Case Studies

Essays

Earth Watch

Health Watch

A Closer Look At

Scientific Inquiry

Links to Everyday Life

BIOLOGY:
LIFE ON EARTH
WITH PHYSIOLOGY

CUSTOM EDITION FOR SAINT LOUIS UNIVERSITY

Teresa Audesirk
Gerald Audesirk
Bruce E. Byers

Taken From:

Biology: Life on Earth with Physiology, Ninth Edition
by Teresa Audesirk, Gerald Audesirk, and Bruce E. Byers

Learning Solutions

New York Boston San Francisco
London Toronto Sydney Tokyo Singapore Madrid
Mexico City Munich Paris Cape Town Hong Kong Montreal

Cover Art: Courtesy of PhotoDisc/Getty Images

Taken from:

Biology: Life on Earth with Physiology, Ninth Edition
by Teresa Audesirk, Gerald Audesirk, and Bruce E. Byers
Copyright © 2011, 2008, 2005 by Pearson Education, Inc.
Published by Benjamin Cummings
San Francisco, California 94111

This special edition published in cooperation with Pearson Learning Solutions.

Pearson Learning Solutions, 501 Boylston Street, Suite 900, Boston, MA 02116
A Pearson Education Company
www.pearsoned.com

Printed in the United States of America

2 3 4 5 6 7 8 9 10 V0CR 15 14 13 12 11 10

000200010270585579

CW

ISBN 10: 0-558-76309-X
ISBN 13: 978-0-558-76309-1

TERRY AND GERRY AUDESIRK

grew up in New Jersey, where they met as undergraduates. After marrying in 1970, they moved to California, where Terry earned her doctorate in marine ecology at the University of Southern California and Gerry earned his doctorate in neurobiology at the California Institute of Technology. As postdoctoral students at the University of Washington's marine laboratories, they worked together on the neural bases of behavior, using a marine mollusk as a model system.

They are now emeritus professors of biology at the University of Colorado Denver, where they taught introductory biology and neurobiology from 1982 through 2006. In their research, funded primarily by the National Institutes of Health, they investigated the mechanisms by which neurons are harmed by low levels of environmental pollutants and protected by estrogen.

Terry and Gerry share a deep appreciation of nature and of the outdoors. They enjoy hiking in the Rockies, walking near their home in Steamboat Springs, and attempting to garden at 7,000 feet in the presence of hungry deer and elk. They are long-time members of many conservation organizations. Their daughter, Heather, provides another welcome focus to their lives.

BRUCE E. BYERS

is a midwesterner transplanted to the hills of western Massachusetts, where he is a professor in the biology department at the University of Massachusetts, Amherst. He's been a member of the faculty at UMass (where he also completed his doctoral degree) since 1993. Bruce teaches introductory biology courses for both non-majors and majors; he also teaches courses in ornithology and animal behavior.

A lifelong fascination with birds ultimately led Bruce to scientific exploration of avian biology. His current research focuses on the behavioral ecology of birds, especially on the function and evolution of the vocal signals that birds use to communicate. The pursuit of vocalizations often takes Bruce outdoors, where he can be found before dawn, tape recorder in hand, awaiting the first songs of a new day.

With love to Jack and Lori and in loving memory of Eve and Joe

T. A. & G. A.

To Bob and Ruth, with gratitude

B. E. B.

Brief Contents

Detailed Contents

Unit 2
Inheritance 143

9 The Continuity of Life: Cellular Reproduction 144

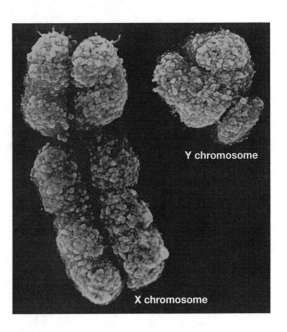

Y chromosome

X chromosome

10   Patterns of Inheritance   173

Case Study *Sudden Death on the Court*   173

10.1   What Is the Physical Basis of Inheritance?   174
Genes Are Sequences of Nucleotides at Specific Locations on Chromosomes   174
An Organism's Two Alleles May Be the Same or Different   175

10.2   How Were the Principles of Inheritance Discovered?   175
Doing It Right: The Secrets of Mendel's Success   175

10.3   How Are Single Traits Inherited?   176
The Inheritance of Dominant and Recessive Alleles on Homologous Chromosomes Can Explain the Results of Mendel's Crosses   177
Simple "Genetic Bookkeeping" Can Predict Genotypes and Phenotypes of Offspring   178
Mendel's Hypothesis Can Be Used to Predict the Outcome of New Types of Single-Trait Crosses   179

Case Study Continued *Sudden Death on the Court*   180

10.4   How Are Multiple Traits Inherited?   180
Mendel Hypothesized That Traits Are Inherited Independently   181
In an Unprepared World, Genius May Go Unrecognized   181

10.5   How Are Genes Located on the Same Chromosome Inherited?   182
Genes on the Same Chromosome Tend to Be Inherited Together   182
Crossing Over Creates New Combinations of Linked Alleles   183

10.6   How Is Sex Determined?   184

10.7   How Are Sex-Linked Genes Inherited?   184
Sex-Linked Genes Are Found Only on the X or Only on the Y Chromosome   184

10.8   Do the Mendelian Rules of Inheritance Apply to All Traits?   186
Incomplete Dominance: The Phenotype of Heterozygotes Is Intermediate Between the Phenotypes of the Homozygotes   186
A Single Gene May Have Multiple Alleles   186
Many Traits Are Influenced by Several Genes   187
Single Genes Typically Have Multiple Effects on Phenotype   187
The Environment Influences the Expression of Genes   187

Case Study Continued *Sudden Death on the Court*   189

10.9   How Are Human Genetic Disorders Investigated?   189

10.10   How Are Human Disorders Caused by Single Genes Inherited?   189
Some Human Genetic Disorders Are Caused by Recessive Alleles   189
Some Human Genetic Disorders Are Caused by Dominant Alleles   191
Some Human Genetic Disorders Are Sex-Linked   191

10.11   How Do Errors in Chromosome Number Affect Humans?   192
Some Genetic Disorders Are Caused by Abnormal Numbers of Sex Chromosomes   192

Health Watch *Muscular Dystrophy*   194

Some Genetic Disorders Are Caused by Abnormal Numbers of Autosomes   195

Case Study Revisited *Sudden Death on the Court*   196

Unit 3
Evolution and Diversity of Life   265

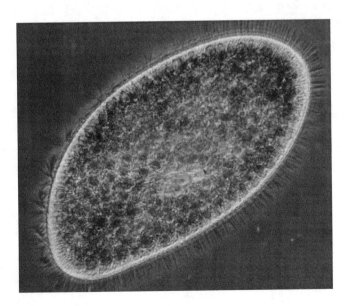

Unit 5
Animal Anatomy and Physiology

Preface

Global warming, biofuels, bioengineered crops in agriculture, stem cells in medicine, potential flu pandemics, the plight of polar bears and pandas—our students are bombarded with buzzwords. The Internet connects them almost instantly to a wealth of reliable information, but also to floods of falsehoods and hype. The concerns that are sweeping our increasingly interconnected world are very real, urgent, and interrelated. Never have scientifically literate societies been more important to humanity's future. As educators, we feel humbled before this massive challenge. As authors, we feel hopeful that with this Ninth Edition of *Biology: Life on Earth*, we can help our introductory biology students along the path to understanding.

Scientific literacy requires a foundation of factual knowledge that provides a solid and accurate cognitive framework into which new information can be integrated. More importantly, however, it endows people with the mental tools they'll need to apply that knowledge to ever-changing situations. A scientifically literate individual recognizes the interrelatedness of concepts and the need to integrate information from many areas before reaching a conclusion. Scientifically literate citizens can readily grasp and evaluate new information from the popular press, allowing them to make informed choices in the political arena as well as in their personal lives.

In this new edition, we strive to:

- Help instructors present biological information in a way that will foster scientific literacy among their students.
- Help inspire students with a sense of wonder about the natural world and their role in it, which, in turn, will foster a lifetime of inquiry and discovery.
- Help students learn to think about the nature of science, and to recognize the importance of what they are learning to their own lives and to their rapidly changing world.

BIOLOGY: LIFE ON EARTH, NINTH EDITION

. . . Is Organized Clearly and Uniformly

Throughout each chapter, users will find navigational aids to help them explore the topics covered.

- Each chapter opens with an "At a Glance" section, which presents the chapter's major sections and essays. Users can readily see what the chapter covers, and how the topics are organized and related to each other. Instructors can easily assign—and students can easily locate—key topics within the chapter.
- Major sections are introduced as questions, to stimulate thinking about the material that will follow, while minor subheadings are summary statements reflecting their more specific content. An important goal of this organization is to present biology as a hierarchy of closely interrelated concepts rather than as a compendium of independent topics.
- A "Summary of Key Concepts" section pulls together important concepts using the chapter's major headings, allowing instructors and students to review the chapter efficiently.

. . . Engages and Motivates Students

Scientific literacy cannot be imposed on students—they must actively participate in acquiring the necessary information and skills. To be inspired to accomplish this, they must first recognize that biology is about their own lives. A major goal for biology educators is to expand students' perception of what is important in their lives. For example, we want to help students appreciate their own bodies as evolutionary marvels, while gaining a basic understanding of how they function.

Further, we hope that our newly biologically literate students will see the entire outside world through different eyes, viewing ponds, fields, and forests as vibrant and interconnected ecosystems brimming with diverse life-forms rather than as mundane features of their everyday surroundings. If we have done our job, our users will also gain the interest, insight, and information they need to look at how humanity has intervened in the natural world. If they ask the question: "Is this activity sustainable?" and then use their knowledge and critical thinking skills to seek some answers, we can be optimistic about the future.

In support of these goals, the Ninth Edition continues to offer these revised and updated features:

- **Case Studies** Each chapter opens with a case study based on major news events, personal interest stories, or particularly fascinating biological topics. The case study is continued in small, boxed features within the text, and is revisited at the end of each chapter, exploring the topic further in light of what the chapter has covered.
- **BioEthics Questions** Many topics explored in the text have ethical implications for human society, such as human cloning, the cultivation of genetically modified foods, and human impacts on other species. BioEthics questions are identified with an icon that alerts students and instructors to the possibility for further discussion and investigation.
- **Boxed Essays** All of our essays, which explore topics relevant both to the chapter and to the goals of this edition, have been thoroughly revised and updated. Five types of essays enliven this text: "Links to Everyday Life" essays illuminate subjects familiar and interesting to students within the context of the chapter topics; "Earth Watch" essays explore pressing environmental issues; "Health Watch" essays cover important and intriguing

medical topics; "Scientific Inquiry" essays explain how scientific knowledge is acquired; and finally, essays titled "A Closer Look At . . ." allow students to explore selected topics in greater depth.

- **Critical Thinking Questions** At the end of each "Case Study Revisited" section, in selected figure captions, and in the "Applying the Concepts" section at the end of each chapter, our critical thinking questions stimulate students to think about science rather than to simply memorize facts.

- **End-of-Chapter Questions** The questions that conclude each chapter allow students to review the material in different formats. Fill-in-the-blank, essay, and critical thinking questions help students to study and test what they've learned. All of the answers to these questions have been revised by the authors and are included in the Study Area of the MasteringBiology Web site. Answers to figure caption and fill-in-the-blank questions appear at the end of the text.

- **Key Terms and a Complete Glossary** Boldfaced key terms are defined clearly within the text as they are introduced. These terms are also listed at the end of each chapter, providing students with a quick reference to the key vocabulary for the chapter. This edition features an outstanding glossary, thoroughly revised by the authors. All key terms and many additional important terms are carefully defined.

. . . Is a Comprehensive Learning Package

The Ninth Edition of *Biology: Life on Earth* is not merely a substantially improved textbook. Thanks to the unprecedented support of our new publishers, Pearson Benjamin Cummings, it has become a superb and complete learning package, providing new and innovative teaching aids for instructors and new learning aids for students, as described in the sections that follow.

WHAT'S NEW IN THIS EDITION?

The Ninth Edition of *Biology: Life on Earth* has undergone substantial revision to help it convey the wonder and relevance of biology even more effectively than in the previous editions.

We have added entirely new features, including:

- **"Have You Ever Wondered?" Questions** This new feature explores high-interest questions that students commonly ask their instructors. One question appears in each chapter, along with a clear, scientific explanation that relates to the chapter's topic. Questions such as "Have you ever wondered . . . why it hurts so much to do a belly flop; why cyanide is so deadly; why dogs lick their wounds; and if the food you eat has been genetically modified?" pique student interest, and demonstrate to them that the subjects being covered in the text are directly related to their everyday experiences.

- **"Case Study Continued" Sections** As in previous editions, "Case Study" and "Case Study Revisited"

sections open and conclude each chapter. In the Ninth Edition, we've added brief "Case Study Continued" sections that relate the case study to material covered at relevant places in the chapter.

- **Fill-in-the-Blank Questions** The "Thinking Through the Concepts" review material now begins with a set of fill-in-the-blank questions, which allow students to better test their recall of key terms and concepts, and cover a wider range of chapter topics than the multiple-choice questions that they replace. But, never fear—an extensive collection of multiple-choice questions for each chapter is readily available on the MasteringBiology Web site.

The text and art have been thoroughly revised to include the latest important developments in biology, as well as to make the text more clear and consistent than ever:

- **New Case Studies** There are six entirely new case studies, covering topics such as "Are Viruses Alive?" (Chapter 1) and "The Migration of the Monarchs" (Chapter 30). All of the case studies retained from the Eighth Edition have been revised for relevance, interest, and currency.

- **Feature Essays** All of our boxed essays—including Health Watch, Earth Watch, Links to Everyday Life, Scientific Inquiry, and A Closer Look At . . . —have been revised and updated.

- **Extensively Revised Text** Each chapter has been reviewed and revised, and has undergone extensive developmental editing for clarity, consistency, and optimal organization.

- **Reinvigorated Art Program** All of the text's art has been extensively reviewed by an expert developmental editor working closely with the authors to ensure that the art clearly explains the concepts and exactly reflects the wording used in the text. Nearly 70% of our art has been revised, and many pieces of complex art have been entirely and beautifully redrawn for clarity and consistency in presentation.

- **A Wealth of New Photos** Throughout the text, returning adopters will find a that we have painstakingly researched eye-catching and informative photographs to illuminate the text, replacing well over 300 of the photos from the last edition.

Chapter-by-Chapter Summary of Important Changes

Unit 1: The Life of a Cell

- **Chapter 1: An Introduction to Life on Earth** features a new case study that explores the question "Are Viruses Alive?," setting the stage for this chapter's discussion of the properties of living things.

- **Chapter 2: Atoms, Molecules, and Life** also begins with a new case study, "Crushed by Ice," which relates the properties of water to the demise of the *Endurance*, the ill-fated ship that carried explorer Ernest Shackleton to the Antarctic in 1914. This chapter also presents a "Links to Everyday Life" essay about the disastrous final flight of the *Hindenburg,* dramatically illustrating how the differing atomic structures of helium and hydrogen influence their chemical properties.

- **Chapter 4: Cell Structure and Function** features beautifully redrawn art of plant and animal cells, as well as a new table that highlights the structure and function of cytoskeletal components.
- In **Chapter 5: Cell Membrane Structure and Function**, new art of both membrane structure and diffusion through membranes helps clarify these critical concepts.
- **Chapter 6: Energy Flow in the Life of a Cell** is revised to better explain how enzyme function is regulated.
- In **Chapter 7: Capturing Solar Energy: Photosynthesis**, the light reactions are depicted with greater precision and clarity. We now provide coverage of CAM photosynthesis, including art comparing the C_4 and CAM photosynthetic pathways. Our "Earth Watch" essay on biofuels stimulates thinking about how the energy that plants capture from sunlight can be used for fuel, and whether current methods for producing biofuels are sustainable.
- **Chapter 8: Harvesting Energy: Glycolysis and Cellular Respiration** has been reorganized, and summary art has been redrawn to make this challenging subject even more accessible.

Unit 2: Inheritance

- The chapters in Unit 2 have been reorganized for better conceptual flow. This unit now begins with cellular reproduction, followed by Mendelian genetics, DNA, gene regulation, and biotechnology.
- **Chapter 9: The Continuity of Life: Cellular Reproduction** has been reorganized to reflect its opening role in the unit, and features an engaging new case study on animal cloning.
- **Chapter 10: Patterns of Inheritance** includes a new "Health Watch" essay on muscular dystrophy and its inheritance.
- **Chapter 12: Gene Expression and Regulation** now opens with a case study about cystic fibrosis. The ingenious experiments demonstrating that most genes code for proteins are now described in a "Scientific Inquiry" essay.
- **Chapter 13: Biotechnology** has been extensively updated to reflect new advances in this explosively expanding field.

Unit 3: Evolution and Diversity of Life

- The major topics of **Chapter 14: Principles of Evolution** have been reorganized to develop this critical topic in the most logical way. This chapter also features an "Earth Watch" essay that describes evolutionary changes that can be directly related to human modification of the biosphere.
- **Chapter 17: The History of Life** includes enhanced art and text coverage of the ribozyme.

- Systematics is undergoing extensive revision based on new genetic information. **Chapter 18: Systematics: Seeking Order Amidst Diversity** helps guide readers through these changes with new art and text describing the importance of cladistics.
- In **Chapter 19: The Diversity of Prokaryotes and Viruses**, users will find both the text and art describing viral replication revised to further clarify this fascinating topic.
- **Chapter 20: The Diversity of Protists** features a clear and careful re-rendering of the malarial life cycle, and coverage of an important taxonomic group, the Rhizarians.
- **Chapter 21: The Diversity of Plants** includes beautifully redrawn plant life cycles throughout the chapter, clarified with numbered steps for each stage of the plant's life.
- Fungal phyla are organized in a comparative table in **Chapter 22: The Diversity of Fungi**, which also now highlights the mycorrhizal fungi (Glomeromycetes), essential components of many of Earth's forests. Every fungal life cycle has been redrawn for better consistency and clarity.
- In **Chapter 24: Animal Diversity II: Vertebrates**, the clades of chordates are described, and a table allows for easy comparison of craniate groups.

Unit 4: Behavior and Ecology

- **Chapter 25: Animal Behavior** provides a new "Links to Everyday Life" essay that features rats trained to detect buried land mines, educating students both about how land mines plague some war-torn countries and about the amazing sensory capabilities of animals.
- **Chapter 26: Population Growth and Regulation** includes a new "Health Watch" essay that describes boom-and-bust population cycles in hazardous algal blooms.
- **Chapter 27: Community Interactions** features beautifully redrawn stages of succession, and a new "Scientific Inquiry" essay that describes the fascinating research leading to the discovery of a parasite that makes some tropical ants resemble berries.
- In **Chapter 28: How Do Ecosystems Work?**, all of the biogeochemical cycles have been redrawn by an outstanding nature artist, with painstaking attention to consistency and clarity.
- **Chapter 29: Earth's Diverse Ecosystems** opens with a new case study highlighting sustainable agriculture in the Tropics. The art for this exceptionally well-illustrated chapter is almost entirely redrawn, and features an abundance of new photos that showcase Earth's diverse ecosystems.
- **Chapter 30: Conserving Earth's Biodiversity** opens with a new case study describing the magnificent migration of monarch butterflies and the challenges they face. This chapter features updated coverage of the loss of species as humanity's ecological footprint grows, and expanded coverage of the increasing threat of global warming to biodiversity.

Unit 5: Animal Anatomy and Physiology

- **Chapter 31: Homeostasis and the Organization of the Animal Body** begins with a new case study about professional football player Korey Stringer, who died of heat stroke at the age of 27, illustrating the importance of homeostasis and the potentially fatal consequences that can result when homeostasis fails. The illustration program in this chapter has been extensively revised, including striking new artwork and new micrographs of tissue types.

- **Chapter 32: Circulation** features a new and inspiring case study about Donald Arthur, a former "couch potato" who became a marathoner after receiving a heart transplant. A new rendering of blood clotting clearly illustrates the steps involved in the process.

- **Chapter 33: Respiration** offers clearer illustrations and explanations of countercurrent exchange, the dynamics of breathing in birds, and the mechanisms of gas transport in blood.

- **Chapter 34: Nutrition and Digestion** features new art of the digestive systems of earthworms and ruminants.

- **Chapter 35: The Urinary System** opens with the story of Anthony DeGiulio, who decided to make a difference by donating a kidney to a stranger, starting a kidney donor chain that resulted in four lives being saved. Both the text and art for the essay "A Closer Look at The Nephron and Urine Formation" have been revised and updated, providing a clearer and more thorough explanation of how human nephrons regulate the composition of urine.

- **Chapter 36: Defenses Against Disease** begins with a new case study on flesh-eating bacteria and what makes these microbes so destructive and virulent. The discussion about the biology of influenza, including swine flu (H1N1) and avian flu (H5N1), has been updated. Coverage of the innate and adaptive immune responses has been expanded, as has coverage of the generation of antibody diversity. Our revision also features new art and text on the lymphatic system.

- **Chapter 37: Chemical Control of the Animal Body: The Endocrine System** begins with an extensively updated case study on anabolic steroids, including their abuse by well-known athletes. The chapter now includes a Health Watch essay describing research into the possibility of using stem cells to cure diabetes.

- **Chapter 38: The Nervous System** is now a stand-alone chapter (the senses are described in Chapter 39), making this chapter shorter and more accessible to students. We have extensively revised illustrations of the human brain, the structure and function of synapses, and the role of ion channels in the resting potential, action potential, and synaptic transmission.

- **Chapter 39: The Senses** is now a separate chapter, beginning with a fascinating case study on how cochlear implants endow people who were once profoundly deaf with the ability to hear. The chapter includes new art and descriptions of sensory transduction and the vestibular system. Coverage of the perception of pain has been expanded and updated and is the basis for a brief essay describing why chili peppers taste hot.

- **Chapter 40: Action and Support: The Muscles and Skeleton** begins with a new case study on Olympic athletes and the role of muscle fiber types in athletic ability. We have added new art and descriptions of the sliding filament mechanism of muscle contraction and also of the role of muscle fiber action potentials and calcium ions in the control of contraction.

- **Chapter 41: Animal Reproduction** begins with a new case study about the increasingly crucial efforts to breed endangered species. The table of contraceptive techniques has been updated, and the mechanisms of erectile dysfunction drugs, such as Viagra™, are explained.

- **Chapter 42: Animal Development** features a new Scientific Inquiry essay tracing the discovery of fundamental mechanisms of animal development, using amphibians as model systems. We have expanded our coverage of homeobox genes, including new art mapping these genes in the fruit fly. The Health Watch essay on stem cells has been updated and includes a discussion of the possibility of using induced pluripotent stem cells in therapeutic applications.

Unit 6: Plant Anatomy and Physiology

- **Chapter 43: Plant Anatomy and Nutrient Transport** is enhanced with extensively revised art of plant anatomy, primary and secondary growth, root uptake of water and minerals, and the mechanisms of opening and closing stomata. The supporting text descriptions have been revised to complement the new art.

- **Chapter 44: Plant Reproduction and Development** includes new and redrawn art of the flowering plant life cycle, the development of male and female gametophytes, pollination and fertilization, and seed development. The chapter also includes a lighthearted look at the botanical confusion in the produce department of grocery stores, where many fruits are sold as vegetables.

- **Chapter 45: Plant Responses to the Environment** features several figures that have been redrawn for clarity in presentation.

ACKNOWLEDGMENTS

When Pearson Education reorganized, *Biology: Life on Earth* had the great good fortune to be acquired by Benjamin Cummings. Our new Editor-in-Chief, Beth Wilbur, accepted the surprise bundle placed on her doorstep with warmth and grace and nurtured it to maturity. Both Beth and Senior Acquisitions Editor Star MacKenzie did a great job of overseeing the process, listening, smoothing out rough spots, and, along with Deborah Gale, Executive Director of Development, helping to coordinate this complex and multifaceted endeavor.

Our Developmental Editor, Mary Ann Murray, carefully examined every word and every piece of art with an awe-inspiring attention to detail. Working tirelessly with the authors (who sometimes got tired), she has brought the text and art to an unprecedented standard of clarity and consistency. Lorretta Palagi, our Copyeditor, put the finishing touches on the text, combining a painstaking attention to detail with tactful suggestions. Many new photos enliven the text, thanks to our Photo Researcher, Yvonne Gerin, who skillfully and cheerfully provided us with an array of selections, and again, to Mary Ann Murray, who examined each photo and helped us to select those that best convey the wonder of life on Earth.

The extensively revised art program, also overseen by Mary Ann, was implemented by two excellent art houses— Imagineering Media Services, under the careful direction of Project Manager Winnie Luong, and McEntee Art and Design. Artist Steve McEntee deserves special praise for his exceptional rendering of natural landscapes, plants, and animals. Thanks to Blakely Kim for his help in developing new art styles for the Ninth Edition. We owe our beautifully redesigned text and cover to Gary Hespenheide. The authors are grateful to Gary and our editors for allowing us to participate actively in the design process and in the selection of the cover photo, and are also grateful for the efforts of Lauren Harp, Executive Marketing Manager, to get this book into your hands.

The production of this text would not have been possible without the considerable efforts of Camille Herrera, Production Supervisor, in coordination with Erin Gregg, Executive Managing Editor, and Michael Early, Managing Editor. Camille and Mary Tindle, Project Editor, S4Carlisle Publishing Services, brought the art, photos, and manuscript together into a seamless whole, graciously handling last-minute changes. In his role as Manufacturing Buyer, Michael Penne's expertise has served us well.

The supplements have evolved into an endeavor fully as important as the text itself. Nina Lewallen Hufford, ably assisted by Erin Mann and Frances Sink, skillfully coordinated the enormous effort of producing a truly outstanding package that complements and supports the text. Jane Brundage oversaw the production of the Study Card that accompanies the text, while James Bruce took the lead on the Instructor's Resource CD-ROM. Finally, thanks to Senior Media Producer Jonathan Ballard for his efforts in developing the outstanding MasteringBiology Web site that accompanies this text.

We are delighted to be under the wings of the Pearson Benjamin Cummings team. This Ninth Edition of *Biology: Life on Earth* reflects their exceptional skill and dedication.

With thanks,

TERRY AUDESIRK, GERRY AUDESIRK, AND BRUCE BYERS

NINTH EDITION REVIEWERS

Mike Aaron,
Shelton State Community College
Ana Arnizaut-Vilella,
Mississippi University for Women

Dan Aruscavage,
State University of New York, Potsdam
Isaac Barjis
New York City College of Technology

Mike Barton,
Centre College
Robert Benard,
American International College
Heather Bennett,
Illinois College
Karen E. Bledsoe,
Western Oregon University
David Brown,
Marietta College
Diep Burbridge,
Long Beach City College
Judy A. Chappell,
Luzerne County Community College
Art Conway,
Randolph-Macon College
Clifton Cooper,
Linn-Benton Community College
Brian E. Corner,
Augsburg College
Peter Cumbie,
Winthrop University
Joe Demasi,
Massachusetts College
Christy Donmoyer,
Winthrop University
Doug Florian,
Trident Technical College
Cynthia Galloway,
Texas A&M University–Kingsville
Janet Gaston,
Troy University
Charles Good,
Ohio State University, Lima
Joan-Beth Gow,
Anna Maria College
Mary Ruth Griffin,
University of Charleston
Wendy Grillo,
North Carolina Central University
Robert Hatherill,
Del Mar College
Kathleen Hecht,
Nassau Community College
Wiley Henderson,
Alabama A&M University
Kristy Y. Johnson,
The Citadel
Ross Johnson,
Chicago State University
Ragupathy Kannan,
University of Arkansas, Fort Smith
Patrick Larkin,
Sante Fe College

Mary Lipscomb,
Virginia Polytechnic and State University
Richard W. Lo Pinto,
Fairleigh Dickinson University
Jonathan Lochamy,
Georgia Perimeter College
Paul Lonquich,
California State University Northridge
Bernard Majdi,
Waycross College
Cindy Malone,
California State University Northridge
Barry Markillie,
Cape Fear Community College
Daniel Matusiak,
St. Charles Community College
Jeanne Minnerath,
St. Mary's University of Minnesota
Russell Nemecek,
Columbia College, Hancock
Murad Odeh,
South Texas College
Luis J. Pelicot,
City University of New York, Hostos
Larry Pilgrim,
Tyler Junior College
Therese Poole,
Georgia State University
Cameron Russell,
Tidewater Community College
Tim Sellers,
Keuka College
Rick L. Simonson,
University of Nebraska, Kearney
Howard Singer,
New Jersey City University
Anthony Stancampiano,
Oklahoma City Community College
Jose G. Tello,
Long Island University
Richard C. Tsou,
Gordon College
Jim Van Brunt,
Rogue Community College
Jerry G. Walls,
Louisiana State University, Alexandria
Holly Walters,
Cape Fear Community College
Winfred Watkins,
McLennan Community College
Richard Whittington,
Pellissippi State Technical Community College

Roger K. Wiebusch,
Columbia College
Taek H. You,
Campbell University
Martin Zahn,
Thomas Nelson Community College
Michelle Zurawski,
Moraine Valley Community College

PREVIOUS EDITION REVIEWERS

W. Sylvester Allred,
Northern Arizona University
Judith Keller Amand,
Delaware County Community College
William Anderson,
Abraham Baldwin Agriculture College
Steve Arch,
Reed College
George C. Argyros,
Northeastern University
Kerri Lynn Armstrong,
Community College of Philadelphia
G. D. Aumann,
University of Houston
Vernon Avila,
San Diego State University
J. Wesley Bahorik,
Kutztown University of Pennsylvania
Peter S. Baletsa,
Northwestern University
John Barone,
Columbus State University
Bill Barstow,
University of Georgia–Athens
Michael C. Bell,
Richland College
Colleen Belk,
University of Minnesota, Duluth
Gerald Bergtrom,
University of Wisconsin
Arlene Billock,
University of Southwestern Louisiana
Brenda C. Blackwelder,
Central Piedmont Community College
Melissa Blamires,
Salt Lake Community College
Raymond Bower,
University of Arkansas
Robert Boyd,
Auburn University

Michael Boyle,
Seattle Central Community College
Marilyn Brady,
Centennial College of Applied Arts and Technology
Virginia Buckner,
Johnson County Community College
Arthur L. Buikema, Jr.,
Virginia Polytechnic Institute
J. Gregory Burg,
University of Kansas
William F. Burke,
University of Hawaii
Robert Burkholter,
Louisiana State University
Matthew R. Burnham,
Jones County Junior College
Kathleen Burt-Utley,
University of New Orleans
Linda Butler,
University of Texas–Austin
W. Barkley Butler,
Indiana University of Pennsylvania
Jerry Button,
Portland Community College
Bruce E. Byers,
University of Massachusetts–Amherst
Sara Chambers,
Long Island University
Nora L. Chee,
Chaminade University
Joseph P. Chinnici,
Virginia Commonwealth University
Dan Chiras,
University of Colorado–Denver
Nicole A. Cintas,
Northern Virginia Community College
Bob Coburn,
Middlesex Community College
Joseph Coelho,
Culver Stockton College
Martin Cohen,
University of Hartford
Jay L. Comeaux,
Louisiana State University
Walter J. Conley,
State University of New York at Potsdam
Mary U. Connell,
Appalachian State University
Jerry Cook,
Sam Houston State University
Sharon A. Coolican,
Cayuga Community College
Joyce Corban,
Wright State University

Ethel Cornforth,
San Jacinto College–South
David J. Cotter,
Georgia College
Lee Couch,
Albuquerque Technical Vocational Institute
Donald C. Cox,
Miami University of Ohio
Patricia B. Cox,
University of Tennessee
Peter Crowcroft,
University of Texas–Austin
Carol Crowder,
North Harris Montgomery College
Mitchell B. Cruzan,
Portland State University
Donald E. Culwell,
University of Central Arkansas
Robert A. Cunningham,
Erie Community College, North
Karen Dalton,
Community College of Baltimore County–Catonsville Campus
Lydia Daniels,
University of Pittsburgh
David H. Davis,
Asheville-Buncombe Technical Community College
Jerry Davis,
University of Wisconsin, LaCrosse
Douglas M. Deardon,
University of Minnesota
Lewis Deaton,
University of Southwestern Louisiana
Lewis Deaton,
University of Louisiana–Lafayette
Fred Delcomyn,
University of Illinois–Urbana
David M. Demers,
University of Hartford
Lorren Denney,
Southwest Missouri State University
Katherine J. Denniston,
Towson State University
Charles F. Denny,
University of South Carolina–Sumter
Jean DeSaix,
University of North Carolina–Chapel Hill
Ed DeWalt,
Louisiana State University

Daniel F. Doak,
University of California–Santa Cruz
Matthew M. Douglas,
University of Kansas
Ronald J. Downey,
Ohio University
Ernest Dubrul,
University of Toledo
Michael Dufresne,
University of Windsor
Susan A. Dunford,
University of Cincinnati
Mary Durant,
North Harris College
Ronald Edwards,
University of Florida
Rosemarie Elizondo,
Reedley College
George Ellmore,
Tufts University
Joanne T. Ellzey,
University of Texas–El Paso
Wayne Elmore,
Marshall University
Thomas Emmel,
University of Florida
Carl Estrella,
Merced College
Nancy Eyster-Smith,
Bentley College
Gerald Farr,
Southwest Texas State University
Rita Farrar,
Louisiana State University
Marianne Feaver,
North Carolina State University
Susannah Feldman,
Towson University
Linnea Fletcher,
Austin Community College–Northridge
Charles V. Foltz,
Rhode Island College
Dennis Forsythe,
The Citadel
Douglas Fratianne,
Ohio State University
Scott Freeman,
University of Washington
Donald P. French,
Oklahoma State University
Harvey Friedman,
University of Missouri–St. Louis
Don Fritsch,
Virginia Commonwealth University

Teresa Lane Fulcher,
Pellissippi State Technical Community College

Michael Gaines,
University of Kansas

Irja Galvan,
Western Oregon University

Gail E. Gasparich,
Towson University

Farooka Gauhari,
University of Nebraska–Omaha

John Geiser,
Western Michigan University

George W. Gilchrist,
University of Washington

David Glenn-Lewin,
Iowa State University

Elmer Gless,
Montana College of Mineral Sciences

Charles W. Good,
Ohio State University–Lima

Margaret Green,
Broward Community College

David Grise,
Southwest Texas State University

Martha Groom,
University of Washington

Lonnie J. Guralnick,
Western Oregon University

Martin E. Hahn,
William Paterson College

Madeline Hall,
Cleveland State University

Georgia Ann Hammond,
Radford University

Blanche C. Haning,
North Carolina State University

Richard Hanke,
Rose State College

Helen B. Hanten,
University of Minnesota

John P. Harley,
Eastern Kentucky University

William Hayes,
Delta State University

Stephen Hedman,
University of Minnesota

Jean Helgeson,
Collins County Community College

Alexander Henderson,
Millersville University

Timothy L. Henry,
University of Texas–Arlington

James Hewlett,
Finger Lakes Community College

Alison G. Hoffman,
University of Tennessee–Chattanooga

Kelly Hogan,
University of North Carolina–Chapel Hill

Leland N. Holland,
Paso-Hernando Community College

Laura Mays Hoopes,
Occidental College

Dale R. Horeth,
Tidewater Community College

Michael D. Hudgins,
Alabama State University

David Huffman,
Southwest Texas State University

Joel Humphrey,
Cayuga Community College

Donald A. Ingold,
East Texas State University

Jon W. Jacklet,
State University of New York–Albany

Rebecca M. Jessen,
Bowling Green State University

James Johnson,
Central Washington University

J. Kelly Johnson,
University of Kansas

Florence Juillerat,
Indiana University–Purdue University at Indianapolis

Thomas W. Jurik,
Iowa State University

Arnold Karpoff,
University of Louisville

L. Kavaljian,
California State University

Joe Keen,
Patrick Henry Community College

Jeff Kenton,
Iowa State University

Hendrick J. Ketellapper,
University of California, Davis

Jeffrey Kiggins,
Blue Ridge Community College

Aaron Krochmal,
University of Houston–Downtown

Harry Kurtz,
Sam Houston State University

Kate Lajtha,
Oregon State University

Tom Langen,
Clarkson University

Stephen Lebsack,
Linn-Benton Community College

Patricia Lee-Robinson,
Chaminade University of Honolulu

David E. Lemke,
Texas State University

William H. Leonard,
Clemson University

Edward Levri,
Indiana University of Pennsylvania

Graeme Lindbeck,
University of Central Florida

Jerri K. Lindsey,
Tarrant County Junior College–Northeast

Jason L. Locklin,
Temple College

John Logue,
University of South Carolina–Sumter

William Lowen,
Suffolk Community College

Ann S. Lumsden,
Florida State University

Steele R. Lunt,
University of Nebraska–Omaha

Daniel D. Magoulick,
The University of Central Arkansas

Cindy Malone,
California State University–Northridge

Paul Mangum,
Midland College

Richard Manning,
Southwest Texas State University

Mark Manteuffel,
St. Louis Community College

Ken Marr,
Green River Community College

Kathleen A. Marrs,
Indiana University–Purdue University Indianapolis

Michael Martin,
University of Michigan

Linda Martin-Morris,
University of Washington

Kenneth A. Mason,
University of Kansas

Margaret May,
Virginia Commonwealth University

D. J. McWhinnie,
De Paul University

Gary L. Meeker,
California State University, Sacramento

Thoyd Melton,
North Carolina State University

Joseph R. Mendelson III,
Utah State University

Karen E. Messley,
Rockvalley College

Timothy Metz,
Campbell University

Steven Mezik,
Herkimer County Community College

Glendon R. Miller,
Wichita State University

Hugh Miller,
East Tennessee State University

Neil Miller,
Memphis State University

Christine Minor,
Clemson University

Jeanne Mitchell,
Truman State University

Lee Mitchell,
Mt. Hood Community College

Jack E. Mobley,
University of Central Arkansas

John W. Moon,
Harding University

Nicole Moore,
Austin Peay University

Richard Mortenson,
Albion College

Gisele Muller-Parker,
Western Washington University

James Mulrooney,
Central Connecticut State University

Kathleen Murray,
University of Maine

Robert Neill,
University of Texas

Harry Nickla,
Creighton University

Daniel Nickrent,
Southern Illinois University

Jane Noble-Harvey,
University of Delaware

David J. O'Neill,
Community College of Baltimore County–Dundalk Campus

James T. Oris,
Miami University of Ohio

Marcy Osgood,
University of Michigan

C. O. Patterson,
Texas A&M University

Fred Peabody,
University of South Dakota

Charlotte Pedersen,
Southern Utah University

Harry Peery,
Tompkins-Cortland Community College

Rhoda E. Perozzi,
Virginia Commonwealth University

Gary B. Peterson,
South Dakota State University

Bill Pfitsch,
Hamilton College

Ronald Pfohl,
Miami University of Ohio

Robert Kyle Pope,
Indiana University South Bend

Bernard Possident,
Skidmore College

Ina Pour-el,
DMACC–Boone Campus

Elsa C. Price,
Wallace State Community College

Marvin Price,
Cedar Valley College

Kelli Prior,
Finger Lakes Community College

Jennifer J. Quinlan,
Drexel University

James A. Raines,
North Harris College

Paul Ramp,
Pellissippi State Technical College

Robert N. Reed,
Southern Utah University

Wenda Ribeiro,
Thomas Nelson Community College

Elizabeth Rich,
Drexel University

Mark Richter,
University of Kansas

Robert Robbins,
Michigan State University

Jennifer Roberts,
Lewis University

Frank Romano,
Jacksonville State University

Chris Romero,
Front Range Community College

Paul Rosenbloom,
Southwest Texas State University

Amanda Rosenzweig,
Delgado Community College

K. Ross,
University of Delaware

Mary Lou Rottman,
University of Colorado–Denver

Albert Ruesink,
Indiana University

Connie Russell,
Angelo State University

Marla Ruth,
Jones County Junior College

Christopher F. Sacchi,
Kutztown University

Eduardo Salazar,
Temple College

Doug Schelhaas,
University of Mary

Brian Schmaefsky,
Kingwood College

Alan Schoenherr,
Fullerton College

Brian W. Schwartz,
Columbus State University

Edna Seaman,
University of Massachusetts, Boston

Patricia Shields,
George Mason University

Marilyn Shopper,
Johnson County Community College

Anu Singh-Cundy,
Western Washington University

Linda Simpson,
University of North Carolina–Charlotte

Steven Skarda,
Linn-Benton Community College

Russel V. Skavaril,
Ohio State University

John Smarelli,
Loyola University

Mark Smith,
Chaffey College

Dale Smoak,
Piedmont Technical College

Jay Snaric,
St. Louis Community College

Phillip J. Snider,
University of Houston

Shari Snitovsky,
Skyline College

Gary Sojka,
Bucknell University

John Sollinger,
Southern Oregon University

Sally Sommers Smith,
Boston University

Jim Sorenson,
Radford University

Mary Spratt,
University of Missouri, Kansas City

Bruce Stallsmith,
University of Alabama–Huntsville

Benjamin Stark,
Illinois Institute of Technology

William Stark,
Saint Louis University

Barbara Stebbins-Boaz,
Willamette University

Kathleen M. Steinert,
Bellevue Community College

Barbara Stotler,
Southern Illinois University

Nathaniel J. Stricker,
Ohio State University

Martha Sugermeyer,
Tidewater Community College

Gerald Summers,
University of Missouri–Columbia

Marshall Sundberg,
Louisiana State University

Bill Surver,
Clemson University

Eldon Sutton,
University of Texas–Austin

Peter Svensson,
West Valley College

Dan Tallman,
Northern State University

David Thorndill,
Essex Community College

William Thwaites,
San Diego State University

Professor Tobiessen,
Union College

Richard Tolman,
Brigham Young University

Sylvia Torti,
University of Utah

Dennis Trelka,
Washington and Jefferson College

Sharon Tucker,
University of Delaware

Gail Turner,
Virginia Commonwealth University

Glyn Turnipseed,
Arkansas Technical University

Lloyd W. Turtinen,
University of Wisconsin, Eau Claire

Robert Tyser,
University of Wisconsin, La Crosse

Robin W. Tyser,
University of Wisconsin, LaCrosse

Kristin Uthus,
Virginia Commonwealth University

Rani Vajravelu,
University of Central Florida

F. Daniel Vogt,
State University of New York–Plattsburgh

Nancy Wade,
Old Dominion University

Susan M. Wadkowski,
Lakeland Community College

Jyoti R. Wagle,
Houston Community College–Central

Lisa Weasel,
Portland State University

Michael Weis,
University of Windsor

DeLoris Wenzel,
University of Georgia

Jerry Wermuth,
Purdue University–Calumet

Diana Wheat,
Linn-Benton Community College

Jacob Wiebers,
Purdue University

Carolyn Wilczynski,
Binghamton University

Lawrence R. Williams,
University of Houston

P. Kelly Williams,
University of Dayton

Roberta Williams,
University of Nevada–Las Vegas

Emily Willingham,
University of Texas–Austin

Sandra Winicur,
Indiana University–South Bend

Bill Wischusen,
Louisiana State University

Michelle Withers,
Louisiana State University

Chris Wolfe,
North Virginia Community College

Stacy Wolfe,
Art Institutes International

Colleen Wong,
Wilbur Wright College

Wade Worthen,
Furman University

Robin Wright,
University of Washington

Taek You,
Campbell University

Brenda L. Young,
Daemen College

Cal Young,
Fullerton College

Tim Young,
Mercer University

Martin Zahn,
Thomas Nelson Community College

Izanne Zorin,
Northern Virginia Community College–Alexandria

Explore the Fascinating World of Biology: Life on Earth

The **Ninth Edition** of *Biology: Life on Earth* engages students by asking and answering questions about the fascinating world of biology.

NEW! *Have you ever wondered?* feature poses high-interest questions that students commonly ask themselves or instructors. Each question is addressed with a clear, scientifically-accurate response.

Have you ever wondered...?

why it hurts so much to do a belly flop?
(Chapter 2, page 29)

how many cells are in the human body?
(Chapter 4, page 62)

why bruises turn color?
(Chapter 12, page 233)

if the food you eat has been genetically modified?
(Chapter 13, page 249)

why antibiotics can't cure a cold?
(Chapter 15, page 297)

Case Studies appear throughout each chapter, tying together important themes.

Page 20

Atoms, Molecules, and Life

Chapter 2

Case Study

Crushed by Ice

IT TOOK JUST 5 MINUTES for the ship *Endurance* to disappear into the ocean depths, but the captain did not go down with his ship, nor was his crew in danger of drowning. They watched— miserable but ~~~ where they ha~~~

Captained ~~~ Sir Ernest Sha~~~ of scientists a~~~ from Plymout~~~ goal: to trave~~~ South Pole. Fi~~~ the Weddell S~~~ unseasonably~~~ around it, lite~~~ slowly crushi~~~ nights onboa~~~ contorted—g~~~ splintering. W~~~ open the dec~~~ Shackleton or~~~ dogsleds to h~~~ they set up camp.

On November 21, 1915, the *Endurance* shifted, its stern rising skyward as it slid benea~ the ice. Shackleton and crew watched in a kind despairing awe from a safe distance. They wer~ to endure three more months of ceaseless cold on their frozen camp, waiting for the ice to release its grip and the sea to become passable for the smaller boats they had rescued from the doomed ship.

The *Endurance* was trapped and ultimately sunk as it was crushed by expanding ice floating on the Antarctic sea. Most liquids, including water, contract and become denser as they cool. But as water freezes, it undergoes an unusual transformation that produces a solid that is less dense and, therefore, floats on the remaining liquid. How does this happen? Why was the *Endurance* crushed as ice froze around it? How do the unique properties of water influence life on Earth?

▲ The *Endurance* trapped in ice

Human-interest case studies open each chapter, engaging students in real world biology from the start. The Ninth Edition includes several new case studies, including the blood doping scandal at the 2008 Tour de France (Chapter 8) and concerns about threatened Monarch butterfly populations (Chapter 30).

Page 30

Case Study continued

Crushed by Ice

The seawater in which the *Endurance* sank provides an excellent illustration of the ability of water to dissolve other molecules. Seawater contains more than 70 different elements, most in trace quantities. The most abundant dissolved elements are sodium and chlorine (NaCl; comprising about 3.2% of seawater by weight) and smaller amounts of sulfur, calcium, magnesium, pota~~~ water also contains dissolved gas~~~ carbon dioxide. Oxygen in seawa~~~ respire, and carbon dioxide allow~~~ makes energy available to aquati~~~

Page 33

Case Study continued

Crushed by Ice

Shackleton and his crew did not lack drinking water during the months they spent waiting; they could simply melt chunks of ice. Although the ice had solidified from salty ocean water, Na⁺ and Cl⁻ ions (and the other substances dissolved in ocean water) do not fit into the lattice of water molecules that make up the crystalline structure of ice (see Fig. 2-14). As ice forms, the remaining water becomes increasingly salty and requires increasingly low temperatures to freeze.

NEW! *Case Study Continued* sections are interspersed throughout each chapter, relating the case study to the chapter topic at hand.

Page 33

Case Study revisited

Crushed by Ice

Although they failed to traverse Antarctica by dogsled, the heroic and ultimately successful efforts of Shackleton and his crew to return home alive are a remarkable true-life adventure. By studying Figure 2-14 you can see why the *Endurance* was crushed—the orderly arrangement of water molecules in ice causes them to occupy more space than they did as a liquid; thus, water expands as it forms ice. You have witnessed this firsthand if you've ever left a full water bottle in the freezer and later found it cracked open by the expanding ice. The expansion of ice also explains why it floats and why the ice formed a safe campground for the crew of the *Endurance*.

Many animals rely on ocean ice, from penguins and walruses that breed on the ice sheets, to polar bears that use the ice as a staging ground to hunt seals. The seals themselves are protected from their polar bear predators by the ice cover as they hunt for fish beneath it, becoming vulnerable when they surface to breathe through holes that they maintain in the ice.

Consider This

Many of water's unique properties are the result of its polar covalent bonds, which allow water molecules to form hydrogen bonds with each other. What if water molecules were nonpolar? How would this have affected the voyage of the *Endurance*?

A *Case Study Revisited* section ends each chapter, summing up the case study in the context of what the student has learned from the chapter. The *Consider This* question within the *Revisited* section allows students to further reflect on themes brought up in the Case Study, encouraging deeper critical thinking.

Questions throughout the text provide opportunities for students to quiz themselves in preparation for tests.

Every major section heading is written as a question. As students read the material, the answers to the question are revealed. This format helps to stimulate analytical thinking and models the importance of asking questions in scientific exploration.

9.3 HOW IS THE DNA IN EUKARYOTIC CHROMOSOMES ORGANIZED?

Eukaryotic chromosomes are separated from the cytopl in a membrane-bound nucleus. Further, eukaryotic cell ways have multiple chromosomes the smallest numbe

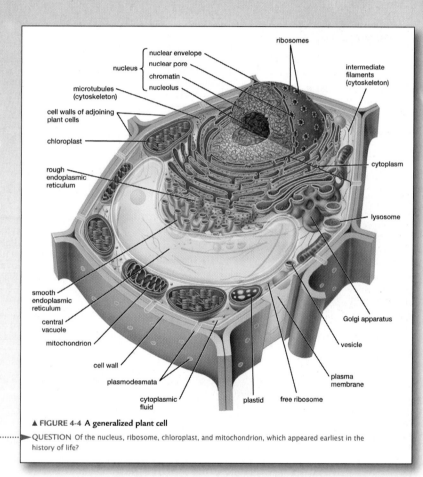

▲ FIGURE 4-4 **A generalized plant cell**

QUESTION Of the nucleus, ribosome, chloroplast, and mitochondrion, which appeared earliest in the history of life?

Figure caption questions ask the student to think critically about the art to ensure they understand the concept being illustrated. Suggested answers appear at the end of the text.

Applying the Concepts

1. **BioEthics** Insects are the largest group of animals on Earth. Insect diversity is greatest in the Tropics, where habitat destruction and species extinction are occurring at an alarming rate. What biological, economic, and ethical arguments can you advance to persuade people and governments to preserve this biological diversity?

2. Discuss at least three ways in which the ability to fly has contributed to the success and diversity of insects.

3. Discuss and defend the attributes you would use to define biological success among animals. Are humans a biological success by these standards? Why?

Applying The Concepts questions are provided at the end of each chapter, challenging students to synthesize information beyond the chapter material and inviting them to apply this knowledge to new situations. Suggested answers appear on the MasteringBiology® Website.

Expanded *BioEthics* questions appear within relevant essay boxes and figure captions, and are included in the end of chapter *Applying the Concepts* section. These questions present bioethical issues and prompt students to carefully consider various points of view.

The significantly revised and invigorated **art program** not only helps draw students into the material, but also teaches concepts more effectively by bringing biological concepts to life.

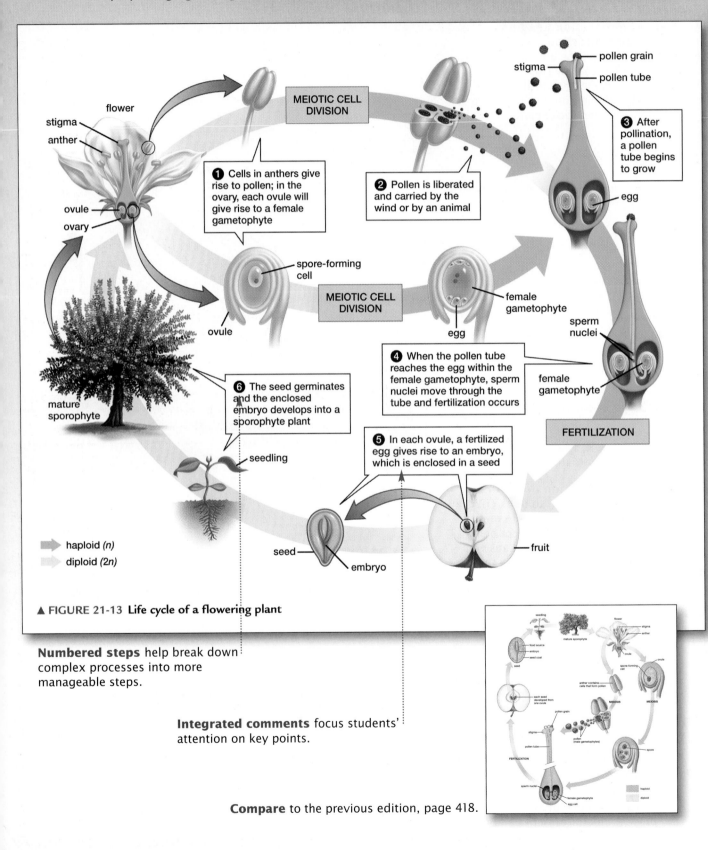

▲ FIGURE 21-13 **Life cycle of a flowering plant**

Numbered steps help break down complex processes into more manageable steps.

Integrated comments focus students' attention on key points.

Compare to the previous edition, page 418.

NEW! Eye-catching photos throughout the text provide an enhanced view into the world of biology and convey the wonder of life on Earth.

chromosomes extending

nuclear envelope re-forming

nucleolus reappearing

Compare to the previous edition, page 199.

Greater consistency in color and illustration format makes it easier for students to intuitively make connections among figures.

lichens and moss on bare rock   bluebell, yarrow   blueberry, juniper   jack pine, black spruce, aspen   balsam fir, paper birch, white spruce, climax forest

time (years)

0   ► 1000

Compare to the previous edition, page 552.

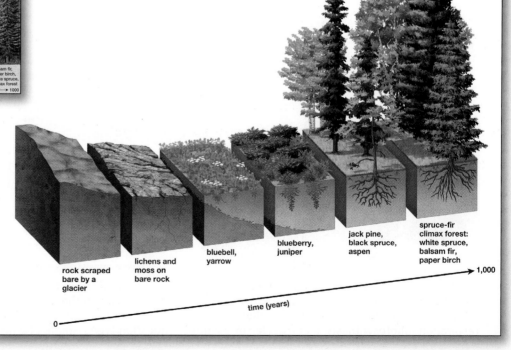

rock scraped bare by a glacier

lichens and moss on bare rock

bluebell, yarrow

blueberry, juniper

jack pine, black spruce, aspen

spruce-fir climax forest: white spruce, balsam fir, paper birch

1,000

0

time (years)

Have you ever wanted to help students make the most of their study time?

NEW! MasteringBiology offers access to Pearson eText, one of the many resources available in the self-study area that students can access 24/7. Other resources include practice quizzes, and personalized study plans. Go to www.masteringbiology.com to get started.

Highlight function lets students highlight what they want to remember.

Annotation feature allows students to take notes.

Google™-based search function lets students search the eText.

Zoom lets students zoom in and out for better viewing.

Hyperlinks connect to quizzes, tests, activities, BioFlix 3-D movie-quality animations, and more.

Pearson eText

Available in the Study Area, Pearson eText gives students access to the text whenever and wherever they can access the Internet. The eText pages look exactly like the printed text, and include powerful interactive and customization functions.

Interactive glossary provides pop-up definitions and terms.

Instructor notes allow you to share notes and highlights with the class.

BioFlix 3-D movie-quality animations and tutorials allow students to visualize the most difficult concepts in biology, such as cellular respiration, photosynthesis, and muscle contraction.

BioFlix activities test students understanding of concepts they learned in the animations. These highly interactive, automatically graded activities include a wide variety of question types—none of which are multiple choice.

how to increase participation and accountability in your non-majors biology course?

MasteringBiology® helps you customize assessment to perfectly match your teaching style and course goals.

MasteringBiology is an online assessment and tutorial system designed to help instructors teach more efficiently, and is pedagogically proven to help students learn. With MasteringBiology, you can...

- **Break free from only offering multiple-choice assessment** but still get automatically graded assignments.

- **Personalize your course** by editing pre-loaded assignments or uploading your own.

- **Take the guesswork out of lectures, quizzes, and tests** by utilizing current data on your students' performance.

- **Assign auto-graded activities** in MasteringBiology that appeal to diverse learning styles: BioFlix™ Activities, *New York Times* Articles, *Discovery Channel* Videos, coaching activities, GraphIt! Activities, Pre-Lecture Quizzes, Post-Lecture Quizzes, and Test Bank Questions.

Customize content with questions and answers that can be easily edited.

Color bar data uses green to indicate correct answers. Red shows the percentage of students who requested an answer. Orange indicates the average number of wrong answers per student.

Pre-lecture quizzes

Help students to arrive at lecture prepared and keep them on track all term.

At-a-glance statistics reveal data for your class as well as national results.

Wrong answer summary gives unique insight into your students' misunderstandings and allows for just-in-time teaching adjustments.

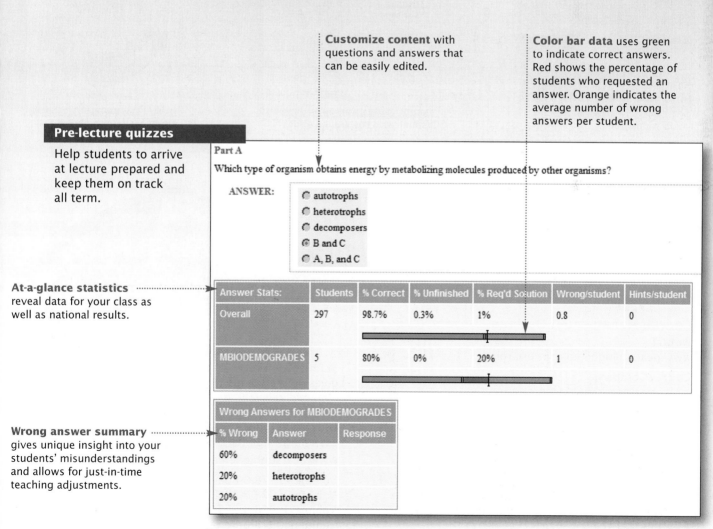

Part A

Which type of organism obtains energy by metabolizing molecules produced by other organisms?

ANSWER:
- ○ autotrophs
- ○ heterotrophs
- ○ decomposers
- ◉ B and C
- ○ A, B, and C

Answer Stats:	Students	% Correct	% Unfinished	% Req'd Solution	Wrong/student	Hints/student
Overall	297	98.7%	0.3%	1%	0.8	0
MBIODEMOGRADES	5	80%	0%	20%	1	0

Wrong Answers for MBIODEMOGRADES		
% Wrong	Answer	Response
60%	decomposers	
20%	heterotrophs	
20%	autotrophs	

Pre-lecture Quiz Student Performance Data

An Introduction to Life on Earth

Case Study

Are Viruses Alive?

IN 1996 IN GABON, AFRICA, a hunting party discovered a recently dead chimpanzee in the bush and butchered it for food. Within a month, the village was devastated. Thirty-seven residents, including the hunters and many of their family members, had fallen ill. Before the scourge had ended, more than half of the victims had died.

The villagers had fallen victim to one of Earth's most sinister pathogens—the Ebola virus (see the inset photo, below). The very mention of Ebola hemorrhagic fever strikes fear in anyone familiar with its symptoms, which begin with fever, headache, joint and muscle aches, and stomach pains, progressing to severe vomiting, bloody diarrhea, and organ failure. Internal hemorrhaging can leave victims bleeding from every orifice. Death usually occurs within 7 to 16 days after the onset of symptoms, and there is no cure. Ebola fever is so contagious and deadly (with up to a 90% fatality rate) that heroic precautions must be taken to protect caregivers from contact with the body fluids of their patients (see the photo to the right).

Ebola fever is one of many infectious diseases caused by viruses. The existence of viruses, entities far smaller than most bacteria, was first surmised in the late nineteenth century. The name "virus" is derived from the Latin word for "poison" because of the disease-causing effects of viruses. Some viruses, such as smallpox and polio, have been largely eradicated, whereas others, such as the common cold and influenza, remain with us but are usually only temporarily debilitating. The viruses of greatest concern to public health officials are the human immunodeficiency virus (HIV), which causes AIDS and kills about 2 million people annually, and the avian influenza virus (H5N1; "bird flu"). Although bird flu's total death toll was about 250 people as of early 2009, its mortality rate is higher than 60%. Health officials are concerned that bird flu may mutate into a far more infectious form, causing a worldwide epidemic.

Measured by the misery they cause, viruses are an unmitigated success. Viruses infect every known form of life on Earth and are the most abundant biological entity on the planet. Viruses can spread from one organism to another, replicate rapidly, and mutate. This tendency to mutate helps them to evade our attempts to develop vaccines against them. In spite of this, most scientists will tell you that viruses are not alive. Why? What is life, anyway?

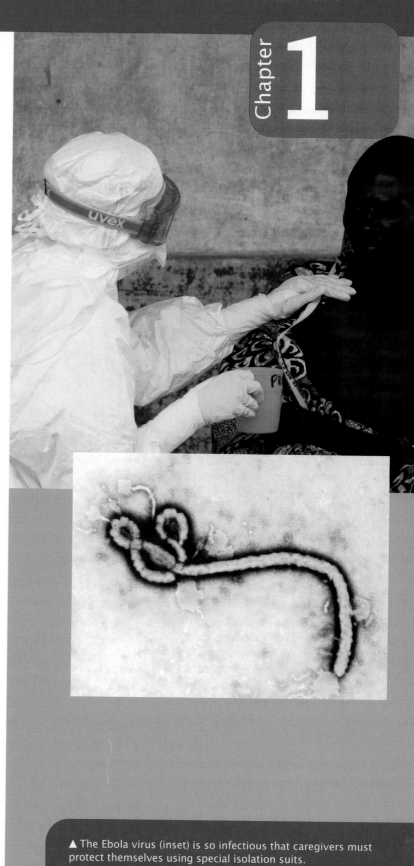

▲ The Ebola virus (inset) is so infectious that caregivers must protect themselves using special isolation suits.

At a Glance

1.1 HOW DO SCIENTISTS STUDY LIFE?

Life Can Be Studied at Different Levels

Just as mud can be formed into bricks that provide the building blocks of a wall, which in turn provide the basis of a structure, the living and nonliving worlds exist at different levels of organization. Each level provides the building blocks for the one above it, and each higher level incorporates many components of each level beneath it (**Fig. 1-1**).

All matter on Earth consists of atoms of substances called **elements,** each of them unique. An **atom** is the smallest particle of an element that retains all the properties of that element. For example, a diamond is a form of the element carbon. The smallest possible unit of a diamond is an individual carbon atom. Atoms may combine in specific ways to form assemblies called **molecules;** for example, one carbon atom can combine with two oxygen atoms to form a molecule of carbon dioxide. Although many simple molecules form spontaneously, only living things manufacture extremely large and complex molecules. The bodies of living things, or **organisms,** are composed primarily of complex molecules called **organic molecules,** meaning that they contain a framework of carbon to which at least some hydrogen is bound.

Although atoms and molecules form the building blocks of life, the quality of life itself emerges on the level of the cell. Just as an atom is the smallest unit of an element, so the **cell** is the smallest unit of life (**Fig. 1-2**). Although many forms of life consist of single cells, in multicellular organisms, cells of similar type combine to form structures known as **tissues;** for example, muscle cells working together form muscle tissue. Different tissues, in turn, may combine to form **organs** (the heart, for example). A group of organs united by a common overall function are called **organ systems** (for example, the heart is part of the circulatory system). Multicellular organisms often have several organ systems.

Levels of organization extend beyond the individual. Within a given area, a group of organisms of the same type (the same species) constitutes a **population.** All organisms capable of breeding with one another are collectively called a **species.** A collection of populations of different species that interact with one another makes up a **community** (see Fig. 1-1). A community and the nonliving environment that surrounds it constitute an **ecosystem.** Finally, the entire surface of Earth and the living things that dwell in and on it is called the **biosphere.**

Biologists work at many different levels, depending on the question they are investigating. For example, to find out how antelope digest their food, a biologist might study the organs of the antelope digestive system or, at a smaller level, the cells that line the digestive tract. Delving deeper, a researcher might investigate the biological molecules secreted into the digestive tract that break down the animal's food. On the other hand, to find out whether habitat destruction is reducing the number of antelope, biologists would investigate

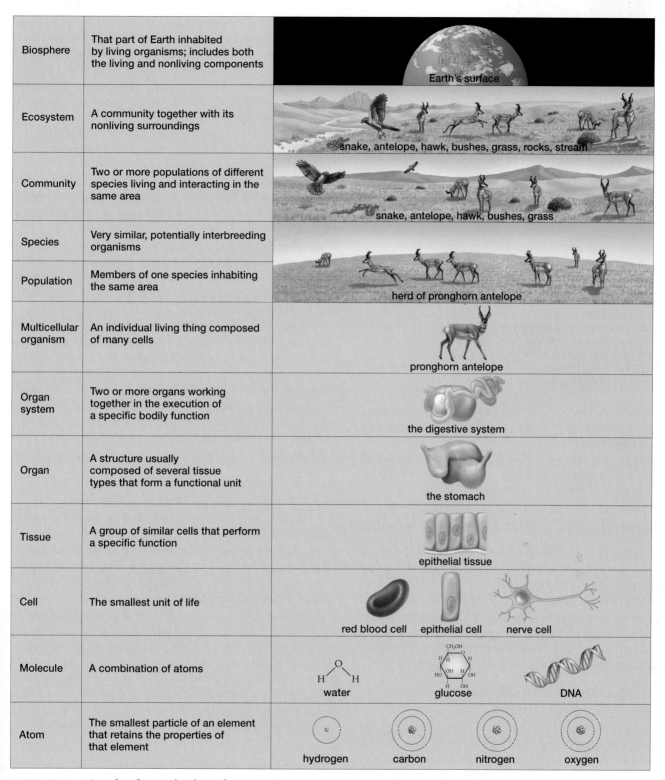

Biosphere	That part of Earth inhabited by living organisms; includes both the living and nonliving components	Earth's surface
Ecosystem	A community together with its nonliving surroundings	snake, antelope, hawk, bushes, grass, rocks, stream
Community	Two or more populations of different species living and interacting in the same area	snake, antelope, hawk, bushes, grass
Species	Very similar, potentially interbreeding organisms	herd of pronghorn antelope
Population	Members of one species inhabiting the same area	
Multicellular organism	An individual living thing composed of many cells	pronghorn antelope
Organ system	Two or more organs working together in the execution of a specific bodily function	the digestive system
Organ	A structure usually composed of several tissue types that form a functional unit	the stomach
Tissue	A group of similar cells that perform a specific function	epithelial tissue
Cell	The smallest unit of life	red blood cell epithelial cell nerve cell
Molecule	A combination of atoms	water glucose DNA
Atom	The smallest particle of an element that retains the properties of that element	hydrogen carbon nitrogen oxygen

▲ FIGURE 1-1 **Levels of organization of matter** Interactions among the components of each level and the levels below it allow the development of the next higher level of organization.

QUESTION What current environmental change is likely to affect the entire biosphere?

nucleus

cell wall

plasma
membrane

organelles

▲ FIGURE 1-2 **The cell is the smallest unit of life** This artificially colored micrograph of a plant cell (a eukaryotic cell) shows the supporting cell wall that surrounds plant (but not animal) cells. Just inside the cell wall, the plasma membrane (found in all cells) has control over which substances enter and leave. The cell also contains several types of specialized organelles, including the nucleus.

antelope populations as well as the interacting populations of other species that make up the community to which antelope belong. It is safe to say that, because biological investigations occur at so many different levels, biology is the most diverse science you will ever encounter.

Scientific Principles Underlie All Scientific Inquiry

Harvard biologist E. O. Wilson defines science as "the organized systematic enterprise that gathers knowledge about the world and condenses the knowledge into testable laws and principles." Scientific inquiry is based on a small set of assumptions. Although these assumptions can never be proven absolutely, they have been so thoroughly tested and validated that we might call them scientific principles. These principles are natural causality, uniformity in space and time, and common perception.

Natural Causality Is the Principle That All Events Can Be Traced to Natural Causes

Over the course of human history, two approaches have been taken to the study of life and other natural phenomena. The first assumes that some events happen through the intervention of supernatural forces beyond our understanding. Ancient Greeks believed that the god Zeus hurled lightning bolts from the sky. Throughout the middle ages, many people were convinced that life arose spontaneously from nonliving matter; for example, that maggots came from rotting meat. Epileptic seizures were once thought to be the result of a visitation from the gods.

Science, in contrast, adheres to the second approach, or the principle of **natural causality,** which states that all events can be traced to natural causes that are potentially within our ability to comprehend. Today, we realize that lightning is an electrical discharge, that maggots are the larval form of flies, and that epilepsy is a brain disorder. The principle of natural causality has an important corollary: The evidence we gather has not been deliberately distorted to fool us. This corollary may seem obvious, yet some people have argued that fossils are not evidence of evolution; rather, they were placed on Earth by God to test our faith. The enormous accomplishments of science rely on the premise of natural causality.

Natural Laws Apply to Every Time and Place

A second fundamental principle of science is that natural laws—laws derived from the study of nature—are uniform in space and time. The laws of gravity, the behavior of light, and the interactions of atoms, for example, are the same today as they were a billion years ago, and they hold true everywhere on Earth, or in our universe. The principle of uniformity in space and time is especially vital to biology, because many important biological events, such as the evolution of today's diversity of living things, happened before humans were around to observe them.

Some people believe that each of the different types of organisms was individually created at one time in the past by the direct intervention of God, a philosophy called creationism. Scientists freely admit that this idea cannot be absolutely disproved, but creationism is contrary to both natural causality and uniformity in time. The overwhelming success of science in explaining natural events through natural causes has led scientists to reject creationism as an explanation for the diversity of life on Earth.

Scientific Inquiry Is Based on the Assumption That People Perceive Natural Events in Similar Ways

A third basic assumption of science is that, generally, people are able to perceive and measure events, and that these perceptions and measurements provide us with reliable, objective information about the natural world. The assumption of common, objective perception is, to some extent, unique to science. Value systems, such as those involved in appreciating art, poetry, and music, do not assume common perception. We may perceive the colors and shapes in a painting in a similar way (the objective aspect of art), but may disagree about its aesthetic value (the subjective, humanistic aspect of art; **Fig. 1-3**). Values differ among individuals, often as a result of cultural or religious beliefs. Because value systems are subjective and not measurable, science cannot answer certain types of philosophical or ethical questions, such as the morality of abortion.

The Scientific Method Is the Basis for Scientific Inquiry

Given these assumptions, how do biologists study the workings of life? Scientific inquiry is a rigorous method for making observations of specific phenomena and searching for the order that underlies those phenomena. Biology and other sciences commonly use the **scientific method,** which consists of six interrelated elements: observation, question, hypothesis, prediction, experiment, and conclusion (**Fig. 1-4**). All scientific inquiry begins with an **observation** of a specific phenome-

▲ **FIGURE 1-3 Value systems differ** Science assumes that people will agree about the colors and shapes in this painting, which are objective aspects of perspection. But subjective questions such as "What does this mean?" or "Is this beautiful?" or "Do I want this on my wall?" will be answered in different ways by different observers.

QUESTION This unique piece of contemporary art by artist and geneticist Hunter Cole is called "Endosymbiosis." The painting features mitochondria and chloroplasts, organelles that are likely to have evolved over millions of years from bacteria living within other cells (see pp. 325–326). Does this objective information change your subjective perception of the art?

non. The observation, in turn, leads to a **question**: "How did this happen?" Then, in a flash of insight—or more often after long, hard thought—a hypothesis is formulated. A **hypothesis** is a supposition, based on previous observations, that is offered as an answer to the question and a natural explanation for the observed phenomenon. To be useful, the hypothesis must lead to a **prediction,** typically expressed in "If . . . then" language. The prediction is tested by carefully controlled manipulations called **experiments.** These experiments produce results that, when analyzed, either support or refute the hypothesis, allowing the scientist to reach a **conclusion** about the validity of the hypothesis. A single experiment is never an adequate basis for a conclusion; the results must be repeatable not only by the original researcher but also by others.

Simple experiments, at least those in the life sciences, test the assertion that a single factor—a **variable**—is the cause of a specific observation. To be scientifically valid, the experiment must rule out other possible variables as the cause of the observation. For this reason, biologists design **controls** into their experiments. Control situations, in which all the variables not being tested remain constant, are then compared with the experimental situation, in which only the vari-

able being tested is changed. In the early 1600s, Francesco Redi used the scientific method to test the hypothesis that flies do not arise spontaneously from rotting meat, and this method is still used today, as illustrated by Malte Andersson's experiment to test the hypothesis that female widowbirds prefer to mate with males with long tails (see "Scientific Inquiry: Controlled Experiments, Then and Now" on pp. 6–7).

You probably use some variation of the scientific method to solve everyday problems (see Fig. 1-4). For example, late for an important date, you rush to your car, turn the ignition key, and make the *observation* that it won't start. Your *question* "Why won't the car start?" immediately leads to a *hypothesis:* The battery is dead. Your hypothesis leads to the *prediction:* A new battery will allow you to start your car. Quickly, you design an *experiment:* You replace your battery with the battery from your roommate's new car and try to start your car again. Your car starts immediately, supporting your hypothesis. But wait, you didn't control for other variables, such as a loose battery cable. To test this, you might replace your old battery, tighten the cables securely, and then attempt to restart the car. If your car repeatedly refuses to start with the old battery and tightened cables but then starts immediately when you put in a new battery, you have isolated a single variable—the battery. Although you are very late for your date, you can now safely draw the conclusion that your old battery is dead.

The scientific method is powerful, but it is important to recognize its limitations. In particular, scientists can seldom be sure that they have controlled for *all* possible variables or made all the possible observations supporting a given hypothesis.

| Observation | → | The car won't start. |

| Question | → | Why won't the car start? |

| Hypothesis | → | The car won't start because the battery is dead. | → Propose a new hypothesis. |

| Prediction | → | IF the hypothesis is correct, THEN the car will start if the battery is replaced. |

| Experiment or Observation | → | The battery is replaced. If the car doesn't start: If the car starts: |

| Conclusion | → | The dead battery hypothesis is supported. |

▲ **FIGURE 1-4 The scientific method** The steps of the scientific method are on the left, with a "real-life" example illustrated on the right.

Scientific Inquiry

Controlled Experiments, Then and Now

A classic experiment by the Italian physician Francesco Redi (1621–1697) beautifully demonstrates the scientific method and helps to illustrate the principle of natural causality, on which modern science is based. Redi investigated why maggots (which are the larval form of flies) appear on spoiled meat. In Redi's time, the appearance of maggots on meat was considered to be evidence of spontaneous generation, the production of living things from nonliving matter.

Redi *observed* that flies swarm around fresh meat and that maggots appear on meat left out for a few days. He formed a testable *hypothesis:* The flies produce the maggots. In his *experiment,* Redi wanted to test just one variable—the access of flies to the meat. Therefore, he took two clean jars and filled them with similar pieces of meat. He left one jar open (the control jar) and covered the other with gauze to keep out flies (the experimental jar). He did his best to keep all the other variables the same (for example, the type of jar, the type of meat, and the temperature). After a few days, he observed maggots on the meat in the open jar, but saw none on the meat in the covered jar. Redi *concluded* that his hypothesis was correct and that maggots are produced by flies, not by the nonliving meat (**Fig. E1-1**). Only through controlled experiments could the age-old hypothesis of spontaneous generation be laid to rest.

More than 300 years after Redi's experiment, today's scientists still use the same approach to design their experiments. Consider the experiment that Malte Andersson designed to investigate the long tails of male widowbirds. Andersson *observed* that male, but

▶ **FIGURE E1-1 The experiments of Francesco Redi**

QUESTION Redi's experiment falsified spontaneous generation of maggots, but did his experiment convincingly demonstrate that flies produce maggots? What kind of follow-up experiment would be needed to more conclusively determine the source of maggots?

not female, widowbirds have extravagantly long tails, which they display while flying across African grasslands. This observation led Andersson to ask the *question:* Why do the males, and only the males, have such long tails? His *hypothesis* was that males have long tails because females prefer to mate with long-tailed males, which therefore have more offspring than shorter-tailed males. From this hypothesis, Andersson *predicted* that if his hypothesis were true, then more females would build

Observation:	Flies swarm around meat left in the open; maggots appear on the meat.
Question:	Where do maggots on the meat come from?
Hypothesis:	Flies produce the maggots.
Prediction:	IF the hypothesis is correct, THEN keeping the flies away from the meat will prevent the appearance of maggots.

Experiment:

Obtain identical pieces of meat and two identical jars

Place meat in each jar

Leave the jar uncovered

Experimental variable: gauze prevents the entry of flies

Cover the jar with gauze

Leave exposed for several days

Controlled variables: time, temperature, place

Leave covered for several days

Flies swarm around and maggots appear

Results

Flies are kept from the meat; no maggots appear

Control situation

Experimental situation

Conclusion:	The experiment supports the hypothesis that flies are the source of maggots and that spontaneous generation of maggots does not occur.

nests on the territories of males with artificially lengthened tails than on the territories of males with artificially shortened tails. He then captured some males, trimmed their tails to about half their original length, and released them (*experimental* group 1). Another group of males had the tail feathers that had been removed from the first group glued on as tail extensions (*experimental* group 2). Finally, Andersson had two *control* groups. In one, the tail was cut and then glued back in place (to control for the effects of capturing the birds and manipulating their feathers). In the other, the birds were simply captured and released. The experimenter was doing his best to make sure that tail length was the only variable that was changed. After a few days, Andersson counted the number of nests that females had built on each male's territory. He found that males with lengthened tails had the most nests on their territories, males with shortened tails had the fewest, and control males (with normal-length tails) had an intermediate number (**Fig. E1-2**). Andersson *concluded* that his hypothesis was correct, and that female widowbirds prefer to mate with males that have long tails.

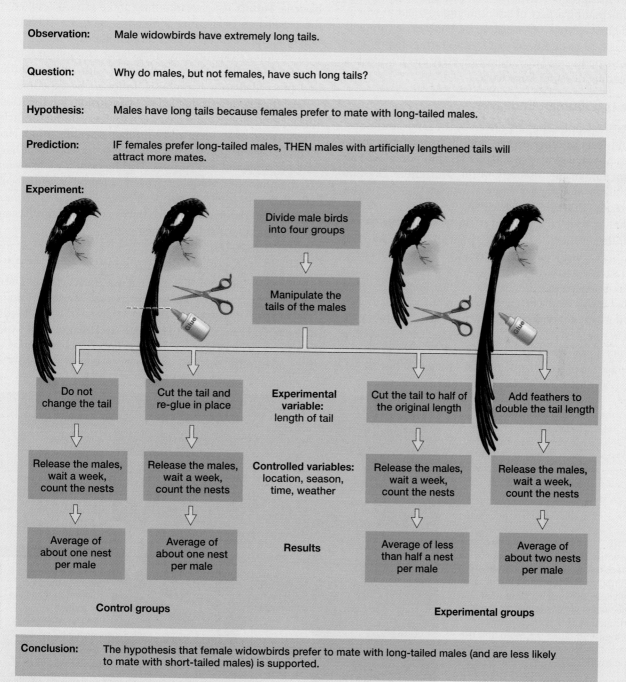

Observation: Male widowbirds have extremely long tails.

Question: Why do males, but not females, have such long tails?

Hypothesis: Males have long tails because females prefer to mate with long-tailed males.

Prediction: IF females prefer long-tailed males, THEN males with artificially lengthened tails will attract more mates.

Experiment:

Divide male birds into four groups

Manipulate the tails of the males

Do not change the tail

Cut the tail and re-glue in place

Experimental variable: length of tail

Cut the tail to half of the original length

Add feathers to double the tail length

Release the males, wait a week, count the nests

Release the males, wait a week, count the nests

Controlled variables: location, season, time, weather

Release the males, wait a week, count the nests

Release the males, wait a week, count the nests

Average of about one nest per male

Average of about one nest per male

Results

Average of less than half a nest per male

Average of about two nests per male

Control groups

Experimental groups

Conclusion: The hypothesis that female widowbirds prefer to mate with long-tailed males (and are less likely to mate with short-tailed males) is supported.

▲ **FIGURE E1-2 The experiments of Malte Andersson**

Therefore, scientific conclusions must always remain subject to revision if new experiments or observations demand it.

Communication Is Crucial to Science

No matter how well designed an experiment is, it is useless if it is not communicated thoroughly and accurately. Redi's experimental design and conclusions survive today only because he carefully recorded his methods and observations. If experiments are not communicated to other scientists in enough detail, they cannot be repeated to verify the conclusions. Without verification, scientific findings cannot be safely used as the basis for new hypotheses and further experiments.

A fascinating aspect of scientific inquiry is that whenever a scientist reaches a conclusion, the conclusion immediately raises further questions that lead to further hypotheses and more experiments (why did your battery die?). Science is a never-ending quest for knowledge.

Science Is a Human Endeavor

Scientists are people. They are driven by the same ambitions, pride, and fears as other people, and they sometimes make mistakes. As you will read in Chapter 11, ambition played an important role in the discovery of the structure of DNA by James Watson and Francis Crick. Accidents, lucky guesses, controversies with competing scientists, and, of course, the intellectual powers of individual scientists contribute greatly to scientific advances. To illustrate what we might call "real science," let's consider an actual case.

To study bacteria, microbiologists use pure cultures—that is, plates of bacteria that are free from contamination by other bacteria or molds. At the first sign of contamination, a culture is usually thrown out, often with mutterings about sloppy technique. On one such occasion, however, in the late 1920s, Scottish bacteriologist Alexander Fleming turned a ruined bacterial culture into one of the greatest medical advances in history.

One of Fleming's bacterial cultures became contaminated with a mold (a type of fungus) called *Penicillium*. Before throwing out the culture dish, Fleming made the observation that no bacteria were growing near the mold (**Fig. 1-5**). Why not? Fleming formulated the hypothesis that *Penicillium* releases a substance that kills bacteria. To test this hypothesis, Fleming performed an experiment. He grew *Penicillium* in a liquid nutrient broth. He then filtered out the mold and placed some of the remaining liquid in a plate with an uncontaminated bacterial culture. Sure enough, something in the liquid killed the bacteria, supporting his hypothesis and leading to the conclusion that *Penicillium* secretes something that kills bacteria. Further research into these mold extracts resulted in the production of the first antibiotic—penicillin, a bacteria-killing substance that has since saved millions of lives.

Fleming's experiments are a classic example of the use of scientific methodology. They began with an observation and proceeded to a hypothesis, followed by experimental tests of the hypothesis that led to a conclusion. But the scientific method alone would have been useless without the lucky combination of accident and a brilliant scientific mind. Had Fleming been a "perfect" microbiologist, he would not have had any contaminated cultures. Had he been less observant, the contamination would have been just another spoiled culture dish. Instead, it was the beginning of antibiotic therapy for bacterial diseases. As French microbiologist Louis Pasteur said, "Chance favors the prepared mind."

Scientific Theories Have Been Thoroughly Tested

Scientists use the word "theory" in a way that is different from its everyday usage. If Dr. Watson were to ask Sherlock Holmes, "Do you have a theory as to the perpetrator of this foul deed?" in scientific terms, he would be asking Holmes for a hypothesis—an "educated guess" based on observable evidence, or clues. A **scientific theory** is far more general and more reliable

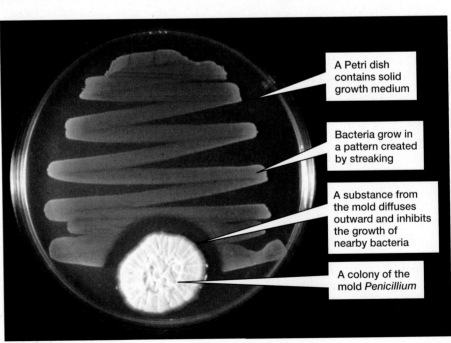

▶ **FIGURE 1-5 Penicillin kills bacteria**
A fuzzy white colony of the mold *Penicillium* has secreted a substance (penicillin) that has inhibited the growth of the disease-causing bacteria *Staphylococcus aureus* (smeared back and forth across this plate of jelly-like growth medium). Both the mold and the bacteria are visible only when they grow at high densities.

QUESTION Why might some molds produce substances that are toxic to bacteria?

A Petri dish contains solid growth medium

Bacteria grow in a pattern created by streaking

A substance from the mold diffuses outward and inhibits the growth of nearby bacteria

A colony of the mold *Penicillium*

than a hypothesis. Far from being an educated guess, a scientific theory is a general explanation of important natural phenomena, developed through extensive and reproducible observations. In common English, it is more like a principle or a natural law. For example, scientific theories such as the atomic theory (that all matter is composed of atoms) and the theory of gravitation (that objects exert attraction for one another) are fundamental to the science of physics. Likewise, the cell theory (that all living things are composed of cells) and the theory of evolution (discussed in Section 1.2) are fundamental to the study of biology. Scientists describe fundamental principles as "theories" rather than "facts" because a basic premise of scientific inquiry is that it must be performed with an open mind. If compelling evidence arises, a scientific theory will be modified.

A modern example of the need to keep an open mind in the light of new scientific evidence is the discovery of prions, which are infectious proteins (see the case study for Chapter 3). Before the early 1980s, all known infectious disease agents possessed genetic material—either DNA or the related molecule, RNA. When neurologist Stanley Prusiner from the University of California at San Francisco published evidence in 1982 that scrapie (an infectious disease that causes the brains of sheep to degenerate) is actually caused and transmitted by a protein with no associated genetic material, his results were met with widespread disbelief. Prions have since been found to cause "mad cow disease" (also called BSE for "bovine spongiform encephalitis"), which has killed not only cattle but also about 200 people who ate infected beef. Prior to the discovery of prions, the concept of an infectious protein was unknown to science. But by being willing to modify accepted beliefs to accommodate new data, scientists maintained the integrity of the scientific process while expanding our understanding of how diseases can occur. For his pioneering work, Stanley Prusiner was awarded the Nobel Prize in Physiology or Medicine in 1997.

Science Is Based on Reasoning

Scientific theories arise through **inductive reasoning,** the process of creating a generalization as a result of making many observations that support it, and none that contradict it. Simplistically, the theory that Earth exerts gravitational forces on objects began from repeated observations of objects falling down toward Earth and from a complete lack of observations of objects "falling up." The cell theory arises from the observation that all organisms that possess the attributes of life are composed of one or more cells, and that nothing that is not composed of cells shares all these attributes.

Once a scientific theory has been formulated, it then can be used to support deductive reasoning. In science, **deductive reasoning** is the process of generating hypotheses about how a specific experiment or observation will turn out, based on a well-supported generalization such as a scientific theory. For example, based on the cell theory, if scientists discover a new organism that exhibits all the attributes of life, scientists can confidently deduce (hypothesize) that it will be composed of cells. Of course, the new organism must be carefully scrutinized under the microscope to determine its cellular structure; if compelling new evidence arises, a scientific theory can be modified.

Scientific Theories Are Formulated in Ways That Can Potentially Be Disproved

A major difference between a scientific theory and a belief based on faith is that a scientific theory can be disproved or falsified, whereas a faith-based assertion cannot. The potential to be falsified is why scientists continue to refer to basic precepts of science as "theories." To explain falsifiability, let's look at elves. The scientific approach to elves is that they do not exist because no objective evidence supports their existence. People with faith in elves might describe them as creatures so secretive that they can never be captured or otherwise detected, or they might claim that elves manifest themselves only to those who believe in them. The scientific theory that elves do not exist could be falsified if someone captured an elf or provided other repeatable, objective evidence of their existence. In contrast, faith-based assertions—for example, that elves exist or that each creature on Earth was separately created—are formulated in ways that can never be disproved or "falsified." For this reason, they are articles of faith rather than science.

1.2 EVOLUTION: THE UNIFYING THEORY OF BIOLOGY

In the words of biologist Theodosius Dobzhansky, "Nothing in biology makes sense, except in the light of evolution." Why don't snakes have legs? Why are there dinosaur fossils but no living dinosaurs? Why are monkeys so like us, not only in appearance but also in the structure of their genes and proteins? The answers to these questions, and thousands more, lie in the processes of evolution, which we will examine in detail in Unit 3.

Evolution, the process by which modern organisms descended, with modifications, from pre-existing forms of life, not only explains the origin of diverse forms of life, but accounts for the remarkable similarities among different organisms as well. Ever since the theory of evolution was formulated in the mid-1800s by two English naturalists, Charles Darwin and Alfred Russel Wallace, it has been supported by fossils, geological studies, radioactive dating of rocks, genetics, molecular biology, biochemistry, and breeding experiments. People who refer to evolution as "just a theory" profoundly misunderstand the concept of a scientific theory.

Three Natural Processes Underlie Evolution

The **scientific theory of evolution** states that modern organisms descended, with modification, from preexisting life-forms. The most important force in evolution is **natural selection,** the process by which organisms with specific traits that help them cope with the rigors of their environment reproduce more successfully than do others that lack these traits. The changes that occur during evolution are a result of natural selection acting on the inherited variation that occurs among individuals in a population, causing changes in the population over successive generations. The variation upon which natural selection acts is a result of small differences in the genetic makeup of the individuals within the population.

Evolution arises as a consequence of three natural occurrences: genetic variation among members of a population owing to differences in their DNA, inheritance of those variations by the offspring of parents who carry the variation, and natural selection, the enhanced reproduction of organisms with variations that help them cope with their environment.

Genetic Variability Among Organisms Is Inherited

Look around at your classmates and notice how different they are, or go to an animal shelter and observe the differences among the dogs in size, shape, and coat color. Although some of this variation (particularly among your classmates) is due to differences in environment and lifestyle, much of it is influenced by genes. For example, most of us could pump iron for the rest of our lives and never develop a body like that of "Mr. Universe."

But what are genes? The hereditary information of all known forms of life is contained within a type of molecule called **deoxyribonucleic acid,** or **DNA** (**Fig. 1-6**). An organism's DNA, which is contained in **chromosomes** in each cell, is the cell's genetic "blueprint" or molecular "instruction manual," a guide to the construction and the operation of its body. Genes are segments of DNA; each gene directs the formation of one of the crucial molecular components of the organism's body. When an organism reproduces, it passes a copy of its chromosomes containing DNA to its offspring.

The accuracy of the DNA copying process is astonishingly high; in people only about 25 mistakes, called **mutations,** occur for every billion subunits of the DNA molecule that are copied. Mutations can also result from damage to DNA, for example, by ultraviolet light, radioactive particles, or toxic chemicals such as those in cigarette smoke. These occasional errors can alter the information in genes or alter the collections of genes within chromosomes. Some mutations are harmful. For example, mutations in skin cells caused by too much ultraviolet light or in lung cells exposed to poisons in cigarette smoke can cause cancer.

On rare occasions, a mutation will occur when a sperm or egg cell is being formed, allowing the change to be passed to the organism's offspring. As a result, each cell in the new individual's body will carry this hereditary mutation. Some of these mutations will prevent the new organism from developing, while other changes in genetic material cause diseases such as Down syndrome. Many mutations have no observable effect or may change the organism in a way that is harmless. On rare occasions, however, a mutation occurs that helps an organism survive and reproduce. Mutations that occurred hundreds of thousands of years ago have been passed from parent to offspring through countless generations, accounting for individual differences in height, body proportions, facial features, and the color of skin, hair, and eyes.

Natural Selection Tends to Preserve Genes That Help an Organism Survive and Reproduce

Organisms that best meet the challenges of their environment will usually leave the most offspring. These offspring will have inherited the genes that made their parents successful. Thus, natural selection preserves genes that help organisms flourish in their environment. For example, we can hypothesize that modern beavers have long front teeth because of an ancient mutation passed to offspring of a single pair of beavers that caused their offspring's teeth to grow larger than usual. Beavers with this mutation could chew down trees more efficiently, build bigger dams and lodges, and eat more bark than could "normal" beavers that lacked the mutation. Because these big-toothed beavers obtained more food and better shelter, they were able to raise more offspring who inherited their parents' genes for larger front teeth. Over time, less-successful, smaller-toothed beavers became increasingly scarce; after many generations, all beavers had large front teeth.

Structures, physiological processes, or behaviors that aid in survival and reproduction in a particular environment are called **adaptations.** Most of the features that we admire so much in our fellow life-forms, such as the long limbs of deer, the wings of eagles, and the mighty trunks of redwood trees, are adaptations that help them escape predators, capture prey, reach the sunlight, or accomplish other feats that ensure their survival and reproduction. These features were molded by millions of years of natural selection acting on random mutations.

Over time, the interplay of environment, genetic variation, and natural selection inevitably results in evolution: a change in the genetic makeup of a species. Evolution has been documented innumerable times both in laboratory settings and in the wild. For example, antibiotics act as agents of natural selection on bacterial populations, causing the evolution of antibiotic-resistant forms. Lawn mowers have caused changes in the genetic makeup of populations of dandelions, favoring those that produce flowers on very short stems. Scientists have documented the spontaneous emergence of entirely new species of plants due to mutations that alter their chromosome number, preventing them from interbreeding with their parent species.

What helps an organism survive today may become a liability tomorrow. If environments change—for example, as global warming occurs—the genetic makeup that best adapts organisms to their environments will also change over time. When random new mutations increase the fitness of an organism in the altered environment, these mutations will spread throughout the population. Populations within a species that live in different environments will be subjected to different types of natural selection. If the differences are great enough and continue for long enough, they may eventually cause the

▲ **FIGURE 1-6 DNA** A model of DNA, the molecule of heredity. As James Watson, its codiscoverer, put it: "A structure this pretty just had to exist."

▲ **FIGURE 1-7 A fossil *Triceratops*** This *Triceratops* died in what is now Montana about 70 million years ago. No one is certain what caused the extinction of the dinosaurs, but we do know that they were unable to evolve new adaptations rapidly enough to keep up with changes in their environment.

populations to become sufficiently different from one another to prevent interbreeding—a new species will have evolved.

If, however, favorable mutations do not occur, a changing environment may doom a species to extinction. Dinosaurs (Fig. 1-7) are extinct not because they were failures—after all, they flourished for 100 million years—but because they did not evolve rapidly enough to adapt to changing conditions. In recent decades, human activities have drastically accelerated the rate of environmental change. Adaptive mutations are relatively rare. Thus, many species are unable to adapt to rapid environmental change, and the rate of extinction has increased dramatically as a result. This concept is explored further in "Earth Watch: Why Preserve Biodiversity?"

1.3 WHAT ARE THE CHARACTERISTICS OF LIVING THINGS?

The word "biology" comes from the Greek root "bio" meaning "life" and "logy" meaning "the study of" (you will find many more word roots in Appendix I). But exactly what is life? If you look up "life" in a dictionary, you will find definitions such as "the quality that distinguishes a vital and functioning being from a dead body," but you won't find out what that "quality" is. Life emerges as a result of incredibly complex, ordered interactions among nonliving molecules. How did life originate? Although scientists have several hypotheses as to how life on Earth first arose (see Chapter 17), these are, of course, untestable. Life is an intangible quality that defies simple definition, even among biologists. However, most will agree that living things share certain characteristics that, taken together, are not shared by nonliving objects. Characteristics of life include the following:

- Living things are composed of cells that have a complex, organized structure.
- Living things actively maintain their complex structure and their internal environment, a process called homeostasis.
- Living things respond to stimuli from their environment.

- Living things acquire and use materials and energy from their environment and convert them into different forms.
- Living things grow.
- Living things reproduce themselves, using the molecular blueprint of DNA.
- Living things, as a whole, have the capacity to evolve.

Let's explore these characteristics in more detail.

Living Things Are Complex, Organized, and Composed of Cells

In Chapter 4 you will learn how researchers in the early 1800s, observing life with primitive microscopes, devised the **cell theory,** which states that the cell is the basic unit of life. Even a single cell has an elaborate internal structure (see Fig. 1-2). All cells contain **genes,** units of heredity that provide the information required to control the life of the cell. Cells also contain structures called **organelles** that are specialized to carry out specific functions such as moving the cell, obtaining energy, or synthesizing large molecules. Cells are always surrounded by a thin **plasma membrane** that encloses the **cytoplasm** (organelles and the fluid surrounding them) and separates the cell from the outside world. Some organisms, mostly invisible to the naked eye, consist of just one cell. Your body—and the bodies of organisms that are most familiar to us—is composed of many cells that are specialized and elaborately organized to perform specific functions. The water flea beautifully illustrates the complexity found in a multicellular form of life that is smaller than the letter "o" in this text (Fig. 1-8).

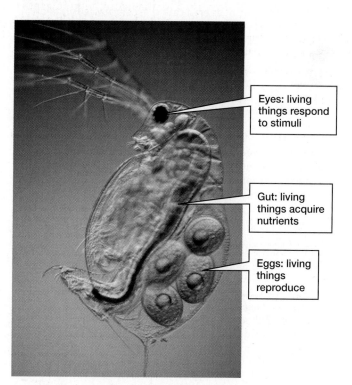

Eyes: living things respond to stimuli

Gut: living things acquire nutrients

Eggs: living things reproduce

▲ **FIGURE 1-8 Life is both complex and organized** The water flea, *Daphnia longispina*, is only 1 millimeter ($\frac{1}{1,000}$ meter) in length, yet it has legs, a mouth, a digestive tract, reproductive organs, light-sensing eyes, and a simple brain.

Earth Watch

Why Preserve Biodiversity?

"The loss of species is the folly our descendants are least likely to forgive us."

—E. O. Wilson,
Professor, Harvard University

What is biodiversity, and why should we be concerned with preserving it? **Biodiversity** refers to the total number of species within a given region. Over the 3.5-billion-year history of life on Earth, evolution has produced an estimated 8 to 10 million unique and irreplaceable species. Of these, scientists have named only about 1.4 million, and only a tiny fraction of this number have been studied. Evolution has not, however, merely churned out millions of independent species. Over thousands of years, organisms in a given area have been molded by forces of natural selection exerted by other living species as well as by the nonliving environment in which they live. The outcome is the community; a highly complex web of interdependent organisms whose interactions sustain one another. By participating in the natural cycling of water, oxygen, and other nutrients, and by producing rich soil and purifying wastes, these communities contribute to the sustenance of human life as well.

The tropics are home to the vast majority of all the species on Earth, perhaps 7 or 8 million of them, living in complex communities. The rapid destruction of habitats in the tropics—from rain forests to coral reefs—as a result of human activities is driving large numbers of species to extinction (**Fig. E1-3**). Most of these species have never been named, and others never even discovered. Aside from ethical concerns over eradicating irreplaceable forms of life, as we drive unknown organisms to extinction, we lose potential sources of medicine, food, and raw materials for industry.

For example, a wild relative of corn that is not only very disease resistant but also perennial (that is, lasts more than one growing season) was found growing only on a 25-acre plot of land in Mexico that was scheduled to be cut and burned within a week of the discovery. The genes of this plant might one day enhance the disease resistance of corn or create a perennial corn plant. The rosy periwinkle, a flowering plant found in the tropical forest of the island of Madagascar (off the eastern coast of Africa; see Fig. E1-3 inset) produces two substances that are now synthesized and marketed for the treatment of childhood leukemia and Hodgkin's disease, a cancer of the lymphatic organs. The periwinkle's wild habitat has been extensively deforested. Only about 3% of the world's flowering plants have been examined for substances that might fight cancer or other diseases. Closer to home, loggers of the Pacific Northwest frequently cut and burned the Pacific yew tree as a "nuisance species" until the active ingredient for the anticancer drug Taxol® was discovered in its bark.

Many ecologists are also concerned that as species are eliminated, either locally or through total extinction, the

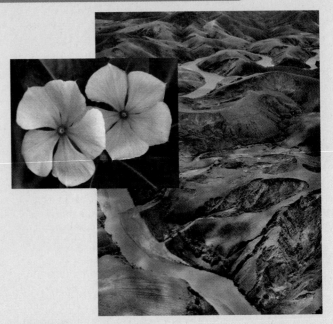

▲ **FIGURE E1-3 Biodiversity threatened** Destruction of tropical rain forests threatens Earth's greatest storehouse of biological diversity. (Inset) The rosy periwinkle's habitat has been dramatically reduced by logging in Madagascar.

communities of which they were a part will change, becoming less stable and more vulnerable to damage by diseases or adverse environmental conditions. Some experimental evidence supports this viewpoint, but the interactions within communities are so complex that these hypotheses are difficult to test. Clearly, some species have a much larger role than others in preserving the stability of a given ecosystem. Which species are most crucial in each ecosystem? No one knows. Human activities have increased the natural rate of extinction by a factor of at least 100 and possibly by as much as 1,000 times the "pre-human" rate. By reducing biodiversity to support increasing numbers of people and wasteful standards of living, we have ignorantly embarked on an uncontrolled global experiment, using planet Earth as our laboratory. Stanford ecologists Paul and Anne Ehrlich compare the loss of biodiversity to the removal of rivets from the wing of an airplane. The rivet-removers continue to assume that there are far more rivets than needed, until one day, when the airplane takes off, they are proven tragically wrong. As human activities drive species to extinction with little knowledge of the role each plays in the complex web of life, we run the risk of removing "one rivet too many."

Living Things Maintain Relatively Constant Internal Conditions Through Homeostasis

Complex, organized structures are not easy to maintain. Whether we consider the molecules of your body or the books and papers on your desk, organization tends to disintegrate into chaos unless energy is used to sustain it (we explore this concept further in Chapter 6). To stay alive and function effectively, organisms must keep the conditions within their bodies fairly constant; in other words, they must maintain **homeostasis** (derived from Greek words meaning "to stay the same"). For example, organisms must precisely regulate the amount of water and salts within their cells. Their bodies must also be maintained at appropriate temperatures for biological functions to occur. Among warm-blooded animals, vital organs such as the brain and heart are kept at a warm, constant temperature despite wide fluctuations in outside temperature. Homeostasis is maintained by a variety of mechanisms. In the case of temperature regulation, these include sweating during hot weather and exercise, dousing oneself with cool water (**Fig. 1-9**), metabolizing more food in cold weather, basking in the sun, or even adjusting a thermostat.

Of course, not everything stays the same throughout an organism's life. Major changes, such as growth and reproduction, occur; but these are not failures of homeostasis. Rather, they are specific, genetically programmed parts of the organism's life cycle.

Living Things Respond to Stimuli

To stay alive, reproduce, and maintain homeostasis, organisms must perceive and respond to stimuli in their internal and external environments. Animals have evolved elaborate

▲ **FIGURE 1-9 Living things maintain homeostasis** Evaporative cooling by water, both from sweat and from a bottle, helps Lance Armstrong (seven-time winner of the Tour de France bicycle race) maintain temperature homeostasis.

sensory organs and muscular systems that allow them to detect and respond to light, sound, touch, chemicals, and many other stimuli from their surroundings. Internal stimuli are perceived by receptors for stretch, temperature, pain, and various chemicals. For example, when you feel hungry, you perceive contractions of your empty stomach and low levels of sugars and fats in your blood. You then respond to external stimuli by choosing appropriate objects to eat, such as a sandwich rather than a plate. Yet animals, with their elaborate nervous systems and motile bodies, are not the only organisms that perceive and respond to stimuli. The plants on your windowsill grow toward light, and even the bacteria in your intestines can move toward favorable conditions and away from harmful substances.

Living Things Acquire and Use Materials and Energy

Organisms need materials and energy to maintain their high level of complexity and organization, to grow, to maintain homeostasis, and to reproduce. Organisms acquire the materials they need, called **nutrients,** from air, water, or soil, or from other living things. Nutrients include minerals, oxygen, water, and all the other chemical building blocks that make up biological molecules. These nutrients are obtained from the environment, where they are continuously exchanged and recycled among living things and their nonliving surroundings (**Fig. 1-10**).

To sustain life, organisms must obtain **energy**—the ability to do work, such as carrying out chemical reactions, growing leaves in the spring, or contracting a muscle. Ultimately, the energy that sustains nearly all life comes from sunlight. Plants and some single-celled organisms capture the energy of sunlight directly and store it in energy-rich molecules, such as sugars, using a process called **photosynthesis.** Only photosynthetic organisms can capture the energy of sunlight. Organisms that cannot photosynthesize, such as animals and fungi, acquire their energy prepackaged in molecules of the bodies of other organisms. Thus, energy flows in a one-way path from the sun through nearly all forms of life. The energy is eventually released as heat, which cannot be used to power life (see Fig. 1-10).

Living Things Grow

At some time in its life cycle, every organism becomes larger—that is, it grows. Although this characteristic is obvious in most animals and plants, even single-celled bacteria grow to about double their original size before they divide. In all cases, growth involves the conversion of materials acquired from the environment into the specific molecules of the organism's body.

Living Things Reproduce Themselves

Organisms reproduce, giving rise to offspring of the same type and creating the continuity of life. The processes by which reproduction occurs differ widely among different

▶ FIGURE 1-10 **The flow of energy and the recycling of nutrients** Energy is acquired from sunlight (yellow arrow) by photosynthetic organisms, is transferred through organisms that consume other forms of life (red arrows), and is lost as heat (orange arrows) in a one-way flow. In contrast, nutrients (purple arrows) are recycled among organisms and the nonliving environment.

forms of life, but the result is the same—the perpetuation of the parents' genes.

Living Things, Collectively, Have the Capacity to Evolve

Populations of organisms evolve in response to changing environments. Although the genetic makeup of a single organism remains essentially the same over its lifetime, the genetic makeup of a population will change over time as a result of natural selection.

Case Study continued
Are Viruses Alive?

Viruses possess only two of the characteristics of life described here—they reproduce and they evolve.

1.4 HOW DO SCIENTISTS CATEGORIZE THE DIVERSITY OF LIFE?

Although all living things share the general characteristics discussed earlier, evolution has produced an amazing variety of life-forms. Scientists generally categorize organisms into three major groups, or **domains:** Bacteria, Archaea, and Eukarya (**Fig. 1-11**). This classification reflects fundamental differences among the cell types that compose them. Members of both the Bacteria and the Archaea usually consist of single, simple cells. Systematists (scientists who classify organisms based on their evolutionary relatedness) have not been able to agree about how to distinguish kingdoms within these two domains, in part because the cells of different organisms within each domain are so simple and have so much in common. In contrast, members of the Eukarya have bodies composed of one or more highly complex cells. This domain includes three major subdivisions or **kingdoms**—the Fungi, Plantae, and Animalia—as well as a

diverse collection of mostly single-celled organisms collectively known as "protists" (see Fig. 1-11).

Categories within kingdoms are phylum, class, order, family, genus, and species. These groupings form a hierarchy in which each category includes all of those below it. Within the final category, the species, all members are so similar that they can interbreed. Biologists use a **binomial system** (from Latin, meaning "two names") for naming species. Why? The animal in Figure 1-8, for example, has the common name *water flea*, but because there are many types of water fleas, people who study them need to be more precise. Each type of organism is assigned a scientific name with two parts: its genus and its species. The genus name is always capitalized, and the species name is not; both are italicized. So *Daphnia longispina*, the water flea in Figure 1-8, is in the genus *Daphnia* (which includes many other water fleas) and the species *longispina* (which refers to a long spine that characterizes this particular type of water flea). People are classified as *Homo sapiens*; we are the only members of this genus and species.

Have you ever wondered

Why Scientists Study Obscure Things— Like Water Fleas?

The more we learn about life, the more we realize how interdependent various forms of life are. *Daphnia* eat microscopic algae, and they in turn are eaten by juvenile fish, allowing the fish to survive, grow, and provide food for other fish, birds, mammals, and people. In addition, by consuming suspended microscopic algae, water fleas help keep lake water relatively clear; this allows sunlight to penetrate the water, allowing submerged plants to thrive. These plants provide food and habitat for a variety of aquatic insects that support adult fish populations. *Daphnia* are also easy to raise in the laboratory and sensitive to toxic chemicals, so scientists sometimes test water quality by determining whether *Daphnia* can thrive in it. The bottom line? You name it, and scientists have good reasons for studying it.

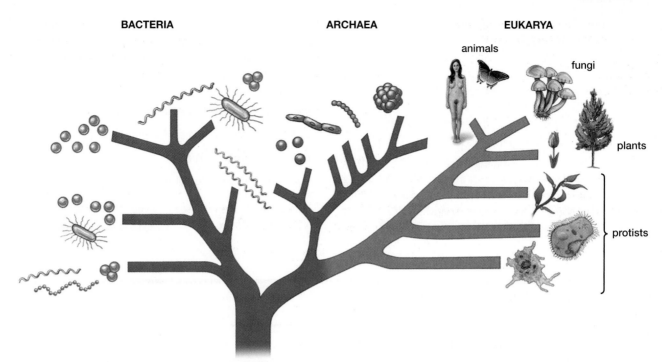

BACTERIA   **ARCHAEA**   **EUKARYA**

animals

fungi

plants

protists

FIRST CELLS

▲ FIGURE 1-11 **The domains and kingdoms of life**

This binomial system of naming organisms allows scientists worldwide to communicate very precisely about any given organism. In the following paragraphs, we provide a brief introduction to the domains and kingdoms of life. You will learn far more about life's incredible diversity and how it evolved in Unit 3.

There are exceptions to any simple set of criteria used to characterize the domains and kingdoms, but three characteristics are particularly useful: cell type, the number of cells in each organism, and how it acquires energy (**Table 1-1**).

The Domains Bacteria and Archaea Consist of Prokaryotic Cells; the Domain Eukarya Is Composed of Eukaryotic Cells

There are two fundamentally different types of cells: **prokaryotic** and **eukaryotic.** "Karyotic" refers to the **nucleus** of a cell, a membrane-enclosed sac containing the cell's genetic material (see Fig. 1-2). "Pro" means "before" in

Greek; prokaryotic cells almost certainly evolved before eukaryotic cells (and, as we will see in Chapter 17, eukaryotic cells almost certainly evolved from prokaryotic cells). Prokaryotic cells do not have a nucleus; their genetic material resides in their cytoplasm. They are usually small—only 1 or 2 micrometers in diameter—and lack membrane-bound organelles. The domains Bacteria and Archaea consist of prokaryotic cells; the cells of Eukarya, however, as the name implies, are eukaryotic. "Eu" means "true" in Greek, and eukaryotic cells possess a "true" membrane-enclosed nucleus. Eukaryotic cells are generally larger than prokaryotic cells and contain a variety of other organelles.

Bacteria and Archaea Are Mostly Unicellular; Members of the Kingdoms Fungi, Plantae, and Animalia Are Nearly All Multicellular

Most members of the domains Bacteria and Archaea are single celled, or **unicellular,** although a few live in strands or mats

Table 1-1	Some Characteristics Used in Classification of Organisms			
Domain	**Kingdom**	**Cell Type**	**Cell Number**	**Energy Acquisition**
Bacteria	(Under discussion)	Prokaryotic	Unicellular	Autotrophic or heterotrophic
Archaea	(Under discussion)	Prokaryotic	Unicellular	Autotrophic or heterotrophic
Eukarya	Fungi	Eukaryotic	Multicellular	Heterotrophic
	Plantae	Eukaryotic	Multicellular	Autotrophic
	Animalia	Eukaryotic	Multicellular	Heterotrophic
	"Protists"*	Eukaryotic	Uni- and multicellular	Autotrophic or heterotrophic

*The "protists" are a diverse collection of organisms that includes several kingdoms under discussion.

of cells with little communication, cooperation, or organization among them. Most members of the kingdoms Fungi, Plantae, and Animalia are many celled, or **multicellular;** their lives depend on intimate communication and cooperation among numerous specialized cells.

Members of the Different Kingdoms Have Different Ways of Acquiring Energy

Photosynthetic organisms—including some archaea, some bacteria, some protists, and most plants, are **autotrophic**—meaning "self-feeding." Organisms that cannot photosynthesize—including some archaea, some bacteria, some protists, and all fungi and animals—are **heterotrophic,** meaning "other feeding." Some heterotrophs, such as archaea, bacteria, and fungi, absorb individual food molecules from outside their bodies; others, including most animals, ingest chunks of food and break them down to molecules in their digestive tracts.

Case Study continued
Are Viruses Alive?

Notice that viruses are not included in our classification system of life. They infect cells of every known form of life, but how and when viruses evolved is unknown.

Links to *Everyday Life*

Knowledge of Biology Illuminates Life

Some people regard science as a "dehumanizing" activity, thinking that too deep an understanding of the world robs us of vision and awe. Nothing could be further from the truth, as we repeatedly discover in our own lives. For example, lupine flowers have two lower petals that form a tube enclosing both the male and the female reproductive parts (**Fig. E1-4**). In young lupine flowers, the weight of a bee on these petals forces pollen (carrying sperm) out of the tube and onto the bee's abdomen (see Fig. E1-4, inset). In older flowers ready to be fertilized, the female reproductive part protrudes through the lower petals. When a pollen-dusted bee visits, it usually leaves behind a few grains of pollen that contain the lupine's sperm.

Do these insights into lupine flowers detract from our appreciation of them? Far from it. We look on lupines with greater delight, because we understand some of the interplay of form and function, bee and flower, that shaped the evolution of the flower. Several years ago, as we crouched beside a wild lupine in Olympic National Park in Washington State, an elderly man stopped to ask what we were looking at so intently. He listened with interest as we explained the structure to him; he then went off to another patch of lupines to watch the bees foraging. He too felt the increased sense of wonder that comes with understanding.

Throughout this text, we try to convey to you that sense of understanding and wonder, and we hope that you, too, will experience it. We also emphasize that biology is not a completed work but an exploration that has really just begun. We cannot urge you strongly enough, even if you are not contemplating a career in biology, to join in the journey of biological discoveries throughout your life. Don't think of biology as just another course to take, just another set of facts to memorize. Biology is a pathway to a new understanding of yourself and of the life on Earth around you.

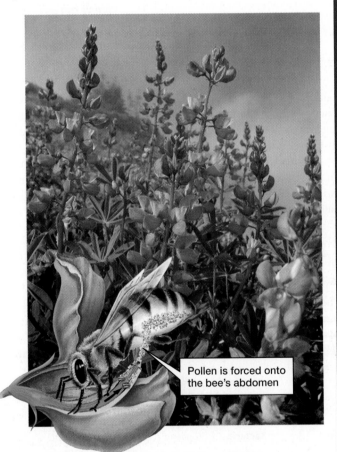

Pollen is forced onto the bee's abdomen

▲ **FIGURE E1-4 Wild lupines** Thousands of people visit Hurricane Ridge in Washington State's Olympic National Park each summer to gaze in awe at Mt. Olympus, but few bother to investigate the small wonders at their feet. (Inset) A lupine flower deposits pollen on a foraging bee's abdomen.

Case Study revisited
Are Viruses Alive?

Researchers got their first blurry glimpse of viruses in the mid-1930s, through the newly invented electron microscope. They discovered that the simplest viruses contain genetic material (DNA or RNA) surrounded by a coat made of proteins. This knowledge provided the first indication that viruses are not composed of cells. Many viruses, including Ebola and herpes, are somewhat more complex, with an outer envelope derived partly from the membrane of the cells they infect (**Fig. 1-12**). Protein spikes protrude from the viral surface and help them attach to and infect the cells of their victims. But this additional complexity still doesn't approach that of an actual cell.

Viruses seem to be inert packages of complex biological chemicals—that is, until they infect a living cell. After penetrating the host cell, the virus hijacks its metabolic processes, using the cell's energy, organelles, and raw materials to produce new viruses. The newly formed viruses then emerge from the host cell, often rupturing it and sometimes acquiring an envelope made of the host's plasma membrane. Errors in copying viral genetic material, or accidental recombination of viral genetic material with genetic material from different viruses or from the host cell itself, produce mutations that allow viruses to evolve. Through evolution, viruses sometimes become more infectious or more deadly, or they may gain the ability to infect new hosts.

The uncomplicated structure of viruses, coupled with amazing advances in biotechnology, has now allowed researchers to synthesize viruses in the laboratory using materials available from chemical supply companies. The first virus to be synthesized was the small, relatively simple poliovirus. This feat was accomplished by Eckard Wimmer and coworkers at the University of New York at Stony Brook in 2002. Did these researchers create life in the laboratory? A few scientists would say "yes"—defining life by its ability to reproduce and to evolve. The more stringent definition of life provided in this chapter explains why most scientists agree that viruses aren't exactly a "life-form": They are not composed of cells, they do not obtain or use their own energy or nutrients, they do nothing to maintain homeostasis, they do not respond to stimuli, nor do they grow. As virologist Luis Villarreal of the University of California at Irvine states, "Viruses are parasites that skirt the boundaries between life and inert matter."

▲ FIGURE 1-12 **A herpes virus**

BioEthics Consider This

Wimmer and coworkers' announcement that they had synthesized the poliovirus created considerable controversy both within and outside of the scientific community. People raised concerns that this research jeopardized the eradication of polio, which has nearly been eliminated by widespread vaccination. They feared that deadly and highly contagious viruses such as Ebola could now be synthesized by bioterrorists. The researchers responded that they were merely applying already established knowledge and techniques to demonstrate the principle that viruses are basically chemical entities that can be synthesized in the laboratory. Do you think scientists should synthesize viruses? What are the implications of forbidding such research?

CHAPTER REVIEW

Summary of Key Concepts

1.1 How Do Scientists Study Life?
Scientists identify a hierarchy of levels of organizations, as illustrated in Figure 1-1. Biology is based on the scientific principles of natural causality, uniformity in space and time, and common perception. Knowledge in biology is acquired through application of the scientific method, which starts with an observation leading to a question, which leads to a hypothesis. The hypothesis leads to a prediction that is tested by controlled experiments. The experimental results, which must be repeatable, either support or refute the hypothesis, leading to a conclusion about the validity of the hypothesis. A scientific theory is a general explanation of natural phenomena, developed through extensive and reproducible experiments and observations.

1.2 Evolution: The Unifying Theory of Biology
Evolution is the scientific theory that modern organisms descended, with modification, from preexisting life-forms. Evolution occurs as a consequence of genetic differences—arising from mutations—among members of a population, inheritance of those variations by offspring, and natural selection of the variations that best adapt an organism to its environment.

1.3 What Are the Characteristics of Living Things?
Organisms possess the following characteristics: Their structure is complex and organized; they maintain homeostasis; they respond to stimuli; they acquire energy and materials from the environment; they grow; they reproduce; and they have the capacity to evolve. Photosynthetic organisms capture and store the energy of sunlight in energy-rich molecules. Most obtain all of their nutrients from their nonliving environment. Organisms that cannot photosynthesize, and therefore eat other organisms, obtain all of their energy and most of their nutrients from the bodies of the organisms that they eat.

1.4 How Do Scientists Categorize the Diversity of Life?
Organisms can be grouped into three major categories, called domains: Archaea, Bacteria, and Eukarya. Within the Eukarya are three kingdoms, Fungi, Plantae, and Animalia, and unicellular eukaryotes known collectively as "protists." Features used to classify organisms include the cell type (eukaryotic or prokaryotic), cell number (unicellular or multicellular), and energy acquisition (autotrophic or heterotrophic). The genetic material of eukaryotic cells is enclosed within a membrane-bound nucleus. Prokaryotic cells do not have a nucleus. Food obtained by heterotrophic organisms is either ingested in chunks or absorbed molecule by

molecule from the environment. The features of the domains and kingdoms are summarized in Table 1-1.

Key Terms

adaptation *10*	kingdom *14*
atom *2*	molecule *2*
autotroph *16*	multicellular *16*
binomial system *14*	mutation *10*
biodiversity *12*	natural causality *4*
biosphere *2*	natural selection *9*
cell *2*	nucleus *15*
cell theory *11*	nutrient *13*
chromosome *10*	observation *4*
community *2*	organ *2*
conclusion *5*	organ system *2*
control *5*	organelle *11*
cytoplasm *11*	organic molecule *2*
deductive reasoning *9*	organism *2*
deoxyribonucleic acid	photosynthesis *13*
(DNA) *10*	plasma membrane *11*
domain *14*	population *2*
ecosystem *2*	prediction *5*
element *2*	prokaryotic *15*
energy *13*	question *5*
eukaryotic *15*	scientific method *4*
evolution *9*	scientific theory *8*
experiment *5*	scientific theory of
gene *11*	evolution *9*
heterotroph *16*	species *2*
homeostasis *13*	tissue *2*
hypothesis *5*	unicellular *15*
inductive reasoning *9*	variable *5*

Thinking Through the Concepts

Fill-in-the-Blank

1. The smallest particle of an element that retains all the properties of that element is a(n) _____. The smallest unit of life is the _____. Most molecules found in cells have frameworks of _____ atoms, and are called _____. Cells of a specific type within multicellular organisms combine to form _____.

2. A(n) _____ is a general explanation of natural phenomena supported by extensive, reproducible tests and observations. In contrast, a(n) _____ is a proposed explanation for observed events. To answer specific questions about life, biologists use a general process called the _____.

3. An important scientific theory that explains why organisms are at once so similar and also so diverse is the theory of _____. This theory explains life's diversity as having originated primarily through the process of _____.

4. The molecule that guides the construction and operation of an organism's body is called (complete term) _____, abbreviated as _____. This large molecule contains discrete segments with specific instructions; these segments are called _____.

5. Fill in the following about living things: Living things maintain a relatively stable internal environment by the process of _____; living things respond to _____; living things acquire and use _____ and _____ from the environment. Living things are composed of cells whose structure is both _____ and _____.

Review Questions

1. List the hierarchy of organization of life from an atom to a multicellular organism, briefly explaining each level.

2. What is the difference between a scientific theory and a hypothesis? Explain how scientists use each operation. Why do scientists refer to basic principles as "theories," not "facts"?

3. Explain the differences between inductive and deductive reasoning, and provide an example, real or hypothetical, of each.

4. Describe the scientific method. In what ways do you use the scientific method in everyday life?

5. What are the differences between a salt crystal and a tree? Which is living? How do you know?

6. Define and explain the terms *natural selection, evolution, mutation, creationism,* and *population.*

7. What is evolution? Briefly describe how evolution occurs.

8. Define *homeostasis.* Why must organisms continuously acquire energy and materials from the external environment to maintain homeostasis?

Applying the Concepts

1. Review the properties of life, and then discuss whether humans are unique.

2. Review Alexander Fleming's experiment that led to the discovery of penicillin. Devise an appropriate control for the experiment in which he applied filtered medium from a *Penicillium* culture to plates of bacteria.

3. Science is based on principles, including uniformity in space and time and common perception. Assume that humans encounter intelligent beings from a planet in another galaxy where they evolved under very different conditions. Discuss the two principles just mentioned, and explain how they would affect the nature of scientific observations on the different planets as well as communications about these observations.

4. Identify two different types of organisms that you have seen interacting, for example, a caterpillar on a plant such as a milkweed, or a beetle in a flower. Now, form a single, simple hypothesis about this interaction. Use the scientific method and your imagination to design an experiment that tests this hypothesis. Be sure to identify variables and control for them.

5. Explain an instance in which your understanding of a phenomenon enhances your appreciation of it.

(MB) *Go to www.masteringbiology.com for practice quizzes, activities, eText, videos, current events, and more.*

Scientific Inquiry

Radioactivity in Research

How do biologists know that DNA is the genetic material of cells? How do paleontologists measure the ages of fossils? How do botanists know how plants transport sugars made in their leaves during photosynthesis to other parts of the plant? These discoveries, and many more, were made possible only through the use of radioactive isotopes. During radioactive decay, the process by which a radioactive isotope spontaneously breaks apart, an isotope emits particles that can be detected with sensitive electronic devices. A particularly fascinating and medically important use of radioactive isotopes is in positron emission tomography, or PET, scans (**Fig. E2-1**). In one common application of PET scans, a subject is given glucose sugar with a radioactive isotope of fluorine attached. As the isotope decays, it emits two bursts of energy that travel in opposite directions. Detectors in a ring around the subject's head capture the emissions, recording the slightly different arrival times of the two energy bursts from each decaying particle.

A powerful computer then calculates the location within the brain where the decay occurred and generates a color-coded map of the frequency of decays within a given "slice" of the brain. The more active a brain region is, the more glucose it uses as an energy source, and the more radioactivity is concentrated there. For example, tumor cells grow and divide rapidly, using large amounts of glucose, so they show up in PET scans as "hot spots" (**Fig. E2-1c**). Normal brain regions activated by a specific mental task (for example, a math problem) will also have higher glucose demands that can be detected by PET scans. Thus, physicians can use PET to locate brain disorders, and researchers can use it to study what parts of the brain are activated by different mental processes.

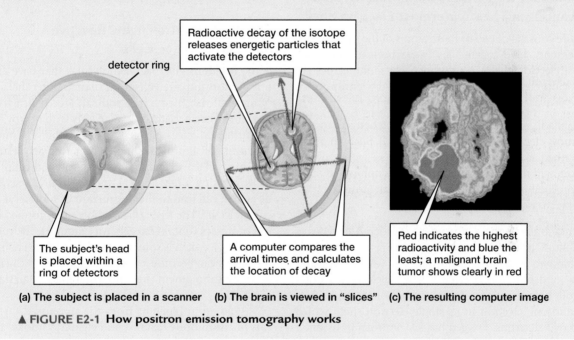

Radioactive decay of the isotope releases energetic particles that activate the detectors

detector ring

The subject's head is placed within a ring of detectors

A computer compares the arrival times and calculates the location of decay

Red indicates the highest radioactivity and blue the least; a malignant brain tumor shows clearly in red

(a) The subject is placed in a scanner   (b) The brain is viewed in "slices"   (c) The resulting computer image

▲ FIGURE E2-1 **How positron emission tomography works**

stability, whereas the electron shells allow attractive interactions, called **chemical bonds,** with other atoms. Nuclei resist disturbance by outside forces; ordinary sources of energy—such as heat, electricity, and light—hardly affect them at all. Because its nucleus is stable, a carbon atom remains carbon whether it is part of a diamond, carbon dioxide, or sugar. Electron shells, however, are dynamic, capable of capturing and releasing energy and forming chemical bonds.

Life Depends on the Ability of Electrons to Capture and Release Energy

Because electron shells correspond to energy levels, when an atom is excited by energy, such as heat or light, this energy causes an electron to jump from a lower-energy electron shell to a higher-energy shell. Soon afterward, the electron spontaneously falls back into its original electron shell, releasing the energy, often as light (**Fig. 2-3**).

We make use of this property of electrons every day. When we switch on an incandescent light bulb, electricity flowing through the filament in the bulb heats it, and the heat energy bumps electrons in the metal filament into higher-energy electron shells. As the electrons drop back down into their original shells, they emit their captured energy as light. Life itself depends on the ability of electrons to capture and release energy, as you will learn in Chapters 7 and 8, when we discuss photosynthesis and cellular respiration.

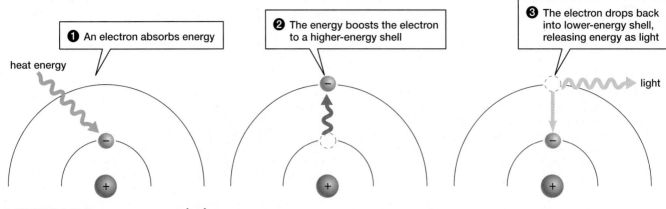

heat energy

❶ An electron absorbs energy

❷ The energy boosts the electron to a higher-energy shell

❸ The electron drops back into lower-energy shell, releasing energy as light

light

▲ **FIGURE 2-3 Energy capture and release**

2.2 HOW DO ATOMS INTERACT TO FORM MOLECULES?

Atoms Interact with Other Atoms When There Are Vacancies in Their Outermost Electron Shells

A **molecule** consists of two or more atoms of the same or different elements, held together by interactions among their outermost electron shells. A substance whose molecules are formed of different types of atoms is called a **compound.** Atoms behave according to two basic principles:

- An atom will not react with other atoms when its outermost electron shell is completely full. Such an atom is described as being inert.
- An atom will react with other atoms if its outermost electron shell is only partially full. Such an atom is described as being reactive.

To demonstrate these principles, consider three types of atoms: helium, hydrogen, and oxygen (see Figs. 2-1 and 2-2). Helium has two protons in its nucleus, and two electrons fill its single (and outermost) electron shell. Because its outer shell is full, helium is inert. Hydrogen has one proton in its nucleus and one electron in its single electron shell, which can hold two electrons. Oxygen has six electrons in its outer shell, which can hold eight. Hydrogen and oxygen atoms, both with partially empty outer shells, are reactive. One way for these atoms to gain stability is by reacting with each other. The single electrons from each of two hydrogen atoms can fill the outer shell of an oxygen atom, forming water (H_2O; see Fig. 2-6b later in the chapter). In fact, hydrogen reacts so vigorously with oxygen that the space shuttle and other rockets use liquid hydrogen as fuel to power liftoff. (See "Links to Everyday Life: Hmm . . . What Gas Should I Use to Inflate My Blimp—Or Fill My Car?")

An atom with an outermost electron shell that is partially full can gain stability by losing electrons (emptying the shell completely), gaining electrons (filling the shell), or sharing electrons with another atom (allowing both atoms to behave as though they had full outer shells). In many instances, reactions that fill or empty outer electron shells produce stable chemical bonds (described later).

However, certain reactions that occur routinely in the body generate molecules called free radicals that are highly unstable and reactive.

Free Radicals Are Highly Reactive and Can Damage Cells

Some reactions give rise to molecules that have atoms with one or more unpaired electrons in their outer shells. This type of molecule is called a **free radical.** Free radicals, which can be charged or uncharged, react readily with nearby molecules, capturing or releasing electrons to achieve a more stable arrangement. But in stealing or donating an electron, a free radical often leaves an unpaired electron in the molecule it attacks, creating a new radical and beginning a series of reactions that can lead to the destruction of biological molecules crucial to life. The free radicals most often formed by biological processes contain oxygen. An example is hydrogen peroxide (H_2O_2), which is sometimes used to bleach hair or whiten teeth. You can become a "peroxide blonde" because H_2O_2 reacts with the pigment (melanin) that makes hair dark, changing it into a colorless substance.

Radiation (such as from the sun and X-rays), chemicals in automobile exhaust and cigarette smoke, and industrial metals such as mercury and lead can enter our bodies and generate free radicals. Most free radicals, however, are generated by reactions that are essential to life because they supply cells with energy, using oxygen in the process. Cell death caused by free radicals contributes to a variety of human ailments, including heart disease and nervous system disorders such as Alzheimer's disease. By damaging genetic material, free radicals can also cause some forms of cancer. The gradual deterioration of the body that accompanies aging is believed by many scientists to result, at least in part, from free-radical damage accumulating over a lifetime of exposure (**Fig. 2-4**). Fortunately molecules called **antioxidants** react with free radicals and render them harmless. Our bodies synthesize several antioxidants, and others can be obtained from a healthy diet. Vitamins E and C are antioxidants, as are a variety of other substances found in fruits and vegetables. To learn about another

Links to *Everyday Life*

Hmm . . . What Gas Should I Use to Inflate My Blimp—Or Fill My Car?

On May 6, 1937, the luxury passenger blimp *Hindenburg* was descending to land in Lakehurst, New Jersey, having departed from Germany three days earlier. As its landing lines were dropped, the crowd of journalists, photographers, and a radio announcer gathered to chronicle its landing watched in horror as flames suddenly appeared. Within 40 seconds, the craft was fully consumed by fire (**Fig. E2-2**), and thirty six people were killed.

The *Hindenburg* was filled with hydrogen gas (H_2). Because of their half empty outer electron shells, the hydrogen atoms in H_2 combine vigorously with oxygen in the atmosphere; in other words, hydrogen burns. The highly combustible nature of hydrogen makes it a dangerous gas to use in blimps, but gives it the potential to replace gasoline as a fuel for vehicles. Burning hydrogen produces only water as a reaction product. Gasoline, however, consists of chains of carbons bonded to hydrogens, and the burning of gasoline not only combines oxygen and hydrogen atoms to produce water, it also combines oxygen with carbon atoms. This generates carbon dioxide gas, now recognized as a major contributor to global warming.

Should cars be fueled with hydrogen? If fossil fuels are used in the energy-intensive stages of generating, compressing, transporting, storing, and delivering hydrogen to cars, this could completely negate the reduction in carbon dioxide emissions that should be an advantage of burning hydrogen. But if solar, wind, or other renewable energy sources could be used to produce and deliver hydrogen, it might become a sustainable and environmentally-friendly replacement for gasoline.

▲ FIGURE E2-2 **The hydrogen-filled *Hindenburg* goes up in flames**

QUESTION Filling the *Hindenburg* with hydrogen rather than helium gave it some extra lift—explain why.

Incidentally, you need not worry that the blimps floating above stadiums at sporting events will burst into flames, because modern blimps are filled with helium. With its full outer electron shell, helium is nonreactive and cannot burn.

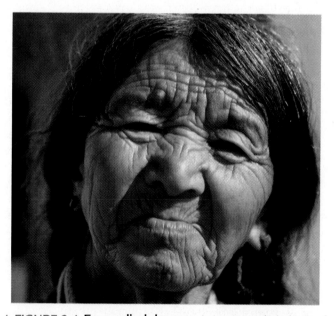

▲ FIGURE 2-4 **Free-radical damage** Aging is partly a result of accumulating free-radical damage to the biological molecules that compose our bodies. For example, sunlight can generate free radicals in skin, damaging molecules that give skin its elasticity and contributing to wrinkles as we age.

QUESTION How do free radicals damage biological molecules?

source of antioxidants, see "Health Watch: Might Chocolate Actually Be Good for You?" on p. 26.

Chemical Bonds Hold Atoms Together in Molecules

Chemical bonds, the attractive forces that hold atoms together in molecules, arise from interactions between adjacent atoms as they gain, lose, or share electrons. The atoms of each element have chemical bonding properties that arise from the configuration of electrons in their outer shells. A **chemical reaction** is a process by which new chemical bonds are formed or existing bonds are broken, converting one substance into another. There are three major types of chemical bonds: ionic bonds, covalent bonds, and hydrogen bonds (**Table 2-2**).

Ionic Bonds Form Among Charged Atoms Called Ions

Atoms that have an almost empty outermost electron shell, as well as atoms that have an almost full outermost shell, can become stable by losing electrons (emptying their outermost shells) or by gaining electrons (filling their outermost shells). The formation of table salt (sodium chloride

Health Watch

Might Chocolate Actually Be Good for You?

Many fruits and vegetables contain vitamins C and E as well as other antioxidants. But did you know that chocolate (**Fig. E2-3**) also contains antioxidants, and so might actually be a type of health food? Although it is extremely difficult to do controlled experiments on the effects of antioxidants in the human diet, there is evidence that diets high in antioxidants may be beneficial. For example, the low incidence of heart disease among the French has been attributed in part to antioxidants in wine, which many French people consume regularly. They also eat considerably more fruits and vegetables than Americans do.

Now, amazingly, researchers have given us an excuse to eat chocolate and feel good about it! Cocoa powder (the dark, bitter powder made from the seeds inside cacao pods; see Fig. E2-3 inset) contains high concentrations of flavenoids, which are powerful antioxidants, chemically related to those found in wine. No studies have yet been done to determine whether eating large quantities of chocolate actually reduces the risk of cancer or heart disease, but there will certainly be no shortage of volunteers for this research. Be aware that the most sinfully delicious chocolates are also high in fat and sugar, and becoming overweight by indulging could counteract any positive effects of the pure cocoa powder. However, slim "chocoholics" have reason to relax and enjoy!

▲ FIGURE E2-3 **Chocolate** Cocoa powder is derived from the cacao beans found inside cacao pods (inset), which grow on trees in tropical regions of the Americas.

or NaCl) demonstrates this principle. Sodium (Na) has only one electron in its outermost electron shell, and chlorine (Cl) has seven electrons in its outer shell, making it one electron short of a full shell (**Fig. 2-5a**).

Sodium can become stable by losing the electron from its outer shell to chlorine. This reaction also fills the outer shell of chlorine. Atoms that have lost or gained electrons, altering the balance between protons and electrons, are charged, and are called **ions.** To form sodium chloride, sodium loses an electron, becoming a positively charged sodium ion (Na^+), while chlorine picks up the electron and becomes a negatively charged chloride ion (Cl^-).

The sodium and chloride in NaCl are held together by **ionic bonds:** the electrical attraction between positively and negatively charged ions (**Fig. 2-5b**). The ionic bonds between sodium and chloride ions result in crystals composed of a

Table 2-2	Common Types of Bonds in Biological Molecules	
Type	**Type of Interaction**	**Example**
Ionic bond	An electron is transferred, creating positive and negative ions that attract one another	Occurs between the sodium (Na^+) and chloride (Cl^-) ions of table salt (NaCl)
Covalent bond	Electrons are shared	
Nonpolar	Equal sharing	Occurs between the two oxygen atoms in oxygen gas (O_2)
Polar	Unequal sharing	Occurs between the hydrogen and oxygen atoms of a water molecule (H_2O)
Hydrogen bond	A slightly positive hydrogen in a polar molecule attracts the slightly negative pole of a nearby polar molecule	Occurs between water molecules; slightly positive charges on hydrogen atoms attract slightly negative charges on oxygen atoms of adjacent molecules

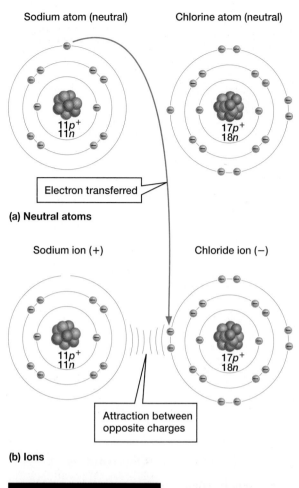

Sodium atom (neutral)   Chlorine atom (neutral)

11p⁺
11n

17p⁺
18n

Electron transferred

(a) Neutral atoms

Sodium ion (+)   Chloride ion (−)

11p⁺
11n

17p⁺
18n

Attraction between
opposite charges

(b) Ions

Cl⁻ Na⁺ Cl⁻
Na⁺ Cl⁻ Na⁺
Cl⁻ Na⁺ Cl⁻

(c) An ionic compound: NaCl

▲ **FIGURE 2-5 The formation of ions and ionic bonds**
(a) Sodium has only one electron in its outer electron shell;
chlorine has seven. **(b)** Sodium can become stable by losing an
electron, and chlorine can become stable by gaining an electron.
Sodium then becomes a positively charged ion and chlorine a
negatively charged ion. **(c)** Because oppositely charged particles
attract one another, the resulting sodium and chloride ions
nestle closely together in a crystal of salt, NaCl. The
arrangement of ions in salt causes it to form cubic crystals.

repeating, orderly array of the two ions (**Fig. 2-5c**). As we will
see later, water will often break ionic bonds.

Covalent Bonds Form Between Uncharged Atoms That Share Electrons

An atom with a partially full outermost electron shell can become stable by sharing electrons with another atom, forming
a **covalent bond** (**Fig. 2-6**).

Most Biological Molecules Utilize Covalent Bonding

Because biological molecules must function in a watery environment where ionic bonds rapidly dissociate (break apart),
the atoms in most biological molecules, such as those found
in proteins, sugars, and fats, are joined by covalent bonds. The
bonds formed by the most common atoms in biological molecules are illustrated in **Table 2-3**.

How Electrons Are Shared Determines Whether a Covalent Bond Is Nonpolar or Polar

The electrons in covalent bonds may be shared equally between the two atoms, or they may spend more time near
one of the two atoms. If the electrons are shared roughly
equally, the bond is called a **nonpolar covalent bond.**
Consider the hydrogen atom, which has one proton in its
nucleus and one electron in its electron shell (which can
hold two electrons). A hydrogen atom can become reasonably stable if it shares its single electron with another hydrogen atom, forming a molecule of hydrogen gas (H_2) in
which each atom behaves almost as if it had two electrons
in its electron shell (**Fig. 2-6a**). Because the two nuclei in H_2
are identical, the shared electrons spend equal time near
each nucleus. Therefore, not only is the molecule as a whole
electrically neutral or uncharged, but each end, or pole, of
the molecule is also uncharged. Other examples of nonpolar molecules include oxygen gas (O_2), nitrogen gas (N_2),
carbon dioxide (CO_2), and biological molecules such as
fats (see pp. 43–44).

In contrast, some pairs of atoms form covalent bonds
in which the shared electrons spend more time near one of
the atoms. This atom thus acquires a slight negative charge,
and the other atom takes on a slight positive charge. This situation produces a **polar covalent bond** (**Fig. 2-6b**). Although the molecule as a whole is electrically neutral, it has
charged poles. In water (H_2O), for example, an electron is
shared between each hydrogen atom and the central oxygen
atom. However, the shared electrons spend far more time
near the oxygen atom than near either of the hydrogen
atoms. By attracting electrons, the oxygen pole of a water
molecule becomes slightly negative, leaving each hydrogen
atom slightly positive (see Fig. 2-6b). Water is an example of
a polar molecule.

Hydrogen Bonds Are Attractive Forces Between Polar Molecules

As you might guess, opposite charges on polar molecules attract one another. A **hydrogen bond** is the attraction between the slightly positive hydrogen in a polar molecule and
the slightly negative pole of a nearby polar molecule.

Polar molecules result when hydrogen atoms form bonds
with nitrogen, oxygen, or fluorine. Although fluorine is rare in
biological molecules, O—H and N—H bonds are common.
Molecules such as water, sugars, proteins, and DNA are polar
and can form hydrogen bonds with other polar molecules or
with different polar regions of the same large molecule. Water

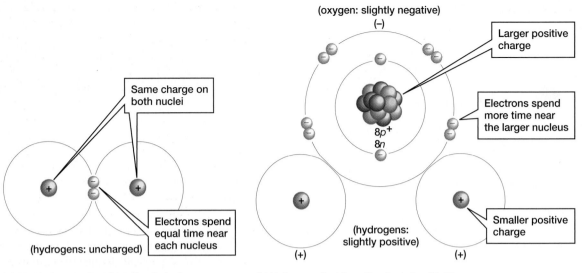

(oxygen: slightly negative)
(−)

Larger positive charge

Same charge on both nuclei

Electrons spend more time near the larger nucleus

$8p^+$
$8n$

Electrons spend equal time near each nucleus

(hydrogens: uncharged)

(hydrogens: slightly positive)

Smaller positive charge

(+)   (+)

(a) Nonpolar covalent bonding in hydrogen gas (H_2)

(b) Polar covalent bonding in water (H_2O)

▲ **FIGURE 2-6 Covalent bonds involve shared electrons (a)** In hydrogen gas, an electron from each hydrogen atom is shared, forming a single nonpolar covalent bond. **(b)** Oxygen lacks two electrons to fill its outer shell, so oxygen can form polar covalent bonds with two hydrogen atoms, creating water. Oxygen exerts a greater pull on the electrons than does hydrogen, so the "oxygen end" of the molecule has a slight negative charge and the "hydrogen end" has a slight positive charge.

molecules form hydrogen bonds with one another between their positive hydrogen poles and negative oxygen poles (**Fig. 2-7**). As we will see shortly, hydrogen bonds give water several unusual properties that are essential to life on Earth.

2.3 WHY IS WATER SO IMPORTANT TO LIFE?

As naturalist Loren Eiseley eloquently stated, "If there is magic on this planet, it is contained in water." Water is extraordinarily abundant on Earth, has unusual properties, and is so essential to life that it merits special consideration. Life is likely to have arisen in the waters of the primeval Earth, and

water makes up from 60% to 90% of the body weight of most organisms. What is so special about water?

Water Molecules Attract One Another

Hydrogen bonds interconnect water molecules. But, like square dancers continually moving from one partner to the next—joining and then releasing hands as they go—hydrogen bonds in liquid water easily break and re-form, allowing the water to flow. **Cohesion** among water molecules, caused by hydrogen bonding, produces **surface tension,** the tendency for the water surface to resist being broken. Surface tension can support fallen leaves, some spiders and water insects, and even a running basilisk lizard (**Fig. 2-8a**).

Table 2-3	Bonding Patterns of Atoms Commonly Found in Biological Molecules			
Atom	**Capacity of Outer Electron Shell**	**Electrons in Outer Shell**	**Number of Covalent Bonds Usually Formed**	**Common Bonding Patterns**
Hydrogen	2	1	1	—H
Carbon	8	4	4	C C C C
Nitrogen	8	5	3	N N N
Oxygen	8	6	2	O O
Phosphorus	8	5	5	P
Sulfur	8	6	2	S

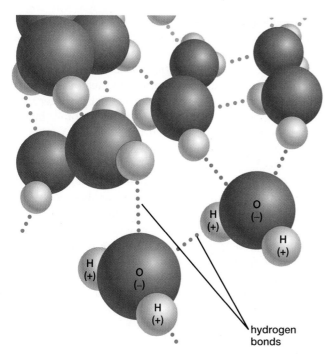

▲ **FIGURE 2-7 Hydrogen bonds in water** The partial charges on different parts of water molecules produce weak attractive forces called hydrogen bonds (dotted lines) between the oxygen and hydrogen atoms in adjacent water molecules. As water flows, these bonds are constantly breaking and re-forming.

Have you ever wondered

Why It Hurts So Much to Do a Belly Flop?

The slap of a belly flop provides firsthand experience of the power of cohesion among water molecules. Because of the hydrogen bonds that interconnect its molecules, the surface of water resists being broken. When you suddenly force water molecules apart over a large area using your body, the result can be a bit painful.

The cohesion of water plays a crucial role in the life of land plants. How does water absorbed through a plant's roots ever reach the leaves, especially if the plant is a 300-foot-tall redwood tree (**Fig. 2-8b**)? Water molecules in plants fill tiny tubes that connect the roots, stem, and leaves. Water molecules evaporating from the leaves pull water up these tubes, much like a chain being dragged up from the top. The system works because the hydrogen bonds that link water molecules are stronger than the weight of the water in the tube and so the water chain doesn't break. Without the cohesion of water, there would be no land plants as we know them, and terrestrial life would have evolved quite differently.

Water also exhibits **adhesion,** a tendency to stick to surfaces having slight charges that attract the polar water molecules. If you touch water with the end of a very narrow glass tube, adhesion will draw the water a short distance up into the tube. In a similar way, adhesion also helps water in plants move up the thin tubes from roots to leaves.

Water Interacts with Many Other Molecules

A **solvent** is a substance that **dissolves** (completely surrounds and disperses) other substances. A solvent containing one or more dissolved substances is called a **solution.** Molecules involved in biochemical reactions are often in solution; this allows them to move around freely and meet one another to react. Water is an excellent solvent; its polar nature attracts it to other polar molecules and to ions, causing it to surround them. Water dissolves many molecules that are important to life, including proteins, salts, sugars, oxygen, and carbon dioxide.

To illustrate water's role as a solvent, let's look at how table salt dissolves. A crystal of table salt is held together by the electrical attraction between positively charged sodium ions and negatively charged chloride ions (see Fig. 2-5c). If a salt crystal is dropped into water, the positively charged hydrogen poles of water molecules will congregate around the negatively charged chloride ions, and the negatively charged oxygen poles of water molecules will attract the positively charged sodium ions. As water molecules enclose the sodium

(a) Cohesion causes surface tension

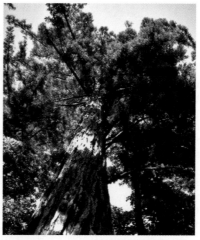

(b) Cohesion helps water to reach treetops

◀ **FIGURE 2-8 Cohesion among water molecules (a)** A basilisk lizard uses surface tension as it races across the water's surface to escape a predator. **(b)** Cohesion caused by hydrogen bonding allows water evaporating from the leaves of plants to pull water up from the roots.

▲ FIGURE 2-9 **Water as a solvent** When a salt crystal is dropped into water, the water surrounds the sodium and chloride ions with oppositely charged poles of its molecules. The ions disperse as the surrounding water molecules isolate them from one another, and the crystal gradually dissolves.

and chloride ions, shielding them from interacting with each other, the ions separate from the crystal and drift away in the water—thus, the salt dissolves (**Fig. 2-9**).

Water also dissolves other polar molecules because its positive and negative poles are attracted to their oppositely charged poles. Because of their electrical attraction for water molecules, ions and polar molecules are described as **hydrophilic** (from the Greek "hydro," meaning "water," and "philic" meaning "loving"). Many biological molecules are hydrophilic and dissolve readily in water.

Gases such as oxygen and carbon dioxide are essential for biochemical reactions but are nonpolar—so how do they dissolve? These molecules are so small that they fit into the spaces among water molecules without disrupting the hydrogen bonds linking the water molecules. Fish swimming below the ice on a frozen lake rely on oxygen that dissolved before the ice formed, and the CO_2 they release dissolves into the water.

Case Study continued

Crushed by Ice

The seawater in which the *Endurance* sank provides an excellent illustration of the ability of water to dissolve other molecules. Seawater contains more than 70 different elements, most in trace quantities. The most abundant dissolved elements are sodium and chlorine (NaCl; comprising about 3.2% of seawater by weight) and smaller amounts of sulfur, calcium, magnesium, potassium, and nitrogen. Ocean water also contains dissolved gases such as oxygen and carbon dioxide. Oxygen in seawater allows aquatic animals to respire, and carbon dioxide allows photosynthesis, which makes energy available to aquatic organisms.

Larger molecules with nonpolar covalent bonds, such as fats and oils, usually do not dissolve in water and hence are called **hydrophobic** (Greek for "water-fearing"). Nevertheless, water has an important effect on such molecules. When oil molecules encounter one another in water, their nonpolar surfaces nestle closely together, surrounded by water molecules that form hydrogen bonds with one another but not with the oil. Thus, the oil molecules remain together in droplets (**Fig. 2-10**). Because oil is less dense than water, these droplets float. The tendency of oil molecules to clump together in water is described as a **hydrophobic interaction.** As we will discuss in Chapter 5, the membranes of living cells owe much of their structure to both hydrophilic and hydrophobic interactions.

In addition to its role as a solvent, water is directly involved in many of the chemical reactions that occur in living cells. For example, the oxygen that plants release into the air is derived from water during photosynthesis. The chemical reactions in cells that manufacture proteins, fats, or nucleic acids liberate water; conversely, water is split apart and used in the reactions that break down these molecules, as described in later chapters.

Water-Based Solutions Can Be Acidic, Basic, or Neutral

Although water is generally regarded as a stable compound, it has a slight tendency to spontaneously form ions that, in turn, can reunite to form water. At any given time, a small

▲ FIGURE 2-10 **Oil and water don't mix** Yellow oil has just been poured into this bottle of water and is rising to the surface. Oil floats because it is less dense than water, and it forms droplets in water because it is a hydrophobic, nonpolar molecule that is not attracted to water's polar molecules.

fraction of water molecules have split into hydroxide ions (OH⁻) and hydrogen ions (H⁺) (**Fig. 2-11**).

water
(H₂O)

hydroxide ion
(OH⁻)

hydrogen ion
(H⁺)

▲ FIGURE 2-11 **Some water is ionized**

A hydroxide ion is negatively charged because it has gained an electron from the hydrogen atom. By losing an electron, the hydrogen atom is converted into a positively charged hydrogen ion. Pure water contains equal concentrations of hydrogen ions and hydroxide ions.

In many solutions, however, the concentrations of H^+ and OH^- are not the same. If the concentration of H^+ exceeds the concentration of OH^-, the solution is **acidic.** An **acid** is a substance that releases hydrogen ions when it dissolves in water. When hydrochloric acid (HCl), for example, is added to pure water, almost all of the HCl molecules separate into H^+ and Cl^-. Therefore, the concentration of H^+ greatly exceeds

the concentration of OH^-, and the resulting solution is acidic. Many acidic substances, such as lemon juice and vinegar, have a sour taste because the sour receptors on your tongue are specialized to respond to an excess of H^+. Bacteria common in your mouth can form a coating on your teeth and break down sugar from trapped food, producing lactic acid. The excess H^+ released by the acid can cause tooth enamel to dissolve and erode away, creating a cavity. Orange juice and many soft drinks are quite acidic, but generally don't remain in your mouth long enough to damage teeth.

If the concentration of OH^- is greater than H^+, the solution is **basic.** A **base** is a substance that combines with hydrogen ions, reducing their number. If, for instance, sodium hydroxide (NaOH) is added to water, the NaOH molecules separate into Na^+ and OH^-. Some OH^- ions combine with H^+ to produce H_2O, reducing the number of H^+ ions and creating a basic solution.

The degree of acidity is expressed on the **pH scale** (**Fig. 2-12**), in which neutrality (equal numbers of H^+ and OH^-) is indicated by the number 7. Pure water, with equal concentrations of H^+ and OH^-, has a pH of 7. Acids have a pH below 7; bases have a pH above 7. Each unit on the pH scale represents a tenfold change in the concentration of H^+. Thus, a soft drink with a pH of 3 has a concentration of H^+ that is 10,000 times that of water, which has a pH of 7.

▲ FIGURE 2-12 **The pH scale** The pH scale reflects the concentration of hydrogen ions in a solution. The pH (upper scale) is the negative log of the H^+ concentration (lower scale). Each unit on the scale represents a tenfold change. Lemon juice, for example, is about 10 times more acidic than orange juice, and the most severe acid rains in the northeastern United States are almost 1,000 times more acidic than normal rainfall. Except for the inside of your stomach, nearly all the fluids in your body are finely adjusted to a pH of about 7.4.

A Buffer Helps Maintain a Solution at a Relatively Constant pH

In most mammals, including humans, both the cell interior (cytoplasm) and the fluids that bathe the cell are nearly neutral (pH about 7.3 to 7.4). Small increases or decreases in pH may cause drastic changes in both the structure and function of biological molecules, leading to the death of cells or entire organisms. Nevertheless, living cells seethe with chemical reactions that take up or give off H^+. How, then, does the pH remain constant overall? The answer lies in the many buffers found in living organisms. A **buffer** is a compound that tends to maintain a solution at a constant pH by accepting or releasing H^+ in response to small changes in H^+ concentration. If the H^+ concentration rises, buffers combine with them; if the H^+ concentration falls, buffers release H^+. Thus, the original concentration of H^+ is maintained. Common buffers in living organisms include phosphate ($H_2PO_4^-$ and HPO_4^{2-}) and bicarbonate (HCO_3^-), both of which can accept or release H^+ depending on the circumstances. Blood pH is precisely regulated by bicarbonate ions.

Water Moderates the Effects of Temperature Changes

Your body and the bodies of other organisms can survive only within a limited temperature range. As we will see in Chapter 6, high temperatures may damage enzymes that promote the chemical reactions essential to life. Low temperatures are also dangerous because enzyme action slows as the temperature drops. Fortunately, water has important properties that moderate the effects of temperature changes. These properties help keep the bodies of organisms within tolerable temperature limits. All of these properties result from the polar nature of water molecules, which allows hydrogen bonds to form among them (see Fig. 2-7).

It Takes a Lot of Energy to Heat Water

The energy required to heat 1 gram of a substance by $1\,°C$ is called its **specific heat.** Water has a very high specific heat, meaning that it takes more energy to heat water than to heat most other substances by the same amount. For example, the energy required to heat a given weight of water by $1\,°C$ would raise the temperature of an equal weight of rock by about $50\,°C$.

At any temperature above absolute zero ($-273\,°C$), the atoms or molecules within a substance are in constant motion. Heat energy speeds up molecular movement. But increasing the rate of movement of water molecules requires that the hydrogen bonds between them be broken at a higher rate. A considerable amount of heat energy must be expended to break these bonds, and this energy is then unavailable to raise the temperature of the water. The high specific heat of water allows organisms, whose bodies are mostly water, to inhabit hot, sunny environments without overheating. The sunbathers in **Figure 2-13a** are taking advantage of this property of water.

It Takes a Lot of Energy to Cause Water to Evaporate

Sunbathers take advantage of another property of water—its high heat of vaporization. The **heat of vaporization** is the amount of heat needed to cause a substance to evaporate (to change from a liquid to a vapor). It takes a great deal of heat energy (539 calories per gram) to convert liquid water to water vapor; in fact, water's heat of vaporization is one of the highest known. This is also due to the polar nature of water molecules and the hydrogen bonds that interconnect them. For a water molecule to evaporate, it must absorb sufficient energy to break all the hydrogen bonds linking it to nearby water molecules. Only the fastest-moving water molecules, carrying the most energy, can break free and escape into the air. The remaining water is cooled by the loss of these high-energy molecules. Sunbathers benefit because their evaporating

(a) Water's high specific heat protects sunbathers

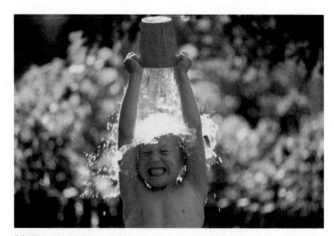

(b) Water's high heat of vaporization cools the body

▲ FIGURE 2-13 **Water's high specific heat and high heat of vaporization affect human behavior (a)** Because our bodies are mostly water, sunbathers can absorb a great deal of heat without sending their body temperatures skyrocketing, a result of water's high specific heat. **(b)** Water's high heat of vaporization (evaporative cooling) and specific heat together make water a very effective coolant on a hot day.

Case Study continued
Crushed by Ice

Shackleton and his crew did not lack drinking water during the months they spent waiting; they could simply melt chunks of ice. Although the ice had solidified from salty ocean water, Na^+ and Cl^- ions (and the other substances dissolved in ocean water) do not fit into the lattice of water molecules that make up the crystalline structure of ice (see Fig. 2-14). As ice forms, the remaining water becomes increasingly salty and requires increasingly low temperatures to freeze.

▲ FIGURE 2-14 **Liquid water (left) and ice (right)**

perspiration carries away a lot of heat without much loss of water. Children playing in water on a hot summer day are cooled as heat energy from their bodies breaks the hydrogen bonds of water, first as the water is warmed and then as it evaporates from their skin (**Fig. 2-13b**).

Water Forms an Unusual Solid: Ice

Even solid water is unusual. Most liquids become denser when they solidify, but ice is less dense than liquid water. The molecules of liquid water are continually moving past one another, breaking and re-forming hydrogen bonds as they shift position. When water freezes, however, each molecule forms stable hydrogen bonds with four other water molecules, creating an open, hexagonal (six-sided) arrangement. This keeps the water molecules further apart than their average distance in liquid water, so ice is less dense than liquid water (**Fig. 2-14**). The beautiful six-sided symmetry of snowflakes is an outgrowth of the hexagonal array of water molecules in ice crystals.

When a pond or lake starts to freeze in winter, the ice floats on top, forming an insulating layer that delays the freezing of the rest of the water. This insulation allows fish and other aquatic animals to survive in the liquid water below. If ice were to sink, many ponds and lakes around the world would freeze solid from the bottom up during the winter, killing plants, fish, and other underwater organisms. The ocean floor at higher latitudes would be covered with extremely thick layers of ice that would never melt.

Case Study revisited
Crushed by Ice

Although they failed to traverse Antarctica by dogsled, the heroic and ultimately successful efforts of Shackleton and his crew to return home alive are a remarkable true-life adventure. By studying Figure 2-14 you can see why the *Endurance* was crushed—the orderly arrangement of water molecules in ice causes them to occupy more space than they did as a liquid; thus, water expands as it forms ice. You have witnessed this firsthand if you've ever left a full water bottle in the freezer and later found it cracked open by the expanding ice. The expansion of ice also explains why it floats and why the ice formed a safe campground for the crew of the *Endurance*.

Many animals rely on ocean ice, from penguins and walruses that breed on the ice sheets, to polar bears that use the ice as a staging ground to hunt seals. The seals themselves are protected from their polar bear predators by the ice cover as they hunt for fish beneath it, becoming vulnerable when they surface to breathe through holes that they maintain in the ice.

Consider This

Many of water's unique properties are the result of its polar covalent bonds, which allow water molecules to form hydrogen bonds with each other. What if water molecules were nonpolar? How would this have affected the voyage of the *Endurance*?

CHAPTER REVIEW

Summary of Key Concepts

2.1 What Are Atoms?

An element is a substance that can neither be broken down nor converted to different substances by ordinary chemical means. The smallest possible particle of an element is the atom, which is itself composed of a central nucleus, containing protons and neutrons, and electrons outside the nucleus. All atoms of a given element have the same number of protons, different from that in every other element. Neutrons cluster with protons in most atomic nuclei, contributing to the atomic weight of the nucleus but not affecting its charge. Electrons orbit the nucleus within specific regions called electron shells. Shells at increasing distances from the nucleus contain electrons with increasing amounts of energy. Each shell can contain a fixed maximum number of electrons. The chemical reactivity of an atom depends on the number of electrons in its outermost electron shell; an atom is most stable when its outermost shell is full.

2.2 How Do Atoms Interact to Form Molecules?

Atoms gain stability by filling or emptying their outermost electron shell by acquiring, losing, or sharing electrons during chemical reactions. This results in stable attractions called chemical bonds among atoms, forming molecules. Some chemical reactions produce unstable and reactive atoms or molecules, called free radicals, with unpaired electrons in their outer shells. These may react with important biological molecules, such as DNA, destroying them. Antioxidants help protect against free-radical damage.

Chemical bonds may be ionic, covalent, or hydrogen bonds. Atoms that have lost or gained electrons are negatively or positively charged particles called ions. Ionic bonds are electrical attractions between charged ions, holding them together in crystals. When two atoms share electrons, covalent bonds form. In a nonpolar covalent bond, the two atoms share electrons equally. In a polar covalent bond, one atom attracts the electron more strongly than the other atom does, giving the molecule slightly positive and negative poles. Polar covalent bonds allow hydrogen bonding, the attraction between the slightly positive hydrogen on one molecule and the slightly negative regions of other polar molecules.

2.3 Why Is Water So Important to Life?

Water has many unique properties that allowed life as we know it to evolve. Water is polar and dissolves polar substances and ions. Water forces nonpolar substances, such as fat, to form clumps. Water also participates directly in some chemical reactions. Water molecules cohere to each other using hydrogen bonds, and adhere to many surfaces. Because of its high specific heat and heat of vaporization, water helps maintain a fairly stable temperature despite wide temperature fluctuations in the environment. Water is almost unique in being less dense in its frozen than in its liquid state.

Key Terms

acid *31*	free radical *24*
acidic *31*	heat of vaporization *32*
adhesion *29*	hydrogen bond *27*
antioxidant *24*	hydrophilic *30*
atom *21*	hydrophobic *30*
atomic mass *22*	hydrophobic interaction *30*
atomic nucleus *21*	ion *26*
atomic number *21*	ionic bond *26*
base *31*	isotope *22*
basic *31*	molecule *24*
buffer *32*	neutron *21*
chemical bond *23*	nonpolar covalent bond *27*
chemical reaction *25*	pH scale *31*
cohesion *28*	polar covalent bond *27*
compound *24*	proton *21*
covalent bond *27*	radioactive *22*
dissolve *29*	solution *29*
electron *21*	solvent *29*
electron shell *22*	specific heat *32*
element *21*	surface tension *28*

Thinking Through the Concepts

Fill-in-the-Blank

1. An atom consists of an atomic nucleus composed of positively charged _____ and uncharged _____. The number of positively charged particles in the nucleus determines the _____ of the element. Orbiting around the nucleus are _____ that occupy confined spaces called _____.

2. An atom that has lost or gained one or more electrons is called a(n) _____. If an atom loses an electron it takes on a(n) _____ charge. If it gains an electron it takes on a(n) _____ charge. Atoms with opposite charges attract one another, forming _____ bonds.

3. Atoms of the same element that differ in the number of neutrons in their nuclei are called _____ of one another. Some of these atoms spontaneously break apart, releasing _____ and forming different atoms in the process. Atoms that behave this way are described as being _____.

4. An atom with an outermost electron shell that is either completely full or completely empty is described as _____. Atoms with partially full outer electron shells are _____. Covalent bonds are formed when atoms _____ electrons, filling their outer shells.

5. Highly reactive atoms or molecules with unpaired electrons in their outer shells are called _____. These can damage biological molecules, including the hereditary molecule called _____. Some of this damage can be prevented by _____.

6. Water is described as _____ because each water molecule has partial negative and positive charges. This property allows water molecules to form _____ bonds with one another. The bonds between water molecules give water a high _____ that produces surface tension.

Review Questions

1. What are the six most abundant elements found in the human body by percent weight?

2. Distinguish between atoms and molecules; between elements and compounds; and among protons, neutrons, and electrons.

3. Compare and contrast covalent bonds and ionic bonds.

4. Why can water absorb a great amount of heat with little increase in its temperature?

5. Describe how water dissolves a salt. How does this phenomenon compare with the effect of water on a hydrophobic substance such as corn oil?

6. Define *pH*, *acid*, *base*, and *buffer*. How do buffers reduce changes in pH when hydrogen ions or hydroxide ions are added to a solution? Why is this phenomenon important in organisms?

Applying the Concepts

1. Fats and oils do not dissolve in water; polar and ionic molecules dissolve easily in water. Detergents and soaps

help clean by dispersing fats and oils in water so that they can be rinsed away. From your knowledge of the structure of water and the hydrophobic nature of fats, what general chemical structures (for example, polar or nonpolar parts) must a soap or detergent have, and why?

2. If the density of ice were greater than that of liquid water, how would this affect aquatic life? Describe some impacts this would have on terrestrial organisms.

3. How does sweating help you regulate your body temperature? Why do you feel hotter and more uncomfortable on a hot, humid day than on a hot, dry day?

4. Free radicals are formed when organisms use oxygen to metabolize sugar to make high-energy molecules. Ross Hardison, of Pennsylvania State University, stated: "Keeping oxygen under control while using it in energy production has been one of the great compromises struck in the evolution of life on Earth." What did he mean by this?

5. Some people have proposed towing huge icebergs to regions where people are short of drinking water. How can ice that formed from salty ocean water be good to drink?

6. Earth's atmosphere is about 20% oxygen (O_2), 79% nitrogen (N_2), and 0.38% carbon dioxide (CO_2). Explain why blimps will float in air if they are filled with either hydrogen (H_2) or helium (He). Which gas is preferable for filling blimps, and why?

(MB) *Go to www.masteringbiology.com for practice quizzes, activities, eText, videos, current events, and more.*

Biological Molecules

▲ Although this cow is healthy, mad cow disease leaves animals drooling and often unable to stand.

Case Study

Puzzling Proteins

"YOU KNOW, LISA, I think something is wrong with me," the vibrant, 22-year-old scholarship winner told her sister. It was 2001 when Charlene began to lose her memory and experience mood swings. During the next three years, her symptoms worsened. Charlene's hands shook, she was subject to uncontrollable episodes of biting and striking people, and became unable to walk or swallow. In June 2004, Charlene became the first U.S. resident to die of the human form of mad cow disease, which she had almost certainly contracted more than 10 years earlier while living in England.

It was not until the mid-1990s that health officials recognized that mad cow disease, or bovine spongiform encephalitis (BSE), could be spread to people who ate meat from infected cattle. Although millions of people may have eaten this tainted beef, only about 200 people worldwide have died from the human version of BSE, or variant Creutzfeldt-Jakob disease (vCJD). For those infected, however, the disease is always fatal, riddling brains of both humans with vCJD and cows with BSE with microscopic holes, giving the brain a spongy appearance.

Where did mad cow disease come from? For centuries, it was known that sheep could suffer from a spongiform encephalitis called scrapie. Scientists believe that a mutated form of scrapie became capable of infecting cattle, perhaps as early as the early 1980s. At that time, cattle feed often contained parts from sheep, some of whom may have harbored scrapie. Since 1986, when BSE was first identified in British cattle, millions of cattle there have been slaughtered and their bodies burned to prevent its spread.

Why is mad cow disease particularly fascinating to scientists? In the early 1980s, Dr. Stanley Prusiner, a researcher at the University of California—San Francisco, startled the scientific world by providing evidence that a protein, which lacks genetic material (DNA or RNA), was the cause of scrapie, and that this protein could transmit the disease to experimental animals in the laboratory. He dubbed the infectious proteins "prions" (pronounced PREE-ons), short for "proteinaceous infectious particles."

What are proteins? How do they differ from DNA and RNA? How can a protein with no hereditary material infect another organism, increase in number, and produce a fatal disease? Read on to find out.

At a Glance

3.1 WHY IS CARBON SO IMPORTANT IN BIOLOGICAL MOLECULES?

You have probably seen fruits and vegetables grown without synthetic fertilizers or pesticides labeled as "organic." But in chemistry, **organic** describes molecules that have a carbon skeleton bonded to some hydrogen atoms. The term is derived from the ability of living organisms to synthesize and use this general type of molecule. **Inorganic** molecules, which include carbon dioxide (which lacks hydrogen atoms) and all molecules without carbon (such as water and salt), are far less diverse and generally far simpler than organic molecules.

Life is characterized by an amazing variety of molecules interacting in ways that are dazzlingly complex. Molecular interactions are governed by the structures of molecules and the chemical properties that arise from these structures. Life is a dynamic condition; as molecules within cells interact with one another, their structures and chemical properties change. Collectively, these precisely orchestrated changes give cells the ability to acquire and utilize nutrients, to eliminate wastes, to move and grow, and to reproduce.

The versatile carbon atom is the key to the tremendous variety of organic molecules that make life on Earth possible. The carbon atom has four electrons in its outermost shell, which can accommodate eight electrons. Therefore, a carbon atom can become stable by bonding with up to four other atoms, or by forming double or even triple bonds. As a result, organic molecules can assume complex shapes, including branched chains, rings, sheets, and helices.

Attached to the carbon backbone of organic molecules are **functional groups,** groups of atoms that help determine the characteristics and chemical reactivity of the molecules. Functional groups are less stable than the carbon backbone and more likely to participate in chemical reactions. A large number of different functional groups may be attached to organic molecules; the six most common functional groups found in biological molecules are shown in **Table 3-1**.

Although the molecules of life are incredibly diverse, most contain the same basic set of functional groups. Further, most large organic molecules are synthesized from repeating subunits, as described in the following section.

3.2 HOW ARE ORGANIC MOLECULES SYNTHESIZED?

Although a complex molecule could be made by combining atom after atom following an extremely detailed blueprint, life takes a modular approach, preassembling smaller molecules and hooking them together. Just as trains are made by joining a series of train cars, small organic molecules (for example, sugars or amino acids) are joined to form longer molecules (for example, starches or proteins)—like cars in a train. The individual subunits are called **monomers** (from Greek words meaning "one part"); chains of monomers are called **polymers** ("many parts").

Table 3-1   Important Functional Groups in Biological Molecules

Group	Structure	Properties	Found In
Hydroxyl	—O—H	Polar; involved in dehydration and hydrolysis reactions	Sugars, starches, nucleic acids, alcohols, some acids, and steroids
Carbonyl		Polar; tends to make parts of molecules hydrophilic (water-soluble)	Sugars, some hormones, some vitamins
Carboxyl		Acidic; the negatively charged oxygen may bond H^+, forming carboxylic acid (—COOH); involved in peptide bonds	Amino acids, fatty acids
Amino		Basic; may bond an additional H^+, becoming positively charged; involved in peptide bonds	Amino acids, nucleic acids
Sulfhydryl	—S—H	Forms disulfide bonds in proteins	Some amino acids; many proteins
Phosphate		Acidic; links nucleotides in nucleic acids; energy-carrier group in ATP (this ionized form occurs in cellular environments)	Nucleic acids, phospholipids

Biological Polymers Are Formed by Removing Water and Split Apart by Adding Water

The subunits of large biological molecules are usually joined by a chemical reaction called **dehydration synthesis,** literally meaning "to form by removing water." In dehydration synthesis, a hydrogen ion (H^+) is removed from one subunit and a hydroxyl ion (OH^-) is removed from a second subunit, leaving openings in the outer electron shells of atoms in the two subunits. These openings are filled when the subunits share electrons, creating a covalent bond that links them. The hydrogen ion and the hydroxyl ion combine to form a molecule of water (H_2O), as shown in **Figure 3-1** using arbitrary subunits.

▲ FIGURE 3-1 Dehydration synthesis

The reverse reaction, **hydrolysis** ("to break apart with water"), splits the molecule back into its original subunits, with water donating a hydrogen ion to one subunit and a hydroxyl ion to the other (**Fig. 3-2**).

▲ FIGURE 3-2 Hydrolysis

Digestive enzymes use hydrolysis to break down food. For example, the starch in a cracker is composed of a series of glucose (simple sugar) molecules (see Fig. 3-8). Enzymes in our saliva and small intestines promote hydrolysis of the starch into individual sugar molecules that can be absorbed into the body.

In spite of the tremendous diversity of biological molecules, most of them fall into one of four general categories: carbohydrates, lipids, proteins, and nucleotides/nucleic acids (Table 3-2).

3.3 WHAT ARE CARBOHYDRATES?

Carbohydrate molecules are composed of carbon, hydrogen, and oxygen in the approximate ratio of 1:2:1. This formula explains the origin of the word "carbohydrate," which literally means "carbon plus water." All carbohydrates are either small, water-soluble **sugars** or polymers of sugar, such as starch. If a carbohydrate consists of just one sugar molecule, it is called a **monosaccharide** (Greek for "single

Table 3-2	Principal Types of Biological Molecules		
Type and Structure of Molecule	**Principal Subtypes and Structures**	**Example**	**Function**
Carbohydrate: Most contain carbon, oxygen, and hydrogen, in the approximate formula $(CH_2O)_{n*}$	*Monosaccharide:* Simple sugar, often with the formula $C_6H_{12}O_6$	Glucose Fructose	Important energy source for cells; subunit of polysaccharides
	Disaccharide: Two monosaccharides bonded together	Sucrose	Energy-storage molecule in fruits and honey
			Principal sugar transported throughout the bodies of land plants
	Polysaccharide: Chain of monosaccharides (usually glucose)	Starch	Energy storage in plants
		Glycogen	Energy storage in animals
		Cellulose	Structural material in plants
Lipid: Contains a high proportion of carbon and hydrogen; most lipids are nonpolar and insoluble in water	*Triglyceride:* Three fatty acids bonded to glycerol	Oil, fat	Energy storage in animals and some plants
	Wax: Variable numbers of fatty acids bonded to a long-chain alcohol	Waxes in plant cuticle	Waterproof covering on leaves and stems of land plants
	Phospholipid: Polar phosphate group and two fatty acids bonded to glycerol	Phosphatidylcholine	Component of cell membranes
	Steroid: Four fused rings of carbon atoms with functional groups attached	Cholesterol	Component of the membranes of eukaryotic cells; precursor for other steroids such as testosterone and bile salts
Protein: Consists of one or more chains of amino acids; may have up to four levels of structure that determine its function	*Peptide:* Short chain of amino acids	Oxytocin	Hormone consisting of nine amino acids; functions include stimulating uterine contractions during childbirth
	Polypeptide: Long chain of amino acids; also called "protein"	Hemoglobin	Globular protein composed of four subunit peptides; transport of oxygen in vertebrate blood
Nucleotide/nucleic acid: *Nucleotide:* Consists of a sugar, a base, and a phosphate group	*Nucleotide:* Composed of a five-carbon sugar (ribose or deoxyribose), a nitrogen-containing base, and a phosphate group	Adenosine triphosphate (ATP)	Principal short-term energy carrier molecule in cells
		Cyclic adenosine monophosphate (cAMP)	Intracellular messenger
Nucleic acid: A polymer made of nucleotides	*Nucleic acid:* A polymer of nucleotide subunits joined by covalent bonds between their phosphate and sugar groups	Deoxyribonucleic acid (DNA)	Genetic material of all cells
		Ribonucleic acid (RNA)	In cells, essential for protein synthesis using the genetic sequence copied from DNA; genetic material of some viruses

*n signifies the number of carbons in the molecule's backbone.

sugar"). When two monosaccharides are linked, they form a **disaccharide** ("two sugars"), and a polymer of many monosaccharides is called a **polysaccharide** ("many sugars"). Sugars and starches are often used to store energy in cells, while other carbohydrates strengthen cell walls in plants, fungi, and bacteria, or form a supportive armor over the bodies of insects, crabs, and their relatives.

If you've stirred sugar into coffee or tea, you know that it dissolves in water. This is because the hydroxyl functional groups of sugars are polar and form hydrogen bonds with polar water molecules (**Fig. 3-3**).

There Are Several Monosaccharides with Slightly Different Structures

Monosaccharides have a backbone of three to seven carbon atoms. Most of these carbon atoms have both a hydrogen (—H) and a hydroxyl group (—OH) attached to them; therefore,

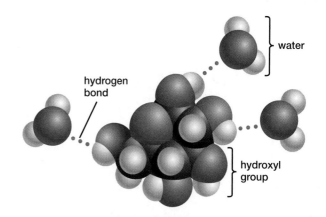

▲ **FIGURE 3-3 Sugar dissolving in water** Glucose dissolves as the polar hydroxyl groups of each sugar molecule form hydrogen bonds with nearby water molecules.

$C_6H_{12}O_6$

(a) Chemical formula

(b) Linear, ball and stick

(c) Ring, ball and stick

(d) Ring, simplified

▲ FIGURE 3-4 **Glucose structure depictions** Chemists draw the same molecule in different ways. **(a)** The chemical formula for glucose; **(b)** the linear form, which occurs when glucose is a solid crystal; **(c, d)** two depictions of the ring form of glucose, which forms when glucose dissolves in water. In (d), each unlabeled joint is a carbon atom; the carbons are numbered for easy reference. Figure 3-3 shows a space-filling depiction of the ring structure of glucose.

carbohydrates generally have the approximate chemical formula $(CH_2O)_n$, where n is the number of carbons in the backbone. When dissolved in water, such as in the cytoplasmic fluid of a cell, the carbon backbone of a sugar usually forms a ring. Figure 3-4 and Figure 3-3 show various ways of depicting the chemical structure of the common sugar **glucose.** When you see simplified structures, keep in mind that every unlabeled "joint" in a ring or chain is actually a carbon atom.

Glucose is the most common monosaccharide in living organisms and is a subunit of many polysaccharides. Glucose has six carbons, so its chemical formula is $C_6H_{12}O_6$. Many organisms synthesize other monosaccharides that have the same chemical

formula as glucose but slightly different structures. These include fructose ("fruit sugar" found in fruits, corn syrup, and honey) and galactose (part of lactose, or "milk sugar") (Fig. 3-5).

fructose

galactose

▲ FIGURE 3-5 **Monosaccharides**

Other common monosaccharides, such as ribose and deoxyribose (found in the nucleic acids of RNA and DNA, respectively), have five carbons. Notice in **Figure 3-6** that deoxyribose ("deoxy" means "remove oxygen") has one fewer oxygen atom than ribose because one of the hydroxyl functional groups in ribose is replaced by a hydrogen atom.

ribose

deoxyribose

Note "missing" oxygen atom

▲ FIGURE 3-6 **Five-carbon monosaccharides**

Disaccharides Consist of Two Single Sugars Linked by Dehydration Synthesis

Monosaccharides can be linked by dehydration synthesis to form disaccharides or polysaccharides (**Fig. 3-7**). Disaccharides are often used for short-term energy storage, especially in plants. When energy is required, the disaccharides are broken apart into their monosaccharide subunits by hydrolysis (see Fig. 3-2), then broken down further to release energy stored in their chemical bonds. Many foods contain disaccharides. Perhaps you had toast and coffee with cream and sugar at breakfast. You stirred **sucrose** (glucose plus fructose, used as

glucose   fructose   dehydration synthesis   sucrose

▲ FIGURE 3-7 **Synthesis of a disaccharide** Sucrose is synthesized by a dehydration reaction in which a hydrogen is removed from glucose and a hydroxyl group is removed from fructose, forming a water molecule and leaving the two monosaccharide rings joined by single bonds to the remaining oxygen atom.

QUESTION Describe hydrolysis of this molecule.

an energy storage molecule in sugarcane and sugar beets) into your coffee, then added cream containing **lactose** (glucose plus galactose). The disaccharide **maltose** (glucose plus glucose) is rare in nature, but it is formed when enzymes in your digestive tract hydrolyze starch, such as that in your toast. Other digestive enzymes then hydrolyze each maltose into two glucose molecules that cells can absorb and break down to liberate energy.

If you are on a diet, you may have used an artificial sugar substitute in your coffee. These interesting molecules are described in "Links to Everyday Life: Fake Foods."

Polysaccharides Are Chains of Single Sugars

Try chewing a cracker for a long time. Does it taste sweeter the longer you chew? It should, because over time, enzymes in saliva cause hydrolysis of the **starch** (a polysaccharide) in crackers into its component glucose sugar molecules (monosaccharides), which taste sweet. Plants often use starch (**Fig. 3-8**) as an energy-storage molecule, and animals commonly store **glycogen,** a similar polysaccharide. Both consist of polymers of glucose molecules. Starch is commonly formed in roots and seeds; a cracker contains starch from wheat seeds. Starch consists of branched chains of up to half a million glucose subunits. Glycogen, stored in the liver and muscles of animals (including ourselves), is also a chain of glucose subunits, but is more highly branched than starch.

Many organisms use polysaccharides as structural materials. One of the most important structural polysaccharides is **cellulose,** which makes up most of the cell walls of plants, the fluffy white bolls of a cotton plant, and about half the bulk of a tree trunk (**Fig. 3-9**). Ecologists estimate that about 1 trillion tons of cellulose are synthesized by organisms each year, making it the most abundant organic molecule on Earth.

Cellulose, like starch, is a polymer of glucose, but in cellulose, unlike starch, every other glucose is "upside down" (compare Fig. 3-8c with Fig. 3-9d). Although most animals can easily digest starch, no vertebrates have enzymes that can break down cellulose. As you will learn in Chapter 6, enzymes must precisely fit the molecules they break down, and the bonding pattern in cellulose prevents any vertebrate enzyme from attacking it. A few animals, such as cows, harbor cellulose-digesting microbes in their digestive tracts and can benefit from the glucose subunits they release. In humans, cellulose fibers pass intact through the digestive system, providing no nutrients, but providing "roughage" that helps prevent constipation.

Links to *Everyday Life*

Fake Foods

In societies blessed with an overabundance of food, obesity is a serious health problem. One goal of food scientists is to modify biological molecules to make them noncaloric; sugar (at 4 Cal/gram) and fat (at 9 Cal/gram) are prime candidates. Several artificial sweeteners such as aspartame (Nutrasweet™) and sucralose (Splenda™) add a sweet taste to foods, while providing few or no calories. The artificial oil called olestra is completely indigestible, ensuring that potato chips made with olestra have no fat calories and far fewer total calories than normal chips (**Fig. E3-1**). How are these "nonbiological molecules" made?

Aspartame is a combination of two amino acids: aspartic acid and phenylalanine (see Fig. 3-18b). For unknown reasons, aspartame is far more effective than sugar in stimulating the sweet taste receptors on our tongues. Sucralose is a modified sucrose molecule in which three hydroxyl groups are replaced with chlorine atoms. Sucralose activates our sweet taste receptors 600 times as effectively as sucrose, but our enzymes cannot digest it, so it provides no calories.

To understand olestra, look at Figure 3-13b and you will see that oils contain a glycerol backbone whose three carbon atoms are each bonded to a fatty acid. In Olestra, the glycerol molecule is replaced by a sucrose molecule with six to eight fatty acids attached to its carbon atoms. The fatty acid chains—extending outward from the rings of the sucrose molecule like the arms of an octopus—prevent digestive

▲ FIGURE E3-1 **Artificial foods** The sucralose in Splenda™ and the olestra in fat-free potato chips are synthetic, indigestible versions of sugar and oil, respectively, that are intended to help people control weight.

enzymes from breaking down the molecule into absorbable fragments. Although it is not digested, olestra adds the same appealing feel and flavor to foods that oil does.

(a) Potato cells

(b) A starch molecule

(c) Detail of a starch molecule

▲ FIGURE 3-8 **Starch is an energy-storage plant polysaccharide made of glucose subunits** **(a)** Starch grains inside individual potato cells. **(b)** A small section of a single starch molecule, which occurs as branched chains of up to half a million glucose subunits. **(c)** The precise structure of the circled portion of the starch molecule in (b). Notice the linkage between the individual glucose subunits for comparison with cellulose (Fig. 3-9).

(a) Wood is mostly cellulose

(b) A plant cell with a cell wall

(c) A close-up of cellulose fibers in a cell wall

Hydrogen bonds cross-linking cellulose molecules

bundle of cellulose molecules

cellulose fiber

Alternating bond configuration differs from starch

(d) Detail of a cellulose molecule

▲ FIGURE 3-9 **Cellulose structure and function (a)** Wood in this 3,000-year-old bristlecone pine is primarily cellulose. **(b)** Cellulose forms the cell wall that surrounds each plant cell. **(c)** Plant cell walls often consist of cellulose fibers in layers that run at angles to each other and resist tearing in both directions. **(d)** Cellulose is composed of glucose subunits. Compare this structure with Figure 3-8c and notice that every other glucose molecule in cellulose is "upside down."

The supportive outer coverings (exoskeletons) of insects, crabs, and spiders are made of **chitin,** a polysaccharide in which the glucose subunits bear a nitrogen-containing functional group (**Fig. 3-10**). Chitin also stiffens the cell walls of many fungi, including mushrooms.

Carbohydrates may also form parts of larger molecules; for example, the plasma membrane that surrounds each cell is studded with proteins to which carbohydrates are attached. Nucleic acids, discussed later, also contain sugar molecules.

3.4 WHAT ARE LIPIDS?

Lipids are a diverse group of molecules that contain regions composed almost entirely of hydrogen and carbon, with non-polar carbon–carbon and carbon–hydrogen bonds. These nonpolar regions make lipids hydrophobic and insoluble in water. Some lipids are used to store energy, some form waterproof coverings on plant or animal bodies, some serve as the primary component of cellular membranes, and still others are hormones.

Lipids are classified into three major groups: (1) oils, fats, and waxes, which are similar in structure and contain only carbon, hydrogen, and oxygen; (2) phospholipids, which are structurally similar to oils, but which also contain phosphorus and nitrogen; and (3) the "fused-ring" family of steroids that are composed of carbon, hydrogen, and oxygen.

Oils, Fats, and Waxes Are Lipids Containing Only Carbon, Hydrogen, and Oxygen

Oils, fats, and waxes are related in three ways. First, they contain only carbon, hydrogen, and oxygen. Second, they contain one or more **fatty acid** subunits, which are long chains of carbon and hydrogen with a carboxylic acid group (—COOH) at one end. Finally, most do not have ring structures.

Fats and **oils** are used primarily as energy-storage molecules; they contain more than twice as many calories per gram as do carbohydrates and proteins (9 Cal/gram for fats; 4 Cal/gram for carbohydrates and proteins). The bear in **Figure 3-11a** has accumulated enough fat to last him through his winter hibernation. To avoid accumulating excess fat, some people turn to foods manufactured with fat substitutes such as olestra, as described in "Links to Everyday Life: Fake Foods."

Fats and oils are formed by dehydration synthesis linking three fatty acid subunits to one molecule of **glycerol,** a three-carbon molecule (**Fig. 3-12**). This structure gives fats and oils their chemical name: **triglycerides.**

Fats (such as butter and lard) are produced primarily by animals, whereas oils (such as corn, canola, and soybean oil) are found primarily in the seeds of plants. The difference between a fat, which is a solid at room temperature, and an oil, which is liquid, lies in the structure of their fatty acid subunits. In fats, the carbons of fatty acids are joined by single bonds, with hydrogen atoms at all the other bonding sites. Such fatty acids are described as **saturated,** because they contain as many hydrogen atoms as possible. Lacking double bonds between carbons, these saturated fatty acid chains are

▲ **FIGURE 3-10 Chitin: a unique polysaccharide** Chitin has the same bonding configuration of glucose molecules as cellulose does. In chitin, however, the glucose subunits have a nitrogen-containing functional group (green) instead of a hydroxyl group. Tough, flexible chitin supports the otherwise soft bodies of arthropods (insects, spiders, and their relatives) and most fungi, such as this shelf fungus.

(a) Fat

(b) Wax

▲ **FIGURE 3-11 Lipids in nature (a)** A fat grizzly bear ready to hibernate. If this bear stored the same amount of energy in carbohydrates instead of fat, he probably would be unable to walk. **(b)** Wax is a highly saturated lipid that remains very firm at normal outdoor temperatures. Its rigidity allows it to be used to form the strong but thin-walled hexagons of this honeycomb.

▲ **FIGURE 3-12 Synthesis of a triglyceride** Dehydration synthesis links a single glycerol molecule with three fatty acids to form a triglyceride and three water molecules.

QUESTION Predict what kind of reaction would occur if a fat-digesting enzyme broke down this molecule.

straight and can pack closely together, forming solid lumps at room temperature (**Fig. 3-13a**).

If there are double bonds between some of the carbons, and consequently fewer hydrogens, the fatty acid is **unsaturated.** The double bonds in the unsaturated fatty acids of oils produce kinks in the fatty acid chains (**Fig. 3-13b**). Oils are liquid at room temperature because these kinks prevent

oil molecules from packing closely together. The commercial process of hydrogenation—which breaks some of the double bonds and adds hydrogens to the carbons—can convert liquid oils to solids, but with some health consequences (see Health Watch: "Cholesterol, Trans Fats, and Your Heart" on p. 46).

Although **waxes** are chemically similar to fats, humans and most other animals do not have the appropriate enzymes to break them down. Waxes are highly saturated and therefore solid at normal outdoor temperatures. Waxes form a waterproof coating over the leaves and stems of land plants. Animals synthesize waxes as waterproofing for mammalian fur and insect exoskeletons. Honey bees use waxes to build elaborate honeycomb structures where they store honey and lay their eggs (**Fig. 3-11b**).

Phospholipids Have Water-Soluble "Heads" and Water-Insoluble "Tails"

The plasma membrane that surrounds each cell contains several types of **phospholipids.** A phospholipid is similar to an oil, except that one of the three fatty acids that form the "fatty acid tails" is replaced by a phosphate group attached to a variable polar functional group that typically contains nitrogen (**Fig. 3-14**). A phospholipid has two dissimilar ends. At one end are two nonpolar fatty acid "tails," which are insoluble in water, and at the other is a phosphate–nitrogen "head" that is polar and water soluble. As you will learn in Chapter 5, these properties of phospholipids are crucial to the structure and function of all the membranes of cells.

Steroids Consist of Four Carbon Rings Fused Together

In contrast to fats and oils, which lack rings, all **steroids** are composed of four rings of carbon atoms, fused together, with various functional groups protruding from them (**Fig. 3-15**).

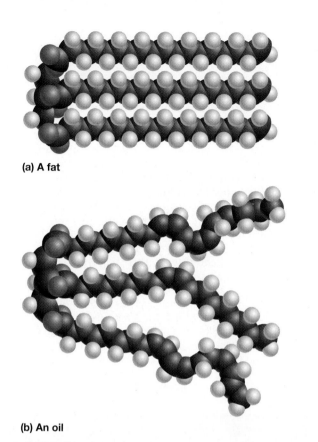

(a) A fat

(b) An oil

▲ FIGURE 3-13 **A fat and an oil** **(a)** Fats have straight chains of carbon atoms in their fatty acid tails. **(b)** The fatty acid tails of oils have double bonds between some of their carbon atoms, creating kinks in the chains. Oils are liquid at room temperature because their kinky tails keep the molecules farther apart.

(b) Estrogen

(a) Cholesterol   **(c) Testosterone**

▲ FIGURE 3-15 **Steroids** All steroids have a similar, nonpolar molecular structure with four fused carbon rings. Differences in steroid function result from differences in functional groups attached to the rings. **(a)** Cholesterol, the molecule from which other steroids are synthesized; **(b)** estradiol (estrogen), the female sex hormone; **(c)** the male sex hormone testosterone. Note the similarities in structure between estrogen and testosterone.

QUESTION Why are steroid hormones able to penetrate plasma membranes and nuclear membranes of cells to exert their effects?

One type of steroid is cholesterol. Cholesterol (**Fig. 3-15a**) is a vital component of the membranes of animal cells. It makes up about 2% of the human brain, where it is an important component of the material used to insulate nerve cells. Cholesterol is used by cells to synthesize other steroids, including the female sex hormone estrogen (**Fig. 3-15b**), the male sex hormone testosterone (**Fig. 3-15c**), and bile that assists in fat digestion. Too much of the wrong form of cholesterol can contribute to heart disease, as explained in "Health Watch: Cholesterol, Trans Fats, and Your Heart."

3.5 WHAT ARE PROTEINS?

Proteins are molecules composed of one or more chains of amino acids. Proteins perform many functions; this diversity of function is made possible by the diversity of protein structures (**Table 3-3**). Most cells contain hundreds of different **enzymes,** proteins that promote chemical reactions. Other types of proteins form structures on or outside the body.

variable
functional phosphate
group group

polar head glycerol
backbone
(hydrophilic)

fatty acid tails

(hydrophobic)

▲ FIGURE 3-14 **Phospholipids** Phospholipids have two hydrophobic fatty acid tails attached to the glycerol backbone. The third position on glycerol is occupied by a polar "head" consisting of a phosphate group to which a second (usually nitrogen-containing) variable functional group is attached. The phosphate group bears a negative charge, and the nitrogen-containing group bears a positive charge, making the heads hydrophilic.

Health Watch

Cholesterol, Trans Fats, and Your Heart

Why are so many foods advertised as "cholesterol free" or "low in cholesterol"? Although cholesterol is crucial to life, medical researchers have found that individuals with high levels of certain cholesterol-containing particles in their blood are at increased risk for heart attacks and strokes. Cholesterol contributes to the formation of obstructions in arteries, called plaques (Fig. E3-2), which in turn can promote the formation of blood clots. If a clot breaks loose and blocks an artery supplying blood to the heart muscle, it can cause a heart attack. If the clot blocks an artery supplying the brain, it causes a stroke.

Cholesterol is found in animal-derived foods including egg yolks, sausages, bacon, whole milk, and butter. Perhaps you have heard of "good" and "bad" cholesterol. Because cholesterol molecules are nonpolar, they do not dissolve in blood but are transported in packets surrounded by polar carrier molecules consisting of protein and phospholipids. These carriers are called lipoproteins (lipids plus proteins).

Lipoproteins that consist of more protein and less lipid are described as "high-density lipoproteins" ("HDL"), because protein is denser than lipid. The "good cholesterol" is carried by HDL. These particles are taken up by the liver, where the cholesterol is metabolized (used in bile synthesis, for example). The bad "low-density lipoprotein" ("LDL") cholesterol packets have less protein and more cholesterol. This form circulates to cells throughout the body and can be deposited in artery walls.

Animals, including humans, can synthesize all the cholesterol their bodies require. Most of the cholesterol in human blood is synthesized by the body. Because of genetic differences, however, some people's bodies manufacture more cholesterol, and some (but not all) people respond to a high-cholesterol diet by manufacturing less. Lifestyle also contributes to blood cholesterol content; exercise tends to increase HDL cholesterol, whereas obesity and smoking increase LDL levels. A high ratio of HDL to LDL is correlated with a reduced risk of heart disease. A cholesterol screening test will distinguish between these two forms.

Perhaps you've heard about **trans fats** as dietary villains. These are produced when oils are artificially hardened by combining them with hydrogen to make them solid at room temperature. The hydrogenation process creates an unusual bonding pattern among carbons and hydrogens in the fatty acid tails, leaving some double bonds intact but eliminating the kinks that these bonds produce in the tails of oils. Research has revealed that trans fats are not metabolized in the same way as naturally-occurring fats, and (for reasons still under investigation) can both increase LDL cholesterol and decrease HDL cholesterol. This suggests that they may place consumers at a higher risk of heart disease.

Until recently, artificially produced trans fats were abundant in commercial food products such as margarine, cookies, crackers, and french fries, because they extended the shelf life and helped retain the flavor of packaged products. The U.S. Food and Drug Administration now requires food labels to include the trans fat content, and most food manufacturers and fast-food chains are reducing or eliminating trans fats in their products.

▲ FIGURE E3-2 **Plaque** A plaque deposit (rippled structure) partially blocks a carotid artery.

Table 3-3 Functions of Proteins

Function of Protein	Examples
Structural	Keratin (forms hair, nails, scales, feathers, and horns); silk (forms webs and cocoons)
Movement	Actin and myosin (found in muscle cells; allow contraction)
Defense	Antibodies (found in the bloodstream; fight disease organisms, some neutralize venoms); venoms (found in venomous animals; deter predators and disable prey)
Storage	Albumin (in egg white; provides nutrition for an embryo)
Signaling	Insulin (secreted by the pancreas; promotes glucose uptake into cells)
Catalyzing reactions	Amylase (found in saliva and the small intestine; digests carbohydrates)

These include keratin, the principal protein of hair, horns, nails, scales, and feathers (**Fig. 3-16**). Silk proteins are secreted outside the body by silk moths and spiders to make cocoons and webs. Still other proteins provide a source of amino acids for developing animals, such as albumin protein in egg white and casein protein in milk. The protein hemoglobin transports oxygen in the blood. Contractile proteins, such as actin and myosin in muscle, allow animal bodies to move. Some hormones, including insulin and growth hormone, are small proteins, as are antibodies (which help fight disease and infection) and many toxins (such as rattlesnake venom) produced by animals.

Proteins Are Formed from Chains of Amino Acids

Proteins are polymers consisting of chains of **amino acids** joined by peptide bonds. All amino acids have the same fundamental structure, consisting of a central carbon bonded to three different functional groups: a nitrogen-containing amino group ($-NH_2$), a carboxylic acid group ($-COOH$), and an "R" group that varies among different amino acids (**Fig. 3-17**).

Twenty amino acids are commonly found in the proteins of organisms, and the R group gives each amino acid distinctive properties (**Fig. 3-18**). Some amino acids are hydrophilic and water soluble because their R groups are polar. Others are hydrophobic, with nonpolar R groups that are insoluble in water. The sulfhydryl R group of one amino acid, cysteine (**Fig. 3-18c**), can form covalent **disulfide bonds** with the sulfur in another cysteine molecule. Although peptide bonds (described later) link amino acids to form the chains that make up a protein, disulfide bonds can link different chains of amino acids to one another or interconnect different parts of the same amino acid chain, causing the protein to bend or fold.

Amino Acids Are Joined to Form Chains by Dehydration Synthesis

Like polysaccharides and lipids, proteins are formed by dehydration synthesis. The nitrogen in the amino group ($-NH_2$) of one amino acid is joined to the carbon in the carboxylic acid group ($-COOH$) of another amino acid by a single covalent bond, and water is liberated (**Fig. 3-19**). This bond is called a **peptide bond,** and the resulting chain of two amino acids is called a **peptide.** More amino acids are added, one by one, until the protein chain is complete. Amino acid chains in living cells vary in length from three to thousands. The terms "protein" and "polypeptide" are often reserved for long chains of more than 50 amino acids, whereas the term "peptide" usually refers to shorter chains.

(a) Hair

(b) Horn

(c) Silk

▲ FIGURE 3-16 **Structural proteins** Common structural proteins include keratin, which is the predominant protein found in **(a)** hair, **(b)** horn, and **(c)** the silk of a spider web.

▲ FIGURE 3-17 **Amino acid structure**

glutamic acid (glu) aspartic acid (asp)

phenylalanine (phe)

leucine (leu)

cysteine (cys)

(a) Hydrophilic functional groups

(b) Hydrophobic functional groups

(c) Sulfur-containing functional group

▲ **FIGURE 3-18 Amino acid diversity** The diversity of amino acids is caused by the variable R group (colored blue), which may be **(a)** hydrophilic or **(b)** hydrophobic. The R group of cysteine **(c)** has a sulfur atom that can form covalent bonds with the sulfur in other cysteines, creating disulfide bonds that can bend a protein or link adjacent polypeptide chains.

A Protein Can Have Up to Four Levels of Structure

Proteins come in many shapes, and exhibit up to four levels of protein structure, with each structural level built on the level below it. A molecule of hemoglobin, the oxygen-carrying protein in red blood cells, illustrates all four structural levels (**Fig. 3-20**). A protein's **primary structure** refers to the sequence of amino acids that make up the protein (**Fig. 3-20a**). This sequence is specified by genes within molecules of DNA. Different types of proteins have different sequences of amino acids.

The amino acid sequence in turn causes each polypeptide chain to assume one of two types of simple, repeating **secondary structures.** Secondary structures are maintained by hydrogen bonds between the polar portions of amino acids. Many proteins, such as keratin in hair and the subunits of the hemoglobin molecule, acquire a coiled, spring-like secondary structure called a **helix** (**Fig. 3-20b**). Hydrogen bonds that form between the oxygens of the carbonyl functional groups (with slightly negative charges) and the hydrogens of the amino functional groups (with slightly positive charges) hold the turns of the coils together. Other proteins, such as silk, contain polypeptide chains that repeatedly fold back upon themselves, with hydrogen bonds holding adjacent segments of the polypeptide together in a **pleated sheet** arrangement (**Fig. 3-21**).

Case Study continued

Puzzling Proteins

Normal, noninfectious prion proteins have a secondary structure that is primarily helical. They perform a variety of beneficial functions in the animal body, including in the brain. Infectious prion proteins, however, fold into pleated sheets, and force normal prion proteins to fold into pleated sheets as well. The sheets are so stable that they cannot be denatured by high temperatures nor by most chemical agents. More importantly, they are unaffected by the enzymes that break down normal prion protein. Because they are so stable, infectious prions accumulate harmfully in the brain.

In addition to their secondary structures, proteins assume **tertiary structures,** consisting of folds determined by interactions of the amino acid functional groups with one another and with their surroundings (**Fig. 3-20c**). Tertiary structure is determined both by the protein's secondary structure and its environment—for example, whether the protein is dissolved in the watery cytoplasmic fluid within a cell or in the lipids of cellular membranes, or both. A protein in water folds in a way that exposes its hydrophilic (polar, "water-loving") amino acids to the water and causes its hydrophobic amino acids to cluster together in the center of the molecule. In

▲ **FIGURE 3-19 Protein synthesis** In protein synthesis, a dehydration reaction joins the carbon of the carboxylic acid group of one amino acid to the nitrogen of the amino group of a second amino acid, releasing water. The resulting covalent bond between amino acids is a peptide bond.

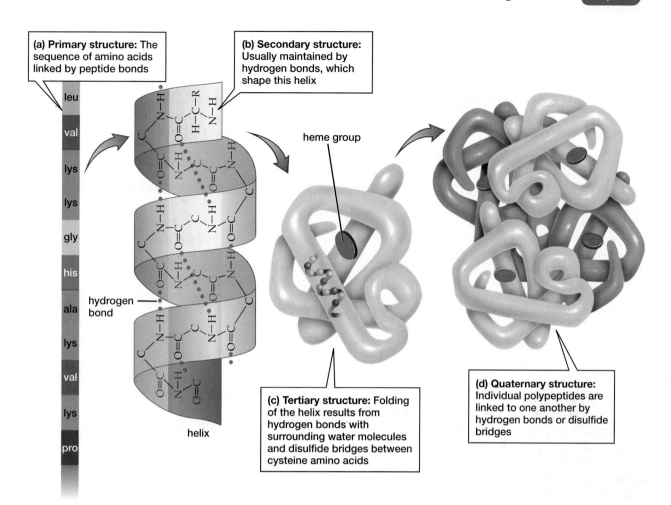

(a) Primary structure: The sequence of amino acids linked by peptide bonds

(b) Secondary structure: Usually maintained by hydrogen bonds, which shape this helix

heme group

hydrogen bond

helix

(c) Tertiary structure: Folding of the helix results from hydrogen bonds with surrounding water molecules and disulfide bridges between cysteine amino acids

(d) Quaternary structure: Individual polypeptides are linked to one another by hydrogen bonds or disulfide bridges

leu
val
lys
lys
gly
his
ala
lys
val
lys
pro

▲ FIGURE 3-20 **The four levels of protein structure** Levels of protein structure are illustrated here with hemoglobin, the oxygen-carrying protein in red blood cells (red disks represent the iron-containing heme group that binds oxygen). Levels of protein structure are generally determined by the amino acid sequence of the protein, interactions among the R groups of the amino acids, and interactions among the R groups and their surroundings.

QUESTION Why do most proteins, when heated, lose their ability to function?

hydrogen bond

pleated sheet

◀ FIGURE 3-21 **The pleated sheet is an example of protein secondary structure** In a pleated sheet, a single polypeptide chain is folded back upon itself repeatedly (loops of peptide connecting the ends of the chains in the sheet are not shown). Adjacent segments of the folded polypeptide are linked by hydrogen bonds (dotted lines), creating a sheet-like configuration. The R groups (green) project alternately above and below the sheet. Despite its accordion-pleated appearance, each peptide chain is in a fully extended state and cannot easily be stretched farther. Silk strands are stretchy because segments of pleated sheets are interspersed with regions of spirally structured proteins, which are highly elastic.

contrast, portions of a protein embedded in the phospholipid cell membrane expose their hydrophobic parts to the surrounding hydrophobic tails of the phospholipid. Disulfide bonds can also contribute to tertiary structure by linking cysteine amino acids from different regions of the polypeptide, as in the hair protein keratin (see Fig. E3-3 in "A Closer Look at Proteins and Hair Texture").

A fourth level of protein organization, called **quaternary structure,** occurs in certain proteins that contain individual polypeptides linked by hydrogen bonds, disulfide bonds, or by attractions between oppositely charged portions of different amino acids. Hemoglobin, for example, consists of four polypeptide chains held together by hydrogen bonds (**Fig. 3-20d**). Each of the four polypeptides holds

A Closer Look At *Proteins and Hair Texture*

Pull out a strand of hair, and notice the root or follicle that was embedded in the scalp. Hair is composed mostly of a helical protein called keratin. Living cells in the hair follicle produce new keratin at the rate of 10 turns of the protein helix every second. The keratin proteins in a hair entwine around one another, held together by disulfide bonds (**Fig. E3-3**). If you pull gently on the hair, you will find it to be both strong and stretchy. When hair stretches, hydrogen bonds that create the helical structure of keratin are broken, allowing the strand of protein to be extended. Most of the covalent disulfide bonds, in contrast, are distorted by stretching, but do not break. When tension is released, these disulfide bonds return the hair to its normal length, and the hydrogen bonds re-form. Wet the hair and you will probably find that it is limp, a bit longer, and easier to stretch. In wet hair, the hydrogen bonds of the keratin helices are broken and replaced by hydrogen bonds between the amino acids and the water molecules surrounding them, so the protein is denatured and the helices collapse. If you roll wet hair around a curler and allow it to dry, hydrogen bonds will re-form in slightly different places, holding the hair in a curl. However, the slightest moisture (even humid air) allows these hydrogen bonds to rearrange into their natural configuration.

If your hair is naturally kinky or curly (because of the sequence of amino acids specified by your genes), the disulfide bonds within and between the individual keratin helices form at locations that bend the keratin molecules, producing curls or kinks (**Fig. E3-4**).

In straight hair, the disulfide bonds occur in places that do not distort the keratin (as shown in Fig. E3-3). When straight hair is given a "permanent wave," two lotions are applied. The first breaks disulfide bonds, denaturing the protein. After the hair is rolled tightly onto curlers, a second solution is applied that re-forms the disulfide bonds. These new bonds reconnect the keratin helices at new positions determined by the curlers, as in the curly hair shown in Figure E3-4. The new bonds are permanent, transforming genetically straight hair into "biochemically curly" hair. Kinky or curly hair can be straightened using the same chemicals and combing and flattening the hair instead of rolling it on a curler.

▲ FIGURE E3-3 **The structure of hair** At the microscopic level, a single hair is organized into bundles of protofibrils within larger bundles called microfibrils. Each protofibril consists of keratin molecules held in a helical shape by hydrogen bonds, with different keratin strands cross-linked by disulfide bonds. These bonds give hair both elasticity and strength. Straight hair is depicted here.

▲ FIGURE E3-4 **Curly hair**

an iron-containing organic molecule called a heme group (red disks in Figs. 3-20c,d), which can bind one molecule (two atoms) of oxygen.

The Functions of Proteins Are Related to Their Three-Dimensional Structures

Within a protein, the exact type, position, and number of amino acids bearing specific R groups determine both the structure of the protein and its biological function. In hemoglobin, for example, amino acids bearing specific R groups must be present in precisely the right places to hold the iron-containing heme group that binds oxygen. In contrast, the polar amino acids on the outside of a hemoglobin molecule serve mostly to keep it dissolved in the cytoplasmic fluid of a red blood cell. Therefore, as long as they are hydrophilic, changes in these amino acids will not alter the protein's function. A mutation that replaces a hydrophilic with a hydrophobic amino acid, however, can have catastrophic effects on the hemoglobin molecule, causing the painful and sometimes life-threatening disorder called sickle-cell anemia (see pp. 190–191).

The importance of higher level protein structure becomes obvious when a protein is **denatured,** meaning that its secondary, tertiary, or quaternary structures are altered while leaving the primary structure intact. A denatured protein has different properties and will no longer perform its function. In a fried egg, for example, the heat of the frying pan causes so much movement of the atoms in the albumin protein that hydrogen bonds are ripped apart. Due to the loss of its secondary and tertiary structure, the egg white changes from clear to white and its texture changes from liquid to solid. When hair is given a permanent wave, the disulfide bonds of keratin are altered, denaturing the natural protein as described in "A Closer Look at Proteins and Hair Texture." Bacteria and viruses are often destroyed by denaturing their proteins. This can be accomplished using heat, ultraviolet rays, or solutions that are salty or acidic. For example, canned foods are sterilized by heating them, water is sometimes sterilized using ultraviolet light, and dill pickles are preserved from bacterial attack in their salty, acidic brine.

3.6 WHAT ARE NUCLEOTIDES AND NUCLEIC ACIDS?

A **nucleotide** is a molecule with a three-part structure: a five-carbon sugar, a phosphate functional group, and a nitrogen-containing **base** that differs among nucleotides. Nucleotides fall into two general classes: deoxyribose nucleotides and ribose nucleotides, depending on which type of sugar they contain (see Fig. 3-6). Bases all have carbon and nitrogen atoms linked in rings, with functional groups attached to some of the carbon atoms. The bases in deoxyribose nucleotides can be adenine, guanine, cytosine, or thymine. Adenine and guanine have double rings, whereas cytosine and thymine have single rings (see Fig. 3-24 and Fig. 11-3). A nucleotide with the adenine base is illustrated in **Figure 3-22.**

▲ FIGURE 3-22 **Deoxyribose nucleotide**

Nucleotides may function as individual energy-carrier molecules or intracellular messengers, or as subunits in polymers called nucleic acids (see below).

Nucleotides Act as Energy Carriers and Intracellular Messengers

Adenosine triphosphate (ATP) is a ribose nucleotide with three phosphate functional groups (**Fig. 3-23**). This unstable molecule carries energy from place to place within a cell, storing the energy in bonds between its phosphate groups. Energy is released to drive energy-demanding reactions (to synthesize a protein, for example) when the bond linking the last phosphate to ATP is broken.

▲ FIGURE 3-23 **The energy-carrier molecule adenosine triphosphate (ATP)**

Other nucleotides (NAD^+ and FAD) are known as "electron carriers" that transport energy in the form of high-energy electrons. You will learn more about these nucleotides in Chapters 6, 7, and 8. The nucleotide cyclic adenosine monophosphate (cAMP) acts as an intracellular messenger molecule, often initiating a series of reactions inside cells.

DNA and RNA, the Molecules of Heredity, Are Nucleic Acids

Single nucleotides (monomers) may be strung together in long chains, forming polymers called **nucleic acids.** In nucleic acids, an oxygen in the phosphate functional group of one nucleotide is covalently bonded to the sugar of the next. The polymer of deoxyribose nucleotides, called **deoxyribonucleic acid (DNA),** can contain millions of nucleotides (**Fig. 3-24**). DNA is found in the chromosomes of all cells. Its sequence of nucleotides, like the dots and dashes of a biological Morse code, spells out the genetic information needed to construct the proteins of each organism. A DNA molecule consists of two strands of nucleotides entwined in the form of a double helix and linked by hydrogen bonds (see Fig. 3-24). Single-stranded chains of ribose nucleotides, called **ribonucleic acid (RNA),** are copied from the DNA and direct the synthesis of proteins (see Chapters 11 and 12).

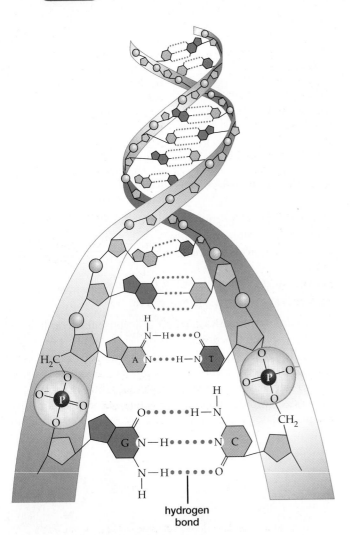

▲ **FIGURE 3-24 Deoxyribonucleic acid** Like a twisted ladder, the double helix of DNA is formed by strands of nucleotides that spiral around one another, linked by hydrogen bonds between the bases of the nucleotides in the two opposing strands. These connected bases form the "rungs" of the ladder. The bases are identified by their initials: A: adenine; C: cytosine; T: thymine; G: guanine.

Case Study continued
Puzzling Proteins

All cells use DNA as a blueprint for producing more cells, and different viruses use either DNA or RNA. Before the discovery of prions, however, no infectious agent had ever been discovered that completely lacked genetic material composed of nucleic acids. Scientists were extremely skeptical of Prusiner's hypothesis that proteins could effectively "reproduce themselves" until repeated studies found no trace of genetic material associated with prions.

Case Study revisited
Puzzling Proteins

Prusiner and his associates identified a misfolded version of a protein found throughout the animal kingdom as the culprit in scrapie, BSE, and vCJD. But how does the infectious prion "reproduce" itself? Prusiner and other researchers have strong experimental evidence supporting a radical hypothesis: The misfolded prion interacts with normal prion proteins and causes them to change configuration, misfolding into the pleated sheet secondary structure of the infectious form. These new misfolded "converts" then go on to transform more normal prion proteins in an ever-expanding chain reaction. As in Charlene's case, it can be years after infection before enough of the proteins have been transformed to cause disease symptoms. Researchers are investigating how the abnormal folding occurs, how it can induce misfolding of normal prion proteins, and how misfolded prions cause disease.

Stanley Prusiner's efforts led to the recognition of a totally new disease process. A major strength of the scientific method is that hypotheses can be tested experimentally. If repeated experiments support the hypothesis, then even well-established scientific principles—for example, that all infectious agents must have genetic material—must be reexamined and sometimes discarded. Although a few scientists still insist that proteins can't be infectious, Prusiner's efforts have been so convincing to the scientific community that he was awarded a Nobel Prize in 1997.

Consider This

A disorder called "chronic wasting disease" has been reported among both wild and captive elk and deer populations in several western states in the United States. Like scrapie and BSE, wasting disease is a fatal brain disorder caused by prions. No human cases have been confirmed. If you were a hunter in an affected region, would you eat deer or elk meat? Explain why or why not.

CHAPTER REVIEW

Summary of Key Concepts

3.1 Why Is Carbon So Important in Biological Molecules?

Organic molecules are so diverse because the carbon atom is able to form many types of bonds. This ability, in turn, allows organic molecules (molecules with a backbone of carbon) to form complex shapes, including branched chains, helices, sheets, and rings. The presence of functional groups produces further diversity among biological molecules (see Table 3-1).

3.2 How Are Organic Molecules Synthesized?

Most large biological molecules are polymers synthesized by linking together many smaller monomer subunits. The subunits are connected by covalent bonds through dehydration synthesis; the chains may be broken apart by hydrolysis reactions. The most important organic molecules fall into one of four classes: carbohydrates, lipids, proteins, and nucleotides/nucleic acids (see Table 3-2).

3.3 What Are Carbohydrates?

Carbohydrates include sugars, starches, chitin, and cellulose. Sugars (monosaccharides and disaccharides) are used for temporary storage of energy and for the construction of other molecules. Starches and glycogen are polysaccharides that provide longer-term energy storage in plants and animals, respectively. Cellulose forms the cell walls of plants, and chitin strengthens the exoskeletons of many invertebrates and the cell walls of fungi. Other polysaccharides form the cell walls of bacteria.

3.4 What Are Lipids?

Lipids are nonpolar, water-insoluble molecules of diverse chemical structure, including oils, fats, waxes, phospholipids, and steroids. Lipids are used for energy storage (oils and fats), as waterproofing for the outside of many plants and animals (waxes), as the principal component of cellular membranes (phospholipids and cholesterol), and as hormones (steroids).

3.5 What Are Proteins?

Proteins are chains of amino acids that possess primary, secondary, tertiary, and sometimes quaternary structure. Both the structure and the function of a protein are determined by the sequence of amino acids in the chain as well as by how these amino acids interact with their surroundings and with each other. Proteins can be enzymes (which promote and guide chemical reactions), structural molecules (e.g., hair, horn), hormones (e.g., insulin), or transport molecules (e.g., hemoglobin).

3.6 What Are Nucleotides and Nucleic Acids?

A nucleotide is composed of a phosphate group, a five-carbon sugar (ribose or deoxyribose), and a nitrogen-containing base. Molecules formed from single nucleotides include intracellular messengers, such as cyclic AMP, and energy-carrier molecules, such as ATP. The nucleic acid molecules deoxyribonucleic acid (DNA) and ribonucleic acid (RNA), which carry the hereditary blueprint for cells and viruses (including the instructions for constructing proteins), are chains of nucleotides.

Key Terms

adenosine triphosphate (ATP) *51*
amino acid *47*
base *51*
carbohydrate *38*
cellulose *41*
chitin *43*
dehydration synthesis *38*
denatured *51*
deoxyribonucleic acid (DNA) *51*
disaccharide *39*
disulfide bond *47*
enzyme *45*
fat *43*
fatty acid *43*
functional group *37*
glucose *40*
glycerol *43*
glycogen *41*
helix *48*
hydrolysis *38*
inorganic *37*
lactose *41*
lipid *43*
maltose *41*
monomer *37*
monosaccharide *38*
nucleic acid *51*
nucleotide *51*
oil *43*
organic *37*
peptide *47*
peptide bond *47*
phospholipid *44*
pleated sheet *48*
polymer *37*
polysaccharide *39*
primary structure *48*
protein *45*
quaternary structure *50*
ribonucleic acid (RNA) *52*
saturated *43*
secondary structure *48*
starch *41*
steroid *44*
sucrose *40*
sugar *38*
tertiary structure *48*
trans fat *46*
triglyceride *43*
unsaturated *44*
wax *44*

Thinking Through the Concepts

Fill-in-the-Blank

1. In organic molecules made of chains of subunits, each subunit is called a(n) _____, and the chains are called _____. Carbohydrates consisting of long chains of sugars are called _____. These sugar chains can be broken down by _____reactions. Three types of carbohydrates consisting of long glucose chains are _____, _____, and _____. Three examples of disaccharides are _____, _____, and _____.

2. Fill in the following with the appropriate type of lipid: Unsaturated, liquid at room temperature: _____; bees use to make honeycombs: _____; stores energy in animals: _____; sex hormones are synthesized from these: _____; the LDL form of this contributes to heart disease: _____; a major component of cell membranes that has polar heads: _____.

3. Proteins are synthesized by a reaction called _____ synthesis, which releases _____. Subunits of proteins are called _____. The sequence of protein subunits is called the _____ structure of the protein. Two regular configurations of secondary protein structure are _____ and _____. Which of these secondary structures is characteristic of infectious prion proteins? _____ When a protein's secondary or higher-order structure is destroyed, the protein is said to be _____.

4. Fill in the following with the most specific term describing the bonds involved: Creates kinks in the carbon chains of fatty acids in oils: _____; maintain the helical structure of many proteins: _____; links polypeptide chains and can cause proteins to bend: _____; join the two strands of the double helix of DNA: _____; link amino acids to form the primary structure of proteins: _____.

5. A nucleotide consists of three parts: _____, _____, and _____. A nucleotide that acts as an energy carrier is _____. The four bases found in deoxyribose nucleotides are _____, _____, _____, and _____. Two important nucleic acids are _____ and _____. The functional group that joins nucleotides in nucleic acids is _____.

6. Infectious prions are unique as infectious agents because they contain no _____. Some people have developed a prion disease called _____. These victims almost certainly ate meat from cows that had a disease called _____. Cows may originally have contracted the disease from sheep who had the disease called _____.

Review Questions

1. What does the term "organic" mean to a chemist?

2. List the four principal types of biological molecules and give an example of each.

3. What roles do nucleotides play in living organisms?

4. One way to convert corn oil to margarine (a solid at room temperature) is to add hydrogen atoms, decreasing the number of double bonds in the molecules of oil. What is this process called? Why does it work?

5. Describe and compare dehydration synthesis and hydrolysis. Give an example of a substance formed by each chemical reaction, and describe the specific reaction in each instance.

6. Distinguish among the following: monosaccharide, disaccharide, and polysaccharide. Give two examples of each, and list their functions.

7. Describe the synthesis of a protein from amino acids. Then describe primary, secondary, tertiary, and quaternary structures of a protein.

8. Where in nature do we find cellulose? Chitin? In what way(s) are these two polymers similar? Different?

9. Which kinds of bonds between keratin molecules are altered when hair is (a) wet and allowed to dry on curlers and (b) given a permanent wave?

Applying the Concepts

1. In Chapter 2, you learned that hydrophobic molecules tend to cluster when immersed in water. In this chapter, you read that a phospholipid has a hydrophilic head and hydrophobic tails. What do you think would be the configuration of phospholipids that are immersed in water? What if they were immersed in oil?

2. Fat contains twice as many calories per unit weight as carbohydrate does, so fat is an efficient way for animals, who must move about, to store energy. Compare the way fat and carbohydrates interact with water, and explain why this interaction also gives fat an advantage for weight-efficient energy storage.

3. Some people think that consuming fat and sugar substitutes is a good way to reduce weight, whereas others object to these dietary "shortcuts." Explain and justify one of these two positions.

4. Saliva from infected deer can transmit chronic wasting disease, caused by misfolded prion proteins. The infectious prions can persist in soil. How might the disease pass from an infected animal to others in the herd?

(MB) *Go to www.masteringbiology.com for practice quizzes, activities, eText, videos, current events, and more.*

Cell Structure and Function

Case Study

Spare Parts for Human Bodies

"I DON'T THINK I've ever screamed so loud in my life." Jennifer looks back on the terrible day when boiling oil from a deep-fat fryer spilled onto her 10-month-old baby, burning over 70% of his body. "The 911 operator said to get his clothes off, but they'd melted onto him. I pulled his socks off and the skin came right with them." A few decades ago, this child's burns would have been fatal. Now, the only evidence of the burn on his chest is slightly crinkled skin. Zachary Jenkins was saved by the bioengineering marvel of artificial skin.

Skin consists of several specialized cell types with complex interactions. The outer cells of skin are masters of multiplication, allowing minor burns to heal without a trace. However, if the deeper (dermal) layers of the skin are completely destroyed, healing occurs very slowly, from the edges of the burn. Deep burns are often treated by grafting skin, including some dermis taken from other sites on the body; but for extensive burns, the lack of healthy skin makes this approach impossible. Although cells from a piece of the patient's healthy skin can be grown in culture and placed over the affected area, growing enough cells to cover extensive burns can take weeks. Until recently, the only other option was to use skin from human cadavers or pigs. At best, these tissues serve as temporary "biological bandages" because the victim's body eventually rejects them. Extensive and disfiguring scars are a common legacy.

The availability of bioengineered skin has radically changed the prognosis for burn victims. The child in this chapter's opening photograph was treated with a bioengineered artificial skin (TransCyte™) that uses skin cells obtained from the donated foreskins of infants who were circumcised at birth. This tissue, which would otherwise be discarded, provides a source of rapidly dividing cells. Cultured in the laboratory on nylon mesh, the cells secrete growth factors and protein fibers that support skin. Although the foreskin cells die, the supporting substances stimulate regeneration of the victim's own skin and new blood vessels. A newer form of bioengineered artificial skin, called Orcel™, retains living foreskin cells on a biodegradable spongy protein matrix.

Bioengineered artificial skin demonstrates our increasing power to manipulate cells, the fundamental units of life. If scientists can shape cells into artificial, but living, skin, might they also be able to sculpt cells into working bones, livers, kidneys, and bladders?

▲ Just 6 months before this photo was taken, this child's chest was severely burned (inset). Because he was treated with bioartificial skin, his healing time was radically reduced, and scarring from the burn is almost nonexistent.

At a Glance

4.1 WHAT IS THE CELL THEORY?

Because cells are so small, they were not seen until the invention of the microscope in the mid-1600s (see "Scientific Inquiry: The Search for the Cell" on pp. 58–59). But seeing cells was only the first step to understanding their importance. In 1838, the German botanist Matthias Schleiden concluded that cells and substances produced by cells form the basic structure of plants, and that plant growth occurs by adding new cells. In 1839, German biologist Theodor Schwann (Schleiden's friend and collaborator) drew similar conclusions for animal cells. The work of Schleiden and Schwann provided a unifying theory of cells as the fundamental units of life. In 1855, the German physician Rudolf Virchow completed the **cell theory** by concluding that all cells come from previously existing cells.

Three principles comprise the cell theory, a fundamental precept of biology:

- Every living organism is made up of one or more cells.
- The smallest living organisms are single cells, and cells are the functional units of multicellular organisms.
- All cells arise from preexisting cells.

All living things, from microscopic bacteria to the human body to a giant sequoia tree, are composed of cells. Whereas each bacterium consists of a single, relatively simple cell, the human body consists of trillions of complex cells, specialized to perform an enormous variety of functions. To survive, all cells must obtain energy and nutrients from their environment, synthesize a variety of proteins and other molecules necessary for their growth and repair, and eliminate wastes. Most cells need to interact with other cells. To ensure the continuity of life, cells must also reproduce. These activities are accomplished by specialized parts of each cell, described later in this chapter.

4.2 WHAT ARE THE BASIC ATTRIBUTES OF CELLS?

All types of cells are derived from common ancestors, and must perform similar functions. As a result, they have many similarities in size and structure.

Cell Function Limits Cell Size

Most cells range in size from about 1 to 100 micrometers (millionths of a meter) in diameter (**Fig. 4-1**). Why are most cells small? The answer lies in the need for cells to exchange nutrients and wastes with their external environment through the plasma membrane. As you will learn in Chapter 5, many nutrients and wastes move into, through, and out of cells by diffusion, the movement of molecules from places of high concentration of those molecules to places of low concentration. This relatively slow process requires that no part of the cell be too far away from the external environment.

All Cells Share Common Features

Despite their diversity, all cells—from the prokaryotic bacteria and archaea to the eukaryotic protists, fungi, plants, and animals—share common features, as described in the following sections.

The Plasma Membrane Encloses the Cell and Allows Interactions Between the Cell and Its Environment

Each cell is surrounded by an extremely thin, rather fluid membrane called the **plasma membrane** (Fig. 4-2). As you will learn in Chapter 5, the plasma membrane and the other

Size

- 100 m — tallest trees
- 10 m —
- 1 m — visible with unaided human eye / adult human
- 10 cm — chicken egg
- 1 cm —
- 1 mm — frog embryo
- 100 μm — visible with light microscope / most eukaryotic cells
- 10 μm —
- 1 μm — visible with conventional electron microscope / mitochondrion / most prokaryotic cells
- 100 nm — virus
- 10 nm — visible with special electron microscope / proteins
- 1 nm — diameter of DNA double helix
- 0.1 nm — atoms

Units of measurement:
1 meter (m) = 39.37 inches
1 centimeter (cm) = 1/100 m
1 millimeter (mm) = 1/1,000 m
1 micrometer (μm) = 1/1,000,000 m
1 nanometer (nm) = 1/1,000,000,000 m

▲ FIGURE 4-1 **Relative sizes** Dimensions commonly encountered in biology range from about 100 meters (the height of the tallest redwood trees) through a few micrometers (the diameter of most cells) to a few nanometers (the diameter of many large molecules).

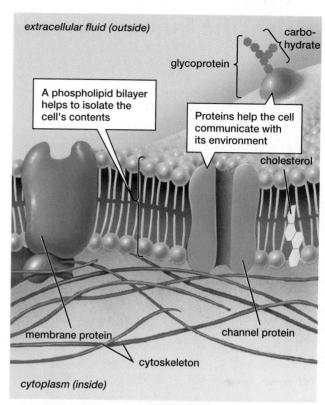

extracellular fluid (outside)

carbo-hydrate

glycoprotein

A phospholipid bilayer helps to isolate the cell's contents

Proteins help the cell communicate with its environment

cholesterol

membrane protein

channel protein

cytoskeleton

cytoplasm (inside)

▲ FIGURE 4-2 **The plasma membrane** The plasma membrane encloses the cell. Like all cellular membranes, it consists of a double layer of phospholipid molecules in which a variety of proteins is embedded. The membrane is supported by the cytoskeleton. In animal cells, cholesterol helps maintain the proper fluidity of the membrane.

membranes within cells consist of a double layer (a bilayer) of phospholipids and cholesterol molecules in which many different proteins are embedded. Important functions of the plasma membrane include:

- Isolating the cell's contents from the external environment.
- Regulating the flow of materials into and out of the cell.
- Allowing interaction with other cells and with the extracellular environment.

The phospholipid and protein components of cellular membranes have very different roles. Each phospholipid has a hydrophilic ("water-loving") head that faces the watery interior or watery exterior of the cell, and a pair of hydrophobic ("water-fearing") tails that face the interior of the membrane (see pp. 44–45). Although some small molecules—including oxygen, carbon dioxide, and water—are able to diffuse through it, the phospholipid bilayer forms a barrier to most hydrophilic molecules and ions. The phospholipid bilayer helps isolate the cell from its surroundings, allowing the cell to maintain crucial differences in concentrations of materials inside and outside.

Proteins embedded in the plasma membrane facilitate communication between the cell and its environment. Some allow specific molecules or ions to move through the plasma

Scientific Inquiry

The Search for the Cell

In 1665, the English scientist and inventor Robert Hooke reported observations with a primitive microscope. He aimed his instrument at an "exceeding thin . . . piece of Cork" and saw "a great many little Boxes" (**Fig. E4-1a**). Hooke called the boxes "cells," because he thought they resembled the tiny rooms, or cells, occupied by monks. Cork comes from the dry outer bark of the cork oak, and we now know that he was looking at the nonliving cell walls that surround all plant cells. Hooke wrote that in the living oak and other plants, "These cells [are] fill'd with juices."

In the 1670s, Dutch microscopist Anton van Leeuwenhoek was constructing his own simple microscopes and observing a previously unknown world. A self-taught amateur scientist, his descriptions of myriad "animalcules" (mostly single-celled organisms) in rain, pond, and well water caused quite an uproar because in those days, water was consumed without being treated. Eventually, van Leeuwenhoek made careful observations of an enormous range of microscopic specimens, including blood cells, sperm, and the eggs of small insects such as aphids and fleas. His discoveries struck a blow to the idea

specimen   location of lens

focusing knob

blood cells photographed through Leeuwenhoek's microscope

(b) Leeuwenhoek's microscope

(a) 17th-century microscope and cork cells

(c) Electron microscope

▲ **FIGURE E4-1 Microscopes yesterday and today (a)** Robert Hooke's drawings of cork cells, as he viewed them with an early light microscope similar to the one shown here. Only the cell walls remain. **(b)** One of Leeuwenhoek's microscopes, and a photograph of blood cells taken through a Leeuwenhoek microscope. The specimen is viewed through a tiny hole just underneath the lens. **(c)** This electron microscope performs as a transmission electron microscope (TEM) and a scanning electron microscope (SEM).

of spontaneous generation; at that time, fleas were believed to emerge spontaneously from sand or dust, and weevils from grain. Although they appear much more primitive than Hooke's microscopes, Leeuwenhoek's microscopes provided much clearer images and higher magnification (**Fig. E4-1b**).

Ever since the pioneering efforts of Robert Hooke and Anton van Leeuwenhoek, biologists, physicists, and engineers have collaborated in the development of a variety of advanced microscopes to view the cell and its components.

Light microscopes use lenses, usually made of glass or quartz, to focus light rays that either pass through or bounce off a specimen, thereby magnifying its image. Light microscopes provide a wide range of images, depending on how the specimen is illuminated and whether it has been stained (**Fig. E4-2a**).

The resolving power of light microscopes—that is, the smallest structure that can be seen—is about 1 micrometer (a millionth of a meter).

Electron microscopes (**Fig. E4-1c**) use beams of electrons instead of light, which are focused by magnetic fields rather than by lenses. Some types of electron microscopes can resolve structures as small as a few nanometers (billionths of a meter). Transmission electron microscopes pass electrons through a thin specimen and can reveal the details of interior cell structure, including organelles and plasma membranes (**Fig. E4-2c**). Scanning electron microscopes bounce electrons off specimens that have been coated with metals and provide three-dimensional images. These can be used to view the surface details of structures that range in size from entire organisms down to cells and even organelles (**Figs. E4-2b,d**).

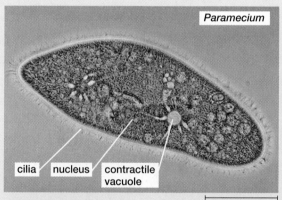

Paramecium

cilia   nucleus   contractile vacuole

50 micrometers

(a) Light microscope

10 micrometers

(b) Scanning electron microscope

basal bodies

mitochondrion

0.5 micrometers

(c) Transmission electron microscope

mitochondria

5 micrometers

(d) Scanning electron microscope

▲ **FIGURE E4-2 A comparison of microscope images (a)** A living *Paramecium* (a single-celled freshwater organism) photographed through a light microscope. **(b)** A false-color scanning electron micrograph (SEM) of *Paramecium*. **(c)** A transmission electron micrograph (TEM) showing the basal bodies at the bases of the cilia that cover *Paramecium*. Mitochondria are also visible. **(d)** An SEM at much higher magnification showing mitochondria (many of which are sliced open) within the cytoplasm. You will see both TEMs and SEMs throughout this text. Any colors you see in electron micrographs have been added artificially to enhance the structures.

membrane, while others promote chemical reactions inside the cell. Some membrane proteins join cells to one another and others receive and respond to signals from molecules (such as hormones) in the fluid surrounding the cell. Glycoproteins embedded in the plasma membrane extend carbohydrate branches outward from the cell (see Fig. 4-2). Some of these glycoproteins—called major histocompatibility complex (MHC) proteins—are responsible for identifying the cell as part of a unique individual. In Chapter 5, we discuss the plasma membrane in detail.

All Cells Contain Cytoplasm

The **cytoplasm** consists of all the fluid and structures that lie inside the plasma membrane, but outside of the nucleus (**Figs. 4-3** and **4-4**). The fluid portion of the cytoplasm in both prokaryotic and eukaryotic cells, called the **cytoplasmic fluid,** contains water, salts, and an assortment of organic molecules, including proteins, lipids, carbohydrates, sugars, amino acids, and nucleotides (described in Chapter 3). Most of the cell's metabolic activities—the biochemical reactions that support life—occur in the cell cytoplasm. Protein synthesis is one example. Cells must synthesize

a variety of proteins, such as those of the cytoskeleton (described later), proteins in the plasma membrane (described in Chapter 5), and all the enzymes that promote biochemical reactions (described in Chapter 6).

Case Study continued
Spare Parts for Human Bodies

Why is skin from cadavers and pigs rejected by burn victims, while synthetic skin substitutes are not? Skin from a different person or animal contains MHC glycoproteins that differ from those of the burn victim. This causes the victim's immune system to treat the skin as foreign, attack it, and eventually reject it. Fortunately, the response is sufficiently gradual that the skin can still help the burn heal before it is rejected. TransCyte™ has no remaining cells to stimulate an immune response, and the developers of Orcel™ hypothesize that the MHC proteins on the original foreskin cells are lost during the extensive culturing process.

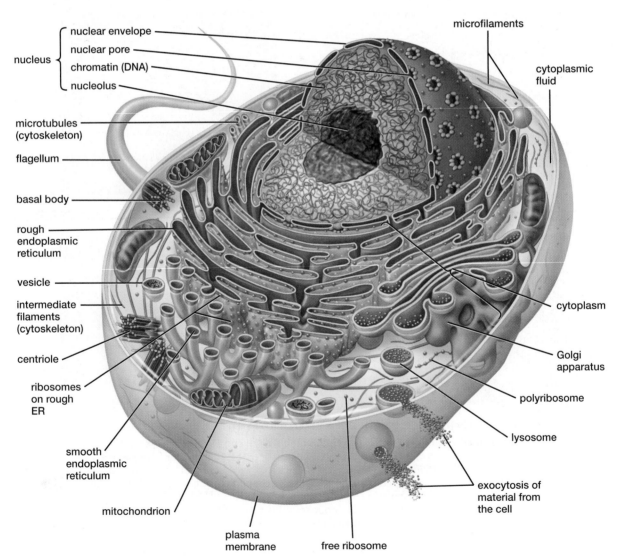

▲ **FIGURE 4-3 A generalized animal cell**

All Cells Use DNA as a Hereditary Blueprint and RNA to Copy the Blueprint and Guide Construction

Each cell contains genetic material, an inherited blueprint that stores the instructions for making the other parts of the cell and for producing new cells. The genetic material in cells is **deoxyribonucleic acid (DNA).** This fascinating molecule, described in detail in Chapter 11, contains genes consisting of precise sequences of nucleotides. During cell division, the original or "parent cells" pass exact copies of their DNA to their newly formed offspring, or "daughter cells." **Ribonucleic acid (RNA)** is chemically related to DNA and comes in different forms that copy the blueprint of genes on DNA and help construct proteins based on this blueprint. All cells contain both DNA and RNA.

All Cells Obtain Raw Materials and Energy from Their Environment

The major elements in biological molecules, including carbon, hydrogen, oxygen, nitrogen, sulfur, and phosphorus, as well as trace amounts of many minerals, ultimately come from the environment, which includes air, water, rocks, and other organisms. To maintain their incredible complexity, cells must continuously acquire and expend energy. As we explain in Chapters 7 and 8, essentially all of the energy powering life on Earth originates in sunlight. Only cells that are capable of photosynthesis can harness this energy. The energy stored by photosynthetic cells fuels the metabolic activities of nearly all other forms of life. Thus, all cells obtain the materials to synthesize the molecules of life and the energy to power this synthesis from their living and nonliving environment.

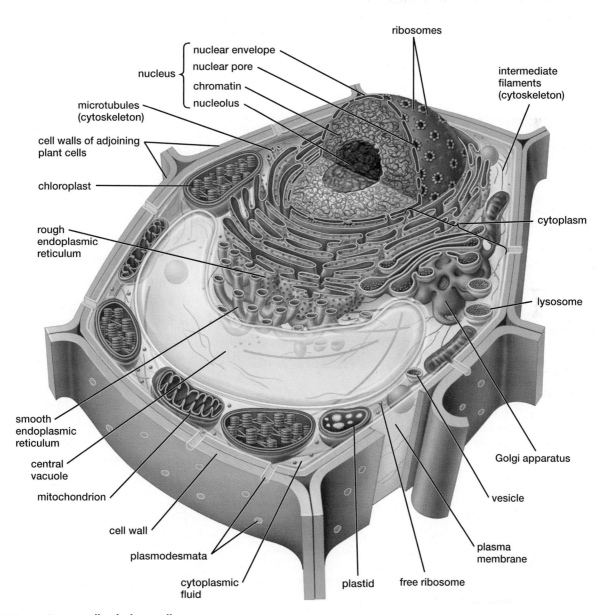

▲ **FIGURE 4-4 A generalized plant cell**

QUESTION Of the nucleus, ribosome, chloroplast, and mitochondrion, which appeared earliest in the history of life?

There Are Two Basic Types of Cells: Prokaryotic and Eukaryotic

All forms of life are composed of only two fundamentally different types of cells. **Prokaryotic** cells ("before the nucleus"; see Fig. 4-19) form the bodies of **bacteria** and **archaea**, the simplest forms of life. **Eukaryotic** cells ("true nucleus"; see Figs. 4-3 and 4-4) are far more complex and comprise the bodies of animals, plants, fungi, and protists.

Have you ever wondered

How Many Cells Are in the Human Body?

Well, scientists have wondered that too, and they can't agree. Estimates range from 10 trillion to 100 trillion. Interestingly, there seems to be a consensus that there are far more bacterial cells in the body than there are human cells—somewhere between 10 and 20 times as many. Does that make us primarily prokaryotic? Hardly. Most of the bacteria are guests that reside in our digestive tracts.

As their names imply, one striking difference between prokaryotic and eukaryotic cells is that the genetic material of eukaryotic cells is contained within a membrane-enclosed nucleus. In contrast, the genetic material of prokaryotic cells is not enclosed within a membrane. Other membrane-enclosed structures, called organelles, contribute to the far greater structural complexity of eukaryotic cells. **Table 4-1** summarizes the features of prokaryotic and eukaryotic cells, which we discuss in the sections that follow.

4.3 WHAT ARE THE MAJOR FEATURES OF EUKARYOTIC CELLS?

Eukaryotic cells comprise the bodies of animals, plants, protists, and fungi; as you might imagine, these cells are extremely diverse. Within the body of any multicellular organism there exists a huge variety of eukaryotic cells specialized to perform different functions. In contrast, the single-celled bodies of protists and some fungi must be sufficiently complex to perform all the necessary activities needed to sustain life, grow, and reproduce independently. Here we emphasize plant and

Table 4-1   Functions and Distribution of Cell Structures

Structure	Function	Prokaryotes	Eukaryotes: Plants	Eukaryotes: Animals
Cell Surface				
Cell wall	Protects and supports the cell	Present	Present	Absent
Cilia	Move the cell through fluid or move fluid past the cell surface	Absent	Absent	Present
Flagella	Move the cell through fluid	Present[1]	Present[2]	Present
Plasma membrane	Isolates the cell contents from the environment; regulates movement of materials into and out of the cell; allows communication with other cells	Present	Present	Present
Organization of Genetic Material				
Genetic material	Encodes the information needed to construct the cell and to control cellular activity	DNA	DNA	DNA
Chromosomes	Contain and control the use of DNA	Single, circular, no proteins	Many, linear, with proteins	Many, linear, with proteins
Nucleus	Membrane-bound container for chromosomes	Absent	Present	Present
Nuclear envelope	Encloses the nucleus; regulates movement of materials into and out of the nucleus	Absent	Present	Present
Nucleolus	Synthesizes ribosomes	Absent	Present	Present
Cytoplasmic Structures				
Mitochondria	Produce energy by aerobic metabolism	Absent	Present	Present
Chloroplasts	Perform photosynthesis	Absent	Present	Absent
Ribosomes	Provide the sites for protein synthesis	Present	Present	Present
Endoplasmic reticulum	Synthesizes membrane components, proteins, and lipids	Absent	Present	Present
Golgi apparatus	Modifies and packages proteins and lipids; synthesizes some carbohydrates	Absent	Present	Present
Lysosomes	Contain intracellular digestive enzymes	Absent	Present	Present
Plastids	Store food, pigments	Absent	Present	Absent
Central vacuole	Contains water and wastes; provides turgor pressure to support the cell	Absent	Present	Absent
Other vesicles and vacuoles	Transport secretory products; contain food obtained through phagocytosis	Absent	Present	Present
Cytoskeleton	Gives shape and support to the cell; positions and moves cell parts	Absent	Present	Present
Centrioles	Produce the microtubules of cilia and flagella	Absent	Absent (in most)	Present

[1]Some prokaryotes have structures called flagella, which lack microtubules and move in a fundamentally different way than do eukaryotic flagella.

[2]A few types of plants have flagellated sperm.

animal cells; the specialized structures of protists and fungi are covered in more detail in Chapters 20 and 22, respectively.

Eukaryotic cells differ from prokaryotic cells in many ways. For example, they are usually larger than prokaryotic cells—typically more than 10 micrometers in diameter. The cytoplasm of eukaryotic cells includes a variety of **organelles**— membrane-enclosed structures, such as the nucleus and mitochondria, that perform specific functions within the cell. The **cytoskeleton,** a network of protein fibers, gives shape and organization to the cytoplasm of eukaryotic cells. Many of the organelles are attached to the cytoskeleton.

Figures 4-3 and 4-4 illustrate the structures that are found in animal and plant cells, respectively (although not all individual cells possess all the features shown). Although they have many structures in common, some structures are unique to one type or the other. For example, plant cells are all surrounded by a cell wall, and they contain chloroplasts, plastids, and a central vacuole, none of which are found in animal cells. Animal cells contain centrioles, which are absent in plant cells. Many animal cells also bear cilia, which are rarely found in plant cells. You may want to refer to Figures 4-3 and 4-4, and Table 4-1, as we describe cell structure in greater detail.

Some Eukaryotic Cells Are Supported by Cell Walls

The outer surfaces of plants, fungi, and some protists are covered with nonliving, relatively stiff coatings called **cell walls** that support and protect the delicate plasma membrane. Single-celled protists that live in the ocean may have cell walls made of cellulose, protein, or glassy silica (see Chapter 20). Plant cell walls are composed of cellulose and other polysaccharides, whereas fungal cell walls are usually made of chitin (see p. 43). Prokaryotic cells also have cell walls, but made of different polysaccharides.

Cell walls are produced by the cells they surround. Plant cells secrete cellulose through their plasma membranes, forming the cell wall (see Fig. 4-4). The walls of adjacent cells are joined by the "middle lamella," a layer made primarily of the polysaccharide pectin. Pectin has a gelatinous texture and is often added to fruit jellies to make them gel. Cell walls support and protect otherwise fragile cells. For example, cell walls allow plants and mushrooms to resist the forces of gravity and wind and to stand erect on land. Cell walls are usually porous, allowing oxygen, carbon dioxide, and water carrying dissolved molecules to flow easily through them. The structure governing the interactions between a cell and its external environment is the plasma membrane, located just beneath the cell wall (when a cell wall is present). The plasma membrane is covered in detail in Chapter 5.

The Cytoskeleton Provides Shape, Support, and Movement

Organelles and other structures within eukaryotic cells do not drift about the cytoplasm haphazardly; most are attached to the network of protein fibers that make up the cytoskeleton (**Fig. 4-5**). Even individual enzymes, which are often a part of a complex series of reactions, may be fastened in sequence to the cytoskeleton, so that molecules can be passed from one enzyme to the next in the correct order for a particular chemical transformation. The cytoskeleton is composed of three types of protein fibers: thin **microfilaments,** medium-sized **intermediate filaments,** and thick **microtubules** (Table 4-2).

The cytoskeleton performs the following important functions:

- **Cell shape** In cells without cell walls, the cytoskeleton, particularly networks of intermediate filaments, determines the shape of the cell.
- **Cell movement** Cell movement occurs as microfilaments or microtubules assemble, disassemble, or slide past one another. Examples of moving cells include single-celled protists propelled by cilia, swimming sperm, and contracting muscle cells.

(a) Cytoskeleton

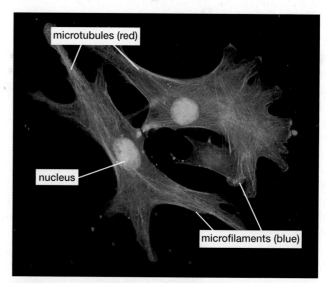

(b) Light micrograph showing the cytoskeleton

▲ **FIGURE 4-5 The cytoskeleton (a)** Eukaryotic cells are given shape and organization by the cytoskeleton, which consists of three types of proteins: microtubules, intermediate filaments, and microfilaments. **(b)** In this light micrograph, cells treated with fluorescent stains reveal microtubules and microfilaments, as well as the nucleus.

Table 4-2 Components of the Cytoskeleton

	Structure	Protein Type and Structure	Functions
Microfilaments	Twisted double strands of protein subunits; about 7 nm in diameter	Actin subunits	Involved in muscle contraction; allow for changes in cell shape; facilitate cytoplasmic division in animal cells
Intermediate filaments	Helical subunits twisted around one another and bundled into clusters of four, which may be further twisted together	Proteins vary with function and cell type subunits	Provide supporting framework within the cell; support the plasma membrane; anchor some organelles within the cytoplasm; attach some cells together
Microtubules	Tubes consisting of spirals of two-part protein subunits; about 25 nm in diameter	Tubulin subunit	Allow movement of chromosomes during cell division; form centrioles and basal bodies; are a major component of cilia and flagella

- **Organelle movement** Microtubules and microfilaments move organelles from place to place within a cell. For example, vesicles budded off the endoplasmic reticulum (ER) and Golgi apparatus (described later) are guided by the cytoskeleton.
- **Cell division** Microtubules and microfilaments are essential to cell division in eukaryotic cells. Cell division is covered in detail in Chapter 9.

Cilia and Flagella Move the Cell Through Fluid or Move Fluid Past the Cell

Both **cilia** (singular, cilium; Latin for "eyelash") and **flagella** (singular, flagellum; "whip") are slender extensions of the plasma membrane, supported internally by microtubules of the cytoskeleton. Each cilium and flagellum contains a ring of nine pairs of microtubules, with another pair in the center (**Fig. 4-6**). Cilia and flagella arise from a **basal body,** which anchors them to the plasma membrane. Basal bodies are derived from **centrioles** (found in pairs in the cytoplasm; see Fig. 4-3). Both consist of barrel-shaped rings of nine microtubule triplets. Centrioles are absent in most plants. They are present in animal cells, where they appear to participate in cell division.

How do cilia and flagella move? In cilia and flagella, tiny "arms" of protein attach neighboring pairs of microtubules (see Fig. 4-6). These arms can flex, using energy released from adenosine triphosphate (ATP) to power their movement. Flexing of the arms slides one pair of microtubules past the adjacent pairs, causing the cilia or flagellum to bend. Cilia and flagella often move almost continuously; the energy to power this motion is supplied by mitochondria, usually found in abundance near the basal bodies.

▲ **FIGURE 4-6 Cilia and flagella** Both cilia and flagella contain an outer ring of nine fused pairs of microtubules surrounding a central unfused pair. The outer pairs have "arms" made of protein that interact with adjacent pairs to provide the force for bending. Cilia and flagella arise from basal bodies, composed of triplets of microtubules, which are located just beneath the plasma membrane.

Cilia and flagella differ in length and number. In general, cilia are shorter and more numerous than flagella. The force generated by cilia can be compared to that created by oars on the sides of a rowboat (**Fig. 4-7a**, left). Flagella are longer than cilia, and cells with flagella usually have only one or two. The force generated by a flagellum can be compared to that created by the engine on a motorboat (**Fig. 4-7b**, left).

Some unicellular organisms, such as *Paramecium* (see Figs. E4-2a,b), use cilia to swim through water; others use flagella. In multicellular animals, cilia usually move fluids and suspended particles past a surface. Ciliated cells line such diverse structures as the gills of oysters (where they move water rich in food and oxygen over the gills), the oviducts of female mammals (where they move an egg through fluid from the ovary to the uterus), and the respiratory tracts of most land vertebrates (where they clear mucus that carries debris and microorganisms out of the trachea and lungs; see Fig. 4-7a, right). Nearly all animal sperm and a few types of plant sperm cells rely on flagella for movement (see Fig. 4-7b, right).

The Nucleus Is the Control Center of the Eukaryotic Cell

A cell's DNA stores all the information needed to construct the cell and direct the countless chemical reactions necessary for life and reproduction. The genetic information in DNA is used selectively by the cell, depending on its stage of development, its environment, and the function of the cell in a multicellular body. In eukaryotic cells, DNA is housed within the nucleus.

The **nucleus** is an organelle (usually the largest in the cell) consisting of three major parts: the nuclear envelope, chromatin, and the nucleolus, shown in **Figure 4-8** and described in the following sections.

The Nuclear Envelope Allows Selective Exchange of Materials

The nucleus is isolated from the rest of the cell by a **nuclear envelope** that consists of a double membrane. The membrane is perforated with tiny protein-lined nuclear pores. Water, ions, and small molecules can pass freely through the pores, but the passage of large molecules—particularly proteins, pieces of ribosomes, and RNA—is regulated by specialized gatekeeper proteins called the **nuclear pore complex** that line each nuclear pore. Ribosomes stud the outer nuclear membrane, which is continuous with membranes of the rough ER, described later (see also Figs. 4-3 and 4-4).

Chromatin Contains DNA, Which Codes for the Synthesis of Proteins

Because the nucleus is darkly colored by stains used in light microscopy, early microscopists, not knowing its function, named the nuclear material **chromatin,** meaning "colored substance." Biologists have since learned that chromatin consists of DNA associated with proteins. Eukaryotic DNA and its associated proteins form long strands called **chromosomes** ("colored bodies"). When cells divide, each chromosome coils upon itself, becoming thicker and shorter. The resulting condensed chromosomes are easily visible, even with a light microscope (**Fig. 4-9**).

The genes on DNA provide a blueprint or a "molecular code" for a huge variety of proteins. Some of these proteins form structural components of the cell. Others regulate the movement of materials through cell membranes, and still others are enzymes that promote chemical reactions within the cell that are responsible for growth and repair, nutrient and energy acquisition and use, and reproduction.

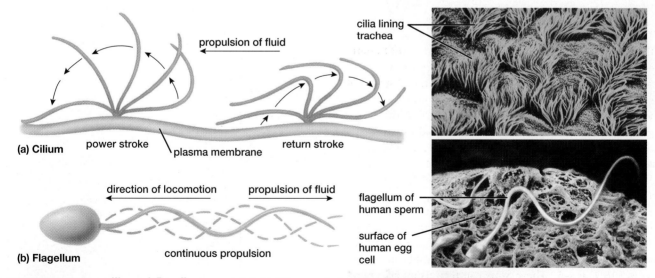

▲ **FIGURE 4-7 How cilia and flagella move (a)** (left) Cilia usually "row," providing a force parallel to the plasma membrane. Their movement resembles the arms of a swimmer doing the breast stroke. (right) SEM of cilia lining the trachea (which conducts air to the lungs); these cilia sweep out mucus and trapped particles. **(b)** (left) Flagella move in a wavelike motion, providing continuous propulsion perpendicular to the plasma membrane. In this way, a flagellum attached to a sperm can move the sperm straight ahead. (right) SEM of a human sperm cell on the surface of a human egg cell.

QUESTION What problems would arise if the trachea were lined with flagella?

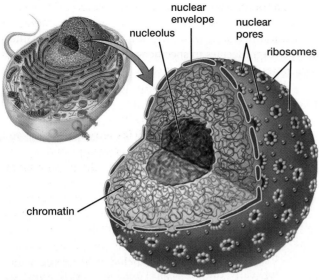

nuclear envelope

nucleolus

nuclear pores

ribosomes

chromatin

(a) The nucleus

nucleus

nuclear pores with nuclear pore complex

(b) Nucleus of a yeast cell

▲ FIGURE 4-8 **The nucleus (a)** The nucleus is bounded by a double outer membrane perforated by pores. Inside are chromatin and a nucleolus. **(b)** SEM of the nucleus of a yeast cell. The "gatekeeper proteins" of the nuclear pore complex are colored pink. These proteins line the nuclear pores.

Because proteins are synthesized in the cytoplasm, copies of the protein blueprints on DNA must be ferried out through the nuclear membrane into the cytoplasm. To accomplish this, genetic information is copied from DNA into molecules of messenger RNA (mRNA), which travel through the pores of the nuclear envelope into the cytoplasm. This information, coded by the sequence of nucleotides in mRNA, is then used to direct the synthesis of cellular proteins, a process that occurs on ribosomes (Fig. 4-10). We take a closer look at these processes in Chapter 12.

chromatin

chromosome

▲ FIGURE 4-9 **Chromosomes** Chromosomes, seen here in a light micrograph of a dividing cell (on the right) in an onion root tip, contain the same material (DNA and proteins) as the chromatin seen in adjacent nondividing cells.

QUESTION Why does the chromatin form discrete structures (chromosomes) in dividing cells?

The Nucleolus Is the Site of Ribosome Assembly

Eukaryotic nuclei have at least one **nucleolus** (plural, nucleoli, meaning "little nuclei"; see Fig. 4-8a). The nucleolus is the site of ribosome synthesis. It consists of ribosomal RNA, proteins, ribosomes in various stages of synthesis, and DNA that carries the genes coding for ribosomal RNA.

A **ribosome** is a small particle composed of ribosomal RNA and proteins that serves as a kind of "workbench" for the synthesis of proteins within the cell cytoplasm. Just as a workbench can be used to construct many different objects, any ribosome can be used to synthesize any of the thousands of proteins made by a cell. In electron micrographs, ribosomes

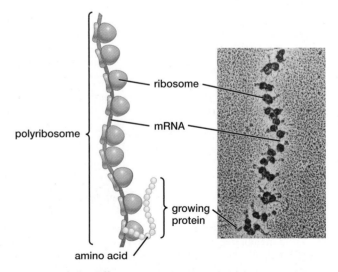

polyribosome

ribosome

mRNA

growing protein

amino acid

▲ FIGURE 4-10 **Ribosomes** Ribosomes in this TEM (right) are strung along a messenger RNA molecule, forming a polyribosome. The ribosomes are synthesizing a protein, indicated by the chain of amino acids.

appear as dark granules, either singly, studding the membranes of the nuclear envelope and endoplasmic reticulum (**Fig. 4-11**), or as polyribosomes ("many ribosomes") clustered along strands of mRNA (see Fig. 4-10).

Eukaryotic Cytoplasm Includes an Elaborate System of Membranes

All eukaryotic cells have an elaborate system of membranes that enclose the cell and create internal compartments within the cytoplasm. Imagine a large factory with many rooms and some separate buildings. Each room houses specialized machinery, and some rooms are interconnected to allow a complex product to be manufactured in stages. Some products must be moved between buildings before they are finished. The factory must import raw materials, but it makes and repairs its own machinery and exports some of its products.

In a comparable way, specialized regions within the cytoplasm, demarcated by membranes, separate a variety of biochemical reactions from one another and process different types of molecules in specific ways. The fluid property of membranes allows them to fuse with one another, so that these internal compartments can interconnect, exchange pieces of membrane among themselves, and transfer their contents to different compartments for various types of processing. Membrane sacs called **vesicles** ferry membrane and specialized contents among the separate regions of the membrane system. Vesicles may also fuse with the plasma membrane, exporting their contents outside the cell. How do the vesicles know where to go within the complex membrane system? Researchers have discovered that specific proteins embedded in membranes serve as "mailing labels" that specify the address to which the sac and its contents are being sent.

The cell's membrane system includes the plasma membrane, nuclear membrane, endoplasmic reticulum, Golgi apparatus, lysosomes, vesicles, and vacuoles, which we explore further in the sections that follow.

The Endoplasmic Reticulum Forms Membrane-Enclosed Channels Within the Cytoplasm

The **endoplasmic reticulum (ER)** is a series of interconnected membranes that form a labyrinth of flattened sacs and channels within the cytoplasm ("reticulum" means "network" and "endoplasmic" means "within the cytoplasm"; see Fig. 4-11). The ER membrane typically makes up at least 50% of the total membrane of the cell. Among its many functions is serving as the site for the synthesis of cell membrane proteins and phospholipids. This is important because ER membrane is constantly being budded off and transported to the Golgi apparatus, lysosomes, and the plasma membrane. Eukaryotic cells have two forms of ER: rough and smooth. Parts of the rough ER are continuous with the nuclear membrane, and some smooth ER is continuous with rough ER (see Fig. 4-3).

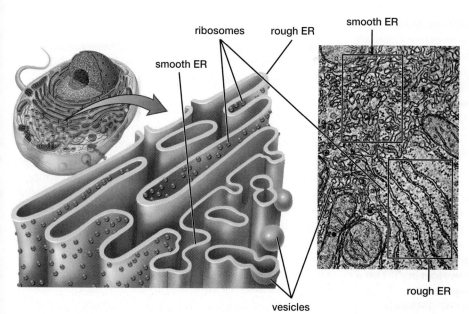

ribosomes   rough ER   smooth ER

smooth ER

vesicles

rough ER

(a) Endoplasmic reticulum may be rough or smooth   **(b) Smooth and rough ER**

◀ FIGURE 4-11 **Endoplasmic reticulum (a)** In some cells, rough and smooth ER are thought to be linked, as depicted in the drawing. In others, smooth ER may be separate. Ribosomes (orange dots) stud the cytoplasmic face of the rough ER membrane. **(b)** A TEM of smooth and rough ER with vesicles.

Smooth Endoplasmic Reticulum Smooth ER lacks ribosomes and is specialized for different activities in different cells. In some cells, smooth ER manufactures large quantities of lipids such as steroid hormones made from cholesterol. For example, sex hormones are produced by smooth ER in mammalian reproductive organs. Smooth ER is also abundant in liver cells, where it contains enzymes that detoxify harmful drugs such as alcohol and metabolic by-products such as ammonia. Other enzymes in the smooth ER of the liver break down glycogen (a carbohydrate stored in the liver) into glucose molecules that provide energy. Smooth ER stores calcium in all cells, but in skeletal muscles it is enlarged and specialized to store large amounts of calcium that are required for muscle contraction.

Rough Endoplasmic Reticulum The ribosomes on rough ER are sites of protein synthesis. For example, the various proteins embedded in cellular membranes are manufactured here. Ribosomes on rough ER are also sites for manufacturing proteins such as digestive enzymes and protein hormones (for example, insulin) that some cells export. As these proteins are synthesized, they are inserted through the ER membrane into the interior compartment. Proteins synthesized either for secretion outside the cell or to be used elsewhere within the cell move through the ER channels. Here they are chemically modified and folded into their proper three-dimensional structures. Eventually the proteins accumulate in pockets of membrane that bud off as vesicles that carry their protein cargo to the Golgi apparatus.

The Golgi Apparatus Sorts, Chemically Alters, and Packages Important Molecules

Named for the Italian physician and cell biologist Camillo Golgi, who discovered it in the late 1800s, the **Golgi apparatus** (or **Golgi**) is a specialized set of membranes derived from the endoplasmic reticulum. It resembles a stack of flattened and interconnected sacs (Fig. 4-12). The main function of the Golgi apparatus is to modify, sort, and package proteins produced by the rough ER. The compartments of the Golgi act like the finishing rooms of a factory, where the final touches are added to products to be packaged and exported. Vesicles from the rough ER fuse with one face of the Golgi apparatus, adding their membranes to the Golgi and emptying their contents into the Golgi sacs. Within the Golgi compartments, some of the proteins synthesized in the rough ER are modified further; for example, carbohydrates may be added to form glycoproteins. Some large proteins are cleaved into smaller fragments. Finally, vesicles bud off from the opposite face of the Golgi, carrying away finished products for use in the cell or export out of the cell.

The Golgi apparatus performs the following functions:

- Modifies some molecules; an important role is to add carbohydrates to proteins to make glycoproteins. It also breaks up some proteins into smaller peptides.
- Synthesizes some polysaccharides used in plant cell walls, such as cellulose and pectin.

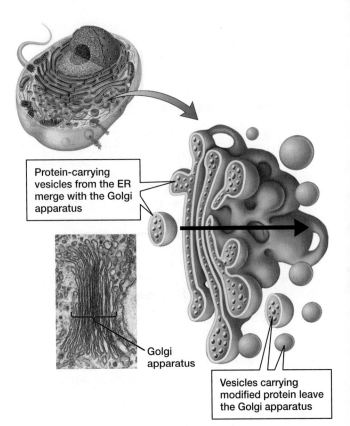

▲ FIGURE 4-12 The Golgi apparatus The Golgi apparatus is a stack of flattened membranous sacs. Vesicles transport both cell membrane and the enclosed material from the ER to the Golgi. The arrow shows the direction of movement of materials through the Golgi as they are modified and sorted. Vesicles bud from the face of the Golgi opposite the ER.

Labels in figure:
Protein-carrying vesicles from the ER merge with the Golgi apparatus
Golgi apparatus
Vesicles carrying modified protein leave the Golgi apparatus

- Separates various proteins and lipids received from the ER according to their destinations. For example, the Golgi apparatus separates the digestive enzymes that are bound for lysosomes from the cholesterol used in new membrane synthesis, and from the protein hormones that the cell will secrete.
- Packages the finished molecules into vesicles that are then transported to other parts of the cell or to the plasma membrane for export.

Secreted Proteins Are Modified as They Move Through the Cell

To understand how some of the components of the membrane system work together, let's look at the manufacture and export of an extremely important protein called an antibody (Fig. 4-13). Antibodies are glycoproteins produced by white blood cells that bind to foreign invaders (such as disease-causing bacteria) and help destroy them. Antibody proteins are synthesized on ribosomes of the rough ER within white blood cells, and they are packaged into vesicles formed from ER membrane. These vesicles travel to the Golgi, where the membranes fuse, releasing the protein into the Golgi apparatus. Within the Golgi, carbohydrates are attached to the protein, which is then repackaged into vesicles formed from

▲ FIGURE 4-13 A protein is manufactured and exported
Here, we illustrate the formation of an antibody as an example of this process.

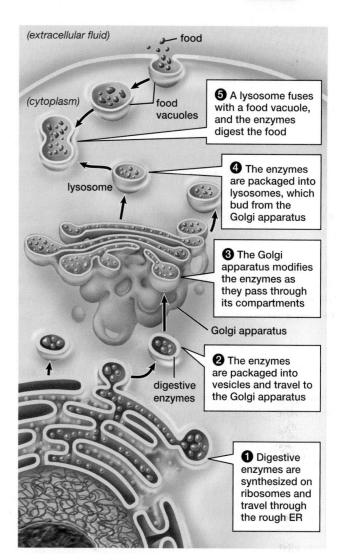

▲ FIGURE 4-14 Formation and function of lysosomes and food vacuoles

QUESTION Why is it advantageous for all membranes associated with the cell to have a fundamentally similar composition?

membrane acquired from the Golgi. The vesicle containing the completed antibody travels to the plasma membrane and fuses with it, releasing the antibody outside the cell, where it will make its way into the bloodstream to help defend the body against infection.

Lysosomes Serve as the Cell's Digestive System

Some of the proteins manufactured in the ER and sent to the Golgi apparatus are intracellular digestive enzymes that can break proteins, fats, and carbohydrates into their component subunits. In the Golgi, these enzymes are packaged in membrane-enclosed vesicles called **lysosomes** (Fig. 4-14). One major function of lysosomes is to digest food particles, which range from individual proteins to complete microorganisms.

As you will learn in Chapter 5, many cells "eat" by phagocytosis—that is, by engulfing particles just outside the cell using extensions of the plasma membrane. The plasma membrane with its enclosed food then pinches off inside the cytoplasm and forms a **food vacuole.** Lysosomes recognize

these food vacuoles and merge with them. The contents of the two vesicles mix, and lysosomal enzymes digest the food into small molecules such as amino acids, monosaccharides, and fatty acids that can be used within the cell. Lysosomes also digest worn out or defective organelles. These are enclosed in vesicles of ER membrane, which fuse with lysosomes, exposing the organelle to digestive enzymes that break it down into its component molecules. These molecules are released into the cytoplasm where they can be reused in metabolic processes.

Membrane Is Exchanged Throughout the Cell

Throughout the cell, membrane is continually exchanged among the nuclear envelope, rough and smooth ER, Golgi apparatus, lysosomes, food vacuoles, and the plasma membrane. By reviewing Figures 4-13 and 4-14, you can get an idea of how the membranes interconnect. For example, the ER synthesizes the phospholipids and proteins that make up the plasma membrane and buds off some of this membrane in vesicles, which then fuse with the Golgi membranes. Some of the ER membrane that fuses with the Golgi carries protein "address labels" that direct it to return to the ER, restoring crucial proteins (such as some enzymes) to the ER membrane. Other parts of the ER membrane are modified by the Golgi; for example, carbohydrates may be added to make membrane glycoproteins. Eventually, this membrane leaves the Golgi as a vesicle that may fuse with the plasma membrane, replenishing or enlarging it.

Vacuoles Serve Many Functions, Including Water Regulation, Support, and Storage

Most cells contain one or more **vacuoles**—sacs of cell membrane filled with fluid containing various molecules. Some, such as the food vacuoles that form during phagocytosis (see Fig. 4-14), are only temporary. However, many cells contain permanent vacuoles that have important roles in maintaining the integrity of the cell, most notably by regulating the cell's water content.

Freshwater Microorganisms Have Contractile Vacuoles

Freshwater protists such as *Paramecium* consist of a single eukaryotic cell. Many of these organisms possess **contractile vacuoles** composed of collecting ducts, a central reservoir, and a tube leading to a pore in the plasma membrane (**Fig. 4-15**). These complex cells live in fresh water, which constantly leaks into them through their plasma membranes (we describe this process, called osmosis, in Chapter 5). The influx of water would soon burst the fragile organism if it did not have a mechanism to excrete the water. Cellular energy is used to pump salts from the cytoplasm of the protist into collecting ducts. Water follows by osmosis and drains into the central reservoir. When the reservoir of the contractile vacuole is full, it contracts, squirting the water out through a pore in the plasma membrane.

Plant Cells Have Central Vacuoles

Three-quarters or more of the volume of many plant cells is occupied by a large **central vacuole** (see Fig. 4-4). The central vacuole has several functions. Filled mostly with water, the central vacuole is involved in the cell's water balance. It also provides a "dump site" for hazardous wastes, which plant cells often cannot excrete. Some plant cells store poisonous substances, such as sulfuric acid, in their vacuoles. These poisons deter animals from munching on the otherwise tasty leaves.

Vacuoles may also store sugars and amino acids not immediately needed by the cell. Blue or purple pigments stored in central vacuoles are responsible for the colors of many flowers. As you will learn in Chapter 5, dissolved substances attract water into the vacuole. The water pressure (called turgor pressure) within the vacuole pushes the fluid portion of the cytoplasm up against the cell wall with considerable force. Cell walls are usually somewhat flexible, so both the overall shape and the rigidity of the cell depend on turgor pressure within the cell. Turgor pressure thus provides support for the non-woody parts of plants. (Look ahead to Fig. 5-10 to see what happens when you forget to water your houseplants.)

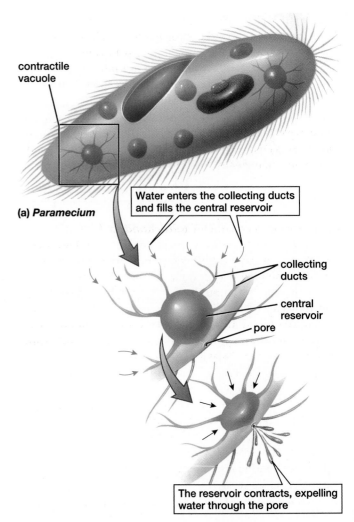

(a) *Paramecium*

Water enters the collecting ducts and fills the central reservoir

collecting ducts

central reservoir

pore

The reservoir contracts, expelling water through the pore

contractile vacuole

(b) Contractile vacuole

▲ FIGURE 4-15 **Contractile vacuoles** Many freshwater protists contain contractile vacuoles. **(a)** The single-celled protist *Paramecium* lives in freshwater ponds and lakes. **(b)** An enlargement of the contractile vacuole showing its structure and activity as it collects and expels water.

Mitochondria Extract Energy from Food Molecules, and Chloroplasts Capture Solar Energy

Every cell requires a continuous supply of energy to manufacture complex molecules and structures, to acquire nutrients from the environment and excrete waste materials, to move, and to reproduce. All eukaryotic cells have mitochondria that capture energy stored in sugar by producing high-energy ATP molecules. The cells of plants (and some protists) also have chloroplasts, which can capture energy directly from sunlight and store it in sugar molecules.

Most biologists accept the hypothesis that both mitochondria and chloroplasts evolved from prokaryotic bacteria that took up residence long ago within the cytoplasm of other prokaryotic cells, by a process called endosymbiosis (literally, "living together inside"). The **endosymbiont hypothesis** of mitochondrial and chloroplast evolution is discussed in more detail in Chapter 17. Mitochondria and chloroplasts are similar to each other and to prokaryotic cells in several ways. Both are about the size of some prokaryotic cells (1 to 5 micrometers in diameter). Both are surrounded by a double membrane; the outer membrane may have come from the original host cell and the inner membrane from the guest cell. Both have assemblies of enzymes that synthesize ATP, as would have been needed by an independent cell. Finally, both possess DNA and ribosomes that more closely resemble prokaryotic than eukaryotic DNA and ribosomes.

Mitochondria Use Energy Stored in Food Molecules to Produce ATP

All eukaryotic cells contain **mitochondria** (singular, mitochondrion), which are sometimes called the "powerhouses of the cell" because they extract energy from food molecules and store it in the high-energy bonds of ATP. As you will see in Chapter 8, different amounts of energy can be released from a food molecule, depending on how it is broken down. The breakdown of food molecules begins with enzymes in the cytoplasmic fluid and does not use oxygen. This **anaerobic** ("without oxygen") breakdown does not convert much food energy into ATP energy. Mitochondria enable a eukaryotic cell to use oxygen to break down high-energy molecules even further. These **aerobic** ("with oxygen") reactions generate energy much more effectively; about 16 times as much ATP is generated by aerobic metabolism in the mitochondria than by anaerobic metabolism in the cytoplasmic fluid. Not surprisingly, mitochondria are found in large numbers in metabolically active cells, such as muscle, and they are less abundant in cells that are less active, such as those of cartilage.

Mitochondria possess a pair of membranes (**Fig. 4-16**). The outer membrane is smooth, whereas the inner membrane forms deep folds called cristae (singular, crista, meaning "crest"). The mitochondrial membranes enclose two fluid-filled spaces: the intermembrane compartment between the inner and outer membranes and the matrix, or inner compartment, within the inner membrane. Some of the reactions that break down high-energy molecules occur in the fluid of the matrix inside the inner membrane; the rest are conducted by a series of enzymes attached to the membranes of the cristae within the intermembrane compartment. The role of mitochondria in energy production is described in detail in Chapter 8.

Chloroplasts Are the Sites of Photosynthesis

Photosynthesis, which captures sunlight and provides the energy to power life on Earth, occurs in the chloroplasts of eukaryotic cells (and on membranes of prokaryotic cells, described later). **Chloroplasts** (**Fig. 4-17**) are specialized organelles surrounded by a double membrane. The inner membrane of the chloroplast encloses a fluid called the stroma. Within the stroma are interconnected stacks of hollow, membranous sacs. The individual sacs are called thylakoids, and a stack of sacs is a granum (plural, grana).

The thylakoid membranes contain the green pigment molecule **chlorophyll** (which gives plants their green color) as well as other pigment molecules. During photosynthesis, chlorophyll captures the energy of sunlight and transfers it to other molecules in the thylakoid membranes. These molecules transfer the energy to ATP and other energy carriers. The energy carriers diffuse into the stroma, where

outer membrane

inner membrane

intermembrane space

matrix

cristae

0.2 micrometer

▲ **FIGURE 4-16 A mitochondrion** Mitochondria contain two membranes enclosing two fluid compartments: the intermembrane compartment between the outer and inner membranes, and the matrix within the inner membrane. The outer membrane is smooth, but the inner membrane forms deep folds called cristae. These structures are visible in the TEM on the right.

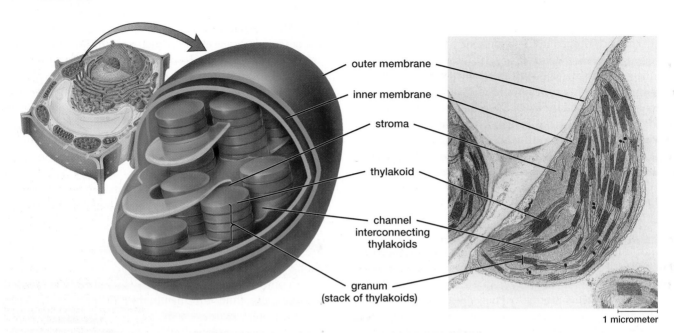

outer membrane

inner membrane

stroma

thylakoid

channel
interconnecting
thylakoids

granum
(stack of thylakoids)

1 micrometer

▲ FIGURE 4-17 **A chloroplast** Chloroplasts are surrounded by a double membrane. The fluid stroma is enclosed by the inner membrane; within the stroma are stacks of thylakoid sacs called grana. Chlorophyll is embedded in the membranes of the thylakoids.

their energy is used to drive the synthesis of sugar from carbon dioxide and water.

Plants Use Plastids for Storage

Chloroplasts are highly specialized **plastids,** organelles found only in plants and photosynthetic protists (Fig. 4-18). Plants and photosynthetic protists use nonchloroplast types of plastids as storage containers for various molecules, including pigments that give ripe fruits their yellow, orange, or red colors. In plants that continue growing from one year to the next, plastids store photosynthetic products from the summer for use during the following winter and spring. Most plants convert the sugars made during photosynthesis into starch, which is also stored in plastids. Potatoes, for example, are composed almost entirely of cells stuffed with starch-filled plastids (see Fig. 4-18).

BioFlix™ Tour of an Animal Cell

BioFlix™ Tour of a Plant Cell

4.4 WHAT ARE THE MAJOR FEATURES OF PROKARYOTIC CELLS?

Prokaryotic Cells Are Relatively Small and Possess Specialized Surface Features

Most prokaryotic cells are small, generally less than 5 micrometers in diameter (most eukaryotic cells are from 10 to 100 micrometers in diameter) with a simple internal structure compared to eukaryotic cells (Fig. 4-19; compare this to Figs. 4-3 and 4-4). Nearly all prokaryotic cells are

plastid

starch
globules

0.5 micrometer

▲ FIGURE 4-18 **A plastid** Plastids, found in the cells of plants and photosynthetic protists, are surrounded by a double outer membrane. Chloroplasts are the most familiar; other types store various materials, such as the starch filling these plastids in potato cells, seen on the right in a TEM.

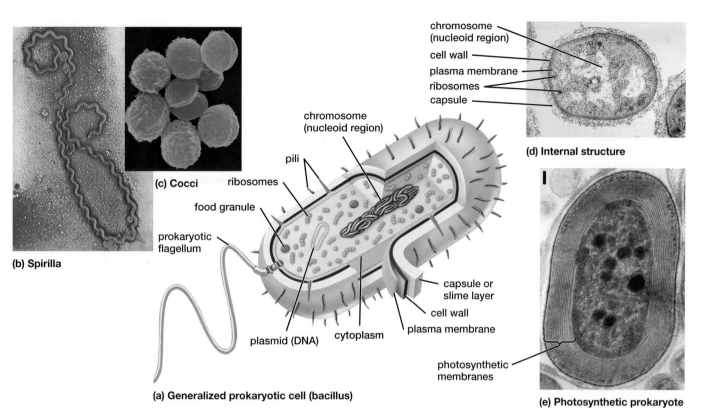

(c) Cocci

(b) Spirilla

(d) Internal structure

(a) Generalized prokaryotic cell (bacillus)

(e) Photosynthetic prokaryote

▲ FIGURE 4-19 **Prokaryotic cells are simpler than eukaryotic cells** Prokaryotes assume a variety of shapes, including **(a)** rod-shaped bacilli, **(b)** spiral-shaped spirilla, and **(c)** spherical cocci. Internal structures are revealed in the TEMs in **(d)** and **(e)**. Some photosynthetic bacteria have internal membranes where photosynthesis occurs, as shown in **(e)**.

surrounded by a stiff cell wall, which protects the cell and confers its characteristic shape. Most prokaryotes take the form of rod-shaped bacilli (**Fig. 4-19a**), spiral-shaped spirilla (**Fig. 4-19b**), or spherical cocci (**Fig. 4-19c**). Several types of antibiotics, including penicillin, fight bacterial infections by interfering with cell wall synthesis, causing the bacteria to rupture. Although no prokaryotic cells possess cilia, some bacteria and archaea are propelled by flagella whose structure differs from eukaryotic flagella.

Bacteria that infect other organisms—such as those that cause tooth decay, diarrhea, pneumonia, or urinary tract infections—possess surface features that help them adhere to specific host tissues, such as the surface of a tooth or the lining of the small intestine, lungs, or bladder. These surface features include capsules and slime layers, which are polysaccharide coatings that some bacteria secrete outside their cell walls. When Anton van Leeuwenhoek observed material scraped from his teeth under his simple microscope, he observed many bacteria that adhere using slime layers (see "Links to Everyday Life: Unwanted Guests" on p. 74). Capsules and slime layers also help some prokaryotic cells avoid drying out. Pili (literally, "hairs") are surface proteins jutting outward from the prokaryotic cell wall (see Fig. 4-19a). Some types of bacteria form sex pili, hollow protein tubes used to exchange genetic material (DNA) between

bacterial cells. The features of prokaryotic cells are discussed and illustrated in more detail in Chapter 19.

Prokaryotic Cells Have Fewer Specialized Structures Within Their Cytoplasm

The cytoplasm of most prokaryotic cells is rather homogeneous in appearance when compared to eukaryotic cells. In the central region of the cell is an area called the **nucleoid** (see Fig. 4-19a). Within the nucleoid, prokaryotic cells generally have a single, circular chromosome consisting of a long coiled strand of DNA that carries essential genetic information. The nucleoid is not separated from the cytoplasm by a membrane, and so is not a true nucleus as seen in eukaryotic cells. Most prokaryotic cells also contain small rings of DNA called plasmids, which are located outside the nucleoid. Plasmids usually carry genes that give the cell special properties; for example, some disease-causing bacteria possess plasmids that allow them to inactivate antibiotics, making them much more difficult to kill.

Prokaryotic cells lack nuclei and the other membrane-enclosed organelles (such as chloroplasts, mitochondria, ER, Golgi, and other components of the membrane system) that eukaryotic cells possess. Nonetheless, some prokaryotic cells do use membranes to organize the enzymes responsible for a series of biochemical reactions. Such enzymes are situated in

Links to *Everyday Life*

Unwanted Guests

In the late 1600s, Dutch microscopist Anton van Leeuwenhoek scraped white matter from between his teeth and viewed it through a microscope that he had constructed himself. To his consternation, he saw millions of cells that he called "animalcules," single-celled organisms that we now recognize as bacteria. Annoyed at the presence of these life-forms in his mouth, he attempted to kill them with vinegar and hot coffee—with little success. The warm, moist environment of the human mouth, particularly the crevices of the teeth and gums, is an ideal habitat for a variety of bacteria. Some produce slime layers that help them and others adhere to the tooth. Each divides repeatedly to form a colony of offspring. Thick layers of bacteria, slime, and glycoproteins from saliva make up the white substance, called plaque, that Leeuwenhoek scraped from his teeth. Sugar in foods and beverages nourishes the bacteria, which break down the sugar into lactic acid. The acid eats away at the tooth enamel, producing tiny crevices in which the bacteria multiply further, eventually producing a cavity. So, although he didn't know why, Leeuwenhoek was right to be concerned about the "animalcules" in his mouth!

a particular sequence along the membrane to promote reactions in the proper order. For example, photosynthetic bacteria possess internal membranes in which light-capturing proteins and enzymes that catalyze the synthesis of high-energy molecules are embedded in a specific order (**Fig. 4-19e**). In prokaryotic cells, reactions that harvest energy from the breakdown of sugars are catalyzed by enzymes that may be either anchored along the inner plasma membrane or floating free in the cytoplasm.

Bacterial cytoplasm contains ribosomes (see Fig. 4-19a). Although their function is similar to that of eukaryotic ribosomes, bacterial ribosomes are smaller and contain different proteins. These ribosomes resemble those found in eukaryotic mitochondria and chloroplasts, providing support for the endosymbiont hypothesis described earlier. Prokaryotic cytoplasm also may contain food granules that store energy-rich molecules, such as glycogen, but these are not enclosed by membranes.

You might wish to go back and look at Table 4-1 at this point to review the differences between prokaryotic and eukaryotic cells. As you compare these cell types, think about the endosymbiont hypothesis. You'll learn more about this concept in Chapter 17.

Case Study revisited
Spare Parts for Human Bodies

Bioengineering of tissues and organs such as skin requires the coordinated efforts of biochemists, biomedical engineers, cell biologists, and physicians.

In laboratories across the world, teams of scientists are working to grow not only skin but also bone, cartilage, heart valves, bladders, and breast tissue on plastic scaffolds. To heal broken bones, for example, teams of researchers are working to develop degradable plastics, incorporating protein growth factors into the material. These growth factors would encourage nearby bone cells and tiny blood vessels to invade the plastic as it breaks down, eventually replacing it with the patient's own bone.

Researchers continue to refine tissue-culturing techniques and to develop better scaffolding materials with the goal of duplicating entire organs. Bioartificial bladders have recently been created using muscle and bladder-lining cells taken from patients with improperly functioning bladders (**Fig. 4-20**). The cells are seeded onto a bladder-shaped scaffold composed of collagen, are incubated for about 7 weeks, and are then transplanted into a patient. The bladders, designed by Dr. Anthony Atala, a surgeon at Wake Forest University, have performed successfully in the seven patients who received

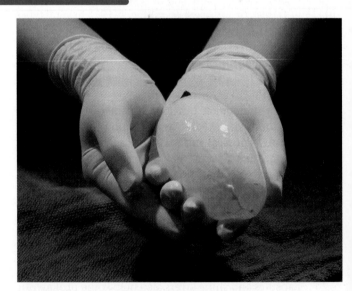

▲ FIGURE 4-20 **A laboratory-grown bladder**

them. A biotechnology company has completed animal studies and hopes to begin further tests of these bladders in humans in 2009, with the goal of bringing the bioengineered "Neo-Bladder" to the medical market.

An exciting new development in tissue engineering is "bioprinting." Using a specially designed instrument (a distant relative of the familiar ink-jet printer), Gabor Forgacs, a biophysicist at the University of Missouri–Columbia, hopes to engineer organs without using scaffolds. His "printer" ejects spheres less than 0.5 millimeter in diameter, which contain from 10,000 to 40,000 cells, onto a gel within which the cells can migrate and interact with one another. The bioprinting technique uses the inherent ability of cells to communicate with one another using physical and chemical signals, and to organize themselves into functional units. In an early test, chicken heart muscle cells were printed onto a dish. After about 90 hours, the heart muscle cells had migrated together and were communicating with one another, contracting in unison, as does a beating heart.

Forgacs and his team are currently working on printing out blood vessels using spheres composed of the three types of cells that comprise a blood vessel. The spheres surround a central core of collagen that will eventually be removed to allow blood to flow through. Over time, the three cell types spontaneously organize themselves around the collagen core just as they do in a natural vessel. Bioprinting offers the possibility of one day building a complete organ from a patient's own cells, and the near future holds the almost certain promise of bioengineered blood vessels.

BioEthics Consider This

Forgacs foresees one of the first uses of his cell-printing technique to be the formation of tissues from human cells on which to test new drugs. What do you think are the advantages of this approach compared to testing drugs on laboratory animals?

CHAPTER REVIEW

Summary of Key Concepts

4.1 What Is the Cell Theory?
The principles of the cell theory are as follows: Every living organism is made up of one or more cells, the smallest living organisms are single cells, cells are the functional units of multicellular organisms, and all cells arise from preexisting cells.

4.2 What Are the Basic Attributes of Cells?
Cells are small because they must exchange materials with their surroundings by diffusion, a slow process that requires that the interior of the cell never be too far from the plasma membrane. All cells are surrounded by a plasma membrane that regulates the interchange of materials between the cell and its environment. All cells use DNA as a genetic blueprint and RNA to direct protein synthesis based on this blueprint. All cells obtain the materials to generate the molecules of life, and the energy to power this synthesis, from their living and nonliving environment. There are two fundamentally different types of cells: prokaryotic and eukaryotic. Prokaryotic cells are small and lack membrane-enclosed organelles. Eukaryotic cells have a variety of organelles, including a nucleus.

4.3 What Are the Major Features of Eukaryotic Cells?
Cells of plants, fungi, and some protists are supported by porous cell walls outside the plasma membrane. All eukaryotic cells have an internal cytoskeleton of protein filaments. The cytoskeleton organizes and shapes the cell, and moves and anchors organelles. Some eukaryotic cells have cilia or flagella, extensions of the plasma membrane that contain microtubules in a characteristic pattern. These structures move fluids past the cell or move the cell through a fluid environment.

Genetic material (DNA) is contained within the nucleus, which is bounded by the double membrane of the nuclear envelope. Pores in the nuclear envelope regulate the movement of molecules between nucleus and cytoplasm. The genetic material is organized into strands called chromosomes, which consist of DNA and proteins. The nucleolus consists of ribosomal RNA and ribosomal proteins, as well as the genes that code for ribosome synthesis. Ribosomes are composed of ribosomal RNA and protein and are the sites of protein synthesis.

The membrane system of a cell includes the plasma membrane, endoplasmic reticulum (ER), Golgi apparatus, vacuoles, and vesicles. Endoplasmic reticulum forms a series of interconnected membranous compartments. The ER is a major site of membrane synthesis within the cell. Smooth ER, which lacks ribosomes, manufactures lipids such as steroid hormones, detoxifies drugs and metabolic wastes, breaks glycogen into glucose, and stores calcium. Rough ER, which bears ribosomes, manufactures and modifies proteins. The Golgi apparatus is a series of membranous sacs derived from the ER. The Golgi processes and modifies materials synthesized in the rough ER. Substances modified in the Golgi are packaged into vesicles for transport elsewhere in the cell. Lysosomes are vesicles that contain digestive enzymes, which digest food particles and defective organelles.

All eukaryotic cells contain mitochondria—organelles that use oxygen to complete the metabolism of food molecules, capturing much of their energy as ATP. Cells of plants and some protists contain plastids. Storage plastids store pigments or starch. Chloroplasts are specialized plastids that capture solar energy during photosynthesis, allowing plant cells to manufacture sugar from water and carbon dioxide. Both mitochondria and chloroplasts probably originated from bacteria.

Many eukaryotic cells contain sacs, called vacuoles, that are bounded by a single membrane and function to store food or wastes, excrete water, or support the cell. Some protists have contractile vacuoles, which collect and expel water. Plants use central vacuoles to support the cell as well as to store wastes and toxic materials.

BioFlix ™ Tour of an Animal Cell

BioFlix ™ Tour of a Plant Cell

4.4 What Are the Major Features of Prokaryotic Cells?
Prokaryotic cells are generally much smaller than eukaryotic cells and have a much simpler internal structure. Most are surrounded by a relatively stiff cell wall. The cytoplasm of prokaryotic cells lacks membrane-enclosed organelles (although some photosynthetic bacteria have extensive internal membranes). A single, circular strand of DNA is found in the nucleoid. Table 4-1

compares prokaryotic cells to the eukaryotic cells of plants and animals.

Study Note

Figures 4-3, 4-4, and 4-19 illustrate the overall structure of animal, plant, and prokaryotic cells, respectively. Table 4-1 lists the principal organelles, their functions, and their occurrence in animals, plants, and prokaryotes.

Key Terms

aerobic   71
anaerobic   71
archaea   62
bacteria   62
basal body   64
cell theory   56
cell wall   63
central vacuole   70
centriole   64
chlorophyll   71
chloroplast   71
chromatin   65
chromosome   65
cilium (plural, cilia)   64
contractile vacuole   70
cytoplasm   60
cytoplasmic fluid   60
cytoskeleton   63
deoxyribonucleic acid
   (DNA)   61
endoplasmic reticulum
   (ER)   67
endosymbiont
   hypothesis   70
eukaryotic   62

flagellum (plural,
   flagella)   64
food vacuole   69
Golgi apparatus   68
intermediate filament   63
lysosome   69
microfilament   63
microtubule   63
mitochondrion (plural,
   mitochondria)   71
nuclear envelope   65
nuclear pore complex   65
nucleoid   73
nucleolus (plural,
   nucleoli)   66
nucleus   65
organelle   63
plasma membrane   56
plastid   72
prokaryotic   62
ribonucleic acid (RNA)   61
ribosome   66
vacuole   70
vesicle   67

Thinking Through the Concepts

Fill-in-the-Blank

1. The plasma membrane is composed of what two major types of molecules? _____ and _____ Which type of molecule is responsible for each of the following functions? Isolation from the surroundings: _____; interactions with other cells: _____; movement of hydrophilic molecules through the membrane: _____.

2. The _____ is composed of a network of protein fibers. The three types of protein fibers are _____, _____, and _____. Which of these supports cilia? _____

3. After each description, fill in the appropriate term: "Workbenches" of the cell: _____; comes in rough and smooth forms: _____; site of ribosome production: _____; a stack of flattened membranous sacs: _____; outermost layer of plant cells: _____; ferries blueprints for protein production from the nucleus to the cytoplasm: _____.

4. Antibody proteins are synthesized on ribosomes associated with the _____. The antibody proteins are packaged into membranous sacs called _____ and are then transported to the _____. Here, what type of molecule is added to the protein? _____ After the antibody is completed, it is packaged into vesicles that fuse with the _____ membrane.

5. After each description, fill in the appropriate structure: "Powerhouses" of the cell: _____; capture solar energy: _____; outermost structure of plant cells: _____; region of prokaryotic cell containing DNA: _____; propel fluid past cells: _____; consists of cytoplasmic fluid and the organelles within it: _____.

6. Two organelles that are believed to have evolved from prokaryotic cells are _____ and _____. Evidence for this hypothesis is that both have _____ membranes, both have groups of enzymes that synthesize _____, both have their own _____, and their _____ is similar to that of prokaryotic cells.

Review Questions

1. What are the three parts of the cell theory?

2. Which organelles are common to both plant and animal cells, and which are unique to each?

3. Define *stroma* and *matrix*.

4. Describe the nucleus and the function of each of its components, including the nuclear envelope, chromatin, chromosomes, DNA, and the nucleolus.

5. What are the functions of mitochondria and chloroplasts? Why do scientists believe that these organelles arose from prokaryotic cells?

6. What is the function of ribosomes? Where in the cell are they found? Are they limited to eukaryotic cells?

7. Describe the structure and function of the endoplasmic reticulum and the Golgi apparatus and how they work together.

8. How are lysosomes formed? What is their function?

9. Diagram the structure of cilia and flagella. Describe how each one beats and what their beating accomplishes.

Applying the Concepts

1. If samples of muscle tissue were taken from the legs of a world-class marathon runner and a sedentary individual, which would you expect to have a higher density of mitochondria? Why?

2. One of the functions of the cytoskeleton in animal cells is to give shape to the cell. Plant cells have a fairly rigid cell wall surrounding the plasma membrane. Does this mean that a cytoskeleton is unnecessary for a plant cell?

3. Most cells are very small. What physical and metabolic constraints limit cell size? What problems would an enormous cell encounter? What adaptations might help a very large cell survive?

 Go to www.masteringbiology.com for practice quizzes, activities, eText, videos, current events, and more.

Cell Membrane Structure and Function

Case Study

Vicious Venoms

WELL BEFORE SCHOOL LET OUT, 13-year-old Justin Schwartz was anticipating his three-week stay at a camp near Yosemite National Park. On July 21, 2002, after a four-and-a-half mile hike, Justin rested on some sunny rocks, hands hanging loosely at his sides. Suddenly, he felt a piercing pain in his left palm. A 5-foot rattlesnake—probably feeling threatened by Justin's dangling arm—had struck without warning.

His campmates stared in alarm as the snake slithered into the undergrowth, but Justin focused on his hand, where the pain was becoming agonizing and the palm was beginning to swell. He suddenly felt weak and dizzy. As counselors and campmates spent the next 4 hours carrying him down the trail, pain and discoloration spread up Justin's arm, and his hand felt as if it were going to burst. A helicopter whisked him to a hospital, where he fell unconscious. A day later, he regained consciousness at the University of California Davis Medical Center. There, Justin spent over a month undergoing 10 surgeries. These relieved the enormous pressure from swelling in his arm, removed dead muscle tissue, and began the long process of repairing the extensive damage to his hand and arm.

Diane Kiehl's ordeal began as she dressed for an informal Memorial Day celebration with her family on May 27, 2006, pulling on blue jeans that she had tossed on the bathroom floor the previous night. Feeling a sting on her right thigh, she ripped off the jeans and watched in dismay as a long-legged brown recluse spider crawled out. Living in an old house in the Kansas countryside, Diane had grown accustomed to spiders as frequent—although uninvited—guests. The two small puncture wounds seemed merely a minor annoyance until the next day, when an extensive, itchy rash appeared at the site. By the third day, intermittent pain pierced like a knife through her thigh. A physician gave her painkillers, steroids to reduce the swelling, and antibiotics to combat bacteria introduced by the spider's mouthparts. The next 10 days were a nightmare of pain from the growing sore, now covered with oozing blisters and underlain with clotting blood. It took 4 months for the lesion to heal. Even after a year, Diane sometimes felt pain in the large scar that remained.

How do rattlesnake and brown recluse spider venoms cause leaky blood vessels, disintegrating skin and tissue, and sometimes life-threatening symptoms throughout the body? What do venoms have to do with cell membranes?

▲ A rattlesnake prepares to strike. (Inset) A brown recluse spider.

At a Glance

5.1 HOW IS THE STRUCTURE OF A MEMBRANE RELATED TO ITS FUNCTION?

Cell Membranes Isolate the Cell Contents While Allowing Communication with the Environment

As you now know, all cells, as well as organelles within eukaryotic cells, are surrounded by membranes. Cell membranes perform several crucial functions:

- They selectively isolate the cell's contents from the external environment, allowing concentration gradients of dissolved substances to be produced across the membrane.
- They regulate the exchange of essential substances between the cell and the extracellular fluid, or between membrane-enclosed organelles and the surrounding cytoplasm.
- They allow communication between cells.
- They create attachments within and between cells.
- They regulate many biochemical reactions.

These are formidable tasks for a structure so thin that 10,000 membranes stacked atop one another would scarcely equal the thickness of this page. The key to membrane function lies in its structure. Membranes are not simply uniform sheets; they are complex, heterogeneous structures whose different parts perform very distinct functions. Membranes vary from one tissue type to another, and they change dynamically in response to their surroundings.

All the membranes of a cell have a similar basic structure: proteins floating in a double layer of phospholipids (see pp. 44–45). Phospholipids are responsible for the isolating function of membranes, whereas proteins are responsible for

selectively exchanging substances and communicating with the environment, controlling biochemical reactions associated with the cell membrane, and forming attachments.

Membranes Are "Fluid Mosaics" in Which Proteins Move Within Layers of Lipids

Prior to the 1970s, although cell biologists knew that cell membranes consist primarily of proteins and lipids, how these molecules create the structure and function of membranes remained unknown. In 1972, cell researchers S. J. Singer and G. L. Nicolson developed the **fluid mosaic model** of cell membranes, which is now known to be accurate. According to this model, each membrane consists of a mosaic, or "patchwork," of different proteins that constantly shift and flow within a viscous (thick, sticky) fluid formed by a double layer of phospholipids (**Fig. 5-1**). Although the components of the plasma membrane remain relatively constant, the overall distribution of proteins and various types of phospholipids can change over time. Let's look more closely at the structure of membranes.

The Phospholipid Bilayer Is the Fluid Portion of the Membrane

As you learned in Chapter 3, a phospholipid consists of two very different parts: a "head" that is polar and hydrophilic (attracted to water) and a pair of fatty acid "tails" that are nonpolar and hydrophobic (not attracted to water). Membranes contain many different phospholipids of the general type shown in **Figure 5-2**. Notice that in this particular phospholipid, a double bond (which makes the lipid unsaturated) creates a kink in the fatty acid tail.

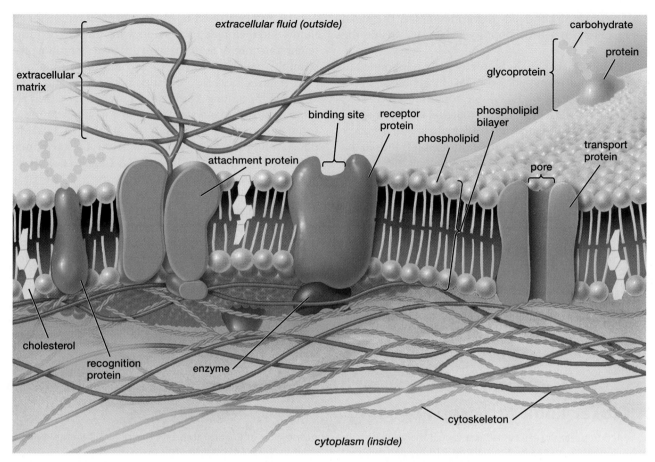

▲ FIGURE 5-1 **The plasma membrane** The plasma membrane is a bilayer of phospholipids interspersed with cholesterol molecules that form a fluid matrix in which various proteins (blue) are embedded. Many proteins have carbohydrates attached to them, forming glycoproteins. Recognition, attachment, receptor, and transport proteins are illustrated.

All cells are surrounded by water. Single-celled organisms may live in fresh water or in the ocean, water saturates the cell walls of plants, and animal cells are bathed in a weakly salty extracellular fluid that filters out of the blood. The fluid portion of the cytoplasm is mostly water. Thus, plasma membranes separate the watery cytoplasmic fluid from its watery external environment, and internal membranes surround watery compartments within the cell. Surrounded by water, phospholipids spontaneously arrange themselves into a double layer called a **phospholipid bilayer** (Fig. 5-3). Hydrogen bonds form between water and the hydrophilic phospholipid heads, causing the heads to orient outward

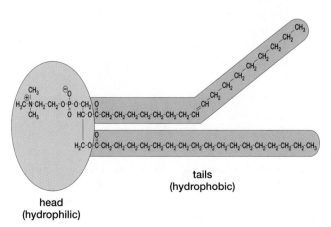

▲ FIGURE 5-2 **A phospholipid** Notice that a double bond in one of the fatty acid tails causes the tail to bend.

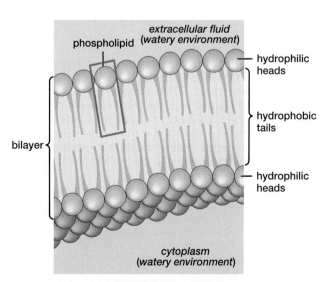

▲ FIGURE 5-3 **The phospholipid bilayer of the cell membrane**

toward the water on either side of the membrane. The phospholipid tails, being hydrophobic, are located inside the bilayer.

Individual phospholipid molecules are not bonded to one another, and membranes contain phospholipids with unsaturated fatty acids whose double bonds introduce kinks into their tails (see Fig. 5-2). These properties allow phospholipids to move about within each layer, making the bilayer reasonably fluid. Membranes with more double bonds in the tails of their phospholipids are more fluid than membranes whose phospholipids have fewer double bonds (**Fig. 5-4**).

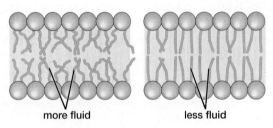

more fluid   less fluid

▲ **FIGURE 5-4 Kinks increase fluidity**

Cells may have different degrees of saturation (and thus fluidity) in their lipid bilayers, allowing them to perform different functions or to function in different environments. For example, membranes tend to become more fluid at high temperatures (because molecules move faster) and less fluid at low temperatures (molecules move more slowly). Cell membranes of organisms living in low-temperature environments are therefore likely to be rich in unsaturated phospholipids, whose kinky tails allow the membrane to retain the necessary fluidity (see "A Closer Look At Form, Function, and Phospholipids").

Most biological molecules, including salts, amino acids, and sugars, are hydrophilic; that is, they are polar and water soluble. Such substances cannot easily pass through the nonpolar, hydrophobic fatty acid tails of the phospholipid bilayer. The phospholipid bilayer is largely responsible for the first of the five membrane functions listed earlier: selectively isolating the cell's contents from the external environment.

The isolation provided by the plasma membrane is not complete, however. As we will describe later, very small molecules—such as water, oxygen, and carbon dioxide—as

A Closer Look At *Form, Function, and Phospholipids*

To function properly, cell membranes must maintain an optimal fluidity. Just as butter melts in a frying pan and oil solidifies in a freezer, the fluidity of cell membranes is sensitive to changing temperatures. Many organisms—including protists and bacteria, plants, "cold-blooded" animals (such as frogs, fish, and snakes), and hibernating mammals—experience large fluctuations in body temperature. Membrane fluidity is influenced by the relative amounts of saturated and unsaturated fatty acid tails in membrane phospholipids. Cells can modify their membrane phospholipid composition to maintain the proper fluidity at different temperatures. At higher temperatures, phospholipids with more saturated fatty acids are inserted into cell membranes, while at lower temperatures, unsaturated fatty acids are added.

A few non-hibernating, warm-blooded mammals have similar adaptations. For example, caribou (which live in the far north) maintain a core temperature of about 100°F (38°C), but allow the temperature of their lower legs to drop almost to freezing (32°F or 0°C), thus conserving body heat as they stand in winter snow (**Fig. E5-1**). In caribou legs, the membranes of cells near the chilly hooves have lots of unsaturated fatty acids, whereas those near the warmer trunk have more saturated fatty acids. This gives plasma membranes the necessary fluidity throughout the leg, despite large temperature differences.

High pressure reduces the fluidity of membranes. Denizens of the deep ocean experience tremendous pressure as well as near-freezing temperatures, a combination that would make human cell membranes much too rigid to function. As you might predict, cell membranes of deep-sea animals have a higher proportion of unsaturated fats (more like vegetable oil than butter). Adapted to high pressure and low temperatures, deep-sea animals rarely survive when brought to the surface. At surface pressure, researchers hypothesize that their cell membranes become too fluid and leaky, preventing their cells from maintaining normal gradients, which leads to death.

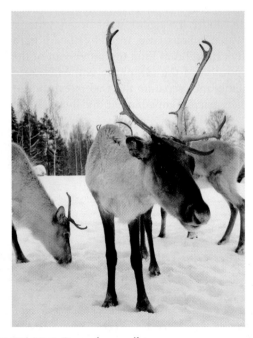

▲ **FIGURE E5-1 Browsing caribou**

Case Study continued

Vicious Venoms

Some of the most devastating effects of certain snake and spider venoms occur because they contain enzymes, called phospholipases, that break down phospholipids in cell membranes, causing the cells to die.

well as larger, uncharged, lipid-soluble molecules, can pass through the phospholipid bilayer.

In most animal cells, the phospholipid bilayer of membranes also contains cholesterol (see Fig. 5-1). Some cellular membranes have relatively few cholesterol molecules; others have as many cholesterol molecules as they do phospholipids. Cholesterol affects membrane structure and function in several ways: It stabilizes the lipid bilayer, making it less fluid at higher temperatures, less solid at lower temperatures, and also less permeable to water-soluble substances such as ions or monosaccharides.

The flexible, fluid nature of the bilayer is very important for membrane function. As you breathe, move your eyes, and turn the pages of this book, cells in your body change shape. If plasma membranes were stiff instead of flexible, cells would break open and die. Further, as you learned in Chapter 4, membranes within eukaryotic cells are in constant motion. Membrane-enclosed compartments ferry substances into the cell, carry materials within the cell, and expel them to the outside, merging membranes in the process. This flow and merger of membranes is made possible by the fluid nature of the phospholipid bilayer.

A Variety of Proteins Form a Mosaic Within the Membrane

Thousands of different membrane proteins are embedded within or attached to the surfaces of the phospholipid bilayer of cell membranes. Many of the proteins in plasma membranes have carbohydrate groups attached to the portion that

is exposed on the outer membrane surface (see Fig. 5-1). These are called **glycoproteins** ("glyco" is from the Greek, meaning "sweet," and refers to the carbohydrate portion with its sugar subunits). Most plasma membrane proteins are embedded, at least partially, in the phospholipid bilayer, but some adhere to the bilayer surface. Membrane proteins may be grouped into five major categories based on their function: receptor proteins, recognition proteins, enzymatic proteins, attachment proteins, and transport proteins.

Most cells bear dozens of types of **receptor proteins** (some of which are glycoproteins) spanning their plasma membranes. To perform their functions, cells must respond to messages sent by other cells. These messages are often molecules (such as hormones) carried in the bloodstream. After diffusing into the extracellular fluid, these message molecules bind to specific sites on receptor proteins, which convey the message to the interior of the cell (**Fig. 5-5**). When the appropriate molecule binds to the receptor, the receptor is "activated"—often by changing shape—and this, in turn, causes a response inside the cell.

The response can take many forms. The shape of a protein inside the cell may be modified, converting it from an inactive form to an active form. This change, in turn, may trigger a sequence of chemical reactions within the cell that alters cellular activities. For example, when the hormone epinephrine (adrenaline) binds to a specific membrane receptor on muscle cells, it stimulates the muscle cells to break down glycogen into glucose, providing more energy for muscle contraction. When other receptor proteins bind messenger molecules, they may cause ion channels to open, or they may start sequences of reactions that stimulate cells to divide or to secrete hormones. Communication among nerve cells also depends on receptors, and receptor proteins allow cells of the immune system to recognize and attack foreign invaders that can cause disease.

Have you ever wondered

What to Do If You Are Bitten by a Poisonous Snake?

If there are a variety of poisonous snakes in your area, notice the color pattern and size of the snake that bit you, to help identify it as you dial 911. Dr. David Erk, a physician at the Wyoming Medical Center who has a particular interest in snakebites, provides the following advice: First, get medical help as quickly as possible. To slow the spread of venom and the swelling it causes, keep the bitten limb immobilized, ideally just below the level of the heart. Remove constricting jewelry and clothing from around the bite. Don't cut the bite, and don't apply suction, a tourniquet, heat, or ice. Don't drink coffee or alcohol or take any medications. Do try to stay as calm as possible.

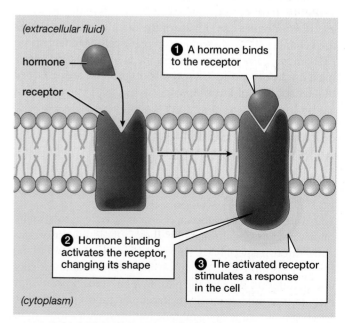

▲ **FIGURE 5-5 Receptor protein activation**

Recognition proteins are glycoproteins that serve as identification tags (see Fig. 5-1). The cells of each individual bear unique glycoproteins that identify them as "self." Immune cells ignore self and attack invading cells, such as bacteria, that have different recognition proteins on their membranes. Recognition glycoproteins on the surfaces of red blood cells bear different sugar groups and determine whether the blood is type A, B, AB, or O (see Table 10-1 on p. 187). Transfusions as well as transplanted organs must have their most important recognition glycoproteins matched to those of the recipient to minimize attack by the immune system.

Enzymes are proteins that promote chemical reactions that synthesize or break apart biological molecules, as described in Chapter 6. Although many enzymes are located within the cytoplasm, some span cell membranes and others are attached to membrane surfaces (see Fig. 5-1). Plasma membrane enzymes include those that are responsible for synthesizing the proteins and carbohydrates of the extracellular matrix (a web of protein and glycoprotein fibers that fills spaces between animal cells).

A diverse group of **attachment proteins** anchors cell membranes in various ways. Some span the plasma membrane, linking the cytoskeleton inside the cell with the extracellular matrix outside (see Fig. 5-1), thus anchoring the cell in place within a tissue. Some attachment proteins help maintain cell shape by linking the plasma membrane to the underlying cytoskeleton, and some help cells adhere to and move along surfaces. Other types of attachment proteins form connections between adjacent cells, as described later in this chapter (see Figs. 5-17 and 5-18).

Transport proteins regulate the movement of hydrophilic molecules through the plasma membrane. Some transport proteins, called **channel proteins,** form channels whose central pores allow water molecules or specific ions to pass through the membrane along their concentration gradients (see Fig. 5-1). Other transport proteins, called **carrier proteins,** have binding sites that can temporarily attach to specific molecules on one side of the membrane. The protein then changes shape (in some cases using cellular energy from ATP), moving the molecule across the membrane, and releasing it on the other side. These transport proteins are described in later sections of this chapter.

5.2 HOW DO SUBSTANCES MOVE ACROSS MEMBRANES?

Molecules in Fluids Move in Response to Gradients

You now know that substances move directly across membranes by diffusing through the phospholipid bilayer or traveling through specialized transport proteins. To understand this process more fully requires some background knowledge and definitions. Because the plasma membrane separates the cytoplasmic fluid from the extracellular fluid environment, let's begin our study of membrane transport with a look at the characteristics of fluids, starting with a few definitions:

- A **fluid** is any substance whose molecules can flow past one another; as a result, fluids have no defined shape. Fluids include gases, liquids, and also cell membranes, whose molecules can flow past one another.
- A **solute** is a substance that can be dissolved (dispersed into individual atoms, molecules, or ions) in a **solvent,** which is a fluid (usually a liquid) capable of dissolving the solute. Water, in which all biological processes occur, dissolves so many different solutes that it is sometimes called the "universal solvent."
- The **concentration** of a substance defines the amount of solute in a given amount of solvent. The concentration of sugar solution, for example, is a measurement of the number of molecules of that sugar contained in a given volume of solution.
- A **gradient** is a physical difference in properties such as temperature, pressure, electrical charge, or concentration of a particular substance in a fluid between two adjoining regions of space. It requires energy to create gradients. Over time, gradients tend to break down unless energy is supplied to maintain them or unless an effective barrier separates them. For example, gradients in temperature cause a flow of energy from a higher-temperature region to a lower-temperature region. Electrical gradients can drive the movement of ions. Gradients of concentration or pressure cause molecules or ions to move from one region to the other in a manner that tends to equalize the difference. Cells use energy and cell membrane proteins to generate **concentration gradients** of various molecules and ions dissolved in their cytoplasmic fluid.

It is important to be aware that, at temperatures above absolute zero ($-459.4\,°F$, or $-273\,°C$), atoms, molecules, and ions are in constant random motion. As the temperature rises, their rate of motion increases, and temperatures that support life cause these particles to move rapidly indeed. As a result of this motion, molecules and ions in solution are continuously bombarding one another and the structures surrounding them. Over time, random movements produce a net movement from regions of high concentration to regions of low concentration, a process called **diffusion.** In a nonliving system, if nothing opposes this movement (opposing factors include electrical charge, pressure differences, or physical barriers), then the random movement of molecules will continue until the substance is evenly dispersed throughout the fluid.

To envision how the random movement of molecules or ions within a fluid eventually breaks down concentration gradients, consider a sugar cube dissolving in hot coffee, or perfume molecules moving from an open bottle into the air. In each case you have a concentration gradient. If you leave the perfume jar open or forget your coffee, eventually you will have an empty perfume bottle and a fragrant room, or cold, but uniformly sweet, coffee. In an analogy to gravity, we describe molecules moving from regions of high concentration to regions of low concentration as moving "down" their concentration gradients.

1 A drop of dye is placed in water

2 Dye molecules diffuse into the water; water molecules diffuse into the dye

3 Both dye molecules and water molecules are evenly dispersed

◄ FIGURE 5-6 Diffusion of a dye in water

drop of dye

water molecule

To watch diffusion in action, place a drop of food coloring in a glass of water (**Fig. 5-6**). Random motion propels dye molecules both into and out of the dye droplet, but there is a net transfer of dye into the water, and of water into the dye. The net movement of dye will continue until it is uniformly dispersed in the water. If you compare the diffusion of a dye in hot and cold water, you will see that heat increases the diffusion rate; this is because heat causes molecules to move faster.

Summing Up   The Principles of Diffusion

- Diffusion is the net movement of molecules down a gradient from high to low concentration.
- The greater the concentration gradient, the faster the rate of diffusion.
- The higher the temperature, the faster the rate of diffusion.
- If no other processes intervene, diffusion will continue until the concentrations become equal throughout; that is, until the concentration gradient is eliminated.

Movement Through Membranes Occurs by Passive Transport and Energy-Requiring Transport

Gradients of ions and molecules across cell membranes are crucial for life; a cell without them is dead. Proteins in cell membranes expend energy to create and maintain these concentration gradients, because many of the biochemical processes of life rely on them. For example, neurons depend on the flow of specific ions down their concentration gradients to produce the electrical signals that underlie sensation and movement. Plasma membranes are described as **selectively permeable** because they selectively allow only certain ions or molecules to pass through (permeate). The selective permeability of the plasma membrane creates a barrier that helps maintain the gradients that characterize all cells.

In its role as gatekeeper of the cell, the cell's plasma membrane permits substances to move through it in two different ways: passive transport and energy-requiring transport (**Table 5-1**). **Passive transport** involves diffusion of substances across cell membranes down their concentration gradients, whereas **energy-requiring transport** requires that the cell expend energy to move substances across membranes or into or out of the cell.

Table 5-1 Transport Across Membranes	
Passive Transport	Diffusion of substances across a membrane down a gradient of concentration, pressure, or electrical charge; does not require cellular energy.
Simple diffusion	Diffusion of water, dissolved gases, or lipid-soluble molecules through the phospholipid bilayer of a membrane.
Facilitated diffusion	Diffusion of water, ions, or water-soluble molecules through a membrane via a channel or carrier protein.
Osmosis	Diffusion of water across a selectively permeable membrane from a region of higher free water concentration to a region of lower free water concentration.
Energy-Requiring Transport	Movement of substances into or out of a cell using cellular energy, usually supplied by ATP.
Active transport	Movement of individual small molecules or ions against their concentration gradients through membrane-spanning proteins.
Endocytosis	Movement of particles or large molecules into a cell; occurs as the plasma membrane engulfs the substance in a membranous sac that pinches off, entering the cytoplasm.
Exocytosis	Movement of particles or large molecules out of a cell; occurs as the plasma membrane encloses the material in a membranous sac that moves to the cell surface and fuses with the plasma membrane, allowing its contents to diffuse out.

Passive Transport Includes Simple Diffusion, Facilitated Diffusion, and Osmosis

Diffusion can occur within a fluid or across a membrane that is permeable to the substance and that separates two fluid compartments. Many molecules cross plasma membranes by diffusion, driven by concentration differences between the cytoplasm and the extracellular fluid.

Some Molecules Move Across Membranes by Simple Diffusion

Very small molecules with no net charge, such as water, oxygen, and carbon dioxide—as well as lipid-soluble molecules that include alcohol, vitamins A, D, and E, and steroid hormones—diffuse directly across the phospholipid bilayer down their concentration gradients. This process is called **simple diffusion** (Fig. 5-7a). A larger concentration gradient, higher temperature, smaller molecular size, and greater solubility in lipids all increase the rate of simple diffusion.

How can water—a polar molecule—diffuse directly through the hydrophobic (literally "water-fearing") phospholipid bilayer? Because water molecules are so small and so abundant in both the cytoplasm and the extracellular fluid, some water molecules stray into the thicket of phospholipid tails, where their random movements bring them through to the far side of the membrane. Simple diffusion of water through the phospholipid bilayer is relatively slow, but in many types of cells, water molecules traverse membranes far more rapidly by facilitated diffusion through transport proteins, as described in the following section.

Some Molecules Cross Membranes by Facilitated Diffusion Using Membrane Transport Proteins

Many substances are unable to simply diffuse through the phospholipid bilayer. These include ions (for example, K^+, Na^+, Cl^-, and Ca^{2+}), which form hydrogen bonds with water molecules. The attached water molecules tend to hold the ions in place, either inside or outside the cell. Molecules such as monosaccharides (simple sugars) are polar, and also form hydrogen bonds with water; thus, their attraction to water and their size inhibits them from entering the bilayer. These ions and molecules can diffuse across membranes only with the aid of specific transport proteins: channel proteins or carrier proteins. The process of moving through cell membranes down a concentration gradient with the aid of transport proteins is called **facilitated diffusion.**

Channel proteins form pores (channels) in the lipid bilayer through which certain ions or water can flow down their concentration gradients (Fig. 5-7b). Channel proteins have a specific interior diameter related to the diameter of the ion whose movement they facilitate, and electrical charges that attract the ion to the amino acids that line the pore. For example, the Na^+ channel is lined with negative charges to attract Na^+. Because cells must maintain gradients of many ions across their membranes, many ion channels include protein "gates" that are opened or closed, depending on the needs of the cell.

Many cells have specialized water channel proteins called **aquaporins** (literally, "water pores"; Fig. 5-7c). The small size of these channels, coupled with positively charged amino acids (which attract the negative pole of water molecules) inside the channels, makes them selective for water molecules. The movement of water through a membrane, either by simple diffusion or facilitated diffusion through

(a) Simple diffusion through the phospholipid bilayer

(b) Facilitated diffusion through channel proteins

(c) Osmosis through aquaporins or the phospholipid bilayer

(d) Facilitated diffusion through carrier proteins

▲ FIGURE 5-7 **Types of diffusion through the plasma membrane (a)** Molecules that are very small, uncharged, or lipid-soluble move directly through the phospholipid bilayer by simple diffusion. Here, oxygen molecules diffuse from the extracellular fluid into the cell down their concentration gradient (red arrow). **(b)** Facilitated diffusion through channel proteins allows ions to cross membranes. Here, chloride ions diffuse down their concentration gradient into the cell through chloride channels. **(c)** Osmosis is the diffusion of water. Water molecules can diffuse directly through the phospholipid bilayer by simple diffusion, or they can pass far more rapidly by facilitated diffusion through water channels called aquaporins. **(d)** Carrier proteins have binding sites for specific molecules (such as the glucose shown here). Binding of the transported molecule causes the carrier to change shape, shuttling the molecule across the membrane down its concentration gradient.

aquaporins, has a special name: osmosis. To learn more about water channels, see "Scientific Inquiry: The Discovery of Aquaporins" on p. 86.

Carrier proteins have active sites that bind specific molecules from the cytoplasmic fluid or the extracellular fluid, such as particular sugars or small proteins. The binding triggers a change in the shape of the carrier that allows the molecules to pass through the protein and across the membrane. These carrier proteins do not use cellular energy, and they can transfer molecules only down their concentration gradients (**Fig. 5-7d**).

Osmosis Is the Diffusion of Water Across Selectively Permeable Membranes

Osmosis is the movement of water across a selectively permeable membrane in response to gradients of concentration, pressure, or temperature. Here, we will focus on osmosis from a region of higher water concentration to a region of lower water concentration. Osmosis may occur directly through the phospholipid bilayer, or (more rapidly) through aquaporin channels composed of membrane-spanning proteins.

What do we mean when we describe a solution as having a "high water concentration" or a "low water concentration"? The answer is simple: Pure water has the highest possible water concentration. Any substance that dissolves in water (any solute) displaces some of the water molecules in a given volume, and it also forms hydrogen bonds with many more of the water molecules, preventing them from moving across a water-permeable membrane. Therefore, the higher the concentration of dissolved substances, the lower the concentration of water that is available to move across a membrane. Consequently, there will be a net movement of water molecules from the solution with with more free water molecules (containing less solute) into the solution with fewer free water molecules (containing more solute). For example, water will move by osmosis from a solution with less dissolved sugar into a solution with more dissolved sugar. Because there are more free water molecules in the less-concentrated sugar solution, more water molecules will collide with—and thus move through—the water-permeable

membrane on that side. The concentration of solute in water determines the solution's "osmotic strength"; the higher the solute concentration, the higher the osmotic strength.

Scientists use the word "tonicity" to compare the concentrations of substances dissolved in water across a membrane that is selectively permeable to water. Solutions with equal concentrations of solute (and thus equal concentrations of water) are described as being **isotonic** to one another (the prefix "iso" means "same"). When isotonic solutions are separated by a water-permeable membrane, there is no net movement of water between them (**Fig. 5-8a**). When a membrane selectively permeable to water separates solutions with different concentrations of a solute, the solution that contains a greater concentration of solute is described as being **hypertonic** (the prefix "hyper" means "greater than") to the less concentrated solution (**Fig. 5-8b**). The more dilute solution is described as **hypotonic** ("hypo" means "below"; **Fig. 5-8c**). Water tends to move from hypotonic solutions into hypertonic solutions.

Summing Up   The Principles of Osmosis

- Osmosis is the movement of water across a selectively water-permeable membrane by simple diffusion or by facilitated diffusion through aquaporins.
- Water moves across a selectively water-permeable membrane down its concentration gradient from the side with a higher concentration of free water molecules to the side with a lower concentration of free water molecules.
- Dissolved substances reduce the concentration of free water molecules in a solution.
- If two solutions are separated by a membrane that is selectively permeable to water, the solution with a higher concentration of solute is hypertonic and has a higher osmotic strength, and the solution with the lower concentration of solute is hypotonic and has a lower osmotic strength.

No net flow of water

(a) A balloon in an isotonic solution

Water flows out; the balloon shrinks

(b) A balloon in a hypertonic solution

Water flows in; the balloon expands

(c) A balloon in a hypotonic solution

◀ FIGURE 5-8 **The effect of solute concentration on osmosis** We start with three balloons made of membrane that is selectively permeable to water (not to sugar; red balls). We place equal volumes of the same concentration of sugar water in each balloon. We then immerse each in a beaker filled with a different concentration of sugar water—**(a)** isotonic, **(b)** hypertonic, or **(c)** hypotonic—to that in the balloon. The figure shows the results after an hour. The blue arrows indicate relative water movement into and out of the balloon.

Scientific Inquiry

The Discovery of Aquaporins

The French microbiologist Louis Pasteur's observation that "Chance favors the prepared mind" is as true today as it was when he first expressed it in the 1800s. Scientists have long realized that osmosis directly through the phospholipid bilayer is much too slow to account for water movement across certain cell membranes, including those of kidney tubules (which reabsorb tremendous quantities of water that the kidney filters from the blood) and those of red blood cells (see Fig. 5-9). But attempts to identify selective transport proteins for water repeatedly failed, partly because water is abundant on both sides of the plasma membrane, and partly because water can also move directly through the phospholipid bilayer.

Then, as often happens in science, chance and prepared minds met. In the mid-1980s, Dr. Peter Agre (Fig. E5-2), then at the Johns Hopkins School of Medicine in Maryland, was attempting to determine the structure of a glycoprotein on red blood cells. The protein he isolated was contaminated, however, with large quantities of another protein. Instead of discarding the unknown protein, he and his coworkers collaborated to determine its structure. They found that it was similar to previously identified membrane channel proteins of unknown function. Agre and colleagues investigated the protein by forcing frog eggs (which are only slightly permeable to water) to insert the protein into their plasma membranes. Whereas eggs without the mystery protein swelled only slightly when placed in a hypotonic solution, those with the protein swelled rapidly and burst in the same solution (Fig. E5-3a). Further studies showed that no other ions or molecules could move through this channel, which was then dubbed "aquaporin." In 2000, Agre and other research teams reported the three-dimensional structure of aquaporin and described how specific polar amino acids in its interior attract water and allow billions of water molecules to move through the channel in single file every second, while repelling other ions or molecules (Fig. E5-3b).

Many types of aquaporins have now been identified, and aquaporins have been found in all forms of life that have been investigated. For example, the plasma membrane of the central vacuole of plant cells is rich in aquaporins, which allow it to fill rapidly when water is available (see Fig. 5-10). In 2003, Agre shared the Nobel Prize in Chemistry for his discovery—the result of chance, careful observation, persistence, and perhaps a bit of what Agre himself describes modestly as "sheer blind luck."

(a) Frog eggs

(b) Aquaporin channel

▲ FIGURE E5-3 **Function and structure of aquaporins** **(a)** The frog egg on the right has aquaporins in its plasma membrane; the egg on the left does not. They have both been immersed in a hypotonic solution for 30 seconds. The egg on the right has burst, whereas that on the left has swollen only slightly. **(b)** The aquaporin channel (shown here in cross-section) is formed by a membrane-spanning protein. Within the channel, charged amino acids interact with water molecules, promoting their movement in either direction while repelling other substances.

▲ FIGURE E5-2 **Peter Agre**

Osmosis Across the Plasma Membrane Plays an Important Role in the Lives of Cells

The extracellular fluid of animals is usually isotonic to the cytoplasmic fluid of their cells, so there is no net tendency for water to enter or leave the cells. Although the concentrations of specific solutes are rarely the same inside and outside the cells, the total concentration of all dissolved particles is equal; therefore, the water concentration is equal inside and outside of cells.

If you immerse red blood cells in salt solutions of varying solute concentrations, you can observe the effects of water movement across their cell membranes. In an isotonic salt solution, the sizes of the cells remain constant (**Fig. 5-9a**). If the salt solution is hypertonic to the cytoplasmic fluid of the red blood cells, water will leave the cells by osmosis, and the cells will shrivel (**Fig. 5-9b**). Conversely, if the salt solution is very dilute and hypotonic to the red blood cell cytoplasmic fluid, water will enter the cells, causing them to swell (**Fig. 5-9c**). If red blood cells are placed in pure water, they will continue to swell until they burst.

Osmosis across plasma membranes is crucial to many biological processes, including water uptake by the roots of plants, absorption of dietary water from the intestine, and the reabsorption of water in kidneys. Organisms that live in fresh water must expend energy to counteract osmosis. Protists such as *Paramecium* have contractile vacuoles that eliminate the water that continuously leaks into their cytoplasmic fluid, which is hypertonic to the fresh water of the ponds in which they live. Cellular energy is used to pump salts from the cytoplasmic fluid into the contractile vacuole. This causes water to follow by osmosis, filling the vacuole, which then contracts, squirting the water out through a pore in the plasma membrane (see Fig. 4-15).

Nearly every living plant cell is supported by water that enters through osmosis. As you learned in Chapter 4, most plant cells have a large, membrane-enclosed central vacuole. The membrane that encloses this vacuole is rich in aquaporins. Dissolved substances stored in the vacuole make its contents hypertonic to the surrounding cytoplasmic fluid, which in turn is usually hypertonic to the extracellular fluid that bathes the cells. Water therefore flows into the cytoplasmic fluid and then into the vacuole by osmosis. The water pressure within the vacuole, called **turgor pressure,** pushes the cytoplasm up against the cell wall with considerable force (**Fig. 5-10a**).

Cell walls are often flexible, so many plant cells depend on turgor pressure for support. If you forget to water a houseplant, the central vacuole and cytoplasmic fluid of each cell loses water and the plasma membrane shrinks away from its cell wall as the vacuole collapses. Just as a balloon goes limp when its air leaks out, the plant droops as its cells lose turgor pressure (**Fig. 5-10b**). Now you know why grocery stores are always spraying their leafy produce: to keep it looking perky and fresh with full central vacuoles.

Energy-Requiring Transport Includes Active Transport, Endocytosis, and Exocytosis

Without concentration gradients across its membranes, a cell is dead. By building gradients and then allowing them to run down under specific circumstances, cells regulate

(a) Red blood cells in an isotonic solution   **(b) Red blood cells in a hypertonic solution**   **(c) Red blood cells in a hypotonic solution**

▲ FIGURE 5-9 **The effects of osmosis on red blood cells (a)** The cells are immersed in an isotonic solution and retain their normal dimpled shape. **(b)** The cells shrink when placed in a hypertonic solution, as more water moves out than flows in. **(c)** The cells expand when placed in a hypotonic solution.

QUESTION A student pours some distilled water into a sample of blood. Returning later, she looks at the blood under a microscope and sees no blood cells at all. What happened?

► FIGURE 5-10 **Turgor pressure in plant cells**
Aquaporins allow water to move rapidly in and out
of the central vacuoles of plant cells. The cell and
plant in part **(a)** are supported by water turgor
pressure, whereas those in part **(b)** have lost
pressure due to dehydration.

QUESTION If a plant cell is placed in water
containing no solutes, will the cell eventually burst?
What about an animal cell? Explain.

cytoplasm   central vacuole

When water is plentiful, it fills
the central vacuole, pushes
the cytoplasm against the cell
wall, and helps maintain the
cell's shape

Water pressure
supports the
leaves of this
impatiens plant

(a) Turgor pressure provides support

cell wall   plasma membrane

When water is scarce, the
central vacuole shrinks and the
cell wall is unsupported

Deprived of the support
from water, the plant
wilts

(b) Loss of turgor pressure causes the plant to wilt

their biochemical reactions, respond to external stimuli, and
obtain chemical energy. The electrical signals of neurons,
the contraction of muscles, and the generation of ATP in mitochondria and chloroplasts (see Chapters 7 and 8) all rely
on concentration gradients of ions. But gradients do not
form spontaneously—they require active transport across a
membrane.

Active Transport Uses Energy to Move Molecules Against Their Concentration Gradients

During **active transport,** membrane proteins use cellular
energy to move molecules or ions across the plasma membrane against their concentration gradients (**Fig. 5-11**).
All cells need to move some materials "uphill" against

concentration gradients. For example, every cell requires
some nutrients that are less concentrated in the environment than in the cell's cytoplasm. Other substances, such as
sodium and calcium ions, are maintained at much lower
concentrations inside the cell than in the extracellular fluid.
Nerve cells maintain large ion concentration gradients because their electrical signals require rapid, passive flow of
ions when channels are opened. After these ions diffuse
into (or out of) the cell, their concentration gradients must
be restored by active transport.

Active-transport proteins span the width of the membrane and have two active sites. One active site—which may
face the inside or outside of the plasma membrane, depending on the transport protein—binds a particular molecule or

(extracellular fluid)

❶ The transport protein binds both ATP and Ca²⁺

❷ Energy from ATP changes the shape of the transport protein and moves the ion across the membrane

❸ The protein releases the ion and the remnants of ATP (ADP and P) and closes

recognition site

ATP binding site

ATP

Ca²⁺

ATP

ADP

P

(cytoplasm)

▲ **FIGURE 5-11 Active transport** Active transport uses cellular energy to move molecules across the plasma membrane against a concentration gradient. A transport protein (blue) has an ATP binding site and a recognition site for the molecules to be transported; in this case, calcium ions (Ca²⁺). Notice that when ATP donates its energy, it loses its third phosphate group and becomes ADP + P.

ion, such as a calcium ion. As shown in **Figure 5-11 ❶**, the second site, always on the inside of the membrane, binds an energy-carrier molecule, usually adenosine triphosphate (ATP; see p. 51). The ATP donates energy to the protein, causing the protein to change shape and move the calcium ion across the membrane (**Fig. 5-11 ❷**). The energy for active transport comes from a high-energy bond that links the last of the three phosphate groups in ATP. Upon releasing its stored energy, ATP becomes ADP (adenosine diphosphate) plus a free phosphate (**Fig. 5-11 ❸**). Active-transport proteins are often called pumps—in an analogy to water pumps—because they use energy to move ions or molecules uphill against a concentration gradient.

Cells Engulf Particles or Fluids by Endocytosis

A cell may need to acquire materials from its extracellular environment that are too large to move directly through the membrane. These materials are engulfed by the plasma membrane and are transported within the cell inside vesicles. This energy-requiring process is called **endocytosis** (Greek for "into the cell"). Here, we describe three forms of endocytosis based on the size and type of material acquired and the method of acquisition: pinocytosis, receptor-mediated endocytosis, and phagocytosis.

Pinocytosis Moves Liquids into the Cell In **pinocytosis** ("cell drinking"), a very small patch of plasma membrane dimples inward as it surrounds extracellular fluid and buds off into the cytoplasm as a tiny vesicle (**Fig. 5-12**). Pinocytosis moves

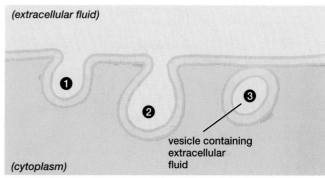

(extracellular fluid)

❶

❷

❸

vesicle containing extracellular fluid

(cytoplasm)

❶ A dimple forms in the plasma membrane, which **❷** deepens and surrounds the extracellular fluid. **❸** The membrane encloses the extracellular fluid, forming a vesicle.

(a) Pinocytosis

❶

extracellular fluid

❷

❸

cytoplasm

(b) TEM of pinocytosis

▲ **FIGURE 5-12 Pinocytosis** The circled numbers correspond to both **(a)** the diagram and **(b)** the transmission electron micrograph.

a droplet of extracellular fluid, contained within the dimpling patch of membrane, into the cell. Therefore, the cell acquires materials in the same concentration as in the extracellular fluid.

Receptor-Mediated Endocytosis Moves Specific Molecules into the Cell In order to selectively concentrate materials that don't move through channels, cells take up specific molecules or complexes of molecules (for example, packets containing protein and cholesterol) using **receptor-mediated endocytosis** (**Fig. 5-13**). Receptor-mediated endocytosis relies on specialized receptor proteins located on the plasma membrane in thickened depressions called coated pits. After the appropriate molecules bind these receptors, the coated pit deepens into a pocket that pinches off as a vesicle that carries the molecules into the cytoplasm.

Phagocytosis Moves Large Particles into the Cell Cells use **phagocytosis** (which means "cell eating") to pick up large particles, including whole microorganisms (**Fig. 5-14a**). When the freshwater protist *Amoeba*, for example, senses a tasty *Paramecium*, the *Amoeba* extends parts of its surface membrane. These membrane extensions are called pseudopods (Latin for "false feet"). The pseudopods fuse around the prey, thus enclosing it inside a vesicle, called a **food vacuole,** for digestion (**Fig. 5-14b**). Like *Amoeba*, white blood cells use phagocytosis followed by intracellular digestion to engulf and destroy invading bacteria, in a drama that occurs constantly within your body (**Fig. 5-14c**).

Exocytosis Moves Material Out of the Cell

Cells also use energy to dispose of undigested particles of waste, or to secrete substances such as hormones into the extracellular fluid, a process called **exocytosis** (Greek for "out of the cell"; **Fig. 5-15**). During exocytosis, a membrane-enclosed vesicle carrying material to be expelled moves to the cell surface, where the vesicle's membrane fuses with the cell's plasma membrane. The vesicle then opens to the extracellular fluid, allowing its contents to diffuse into the fluid outside the cell.

Exchange of Materials Across Membranes Influences Cell Size and Shape

As you learned in Chapter 4, most cells are too small to be seen with the naked eye; they range from about 1 to

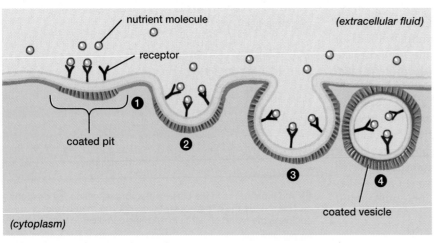

1 Receptor proteins for specific molecules or complexes of molecules are localized at coated pit sites.

2 The receptors bind the molecules and the membrane dimples inward.

3 The coated pit region of the membrane encloses the receptor-bound molecules.

4 A vesicle ("coated vesicle") containing the bound molecules is released into the cytoplasm.

(a) Receptor-mediated endocytosis

(b) TEM of receptor-mediated endocytosis

▲ **FIGURE 5-13 Receptor-mediated endocytosis** The circled numbers correspond to both **(a)** the diagram and **(b)** the transmission electron micrograph.

❶ The plasma membrane extends pseudopods toward an extracellular particle (for example, food). ❷ The ends of the pseudopods fuse, encircling the particle. ❸ A vesicle called a food vacuole is formed containing the engulfed particle.

(a) Phagocytosis

(b) An *Amoeba* engulfs a *Paramecium*

(c) A white blood cell ingests bacteria

▲ FIGURE 5-14 **Phagocytosis (a)** The mechanism of phagocytosis. The photographs of **(b)** an *Amoeba* and **(c)** a white blood cell were taken with a scanning electron microscope, which provides a three-dimensional image. The color is computer generated to help distinguish the cells.

Material is enclosed in a vesicle that fuses with the plasma membrane, allowing its contents to diffuse out

0.2 micrometer

◀ FIGURE 5-15 **Exocytosis** Exocytosis is functionally the reverse of endocytosis.

QUESTION How does exocytosis differ from diffusion of materials out of a cell?

100 micrometers (millionths of a meter) in diameter (see Fig. 4-1). Why? As a roughly spherical cell becomes larger, its innermost regions become farther away from the plasma membrane, which is responsible for acquiring all the cell's nutrients and eliminating its waste products. Much of the exchange occurs by the slow process of diffusion. In a hypothetical giant cell 8.5 inches (20 centimeters) in diameter, oxygen molecules would take more than 200 days to diffuse to the center of the cell, by which time the cell would be long dead for lack of oxygen. In addition, as a sphere enlarges, its volume increases more rapidly than does its surface area. So a large, roughly spherical cell (which would require more nutrients and produce more wastes) would have a relatively smaller area of membrane to accomplish this exchange than would a small spherical cell (**Fig. 5-16**).

In a very large, roughly spherical cell, the surface area of the plasma membrane would be too small, and the diffusion distances within the cell too large, to supply the

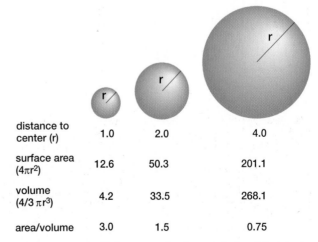

distance to center (r)	1.0	2.0	4.0
surface area ($4\pi r^2$)	12.6	50.3	201.1
volume ($\frac{4}{3}\pi r^3$)	4.2	33.5	268.1
area/volume	3.0	1.5	0.75

▲ FIGURE 5-16 **Surface area and volume relationships** As the size of a sphere increases, its volume increases much more than its surface area. Thus, a large spherical cell will have a relatively small surface area through which to obtain nutrients and eliminate wastes. As a result, roughly spherical cells are extremely small.

cell's metabolic needs. This constraint limits the size of most cells. However, some cells, such as nerve and muscle cells, can become very large because their elongated shape increases their membrane surface area, keeping the ratio of surface area to volume relatively high. In another example, cells lining the small intestine have plasma membranes that project out in fringe-like folds called **microvilli** (see Fig. 5-17a, middle). These microvilli create an enormous surface area of membrane to absorb nutrients from digested food.

BioFlix ™ Membrane Transport

5.3 HOW DO SPECIALIZED JUNCTIONS ALLOW CELLS TO CONNECT AND COMMUNICATE?

In multicellular organisms, specialized structures on plasma membranes hold together clusters of cells and provide avenues through which cells communicate with their neighbors. Depending on the organism and the cell type, four types of connection may occur between cells: desmosomes, tight junctions, gap junctions, and plasmodesmata. Plasmodesmata are restricted to plant cells, whereas the other three types of junctions are found only in animal cells.

Desmosomes Attach Cells Together

Many of an animal's tissues are stretched, compressed, and bent as the animal moves. Cells in the skin, intestine, urinary bladder, and other organs must adhere firmly to one another to avoid tearing under the stresses of movement. Such animal tissues have junctions called **desmosomes,** which link adjacent cells (**Fig. 5-17a**). In a desmosome, the membranes of adjacent cells are tacked together by a complex of different attachment proteins. Intermediate filament proteins of the cytoskeleton are linked to the insides of the desmosomes and extend into the interior of each cell, further strengthening the attachment.

▶ FIGURE 5-17 **Cell attachment structures (a)** Cells lining the small intestine are attached by desmosomes. Protein filaments bound to the inside surface of each desmosome extend into the cytoplasm and attach to other filaments inside the cell, strengthening the connection between cells. **(b)** Tight junctions prevent leakage between cells, such as those of the urinary bladder.

(a) Desmosomes

(b) Tight junctions

Tight Junctions Make Cell Attachments Leakproof

The animal body contains many tubes and sacs that must hold their contents without leaking; for example, leaky skin or a leaky urinary bladder would spell disaster for the rest of the body. When cells must create a leakproof barrier, the spaces between them are blocked with special attachment proteins that are embedded in the membranes of each of adjacent linked cells. These proteins form **tight junctions** by adhering to one another, joining cells along defined pathways, almost as if the two membranes had been stitched together (**Fig. 5-17b**).

Gap Junctions and Plasmodesmata Allow Direct Communication Between Cells

Multicellular organisms must coordinate the actions of their component cells. In animals, a large proportion of the cells of the body communicate through protein channels formed by attachment proteins that connect the insides of adjacent cells. These cell-to-cell channels are called **gap junctions** (**Fig. 5-18a**). Hormones, nutrients, ions, and electrical signals can pass through the channels formed by gap junctions.

Virtually all of the living cells of plants are connected to one another by **plasmodesmata.** Plasmodesmata are holes in the walls of adjacent plant cells. These openings, lined with plasma membrane and filled with cytoplasmic fluid, link the insides of adjacent cells (**Fig. 5-18b**). Many plant cells have thousands of plasmodesmata, allowing water, nutrients, and hormones to pass quite freely from one cell to another.

Throughout this text, we will return many times to the concepts of membrane structure and transport described in this chapter. Understanding the diversity of membrane lipids and proteins is the key to understanding not just the isolated cell but also entire organs, which could not perform as they do without the specialized membrane properties of their component cells.

(a) Gap junctions

◀ FIGURE 5-18 **Cell communication structures (a)** Gap junctions, such as those between cells of the liver, contain cell-to-cell channels that interconnect the cytoplasm of adjacent cells. **(b)** Plant cells are interconnected by plasmodesmata, which link the cytoplasm of adjacent cells.

In gap junctions, channel proteins connect the insides of adjacent cells

In plasmodesmata, membrane-lined channels connect the insides of adjacent cells

(b) Plasmodesmata

Case Study revisited
Vicious Venoms

Both rattlesnake and brown recluse spider venoms are complex mixtures of poisonous proteins. In each case, the proteins responsible for the worst symptoms are enzymes. As you will learn in Chapter 6, enzymes cause the breakdown of biological molecules while remaining unchanged themselves.

Enzymes are often named after the molecules they break apart, with the suffix "–ase" added to identify the protein as an enzyme. Several of the toxic enzymes in snake and spider venoms are phospholipases; the name tells us that they break down phospholipids. You now know that within cell membranes, the fluid bilayer portion—which allows the membrane to maintain the gradients that are crucial to life—consists of phospholipids.

Although the phospholipases and the other toxic proteins that form the "witches brew" of spider and rattlesnake venoms differ among species, in both cases, the venom attacks cell membranes, causing cells to rupture and die. Cell death destroys the tissue around a rattlesnake or brown recluse spider bite (Fig. 5-19). Phospholipases also attack the membranes of capillary cells, rupturing these tiny blood vessels and releasing blood under the skin around the wound. They also attack the membranes of red blood cells (which carry oxygen throughout the body), and so these venoms can cause anemia (an inadequate number of red blood cells), although this is far more common in rattlesnake than in brown recluse bites. In extreme cases, capillary damage can lead to bleeding—not just at the wound site, but internally as well. Rattlesnake phospholipases also attack muscle cells; this caused extensive damage in Justin's forearm.

Justin required large quantities of antivenin, which contains specialized proteins that bind and neutralize the toxins in snake venom. Unfortunately, no antivenin is available for brown recluse bites, and treatment generally consists of preventing infection, controlling pain and swelling, and waiting patiently—sometimes for months—for the wound to heal.

Although both snake and spider bites can have serious consequences, very few of the spiders and snakes found in the Americas are dangerous to people. The best defense is to learn which of these live in your area and where they prefer to hang out. If your activities bring you to such places, wear protective clothing—and always look before you reach! Knowledge can help us to comfortably coexist with spiders and snakes, to avoid their bites, and to keep our cell membranes intact.

Consider This

Phospholipases and other digestive enzymes are found in animal digestive tracts (including those of humans, snakes, and spiders) as well as in snake and spider venom. What different roles do phospholipases play in snake and spider venom as compared to the role of these phospholipases in digestive enzymes?

(a) Brown recluse spider bite

(b) Justin's rattlesnake bite

▲ FIGURE 5-19 **Phospholipases in venoms can destroy cells** Both **(a)** a brown recluse spider bite and **(b)** Justin's hand 36 hours after the rattlesnake bite show extensive tissue destruction caused by phospholipases.

CHAPTER REVIEW

Summary of Key Concepts

5.1 How Is the Structure of a Membrane Related to Its Function?

The plasma membrane consists of a bilayer of phospholipids in which a variety of proteins are embedded. It isolates the cytoplasm from the external environment, regulates the flow of materials into and out of the cell, allows communication between cells, allows attachments within and between cells, and regulates many biochemical reactions. There are five major types of membrane protein: (1) receptor proteins, which bind molecules and trigger changes within the cell; (2) recognition proteins, which label the cell; (3) enzymes, which promote chemical reactions; (4) attachment proteins, which anchor the plasma membrane to the cytoskeleton and extracellular matrix or bind cells to one another; and (5) transport proteins, which regulate the movement of most water-soluble substances through the membrane.

5.2 How Do Substances Move Across Membranes?

Diffusion is the movement of particles from regions of higher concentration to regions of lower concentration. In simple diffusion, water, dissolved gases, and lipid-soluble molecules diffuse through the phospholipid bilayer. During facilitated diffusion, carrier proteins or channel proteins allow water and water-soluble molecules to cross the membrane down their concentration gradients, without expending cellular energy.

Osmosis is the diffusion of water across a selectively permeable membrane down its concentration gradient through the phospholipid bilayer or through aquaporins.

Energy-requiring transport includes active transport, in which carrier proteins use cellular energy (ATP) to drive the movement of molecules across the plasma membrane against concentration gradients. Extracellular fluid, large molecules, and food particles may be acquired by endocytosis, which includes pinocytosis, receptor-mediated endocytosis, and phagocytosis. The secretion of substances, such as hormones, and the excretion of particulate cellular wastes are accomplished by exocytosis.

BioFlix™ Membrane Transport

5.3 How Do Specialized Junctions Allow Cells to Connect and Communicate?

Animal cell junctions include (1) desmosomes, which attach adjacent cells and prevent tissues from tearing apart during ordinary movements; (2) tight junctions, which leak-proof the spaces between adjacent cells; and (3) gap junctions that connect the cytoplasm of adjacent cells. Plasmodesmata interconnect the cytoplasm of adjacent plant cells.

Key Terms

active transport 88	hypertonic 85
aquaporin 84	hypotonic 85
attachment protein 82	isotonic 85
carrier protein 82	microvilli 92
channel protein 82	osmosis 85
concentration 82	passive transport 83
concentration gradient 82	phagocytosis 90
desmosome 92	phospholipid bilayer 79
diffusion 82	pinocytosis 89
endocytosis 89	plasmodesmata 93
energy-requiring	receptor-mediated
transport 83	endocytosis 90
enzyme 82	receptor protein 81
exocytosis 90	recognition protein 82
facilitated diffusion 84	selectively permeable 83
fluid 82	simple diffusion 84
fluid mosaic model 78	solute 82
food vacuole 90	solvent 82
gap junction 93	tight junction 93
glycoprotein 81	transport protein 82
gradient 82	turgor pressure 87

Thinking Through the Concepts

Fill-in-the-Blank

1. Membranes consist of a bilayer of _____ in which are suspended proteins of five major categories based on function: _____, _____, _____, _____, and _____ proteins.

2. A membrane that is permeable to some substances but not to others is described as being _____. The movement of a substance through a membrane down its concentration gradient is called _____. When applied to water, this process is called _____. In many cells, water travels through channels called _____. The process by which substances are moved through the membrane against their concentration gradient is called _____.

3. Membranes that are more fluid have phospholipids with more _____ in their fatty acid tails. Two environmental factors that decrease membrane fluidity are high _____ and low _____.

4. Facilitated diffusion involves either _____ proteins or _____ proteins. Diffusion directly through the phospholipid bilayer is called _____ diffusion, and molecules that take this route must be soluble in _____ or be very small and have no net electrical charge.

5. Energy-requiring transport includes the following three processes: _____, _____, and _____. Which of these uses ATP directly? _____

6. After each molecule, place the term that most specifically describes the process by which it moves through a plasma membrane: Carbon dioxide: _____; ethyl alcohol: _____; a sodium ion: _____; glucose: _____.

7. The general process by which fluids or particles are transported into cells is called _____. Does this process require energy? _____ The specific term for engulfing fluid is _____, and the term for engulfing particles is _____. The engulfed substances are taken into the cell in membrane-lined sacs called _____.

Review Questions

1. Describe and diagram the structure of a plasma membrane. What are the two principal types of molecules in plasma membranes, and what is the general function of each?

2. What are the five categories of proteins commonly found in plasma membranes, and what is the function of each one?

3. Define *diffusion*, and compare that process to osmosis. How do these two processes help plant leaves remain firm?

4. Define *hypotonic, hypertonic,* and *isotonic.* What would be the fate of an animal cell immersed in each of these three types of solution?

5. Describe the following types of transport processes in cells: simple diffusion, facilitated diffusion, active transport, pinocytosis, receptor-mediated endocytosis, phagocytosis, and exocytosis.

6. Name the protein that allows facilitated diffusion of water. What experiment demonstrated the function of this protein?

7. Imagine a container of glucose solution, divided into two compartments (A and B) by a membrane that is permeable to water and glucose but not to sucrose. If some sucrose is added to compartment A, how will the contents of compartment B change? Explain.

8. Name four types of cell-to-cell junctions, and describe the function of each. Which function in plants, and which in animals?

Applying the Concepts

1. Different cells have somewhat different plasma membranes. The plasma membrane of a *Paramecium,* for example, is only about 1% as permeable to water as the plasma membrane of a human red blood cell. Hypothesize about why this is the case. Is *Paramecium* likely to have aquaporins in its plasma membrane? Explain your answer.

2. Predict and sketch the configuration of phospholipids that are placed in vegetable oil. Explain your prediction.

3. The fluid portion of blood, in which red blood cells are suspended, is called plasma. Is the plasma likely to be isotonic, hypertonic, or hypotonic to the red blood cells? Explain.

4. Some cells in the nervous system wrap themselves around parts of neurons, serving as insulation for the electrical signals that flow inside neurons. These signals along the inside of neurons are carried by ions. Given the general roles of protein and lipids in the cell membrane, which component would you predict to be more abundant in these cells? Explain.

(MB) *Go to www.masteringbiology.com for practice quizzes, activities, eText, videos, current events, and more.*

Energy Flow in the Life of a Cell

Chapter

6

Energy Unleashed

Picture a huge crowd that includes people powering along in wheelchairs, a woman battling cancer, a supporter of wildlife dressed as a rhino, a 91-year-old man proceeding at a slow shuffle, a fireman wearing full firefighting gear to honor his fallen comrades, a man with only one leg using crutches, and blind people guided by the sighted. All participate in a 26-mile journey; a personal odyssey for each individual and a collective testimony to human hope, persistence, and endurance.

The 20,000-plus runners in the New York Marathon collectively expend more than 50 million Calories, and travel roughly 520,000 miles. Once finished, they douse their overheated bodies with water and refuel on high-energy drinks and snacks. Finally, cars, buses, and airplanes—burning vast quantities of fuel and releasing enormous amounts of heat—carry the runners back to their homes throughout the world.

What exactly is energy? Do our bodies use it according to the same principles that govern energy use in the engines of cars and airplanes? Why do our bodies generate heat, and why do we give off more heat when exercising than when watching TV?

▲ The bodies of these runners in the New York Marathon convert stored energy to the energy of movement and heat. Their pounding footsteps shake the Verrazano Narrows Bridge.

At a Glance

6.1 WHAT IS ENERGY?

Energy is the capacity to do work. **Work,** in turn, is the transfer of energy to an object, causing the object to move. The objects upon which energy acts are not always easy to see or even to measure. It is obvious that the marathoners in our case study are doing work by moving things: Their chests heave, their arms pump, and their legs stride, pushing their bodies relentlessly forward for 26 miles. **Chemical energy,** which is energy that is contained in molecules and released by chemical reactions, powers this muscular work. Molecules that provide chemical energy—including sugar, glycogen, and fat—are stored in the runners' bodies. Cells utilize specialized molecules such as ATP to accept, briefly store, and transfer energy from one chemical reaction to the next. Muscle contraction results from interactions among specialized proteins that are driven by chemical energy released from molecules of ATP. The synchronized contractions of muscle cells move runners' bodies, using chemical energy to do work.

There are two fundamental types of energy: potential energy and kinetic energy, each of which takes several forms. **Potential energy,** or stored energy, includes chemical energy maintained in the bonds that bind atoms together in molecules, electrical energy housed in a battery, and positional energy stored in a penguin poised to plunge (**Fig. 6-1**). **Kinetic energy** is the energy of movement. It includes light (movement of photons), heat (movement of molecules), electricity (movement of electrically charged particles), and any movement of larger objects—the plummeting penguin (see Fig. 6-1), your eyes flicking across this page, and marathon

▲ FIGURE 6-1 **From potential to kinetic energy** Perched atop an ice floe, the body of the penguin has potential energy. As it dives, the potential energy is converted to the kinetic energy of motion of the penguin's body. Finally, some of this kinetic energy transferred to the water causes the water to splash and ripple.

runners as they strive to complete a grueling race. Under the right conditions, kinetic energy can be transformed into potential energy, and vice versa. For example, a penguin converts kinetic energy of movement into potential energy of position when it climbs back up from the water onto the ice. During photosynthesis (see Chapter 7), the kinetic energy of light is captured and transformed into the potential energy of chemical bonds. To understand energy flow and change, we need to know more about the properties and behavior of energy, described by the laws of thermodynamics.

The Laws of Thermodynamics Describe the Basic Properties of Energy

The **laws of thermodynamics** describe the quantity (the total amount) and the quality (the usefulness) of energy. The **first law of thermodynamics** states that energy can neither be created nor destroyed by ordinary processes (nuclear reactions, in which matter is converted into energy, are the exception). Energy can, however, change form—for example, from light energy to heat and chemical energy. If you had a **closed system,** where neither energy nor matter could enter or leave, and if you could measure energy in all its forms both before and after a particular process occurred, you would find the total energy before and after the process to be unchanged. Therefore, the first law of thermodynamics is often called the **law of conservation of energy.**

To illustrate the first law, consider your car. Before you turn the ignition key, the energy in the car is all potential energy, stored in the chemical bonds of its fuel. As you drive, only about 25% of this potential energy is converted into the kinetic energy of motion. According to the first law of thermodynamics, however, energy is neither created nor destroyed. So where is the "missing" energy? The burning gas not only moves the car but also heats up the engine, the exhaust system, and the air around the car. The friction of tires on the pavement slightly heats the road. So, as the first law dictates, no energy is lost; the total amount of energy remains the same, although it has changed in form.

The **second law of thermodynamics** states that when energy is converted from one form to another, the amount of useful energy decreases. Put another way, the second law states that all reactions or physical changes cause energy to be converted from more-useful into less-useful forms. For example, the 75% of the energy stored in gasoline that did not move the car was converted into heat (**Fig. 6-2**). Heat is a less-usable form of energy because it merely increases the random movement of molecules in the car, the air, and the road.

Similarly, the heat energy that runners liberate to the air when food "burns" in their bodies cannot be harnessed to allow them to run farther or faster. Thus, the second law tells us that no energy conversion process, including those that occur

100 units chemical energy   75 units heat + 25 units kinetic energy
(concentrated)   energy   (motion)

▲ **FIGURE 6-2 Energy conversions result in a loss of useful energy**

Case Study continued
Energy Unleashed

Like a car's engine, the marathoner's body is only about 25% efficient in converting chemical energy into movement; much of the other 75% is lost as heat. A highly trained marathoner completing the race in 2 hours generates enough heat to raise his or her body temperature by about 1.8°F (1°C) every 3 minutes. If unable to dissipate the heat, the runner would collapse from overheating within 10 minutes. Fortunately—thanks to the high heat of vaporization of water (see pp. 32–33)—most of this excess body heat (up to 98% in hot, dry weather) is dissipated by the evaporative cooling of sweat.

in the body, is 100% efficient in using energy to achieve a specific outcome.

The second law of thermodynamics also tells us something about the organization of matter. Useful energy tends to be stored in highly ordered matter, and whenever energy is used within a closed system, there is an overall increase in randomness and disorder of matter. We all experience this in our homes. Without energy-demanding cleaning and organizing efforts, dirty dishes accumulate; books, newspapers, and clothes collect in confusion on the floor; and the bed remains rumpled.

In the case of chemical energy, the eight carbon atoms in a single molecule of gasoline have a much more orderly arrangement than do the carbon atoms of the eight separate, randomly moving molecules of carbon dioxide and the nine molecules of water that are formed when the gasoline burns. The same is true for the glycogen molecules stored in a runner's muscles, which are converted from highly organized chains of sugar molecules into simpler water and carbon dioxide as they are used by the muscles. This tendency toward loss of complexity, orderliness, and useful energy—and the concurrent increase in randomness, disorder, and less-useful energy—is called **entropy.** To counteract entropy, energy must be infused into the system from an outside source.

When the eminent Yale scientist Evelyn Hutchinson stated, "Disorder spreads through the universe, and life alone battles against it," he made an eloquent reference to entropy and the second law of thermodynamics. Fortunately, Earth is not a closed system, for life as we know it depends on a constant infusion of energy from a source that is 93 million miles away—the sun.

Living Things Use the Energy of Sunlight to Create the Low-Entropy Conditions of Life

If you think about the second law of thermodynamics, you may wonder how life can exist at all. If chemical reactions, including those inside living cells, cause the amount of unusable energy to increase, and if matter tends toward increasing randomness and disorder, how can organisms accumulate the usable energy and precisely ordered molecules that characterize life? The answer is that nuclear reactions in the sun generate kinetic energy in the form of sunlight, a process that also produces vast increases in entropy within the sun in the form of heat. In fact, the temperature of the sun's core is estimated to be 27 million degrees F (16 million degrees C).

Living things use a continuous input of solar energy to synthesize complex molecules and maintain orderly structures, to "battle against disorder." The highly organized, low-entropy systems that characterize life do not violate the second law of thermodynamics because they are achieved through a continuous influx of usable light energy from the sun. The solar reactions that provide light energy here on Earth cause a far greater loss of useful energy in the sun, which will eventually burn out (but fortunately, not for billions of years). Because the solar energy that powers life on Earth occurs with an enormous net increase in solar entropy, life does not violate the second law of thermodynamics.

6.2 HOW DOES ENERGY FLOW IN CHEMICAL REACTIONS?

A **chemical reaction** is a process that forms or breaks the chemical bonds that hold atoms together. Chemical reactions convert one set of chemical substances, the **reactants,** into another set, the **products.** All chemical reactions either release energy or require an overall (net) input of energy. A reaction is **exergonic** (Greek for "energy out") if it releases energy; that is, if the starting reactants contain more energy than the end products. All exergonic reactions give off some of their energy as heat (Fig. 6-3).

▲ FIGURE 6-3 An exergonic reaction

A reaction is **endergonic** ("energy in") if it requires a net input of energy; that is, if the products contain more energy than the reactants. Endergonic reactions require a net influx of energy from an outside source (Fig. 6-4).

▲ FIGURE 6-4 An endergonic reaction

In the following sections, we examine the exergonic process of burning sugar and the endergonic process of photosynthesis.

Exergonic Reactions Release Energy

In an exergonic reaction, the reactants contain more energy than the products. Sugar can be burned, as any cook can tell you. As it is burned, sugar (glucose, for example) undergoes the same overall reaction as sugar in the body of a runner (or nearly any other form of life): sugar ($C_6H_{12}O_6$) is combined with oxygen (O_2) to produce carbon dioxide (CO_2) and water (H_2O), releasing energy (Fig. 6-5).

▲ FIGURE 6-5 Reactants and end products of burning glucose

Because molecules of sugar contain much more energy than do molecules of carbon dioxide and water, the reaction releases energy. Once ignited, sugar will continue to burn. It may be helpful to think of exergonic reactions as running "downhill," from high energy to low energy, as shown in Figure 6-6.

Heat, generated as a by-product of every biochemical transformation, is used by people and other "warm-blooded" animals to maintain a high body temperature. An elevated

▲ FIGURE 6-6 Activation energy in exergonic reactions An exergonic ("downhill") reaction, such as burning sugar, proceeds from high-energy reactants (here, glucose and O_2) to low-energy products (CO_2 and H_2O). The energy difference between the chemical bonds of the reactants and products is released as heat. To start the reaction, however, an initial input of energy—the activation energy—is required.

QUESTION In addition to heat and sunlight, what are some other possible sources of activation energy?

Marathoners rely on glycogen, stored in their muscles and liver, for the energy to power their run. Glycogen consists of chains of glucose molecules, which are first cleaved from the chain and then broken down into carbon dioxide and water. This exergonic reaction generates heat and the ATP required for muscle contraction. The carbon dioxide is exhaled as the runners breathe rapidly to supply their muscles with adequate oxygen. The water produced (and a lot more that the runners drink during the race) is lost as sweat. As the sweat evaporates, it carries away the heat generated by the chemical reactions in their muscles, preventing the runners' bodies from overheating.

body temperature speeds up biochemical reactions, allowing animals to move faster and respond more quickly to stimuli than if their body temperatures were lower.

All Chemical Reactions Require Activation Energy to Begin

Although burning sugar releases energy, sugar doesn't burst into flames by itself. This observation leads to an important concept: All chemical reactions, even those that can continue spontaneously, require energy to get started. Think of a rock sitting at the top of a hill. It will remain there indefinitely unless something gives it a push to start it rolling down. In chemical reactions, the energy "push" is called the **activation energy** (see Fig. 6-6). Chemical reactions require activation energy to get started because shells of negatively charged electrons surround all atoms and molecules. For two molecules to react with each other, their electron shells must be forced together, despite their mutual electrical repulsion. Forcing the electron shells together requires activation energy.

Activation energy can be provided by the kinetic energy of moving molecules. At any temperature higher than absolute zero ($-460°F$, or $-273°C$), atoms and molecules are in constant motion. Reactive molecules moving with sufficient speed collide hard enough to force their electron shells to mingle and react. Because molecules move faster as the temperature increases, most chemical reactions occur more readily at high temperatures. For example, heat provided by a match can set sugar on fire. The combination of sugar with oxygen then releases enough of its own heat to sustain the reaction, allowing it to continue spontaneously. How is adequate activation energy generated in the body to allow it to "burn" sugar? Keep this question in mind—you'll find the answer later in this chapter.

Endergonic Reactions Require a Net Input of Energy

In contrast to what happens when sugar is burned, many reactions in living systems result in products that contain more energy than the reactants do. Sugar, produced by photosynthetic organisms such as plants, contains far more energy than does

the carbon dioxide and water from which it was formed. The protein in a muscle cell contains more energy than the individual amino acids that were joined together to synthesize it. In other words, synthesizing complex biological molecules requires an input of energy; these reactions are endergonic. As we will see in Chapter 7, photosynthesis in green plants uses solar energy to produce sugar from water and carbon dioxide (**Fig. 6-7**). The oxygen produced by this reaction is used when glucose is broken down by cells to release its stored energy.

▲ FIGURE 6-7 **Photosynthesis**

Endergonic reactions are not spontaneous; we might call them "uphill" reactions, because the reactants contain less energy than the products do. Going from low energy to high energy is like pushing a rock up to the top of the hill. Where do we and other animals get the energy to fuel endergonic reactions such as synthesizing muscle protein and other complex biological molecules?

6.3 HOW IS ENERGY TRANSPORTED WITHIN CELLS?

Most organisms are powered by the breakdown of sugar (usually glucose). By combining glucose with oxygen and releasing carbon dioxide and water, cells acquire chemical energy from the glucose molecule. This energy is used to do cellular work, such as constructing complex biological molecules and powering muscle contraction. But glucose cannot be used directly to fuel these endergonic processes. Instead, the energy released by glucose breakdown is first transferred to an energy-carrier molecule. **Energy-carrier molecules** are high-energy, unstable molecules that are synthesized at the site of an exergonic reaction, capturing some of the released energy. These energy carriers work something like rechargeable batteries; they pick up an energy charge at an exergonic reaction, move to another location within the cell, and then release the energy to drive an endergonic reaction. Because energy-carrier molecules are unstable, they are used only to capture and transfer energy within cells. They cannot ferry energy from cell to cell, nor are they used for long-term energy storage.

ATP Is the Principal Energy Carrier in Cells

Many exergonic reactions in cells produce **adenosine triphosphate,** or **ATP,** the most common energy-carrier molecule in the body. Because it provides energy to drive such a wide variety of endergonic reactions, ATP is sometimes called

(a) ATP synthesis: Energy is stored in ATP

(b) ATP breakdown: Energy is released

▲ FIGURE 6-8 **The interconversion of ADP and ATP**
(a) Energy is captured when a phosphate group (P) is added to adenosine diphosphate (ADP) to make adenosine triphosphate (ATP). **(b)** Energy to accomplish cellular work is released when ATP is broken down into ADP and P.

the "energy currency" of cells. As you learned in Chapter 3, ATP is a nucleotide composed of the nitrogen-containing base adenine, the sugar ribose, and three phosphate groups (see Fig. 3-23). Energy released in cells during glucose breakdown or other exergonic reactions is used to combine the relatively low-energy molecules **adenosine diphosphate (ADP)** and phosphate (HPO_4^{2-}, also called P) into the much less stable, high-energy molecule ATP (**Fig. 6-8a**). The formation of ATP is endergonic—it requires an input of energy which is captured in this newly formed high energy molecule.

ATP stores energy within its chemical bonds and diffuses throughout the cell, carrying the energy to sites where energy-requiring reactions occur. Its energy is liberated as the ATP is broken down, regenerating ADP and P (**Fig. 6-8b**). The life span of an ATP molecule in a living cell is very short. If the molecules of ATP that you use just sitting at your desk all day could be captured (instead of recycled), they would weigh around 90 pounds (about 40 kg). A marathon runner may recycle the equivalent of a pound of ATP every minute, so without rapid reconversions, it would be a very brief run. As you can see, ATP is *not* a long-term energy-storage molecule. Relatively stable molecules such

as glycogen and fat can store energy for hours, days, or—in the case of fat—years.

Electron Carriers Also Transport Energy Within Cells

ATP is not the only energy-carrier molecule within cells. In some exergonic reactions, including both glucose breakdown and the light-capturing stage of photosynthesis, some energy is transferred to electrons. These energetic electrons, along with hydrogen ions (H^+; present in the cytoplasmic fluid) are captured by special energy-carrier molecules called **electron carriers.** Common electron carriers include nicotinamide adenine dinucleotide (NADH) and its relative, flavin adenine dinucleotide (FADH$_2$). The loaded electron carriers then donate their high-energy electrons to other molecules, which are often involved in pathways that generate ATP. You will learn more about electron carriers and their role in cellular metabolism in Chapters 7 and 8.

Coupled Reactions Link Exergonic with Endergonic Reactions

In a **coupled reaction,** an exergonic reaction provides the energy needed to drive an endergonic reaction (**Fig. 6-9**). During photosynthesis, for example, plants use sunlight (from exergonic reactions in the sun's core) to drive the endergonic synthesis of high-energy glucose molecules from lower energy reactants (carbon dioxide and water). Nearly all organisms use the energy released by exergonic reactions (such as the breakdown of glucose into carbon dioxide and water) to drive endergonic reactions (such as the synthesis of proteins from amino acids). Because energy is lost as heat every time it is transformed, in coupled reactions the energy released by exergonic reactions must exceed the energy needed to drive the endergonic reactions.

The exergonic and endergonic portions of coupled reactions often occur in different places within a cell, so there must be some way to transfer the energy from the exergonic reactions that release energy to the endergonic reactions that require it. In coupled reactions, energy is transferred from place to place by energy-carrier molecules such as ATP. In its role as an intermediary in coupled reactions, ATP is constantly being synthesized to capture the energy released during exergonic reactions and then broken down to power endergonic reactions, as shown in Figure 6-9.

▶ FIGURE 6-9 **Coupled reactions within living cells**
Exergonic reactions (such as glucose breakdown) drive the endergonic reaction that synthesizes ATP from ADP and P. The ATP molecule carries its chemical energy to a part of the cell where energy is needed to drive an endergonic reaction (such as protein synthesis). The ADP and P are rejoined to form ATP via endergonic reactions.

6.4 HOW DO ENZYMES PROMOTE BIOCHEMICAL REACTIONS?

You now know that cells couple reactions together, powering energy-requiring endergonic reactions with the energy released by exergonic reactions. You have also learned that cells synthesize energy-carrier molecules that capture energy from exergonic reactions and transport it to endergonic reactions. But how do cells promote and control the multitude of biochemical reactions required to maintain the precise chemical balance necessary for life?

At Body Temperatures, Spontaneous Reactions Proceed Too Slowly to Sustain Life

In general, the speed at which a reaction occurs is determined by its activation energy; that is, how much energy is required to start the reaction (see Fig. 6-6). Some reactions, such as table salt dissolving in water (see Fig. 2-9), have low activation energies and occur readily at human body temperature (approximately $98.6\,°F$, or $37\,°C$). In contrast, you could maintain sugar at body temperature for decades and it would appear unchanged.

The reaction of sugar with oxygen to yield carbon dioxide and water is exergonic, but it has a high activation energy. The heat of a match flame increases the rate of movement of sugar and nearby oxygen molecules, causing them to collide with sufficient force to overcome their activation energy and react; the sugar burns. The energy released by this exergonic reaction speeds up the movement of more sugar and oxygen molecules, allowing the sugar to continue to burn on its own. At the temperatures found in living organisms, however, sugar and many other energy-containing molecules would almost never break down and give up their energy. Promoting reactions with high activation energies is the job of catalysts.

Catalysts Reduce Activation Energy

Catalysts are molecules that speed up the rate of a reaction without themselves being used up or permanently altered. A catalyst speeds up a reaction by reducing the reaction's activation energy (**Fig. 6-10**). For example, consider the catalytic converters on automobile exhaust systems. Flaws in the gasoline combustion process generate poisonous carbon monoxide (CO). Carbon monoxide reacts spontaneously but slowly with oxygen in the air to form carbon dioxide:

$$2\,CO + O_2 \rightarrow 2\,CO_2 + \text{heat energy}$$

In heavy traffic, the spontaneous reaction of CO with O_2 can't keep pace with the CO emitted, and unhealthy levels of CO accumulate. Enter the catalytic converter. Catalysts such as platinum in the converter provide a specialized surface upon which O_2 and CO combine more readily, hastening the conversion of CO to CO_2 and reducing air pollution.

All catalysts share three important properties:

- Catalysts speed up reactions by lowering the activation energy required for the reaction to begin.

▲ **FIGURE 6-10 Catalysts such as enzymes lower activation energy** A high activation energy (red curve) means that reactant molecules must collide very forcefully in order to react. Catalysts lower the activation energy of a reaction (blue curve), so a much higher proportion of molecules moves fast enough to react when the molecules collide. Therefore, the reaction proceeds much more rapidly.

QUESTION Can a catalyst make an endergonic reaction occur spontaneously?

- Catalysts can speed up both exergonic and endergonic reactions, but they cannot make an endergonic reaction occur spontaneously. An endergonic reaction will still need a net input of energy, with or without an assist from a catalyst.
- Catalysts are not consumed or permanently changed by the reactions they promote.

Enzymes Are Biological Catalysts

Inorganic catalysts, such as the platinum in a catalytic converter, speed up a great number of chemical reactions. Indiscriminately speeding up dozens of reactions would not be useful, and indeed would almost certainly be deadly, to living organisms. Instead, cells employ highly specific biological catalysts called **enzymes,** which are composed primarily of proteins. A given enzyme catalyzes only a few types of chemical reactions, at most. The majority of enzymes catalyze a single reaction involving specific molecules, while leaving even very similar molecules unchanged.

Both exergonic and endergonic reactions are catalyzed by enzymes. The synthesis of ATP from ADP and P, for example, is catalyzed by the enzyme ATP synthase. This enzyme is responsible for capturing some of the energy released during the series of reactions that break down glucose and then storing it in ATP. When energy is required to drive endergonic reactions, ATP is broken down by ATPase. (Notice that some enzymes are named by adding the suffix "ase" to a description of what the enzyme does [ATP synthase] and some others by adding "ase" to the molecule upon which the enzyme acts [ATPase].)

Some enzymes require small nonprotein helper molecules called **coenzymes** in order to function. Many water-soluble vitamins (such as the B vitamins) are essential to humans because they are used by the body to synthesize coenzymes. Enzymes, which can catalyze several million reactions per second, use their precise three-dimensional structures to orient, distort, and reconfigure other molecules while emerging unchanged themselves.

Enzyme Structures Allow Them to Catalyze Specific Reactions

The function of an enzyme is determined by its structure. Each enzyme has a pocket, called the **active site,** into which one or more reactant molecules, called **substrates,** can enter. You may recall from Chapter 3 that proteins have complex three-dimensional shapes (see Fig. 3-20). Their primary structure is determined by the precise order in which amino acids are linked. The chain of amino acids then folds around itself in a configuration (often a helix or a pleated sheet) called secondary structure. The protein then acquires the additional twists and bends of tertiary structure. Some enzymes also contain peptide subunits joined into a quaternary structure. The order of amino acids, and the precise way in which the amino acid chains of a protein are twisted and folded, creates the distinctive shape of the active site and a specific distribution of electrical charges within the site.

Because the enzyme and its substrate fit together precisely, only certain molecules can enter the active site. Take the enzyme amylase, for example. Amylase breaks down starch molecules by hydrolysis, but leaves cellulose molecules intact, even though both consist of chains of glucose molecules. A different bonding pattern between the glucose molecules in cellulose prevents them from fitting into the enzyme's active site. (If you chew a soda cracker long enough, you'll notice a sweet flavor caused by the release of sugar molecules from the starch in the cracker by amylase in your saliva.) The stomach enzyme pepsin is selective for proteins, attacking them at many sites along their amino acid chains. Certain other protein-digesting enzymes (trypsin, for example) will break bonds only between specific amino acids. Digestive systems manufacture several different enzymes that work together to completely break down dietary protein into its individual amino acids.

How does an enzyme catalyze a reaction? First, both the shape and the charge of the active site allow substrates to enter the enzyme only in specific orientations (**Fig. 6-11 ❶**). Second, when substrates enter the active site, both the substrate and active site change shape (**Fig. 6-11 ❷**). Certain amino acids within the enzyme's active site may temporarily bond with atoms of the substrates, or electrical interactions between the amino acids in the active site and substrates may distort chemical bonds within the substrates. The combination of substrate selectivity, substrate orientation, temporary chemical bonds, and the distortion of existing bonds promotes the specific chemical reaction catalyzed by a particular enzyme. When the reaction between the substrates is finished, the

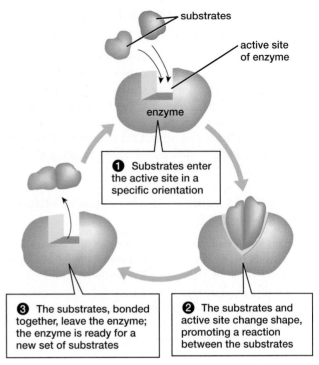

▲ FIGURE 6-11 The cycle of enzyme–substrate interactions

product(s) no longer fit properly into the active site and drift away (**Fig. 6-11 ❸**). The enzyme reverts to its original configuration, and it is ready to accept another set of substrates.

Enzymes, Like All Catalysts, Lower Activation Energy

How do enzymes speed up the rate of chemical reactions? The breakdown or synthesis of a molecule within a cell usually occurs in many small, discrete steps, each catalyzed by a different enzyme (see Fig. 6-12). Each of these enzymes lowers the activation energy for its particular reaction, allowing the reaction to occur readily at body temperature. Think of a rock climber ascending a steep cliff by finding a series of hand- and footholds that allow her to scale it one small step at a time. In a similar manner, a series of reaction steps, each requiring a small amount of activation energy and each catalyzed by an enzyme that lowers activation energy, allows the overall reaction (in this case, oxidizing sugar) to surmount its high overall activation energy "cliff" and to proceed at body temperature.

Enzymes Control the Rate of Energy Release and Capture Some Energy in ATP

Ignite sugar and it will go up in flames as it combines rapidly with oxygen, releasing carbon dioxide and water. The same overall reaction occurs in our cells, but they are in no danger of catching on fire. Thanks to a series of chemical transformations, each catalyzed by a different enzyme, the energy stored in sugar is released gradually. Some is lost as heat, keeping our bodies warm, while some is harnessed to power endergonic reactions that lead to ATP synthesis.

What Makes a Firefly Glow?

The almost magical glow of fireflies comes from specialized cells in their abdomens that are bioluminescent, meaning that they produce "biological light." These cells are rich in ATP and the fluorescent chemical luciferin (Latin, meaning "light-bringer"). Luciferin and ATP serve as substrates for the enzyme luciferase. In the presence of oxygen, luciferase catalyzes a reaction that modifies luciferin and uses the energy from ATP to boost electrons briefly into a higher-energy electron shell. As they fall back into their original shell, the electrons emit their excess energy as light. The process produces so little heat that these beetles are often described as emitting "cold light."

6.5 HOW DO CELLS REGULATE THEIR METABOLIC REACTIONS?

Cells are incredibly complex chemical factories. The **metabolism** of a cell is the sum of all its myriad chemical reactions. Many of these reactions are linked in sequences called **metabolic pathways** (Fig. 6-12). In a metabolic pathway, an initial reactant molecule is modified by an enzyme, forming a slightly different intermediate molecule, which is modified by another enzyme to form a second intermediate, and so on, until an end product is produced. Within metabolic pathways, molecules are both synthesized and broken down, so that the end product may be a waste molecule (such as carbon dioxide formed when glucose is broken down). Alternatively, the end product may be a molecule (such as an amino acid; see Fig. 6-14) synthesized by the metabolic pathway. Photosynthesis (Chapter 7) is a metabolic pathway that results in the synthesis of high-energy molecules, including glucose. Another metabolic pathway, glycolysis, begins the breakdown of glucose (Chapter 8). Different metabolic pathways often use some of the same molecules; as a result, all the thousands of metabolic pathways within a cell are directly or indirectly interconnected (see Fig. 6-12).

Reaction Rates Tend to Increase as Substrate or Enzyme Levels Increase

In a test tube containing an enzyme and its substrate (under constant, ideal conditions), the rate of the reaction will depend on how many substrate molecules encounter the active sites of enzyme molecules in a given time period. As you might guess, if you added either more enzyme or more substrate molecules, the reaction rate would increase. For a given amount of enzyme, as substrate levels increase, the reaction rate will increase until the active sites of all the enzyme molecules are being continuously occupied by new substrate molecules. To increase the rate further, more enzymes would be needed.

But consider the needs of a cell. When glucose molecules flood in after a meal, it would not be desirable to metabolize them all and form far more unstable ATP molecules than the cell can use. To be effective, the metabolic reactions within cells must be precisely regulated; they must occur at the proper time and proceed at the proper rate. This fine-tuning of metabolic reactions is accomplished in several ways.

Case Study continued
Energy Unleashed

If a runner preparing for a marathon eats a huge dish of pasta, a few hours later the starch-digesting enzymes in his or her small intestine will encounter an enormous quantity of carbohydrates. Because of their abundance, these substrate molecules will encounter the active sites of amylase enzymes far more often than before the meal, and the rate at which amylase enzymes break down carbohydrate will increase dramatically.

Cells Regulate Enzyme Synthesis

Cells exert tight control over all the types of proteins they produce. Genes that code for specific proteins are turned on or off depending on the need for that protein, a process described in detail in Chapter 12. Enzyme proteins govern all of the cell's metabolic activities, and these activities must be able to change to meet the cell's changing needs. Some enzymes, therefore, are synthesized in larger quantities when more of their substrate is available. Larger amounts of the enzyme then speed up the rate at which a substance is metabolized, because more substrate molecules are bound to enzyme molecules at

◀ FIGURE 6-12 **Simplified metabolic pathways** The initial reactant molecule (A) undergoes a series of reactions, each catalyzed by a specific enzyme. The product of each reaction serves as the reactant for the next reaction in the pathway. Metabolic pathways are commonly interconnected such that the product of a step in one pathway may serve as a reactant for the next reaction or for a reaction in another pathway.

any given time. For example, the livers of people who regularly drink large quantities of alcohol produce more alcohol dehydrogenase, an enzyme that breaks down alcohol. Unfortunately, this and other liver enzymes convert alcohol into toxic substances, so that alcoholics frequently suffer liver damage.

Mutations (accidental changes) in genes can alter enzyme production, as described in "Health Watch: Lacking an Enzyme Can Lead to Lactose Intolerance or Phenylketonuria."

Cells Regulate Enzyme Activity

Enzymes are complex proteins, and many have properties that cause them to be regulated by their chemical surroundings. This allows enzymes to become active when and where they are needed.

Some Enzymes Are Synthesized in Inactive Forms

Some enzymes are synthesized in an inactive form that is activated under the conditions found where the enzyme is needed.

Examples are the protein-digesting enzymes pepsin and trypsin, mentioned earlier. Cells synthesize and release each of these enzymes in an inactive form, preventing the enzyme from digesting and killing the cell that manufactures it. In the stomach, acid modifies the shape of pepsin, exposing its active site and allowing it to begin breaking down proteins that have been eaten. Trypsin, which helps complete protein digestion, works best in the more basic (higher pH) conditions of the small intestine (see Fig. 6-15a). The small intestine secretes an enzyme that acts on trypsin, altering its configuration and allowing it to function.

Enzyme Activity May Be Inhibited Competitively or Noncompetitively

It is not in the cell's best interest to have its enzymes churning out products all the time. Many enzymes need to be inhibited so that the cell does not use up all of its substrate or become overwhelmed by too much product. You'll recall that

Health Watch

Lacking an Enzyme Can Lead to Lactose Intolerance or Phenylketonuria

Is it difficult for you to imagine life without milk, ice cream, or even pizza (**Fig. E6-1**)? Although some people consider these foods to be staples of the U.S. diet, they are not enjoyed by most of the world's population. Why? About 75% of people worldwide, including 25% of people in the United States, lose the ability to digest lactose, or milk sugar, in early childhood. Roughly 75% of African Americans, Hispanics, and Native Americans, as well as 90% of Asian Americans, experience **lactose intolerance.**

▲ FIGURE E6-1 **Risky behavior?** For most of the world's adults, drinking a glass of milk invites unpleasant consequences.

From an evolutionary perspective, this makes perfect sense. The lactose enzyme, called lactase, is found in the small intestines of all healthy young children. After being weaned in early childhood, our early ancestors no longer consumed milk—the main source of lactose. Because it takes energy to synthesize enzymes, losing the ability to synthesize an unnecessary enzyme is adaptive. However, some populations experienced mutations that conferred the ability to continue to digest lactose into adulthood, such as populations in northern Europe, who raised cattle for milk and made dairy products a regular part of their diet. Their descendants continue to enjoy this healthy food.

Compared to other consequences of enzyme deficiency, the inability to tolerate milk is a relatively minor inconvenience. Because enzymes are crucial to all aspects of cellular life, mutations that render them nonfunctional may cause life-threatening disorders or may prevent an embryo from developing at all. One serious result of a defective enzyme is **phenylketonuria (PKU),** a disorder that occurs most frequently in Caucasians (affecting about 1 in 10,000). This mutation cripples the enzyme that oxidizes the common amino acid phenylalanine, causing a buildup of phenylalanine in the blood. Untreated, PKU causes severe mental retardation. Today, in the United States, newborns are usually screened for PKU, and affected individuals can develop normally on a diet that severely limits phenylalanine intake for the first 10 years of life. This dietary requirement is why NutraSweet™ (aspartame; an artificial sweetener synthesized from aspartic acid and phenylalanine) carries a warning. If a woman with PKU becomes pregnant, she must resume this very restricted diet to prevent harm to her developing child.

for an enzyme to catalyze a reaction, its substrate must bind to the enzyme's active site (**Fig. 6-13a**). There are two general ways in which enzymes can be inhibited.

In **competitive inhibition,** a substance that is not the enzyme's normal substrate binds to the active site of the enzyme, competing with the substrate for the active site (**Fig. 6-13b**). For example, along the metabolic pathway that breaks down glucose, one enzyme in the sequence of reactions is competitively inhibited by the product molecule formed two steps further along. This product diffuses in and out of the active site, so the binding is reversible. This means that the normal substrate and the inhibitor can each displace the other if its concentration is high enough, which helps control the rate of glucose breakdown.

In **noncompetitive inhibition,** a molecule binds to a noncompetitive inhibitor site on the enzyme that is distinct from the active site. As a result, the enzyme active site is distorted, making it less able to catalyze the reaction (**Fig. 6-13c**). Many noncompetitive inhibitor molecules are poisons, as described later.

Some Enzymes Are Controlled by Allosteric Regulation

Some enzymes, called allosteric enzymes, switch readily and spontaneously between two different configurations ("allosteric" literally means "other shape")—one configuration is active, while the other is inactive. Such enzymes are controlled by **allosteric regulation,** which occurs when molecules described as "allosteric activators" or "allosteric inhibitors" bind reversibly to the regulatory sites of the enzyme—sites distinct from the enzyme's active site. Reversible binding of the activator and inhibitor molecules means that they bind temporarily, so that the number of enzymes being activated (or inhibited) is proportional to the numbers of activator (or inhibitor) molecules that are present at any given time.

Allosteric *activators* stabilize the enzyme in its active form; when there are large numbers of allosteric activators present, the enzyme activity will be high. Allosteric *inhibitors* bind to a different regulatory site that stabilizes the enzyme in its inactive form. Thus, the overall level of allosteric enzyme activity is regulated by the relative quantities of activators and inhibitors available. An example of an allosteric activator molecule is ADP, from which ATP is synthesized. An abundance of ADP in a cell means that a lot of ATP has been used up, and more ATP is needed. ADP activates allosteric enzymes in metabolic pathways that produce ATP, stabilizing them in their active state.

An important form of allosteric regulation is feedback inhibition. **Feedback inhibition** (**Fig. 6-14**) causes a metabolic pathway to stop producing its product when the product concentration reaches an optimal level, much as a thermostat turns off a heater when a room becomes warm enough. In feedback inhibition, the activity of an enzyme near the beginning of a metabolic pathway is inhibited by the end product of that pathway. The end product acts as an allosteric inhibitor molecule.

In the metabolic pathway illustrated in Figure 6-14, a series of reactions, each catalyzed by a different enzyme, converts one amino acid to another. As levels of the end product amino acid increase, it increasingly encounters and binds to the al-

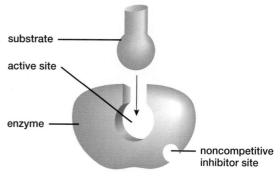

substrate

active site

enzyme

noncompetitive inhibitor site

(a) A substrate binding to an enzyme

A competitive inhibitor molecule occupies the active site and blocks entry of the substrate

(b) Competitive inhibition

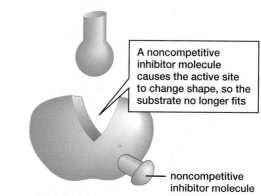

A noncompetitive inhibitor molecule causes the active site to change shape, so the substrate no longer fits

noncompetitive inhibitor molecule

(c) Noncompetitive inhibition

▲ **FIGURE 6-13 Competitive and noncompetitive enzyme inhibition (a)** The normal substrate fits easily into the enzyme's active site when the enzyme is not being inhibited. **(b)** In competitive inhibition, a competitive inhibitor molecule that resembles the substrate blocks the active site. **(c)** In noncompetitive inhibition, a molecule binds to a different site on the enzyme, distorting the active site so it no longer fits its substrate.

losteric regulatory site on an enzyme early in the pathway, inhibiting it. Thus, when enough of the end product is present, the pathway is slowed or halted. Another allosteric inhibitor is ATP, which inhibits enzymes in metabolic pathways that lead to ATP synthesis. When a cell has all the ATP it needs, there is enough ATP around to block ATP production. As ATP is used up, the pathways that produce it become active again.

Poisons, Drugs, and Environmental Conditions Influence Enzyme Activity

Poisons and drugs that act on enzymes usually inhibit them, either competitively or noncompetitively. Environmental

▲ **FIGURE 6-14 Allosteric regulation of an enzyme by feedback inhibition** Here, we illustrate a metabolic pathway that converts one amino acid into another by way of a series of intermediate molecules (colored shapes), each acted upon by a different enzyme (arrows). In this example, the first enzyme in the pathway that converts threonine into isoleucine is inhibited by high concentrations of isoleucine, which acts as an allosteric inhibitor molecule. If a cell lacks isoleucine, the reactions proceed. As isoleucine builds up, it inhibits enzyme 1, blocking the pathway. When concentrations of isoleucine drop and fewer isoleucine molecules are available to inhibit the enzyme, it becomes active again, and isoleucine production resumes.

conditions can denature enzymes, distorting the three-dimensional structure that is crucial for their function.

Some Poisons and Drugs Compete with the Substrate for the Active Site of the Enzyme

Some poisons, such as methanol (a toxic alcohol used as a solvent and antifreeze), act as competitive inhibitors of enzymes. Methanol competes for the active site of the enzyme alcohol dehydrogenase, whose normal substrate is ethanol (found in alcoholic beverages). Alcohol dehydrogenase can break down methanol, but in the process it produces formaldehyde, which can cause blindness. Taking advantage of competitive inhibition, doctors administer ethanol to victims of methanol poisoning. By competing with methanol for the active site of alcohol dehydrogenase, ethanol blocks formaldehyde production.

Some drugs work because they act as competitive inhibitors of enzymes. For example, ibuprofen (Advil™) acts as a competitive inhibitor of an enzyme that catalyzes the synthesis of molecules that contribute to swelling, pain, and fever. Some anticancer drugs are competitive inhibitors of enzymes. Rapidly dividing cancer cells are constantly synthesizing new strands of DNA. Some anticancer drugs resemble the subunits that comprise DNA. These drugs compete with the normal subunits, tricking enzymes into building defective DNA, which in turn prevents the cancer cells from proliferating. Unfortunately, these drugs also interfere with the growth of other rapidly dividing cells, including those in hair follicles and lining the digestive tract. This explains why hair loss and nausea are side effects of some types of cancer chemotherapy drugs.

Some Poisons and Drugs Bind Permanently to the Enzyme

Some poisons and drugs bind irreversibly to enzymes. These irreversible inhibitors may permanently block the enzyme's active site, or they may attach to another part of the enzyme, noncompetitively changing the enzyme's shape or charge so that it can no longer bind its substrates properly.

For example, some nerve gases and insecticides permanently block the active site of acetylcholinesterase, an enzyme that breaks down acetylcholine (a substance that nerve cells release to activate muscles). This allows acetylcholine to build up and overstimulate muscles, causing paralysis. Death ensues because victims are unable to breathe. Penicillin kills bacteria because it is an irreversible competitive inhibitor of an enzyme that helps bacteria produce their cell walls, without which they will burst. Penicillin is harmless to animal cells, which lack cell walls.

Other poisons—including arsenic, mercury, and lead—are noncompetitive inhibitors that bind permanently to other parts of various enzymes, inactivating them.

The Activity of Enzymes Is Influenced by the Environment

The complex three-dimensional structures of enzymes are sensitive to environmental conditions. You may recall from Chapter 3 that much of the three-dimensional structure of proteins is produced by hydrogen bonds between partially charged amino acids. These bonds only occur within a narrow range of chemical and physical conditions, including the proper pH, temperature, and salt concentration. Thus, most enzymes have a very narrow range of conditions in which they function optimally. When conditions fall outside this range, the enzyme becomes **denatured,** meaning that it loses the exact three-dimensional structure required for it to function properly.

In humans, cellular enzymes generally work best at a pH around 7.4, the level maintained in and around our cells (**Fig. 6-15a**). For these enzymes, an acid pH alters the charges on amino acids by adding hydrogen ions to them, which in turn will change the enzyme's shape and compromise its ability to function. Stomach acid kills many bacteria by denaturing their enzymes. Enzymes that operate in the human digestive tract, however, may function outside of the pH range maintained within cells. The protein-digesting enzyme pepsin, for example, requires the acidic conditions of the stomach (pH around 2). In contrast, the protein-digesting enzyme trypsin, found in the small intestine where alkaline conditions prevail, works best at a pH close to 8 (see Fig. 6-15a).

In addition to pH, temperature affects the rate of enzyme-catalyzed reactions, which are slowed by lower temperatures and accelerated by moderately higher temperatures. This is because the rate of movement of molecules determines how likely they are to encounter the active site of an enzyme (**Fig. 6-15b**). Cooling the body can drastically slow human metabolic reactions. In one actual case, a young boy who fell through the ice on a lake was rescued and survived unharmed after 20 minutes under water. Although at normal body temperature the brain dies after about 4 minutes without oxygen, the boy's body temperature and metabolic rate were lowered by the icy water, drastically reducing his need for oxygen.

In contrast, when temperatures rise too high, the hydrogen bonds that regulate protein shape may be broken apart by the excessive molecular motion, denaturing the protein. Think of the protein in egg white, and how its appearance and texture are completely altered by cooking. Far lower temperatures than those required to fry an egg can still be too hot to allow enzymes to function properly. Excessive heat may be fatal; every summer, many children in the United States die from heat stroke when left unattended in overheated cars.

Bacteria and fungi, which exist in nearly all our food, can cause it to spoil. Food remains fresh in the refrigerator or freezer because cooling slows the enzyme-catalyzed reactions upon which these microorganisms rely to grow and reproduce. Before the advent of refrigeration, meat was commonly preserved by using concentrated salt solutions (think of bacon or salt pork), which kill most bacteria. Salts dissociate into ions, which form bonds with amino acids in enzyme proteins. Too much (or too little) salt interferes with the three-dimensional structure of enzymes, destroying their activity. Dill pickles are very well preserved in a vinegar-salt solution, which combines both highly salty and acidic conditions. Organisms that live in saline environments, as you might predict, have enzymes whose configuration depends on a relatively high concentration of salt ions.

(a) Effect of pH on enzyme activity

(b) Effect of temperature on enzyme activity

▲ **FIGURE 6-15 Human enzymes function best within narrow ranges of pH and temperature (a)** The digestive enzyme pepsin, released into the stomach, works best at an acidic pH. Trypsin, released into the small intestine, works best at a basic pH. Most enzymes from cells, however, work best at the precisely regulated pH found in the extracellular fluid and cytoplasm (about 7.4). **(b)** The maximum activity of most human enzymes occurs at human body temperature.

Case Study r e v i s i t e d

Energy Unleashed

Needless to say, during the course of a 26-mile race, a marathoner burns a great deal of glucose to provide enough ATP to power muscles through roughly 34,000 running steps. People store glucose molecules linked together in long branched chains of glycogen, primarily in the muscles and liver. Adults typically store about 3.5 ounces (100 grams) of glycogen in the liver, and another 9.9 ounces (280 grams) in muscles. Trained distance athletes can increase liver glycogen storage capacity by more than 50%, and can more than double the glycogen storage capacity of their muscles.

This is important because during a marathon, a runner depletes essentially all of his or her body's stored glycogen. At this point, often about 90 minutes into the race, the runner may experience extreme muscle fatigue, loss of motivation, and occasionally even hallucinations, because both muscles and brain are starving for energy. Runners describe this sensation as "hitting the wall" or "bonking." To store the greatest possible amount of glycogen, endurance athletes practice "carbo-loading," consuming large quantities of carbohydrates (starches and sugars) during the three days preceding the race. By packing their livers and muscles with glycogen before the race, and by consuming energy drinks during the race, some runners manage to cross the finish line before they hit the wall.

Consider This

When a runner's body temperature begins to rise, the body activates several mechanisms, including sweating and circulating more blood to the skin. Compare this response to overheating with feedback inhibition in enzymes.

CHAPTER REVIEW

Summary of Key Concepts

6.1 What Is Energy?
Energy is the capacity to do work. Potential energy is stored energy (chemical energy, positional energy). Kinetic energy is the energy of movement (light, heat, electricity, movement of objects). The first law of thermodynamics, the law of conservation of energy, states that in a closed system, although energy may change in form, the total amount of energy remains constant. The second law of thermodynamics states that any use of energy causes a decrease in the quantity of useful energy and an increase in entropy (disorder and less-useful energy). The highly organized, low-entropy systems that characterize life do not violate the second law of thermodynamics, because they are achieved through a continuous influx of usable energy from the sun, accompanied by an enormous increase in solar entropy.

6.2 How Does Energy Flow in Chemical Reactions?
Chemical reactions fall into two categories. In exergonic reactions, the reactant molecules have more energy than do the product molecules, so the reaction releases energy. In endergonic reactions, the reactants have less energy than do the products, so the reaction requires a net input of energy. Exergonic reactions can occur spontaneously, but all reactions, including exergonic ones, require an initial input of energy (the activation energy) to overcome electrical repulsions between reactant molecules. Exergonic and endergonic reactions may be coupled such that the energy liberated by an exergonic reaction drives the endergonic reaction. Organisms couple exergonic reactions, such as capturing light or breaking down sugar, with endergonic reactions, such as synthesizing organic molecules.

6.3 How Is Energy Transported Within Cells?
Energy released by chemical reactions within a cell is captured and transported within the cell by unstable energy-carrier molecules, such as ATP and the electron carriers NADH and $FADH_2$. These molecules are the major means by which cells couple exergonic and endergonic reactions occurring at different places in the cell.

6.4 How Do Enzymes Promote Biochemical Reactions?
Cells control their metabolic reactions by regulating the synthesis and the use of enzyme proteins, which are biological catalysts that help overcome activation energy. High activation energies slow many reactions, even exergonic ones, to an imperceptible rate under normal environmental conditions. Catalysts lower the activation energy and thereby speed up chemical reactions without being permanently changed themselves. Organisms synthesize enzyme catalysts that promote one or a few specific reactions. The reactants temporarily bind to the active site of the enzyme, making it easier to form the new chemical bonds of the products and, thus, reducing activation energy. Enzymes also allow the breakdown of energy-rich molecules such as glucose in a series of small steps so that energy is released gradually and can be captured in ATP for use in endergonic reactions.

6.5 How Do Cells Regulate Their Metabolic Reactions?
Enzyme action is regulated in several ways; these include altering the rate of enzyme synthesis, activating previously inactive enzymes, competitive and noncompetitive inhibition, and allosteric regulation, which includes feedback inhibition. Many poisons act as enzyme inhibitors. These include methanol, some nerve gases, and insecticides. Ibuprofen and cancer chemotherapy drugs also act as competitive enzyme inhibitors. Environmental conditions—including pH, salt concentration, and temperature—can promote or inhibit enzyme function by altering the enzyme's three-dimensional structure.

Key Terms

activation energy   *101*
active site   *104*
adenosine diphosphate (ADP)   *102*
adenosine triphosphate (ATP)   *101*
allosteric regulation   *107*
catalyst   *103*
chemical energy   *98*
chemical reaction   *100*
closed system   *99*
coenzyme   *104*
competitive inhibition   *107*
coupled reaction   *102*
denature   *108*
electron carrier   *102*
endergonic   *100*
energy   *98*
energy-carrier molecule   *101*
entropy   *99*
enzyme   *103*

exergonic   *100*
feedback inhibition   *107*
first law of thermodynamics   *99*
kinetic energy   *98*
lactose intolerance   *106*
law of conservation of energy   *99*
laws of thermodynamics   *99*
metabolic pathway   *105*
metabolism   *105*
noncompetitive inhibition   *107*
phenylketonuria (PKU)   *106*
potential energy   *98*
product   *100*
reactant   *100*
second law of thermodynamics   *99*
substrate   *104*
work   *98*

Thinking Through the Concepts

Fill-in-the-Blank

1. According to the first law of thermodynamics, energy can neither be _____ nor _____. Energy occurs in two major forms: _____, the energy of movement, and _____, or stored energy.

2. According to the second law of thermodynamics, when energy changes forms it tends to be converted from _____ useful to _____ useful forms. This leads to the conclusion that matter spontaneously tends to become less _____. This tendency is called _____.

3. The energy needed to start any chemical reaction is called _____ energy. This energy is required to force the _____ of the reactants together. This energy is usually supplied by _____.

4. Once started, some reactions release energy and are called _____ reactions. Others require a net input of energy and are called _____ reactions. Which type will continue spontaneously once it starts? _____ Which type allows the formation of complex biological molecules from simpler molecules (for example, proteins from amino acids)? _____ When the energy released from one reaction provides the energy required by another, the two reactions are described as _____ reactions.

5. The abbreviation "ATP" stands for _____. This molecule is the principal _____ molecule in living cells. The molecule is synthesized by cells from _____ and _____. This synthesis requires _____, which is then stored in the molecule of ATP.

6. Enzymes are (type of biological molecule) _____. Enzymes promote reactions in cells by lowering the _____. Each enzyme possesses a specialized region called a(n) _____ into which the reactant molecules fit. Each of these specialized regions has a distinctive _____ and a distinctive distribution of _____ that make it quite specific for its substrate molecules.

Review Questions

1. Explain why organisms do not violate the second law of thermodynamics. What is the ultimate energy source for most forms of life on Earth?

2. Define *metabolism*, and explain how reactions can be coupled to one another.

3. What is activation energy? How do catalysts affect activation energy? How do catalysts change the rate of reactions?

4. Describe some exergonic and endergonic reactions that occur regularly in plants and animals.

5. Describe the structure and function of enzymes. How is enzyme activity regulated?

Applying the Concepts

1. One of your nerdiest friends walks in while you are vacuuming. Trying to impress her, you casually mention that you are infusing energy into your room to create a lower-entropy state, with the energy coming from electricity. She comments that, ultimately, you are taking advantage of the increase in entropy of the sun to clean your room. What is she talking about? (Look for clues in Chapter 7.)

2. As you learned in Chapter 3, the subunits of virtually all organic molecules are joined by condensation reactions and can be broken apart by hydrolysis reactions. Why, then, does your digestive system produce separate enzymes to digest proteins, fats, and carbohydrates?

3. Suppose someone tried to refute evolution using the following argument: "According to evolutionary theory, organisms have increased in complexity through time. However, the increase in complexity contradicts the second law of thermodynamics. Therefore, evolution is impossible." Is this a valid statement?

4. When a brown bear eats a salmon, does the bear acquire all the energy contained in the body of the fish? Why or why not? What implications do you think this answer would have for the relative abundance (by weight) of predators and their prey?

(MB) *Go to www.masteringbiology.com for practice quizzes, activities, eText, videos, current events, and more.*

Capturing Solar Energy: Photosynthesis

Did the Dinosaurs Die from Lack of Sunlight?

ABOUT 65 MILLION YEARS AGO, the Cretaceous period came to a violent end, and life on Earth suffered a catastrophic blow. Within a short time, most of the species on the planet became extinct. This devastating mass extinction eliminated more than 70% of the species then existing, including the dinosaurs. *Triceratops*, *Tyrannosaurus*, and all the other dinosaur species disappeared forever. Land and sea were nearly emptied of life, and it would be many millions of years before new species arose to take the places of those that had disappeared.

Most scientists believe that this devastation began when a gigantic meteorite, roughly six miles in diameter, entered the atmosphere and crashed into Earth. As the meteorite plowed into the ocean at the tip of the Yucatán Peninsula in southeastern Mexico, it dug a crater a mile deep and 120 miles long. Any organism in the immediate area was, of course, killed by the blast wave from the impact. This kind of direct destruction, however, must have been limited to a relatively small area. How, then, did the meteorite impact eliminate thousands of species all over the globe? In all likelihood, the most serious damage was done not by the meteorite itself, but by the lingering effects of its sudden arrival. In particular, the meteorite's most damaging long-term effect was disruption of the most important chemical reaction on Earth: photosynthesis.

What exactly does photosynthesis do? What makes it so important that interrupting it may have brought down the mighty dinosaurs? To find out, read on.

▲ A giant meteorite may have ended the reign of *Tyrannosaurus* and the other dinosaurs.

At a Glance

7.1 WHAT IS PHOTOSYNTHESIS?

All cells require energy to live, but as you learned in Chapter 6, the first law of thermodynamics tells us that energy cannot be created. Therefore, life relies on energy from outside sources. For nearly all forms of life on Earth, energy is derived from sunlight, either directly or indirectly. The only organisms capable of directly trapping this abundant energy source are those that perform **photosynthesis,** the process by which solar energy is trapped and stored as chemical energy in the bonds of organic molecules such as sugar. The evolution of photosynthesis made life as we know it possible. This amazing process provides not only fuel for life, but the oxygen required to "burn" this fuel, as we will describe in Chapter 8. Photosynthesis occurs in plants, photosynthetic protists, and certain types of bacteria. Here, we will concentrate on the most familiar of these: land plants.

Leaves and Chloroplasts Are Adaptations for Photosynthesis

Photosynthesis in plants takes place within **chloroplasts,** most of which are contained within leaf cells. The leaves of most land plants are only a few cells thick, a structure that is elegantly adapted to the demands of photosynthesis (**Fig. 7-1**). The flattened shape of leaves exposes a large surface area to the sun, and their thinness ensures that sunlight can penetrate to reach the light-trapping chloroplasts inside. Both the upper and lower surfaces of a leaf consist of a layer of transparent cells, the **epidermis.** The outer surface of both epidermal layers is covered by the **cuticle,** a transparent, waxy, waterproof covering that reduces the evaporation of water from the leaf.

A leaf obtains the CO_2 necessary for photosynthesis from the air, through adjustable pores in the epidermis called **stomata** (singular, **stoma;** Greek for "mouth"; **Fig. 7-2** on page 115). Inside the leaf are layers of cells collectively called **mesophyll** (which means "middle of the leaf"). The mesophyll cells contain most of a leaf's chloroplasts and, consequently, photosynthesis occurs principally in these cells. Vascular bundles, which form veins in the leaf, (**Fig. 7-1b**), supply water and minerals to the mesophyll cells and carry the sugars they produce to other parts of the plant. Cells that surround these bundles are called **bundle sheath cells,** and in most plants, these lack chloroplasts.

A single mesophyll cell often has 40 to 50 chloroplasts (**Fig. 7-1c**), which are so small (about 5 micrometers in diameter) that 2,500 of them lined up would span an average thumbnail. As described in Chapter 4, chloroplasts are organelles that consist of a double outer membrane enclosing a semifluid medium, the **stroma.** Embedded in the stroma are disk-shaped, interconnected membranous sacs called **thylakoids** (**Fig. 7-1d**). Each of these sacs encloses a fluid-filled region called the thylakoid space. The chemical reactions of photosynthesis that depend on light (light reactions) occur in and adjacent to the membranes of the thylakoids. The reactions of the Calvin cycle that capture carbon from CO_2 and produce sugar occur in the surrounding stroma.

(a) Leaves

stoma

outer membrane
inner membrane
thylakoid
stroma

(d) Chloroplast

channel
interconnecting
thylakoids

cuticle

upper
epidermis

mesophyll
cells

lower
epidermis

stoma
chloroplasts
bundle sheath cells

vascular bundle
(vein)

(b) Internal leaf structure

(c) Mesophyll cell containing chloroplasts

▲ FIGURE 7-1 **An overview of photosynthetic structures (a)** In land plants, photosynthesis occurs primarily in the leaves. **(b)** A section of a leaf, showing mesophyll cells, where chloroplasts are concentrated, and the waterproof cuticle that coats the leaf on both surfaces. **(c)** A light micrograph of a single mesophyll cell, packed with chloroplasts. **(d)** A single chloroplast, showing the stroma and thylakoids where photosynthesis occurs.

Photosynthesis Consists of the Light Reactions and the Calvin Cycle

Starting with the simple molecules of carbon dioxide (CO_2) and water (H_2O), photosynthesis converts the energy of sunlight into chemical energy stored in the bonds of glucose ($C_6H_{12}O_6$) and releases oxygen (O_2) as a by-product (**Fig. 7-3**). The simplest overall chemical reaction for photosynthesis is:

$$6\ CO_2 + 6\ H_2O + \text{light energy} \rightarrow C_6H_{12}O_6 + 6\ O_2$$

This simple equation obscures the fact that photosynthesis actually involves dozens of individual reactions catalyzed by dozens of enzymes. These reactions occur in two distinct stages: the light reactions and the Calvin cycle. Each stage occurs within different regions of the chloroplast, but the two processes are connected through an important link: energy-carrier molecules.

In the **light reactions,** chlorophyll and other molecules embedded in the membranes of the chloroplast thylakoids capture sunlight energy and convert some of it into chemical energy stored in the energy-carrier molecules ATP (adenosine triphosphate) and NADPH (nicotinamide adenine dinucleotide phosphate). Water is split apart, and oxygen gas is released as a by-product. In the reactions of the **Calvin cycle,** enzymes in the fluid stroma located outside the thylakoids use CO_2 from the atmosphere and chemical energy from the energy-carrier

(a) Stomata open

(b) Stomata closed

◀ FIGURE 7-2 **Stomata (a)** Open stomata allow CO_2 to diffuse in and oxygen to diffuse out. **(b)** Closed stomata reduce water loss by evaporation, but prevent CO_2 from entering and oxygen from leaving.

molecules to drive the synthesis of a three-carbon sugar that will be used to make glucose. Figure 7-3 shows the relationship between the light reactions and the Calvin cycle, illustrating the interdependence of the two processes and placing each in its appropriate location within the chloroplast. Simply put, the "photo" part of photosynthesis refers to the capture of light energy by the light reactions in the thylakoid membranes. These reactions use light energy to "charge up" the energy-carrier molecules ADP (adenosine diphosphate) and NADP⁺ (the energy-depleted form of NADPH) to form ATP and NADPH. The "synthesis" part of photosynthesis refers to the Calvin cycle, which captures carbon and uses it to synthesize sugar, powered by energy provided by ATP and NADPH. The depleted carriers ADP and NADP⁺ are then recharged by the light reactions into ATP and NADPH, which will fuel the synthesis of more sugar molecules.

Now that you have an overview of photosynthesis, let's look at each stage in greater detail.

Case Study continued
Did the Dinosaurs Die from Lack of Sunlight?

More than 2 billion years ago, some bacterial (prokaryotic) cells, through chance mutations in their genetic makeup, acquired the ability to harness the energy of sunlight. Exploiting this abundant energy source, early photosynthetic cells filled the seas. As their numbers increased, oxygen began to accumulate in the atmosphere. Later, plants evolved, made the transition to land, and eventually grew in luxuriant profusion. By the time of the dinosaurs, plants had become abundant and provided enough food to support plant-eating giants, such as the 85-foot-long, 35-ton *Apatosaurus*, on which *Tyrannosaurus* may have preyed.

▲ FIGURE 7-3 **An overview of the relationship between the light reactions and the Calvin cycle** The simple molecules that provide the raw ingredients for photosynthesis (H_2O and CO_2) enter at different stages of the process and are used in different parts of the chloroplast. You can also see here that the O_2 liberated by photosynthesis is derived from H_2O, while the carbon used in the synthesis of sugar is obtained from CO_2. In later figures in this chapter, you will see smaller versions of this figure, indicating where the specific processes are occurring.

7.2 LIGHT REACTIONS: HOW IS LIGHT ENERGY CONVERTED TO CHEMICAL ENERGY?

The light reactions capture the energy of sunlight, storing it as chemical energy in two different energy-carrier molecules: ATP and NADPH. The molecules that make these reactions possible, including light-capturing pigments and enzymes, are anchored in a precise array within the membranes of the thylakoid. As you read this section, notice how the thylakoid membranes and their enclosed spaces support these crucial reactions.

Light Is Captured by Pigments in Chloroplasts

The sun emits energy in a broad spectrum of electromagnetic radiation. The **electromagnetic spectrum** ranges from short-wavelength gamma rays, through ultraviolet, visible, and infrared light, to very long-wavelength radio waves (**Fig. 7-4**). Light and other electromagnetic waves are composed of individual packets of energy called **photons.** The energy of a photon corresponds to its wavelength: short-wavelength photons, such as gamma and X-rays, are very energetic, whereas longer-wavelength photons such as radio waves carry lower energies. Visible light consists of wavelengths with energies that are strong enough to alter biological **pigment molecules** (light-absorbing molecules) such

as chlorophyll, but weak enough not to break the bonds of crucial molecules such as DNA. It is no coincidence that these wavelengths, with just the right amount of energy, not only power photosynthesis, but also stimulate the pigments in our eyes, allowing us to see.

One of three events occurs when a specific wavelength of light strikes an object such as a leaf; the light may be absorbed (captured), reflected (bounced back), or transmitted (passed through). Light that is absorbed can heat up the object or drive biological processes, such as photosynthesis. Light that is reflected or transmitted is not captured, and thus can reach the eyes of an observer, allowing her to perceive this light as the color of the object .

Chloroplasts contain various pigment molecules that absorb different wavelengths of light. **Chlorophyll a,** the key light-capturing pigment molecule in chloroplasts, strongly absorbs violet, blue, and red light, but reflects green, thus giving green leaves their color (see Fig. 7-4). Chloroplasts also contain other molecules, collectively called **accessory pigments,** which absorb additional wavelengths of light energy and transfer them to chlorophyll *a*. Chlorophyll *b* is a slightly different form of green chlorophyll that serves as an accessory pigment, absorbing blue and red-orange wavelengths of light that are missed by chlorophyll *a*, and reflecting yellow-green light. **Carotenoids** are accessory pigments found in all chloroplasts. They absorb blue and green light and appear mostly yellow or orange because they reflect these wavelengths to our eyes (see Fig. 7-4).

Although carotenoids are present in leaves, their color is usually masked by the more abundant green chlorophyll. In the autumn, as leaves begin to die, chlorophyll breaks down before carotenoids do, revealing the bright yellow and orange carotenoid pigments as fall colors. The chlorophyll in the aspen leaves in **Figure 7-5** has broken down and faded, revealing yellow carotenoids. (Red and purple fall leaf colors are not involved in photosynthesis.)

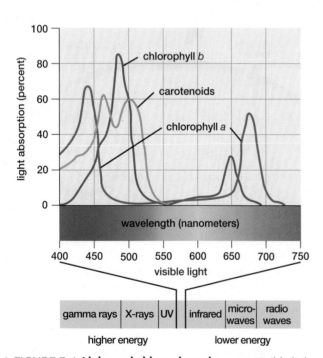

▲ FIGURE 7-4 **Light and chloroplast pigments** Visible light, a small part of the electromagnetic spectrum, consists of wavelengths that correspond to the colors of the rainbow. Chlorophyll *a* and *b* (green and blue curves, respectively) strongly absorb violet, blue, and red light. Carotenoids (orange curve) absorb blue and green wavelengths.

▲ FIGURE 7-5 **Loss of chlorophyll reveals yellow carotenoid pigments** As winter approaches, chlorophyll in these aspen leaves breaks down, revealing yellow carotenoid pigments.

You may have heard of the carotenoid beta-carotene. This pigment helps capture light in chloroplasts, and it produces the orange color of vegetables such as carrots. Beta-carotene is converted by animals into vitamin A, which forms the basis of the light-capturing pigment in the eyes of animals, including people. In a beautiful symmetry, the carotenoids that capture light energy in plants are converted into substances that capture light in animals as well.

The Light Reactions Occur in Association with the Thylakoid Membranes

Light energy is captured and converted into chemical energy by the light reactions that occur in and on the thylakoid membranes. These membranes contain many **photosystems,** each consisting of a cluster of chlorophyll and accessory pigment molecules surrounded by various proteins. Two photosystems—photosystem II (PS II) and photosystem I (PS I)—work together during the light reactions. (These photosystems are named in the order in which they were discovered; however, the order in which they proceed within the light reactions is from photosystem II to photosystem I.)

Each type of photosystem has a different electron transport chain located adjacent to it. These **electron transport chains (ETC)** each consist of a series of electron carrier molecules embedded in the thylakoid membrane. In this discussion, we will refer to these as ETC II and ETC I, according to the photosystem with which they are associated. Thus, within the thylakoid membrane, the overall path of electrons is as follows: PS II → ETC II → PS I → ETC I → NADP$^+$ (see Fig. 7-7).

You can think of the light reactions as a sort of pinball game. Energy (light) is transferred to a ball (an electron) by spring-driven pistons (chlorophyll molecules). The ball is propelled upward (enters a higher energy level). As the ball bounces back downhill, the energy it releases can be used to turn a wheel (generate ATP) or ring a bell (generate NADPH). With this overall scheme in mind, let's look more closely at the actual sequence of events in the light reactions.

Photosystem II Uses Light Energy to Create a Hydrogen Ion Gradient and Split Water

The light reactions begin when photons of light are absorbed by pigment molecules clustered in photosystem II (**Fig. 7-6 ❶**). The energy hops from one pigment molecule to the next until it is funneled into the reaction center (**Fig. 7-6 ❷**). The **reaction center** within each photosystem consists of a pair of specialized chlorophyll *a* molecules and a **primary electron acceptor** molecule embedded in a complex of proteins. When it reaches the reaction center, the energy from light boosts an electron from one of the reaction center chlorophylls to the primary electron acceptor, which captures the energized electron (**Fig. 7-6 ❸**).

The reaction center of photosystem II must be continuously supplied with electrons to replace the ones that jump out of it when they are energized by light. These replacement electrons come from water (see photosystem II in Fig. 7-6). An enzyme associated with PS II splits water molecules, liberating electrons that will replace those lost by the reaction center chlorophyll molecules. This reaction also releases hydrogen ions that contribute to the H$^+$ gradient that drives ATP synthesis (see Fig. 7-7 ❷). For every two molecules of water that are split, one molecule of oxygen gas (O$_2$) is produced.

Once the primary electron acceptor captures the electron, it passes it on to the first molecule of ETC II. The electron then travels from one electron carrier molecule to the next, losing energy as it goes (**Fig. 7-6 ❹**). Some of this energy is harnessed to pump hydrogen ions (H$^+$) across the thylakoid membrane and into the thylakoid space, where they will be used to generate ATP (to be discussed shortly; **Fig. 7-6 ❺** and see Fig. 7-7). Finally, the energy-depleted electron leaves ETC II and enters the reaction center of photosystem I, where it replaces the electron ejected when light strikes photosystem I.

Photosystem I Generates NADPH

Meanwhile, light has also been striking the pigment molecules of PS I (**Fig. 7-6 ❻**). As in PS II, light energy is captured by these pigment molecules and is funneled to a chlorophyll *a* molecule in the reaction center. This ejects an energized electron that is picked up by the primary electron acceptor of PS I (**Fig. 7-6 ❼**). (The energized electron is immediately replaced by an energy-depleted electron from ETC II.) From the primary electron acceptor of PS I, the energized electron is passed along ETC I (**Fig. 7-6 ❽**) until it reaches NADP$^+$. The energy-carrier molecule NADPH is formed when each NADP$^+$ molecule (dissolved in the fluid stroma) picks up two energetic electrons, along with one hydrogen ion (**Fig. 7-6 ❾**).

The Hydrogen Ion Gradient Generates ATP by Chemiosmosis

Figure 7-7 shows the movement of electrons through the thylakoid membrane. It also shows how the energy of these electrons is used to create the H$^+$ gradient that drives ATP synthesis, in a process called **chemiosmosis.** As the energized electron travels along ETC II, some of the energy it liberates is used to pump hydrogen ions into the thylakoid space

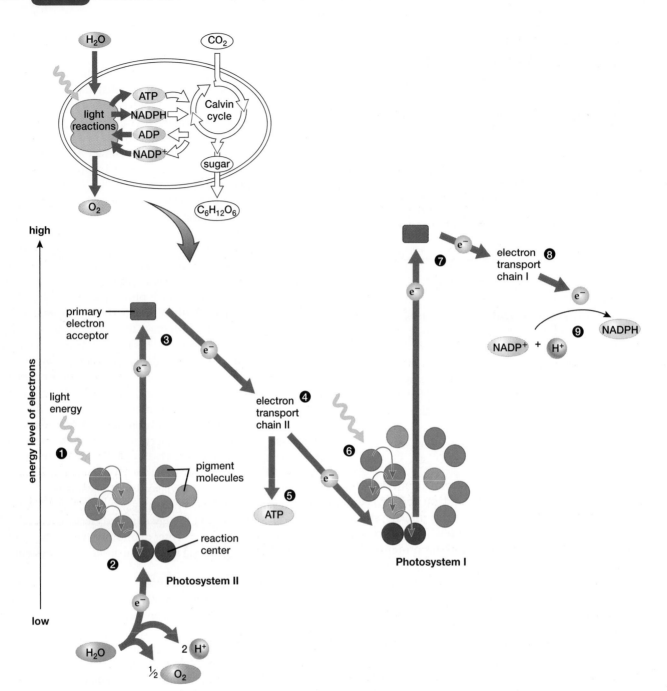

▲ **FIGURE 7-6 Energy transfer and the light reactions of photosynthesis** Light reactions involve a series of molecules and reactions that occur within or adjacent to the thylakoid membrane. ❶ Light is absorbed by photosystem II, and the energy is passed to an electron in one of the reaction center chlorophyll a molecules. ❷ The energized electron is ejected from the chlorophyll a molecule. ❸ The electron is captured by a primary electron acceptor, also in the reaction center. ❹ The electron is passed through the electron transport chain (ETC II). ❺ As the ETC II transfers the electron along, some of the released energy is used to pump H^+ into the thylakoid space. In a separate process, the resulting H^+ gradient is used to generate ATP. The energy-depleted electron then enters the reaction center of photosystem I, replacing an ejected electron. ❻ Light strikes photosystem I, and the energy is passed to the electron in the reaction center chlorophyll molecules. ❼ The energized electron is ejected from the reaction center and is captured by the primary electron acceptor. ❽ The electron moves down the ETC I. ❾ NADPH is formed when $NADP^+$ in the stroma picks up two energized electrons, along with one H^+.

▲ FIGURE 7-7 **Events of the light reactions occur in and near the thylakoid membrane** Here, you can trace the pathway of an energized electron as it travels through the molecules associated with the thylakoid membrane. ❶ Energy released as the electron passes through ETC II is harnessed to pump H^+ across the thylakoid membrane and into the thylakoid space. ❷ A concentration gradient of H^+ is generated as electrons are passed along the ETC II, and their energy is used to pump H^+ across the membrane into the thylakoid space. ❸ During chemiosmosis, H^+ flow down their concentration gradient through an ATP synthase channel, which uses energy from the gradient to generate ATP. About one ATP molecule is synthesized for every three hydrogen ions that pass through the channel.

(Fig. 7-7 ❶), creating a high concentration of H^+ inside the space (Fig. 7-7 ❷), and a low concentration in the surrounding stroma. During chemiosmosis, H^+ flow back down their concentration gradient through a special channel that spans the thylakoid membrane. This channel, called **ATP synthase,** generates ATP from ADP and phosphate dissolved in the stroma as the H^+ flow through the channel (Fig. 7-7 ❸).

How is a gradient of H^+ used to synthesize ATP? Compare the H^+ gradient to water stored behind a dam at a hydroelectric plant (Fig. 7-8). The water flows out over turbines, rotating them. The turbines convert the energy of moving water into electrical energy. Hydrogen ions in the thylakoid space (like water stored behind a dam) can move down their gradient into the stroma only through ATP synthase channels. Like turbines generating electricity, ATP synthase captures the energy liberated by the flow of H^+ and uses it to drive ATP synthesis from ADP plus phosphate.

▲ FIGURE 7-8 **Energy stored in a water "gradient" can be used to generate electricity**

Summing Up **Light Reactions**

Summing Up **Light Reactions**

- Chlorophyll and carotenoid pigments of PS II absorb light that energizes and ejects an electron from a reaction center chlorophyll molecule. The energized electron is caught by the primary electron acceptor molecule.
- The electron is passed from the primary electron acceptor to the adjacent ETC II, where it moves from molecule to molecule, releasing energy. Some of the energy is used to create a hydrogen ion gradient across the thylakoid membrane. This gradient is used to drive ATP synthesis by chemiosmosis.
- The splitting of water by enzymes associated with PS II releases electrons (replacing those ejected from the reaction center chlorophylls), supplies H^+ that enhance the H^+ gradient for ATP production, and generates oxygen.
- Chlorophyll and carotenoid pigments in PS I absorb light that energizes and ejects an electron from a reaction center chlorophyll molecule. The electron is replaced by an energy-depleted electron from ETC II.
- The energized electron passes from the primary electron acceptor into the ETC I.
- For every two energized electrons that exit the ETC I, one molecule of the energy carrier NADPH is formed, from $NADP^+$ and H^+.
- The products of the light reactions are the energy carriers NADPH and ATP; O_2 is released as a by-product (**Fig. 7-9**).

▲ **FIGURE 7-9 Oxygen is a by-product of photosynthesis**
Oxygen released by the leaves of this aquatic plant (*Elodea*) forms bubbles in the surrounding water.

QUESTION Would you expect bubbles of oxygen to form in the dark? Explain.

7.3 THE CALVIN CYCLE: HOW IS CHEMICAL ENERGY STORED IN SUGAR MOLECULES?

Although we inhale some carbon dioxide with every breath, and drink it in carbonated beverages, our bodies can't capture it in organic molecules; only photosynthetic organisms can do this. In fact, every carbon atom in your body was originally captured from the atmosphere by a photosynthetic organism using a process called carbon fixation.

The Calvin Cycle Captures Carbon Dioxide

The ATP and NADPH synthesized during the light reactions are dissolved in the fluid stroma that surrounds the thylakoids. There, these energy carriers power the synthesis of a simple, three-carbon sugar (glyceraldehyde-3-phosphate or G3P) from CO_2. This is accomplished through a series of reactions, called the Calvin cycle, which is catalyzed by enzymes dissolved in the stroma. For every three CO_2 molecules captured by the Calvin cycle, one molecule of G3P is produced.

This metabolic pathway is described as a "cycle" because it begins and ends with the same molecule, a five-carbon sugar called ribulose bisphosphate (RuBP). RuBP is recycled continuously. The Calvin cycle is best understood if we divide it into three parts: (1) carbon fixation, (2) the synthesis of G3P (used to synthesize glucose and other molecules), and (3) the regeneration of RuBP (**Fig. 7-10**). For simplicity, in our cycle we show the number of molecules required to produce one molecule of G3P as an end product.

Carbon Fixation During **carbon fixation**, carbon from CO_2 is incorporated or "fixed" into a larger organic molecule. The Calvin cycle uses the enzyme **rubisco** to combine each CO_2 molecule with an RuBP molecule. This produces an unstable six-carbon molecule that immediately splits in half, forming two molecules of PGA (phosphoglyceric acid; a three-carbon molecule). Because carbon fixation generates this three-carbon PGA molecule, the Calvin cycle is often referred to as the **C_3 pathway** (**Fig. 7-10**).

Case Study continued
Did the Dinosaurs Die from Lack of Sunlight?

Any event that reduces light availability—such as the dust, smoke, and ash that would accompany a meteorite collision with Earth—decreases the ability of plants to synthesize glucose, starch, and other high-energy molecules that they use as food. Because the food that plants synthesized for themselves also fed the dinosaurs, a loss of the ability to photosynthesize would spell disaster for both.

◄ FIGURE 7-10 **The Calvin cycle fixes carbon from CO_2 and produces G3P**

1 Carbon fixation combines three CO_2 with three RuBP using the enzyme rubisco

2 Energy from ATP and NADPH is used to convert the six molecules of PGA to six molecules of G3P

3 Using the energy from ATP, five of the six molecules of G3P are converted to three molecules of RuBP

4 One molecule of G3P leaves the cycle

5 Two molecules of G3P combine to form glucose and other molecules

Synthesis of G3P In a series of enzyme-catalyzed reactions, energy donated by ATP and NADPH (generated by the light reactions) is used to convert six PGA molecules into six molecules of the three-carbon sugar G3P (**Fig. 7-10 ❷**).

Regeneration of RuBP Through a series of enzyme-catalyzed reactions requiring ATP from the light reactions, five of the six G3P molecules are used to regenerate the RuBP necessary to repeat

the cycle (**Fig. 7-10 ❸**). The remaining G3P molecule, which is the end product of photosynthesis, exits the cycle (**Fig. 7-10 ❹**).

Carbon Fixed During the Calvin Cycle Is Used to Synthesize Sugar

Using simple "carbon accounting," if you start and end one turn of the cycle with three molecules of RuBP and capture three molecules of CO_2, one molecule of G3P is left over. In reactions that occur outside of the Calvin cycle, two G3P molecules can be combined to form one six-carbon glucose molecule (**Fig. 7-10 ❺**). Most of these are then used to form sucrose (table sugar; a disaccharide storage molecule consisting of a glucose linked to a fructose), or linked together in long chains to form starch (another storage molecule) or cellulose (a major component of plant cell walls). Most of the synthesis of glucose from G3P and the subsequent synthesis of more complex molecules from glucose occurs outside the chloroplast. Later, glucose molecules may be broken down during cellular respiration to provide energy for the plant cells.

In recent years, countries throughout the world have been attempting to reduce their reliance on fossil fuels and to obtain more of their energy from the products of photosynthesis by converting plant material into oil and ethanol. These "biofuels" have the potential advantage of not adding more carbon dioxide (a "greenhouse gas" that contributes to global warming) to the atmosphere, but do they live up to their promise? We explore this in "Earth Watch: Biofuels—Are Their Benefits Bogus?" on p. 124.

Summing Up **The Calvin Cycle**

The Calvin cycle can be divided into three stages:

- **Carbon fixation:** Three RuBP capture three CO_2, forming six PGA.
- **G3P synthesis:** A series of reactions, driven by energy from ATP and NADPH (from the light reactions), produces six G3P, one of which leaves the cycle and is available to form glucose.
- **RuBP regeneration:** ATP energy is used to regenerate three RuBP molecules from the remaining five G3P molecules, allowing the cycle to continue.

Two G3P molecules produced by the Calvin cycle combine to form glucose.

BioFlix ™ Photosynthesis

7.4 WHY DO SOME PLANTS USE ALTERNATE PATHWAYS FOR CARBON FIXATION?

Plant leaf structure represents a compromise between obtaining adequate light and CO_2 and minimizing water loss through evaporation. Most leaves have a large surface area for intercepting light, a waterproof cuticle to reduce evaporation, and adjustable stomata. When there is adequate water, the stomata open, letting in CO_2. If the plant is in danger of drying out, the stomata close (see Fig. 7-2). Closing the stomata reduces evaporation, but prevents CO_2 intake and also limits the ability of the leaf to release O_2, a by-product of photosynthesis.

When Stomata Are Closed to Conserve Water, Wasteful Photorespiration Occurs

In hot, dry conditions, stomata remain closed much of the time. As a result, the amount of CO_2 inside the leaf decreases and the amount of O_2 increases. Unfortunately, the enzyme rubisco that catalyzes carbon fixation is not very selective. Either CO_2 or O_2 can bind to the active site of rubisco and combine with RuBP, an example of competitive inhibition (see Fig. 6-13b). When O_2 (rather than CO_2) is combined with RuBP, a wasteful process called **photorespiration** occurs. Photorespiration prevents the Calvin cycle from synthesizing sugar, effectively derailing photosynthesis. Plants, particularly fragile seedlings, may die under these circumstances because they are unable to capture enough energy to meet their metabolic needs.

Rubisco is the most abundant enzyme on Earth, and arguably one of the most important. It catalyzes the reaction by which carbon enters the biosphere, and all life is based on carbon. Why, then, is rubisco so nonselective? Scientists hypothesize that, because Earth's early atmosphere contained far less oxygen and far more carbon dioxide, there was very little natural selection pressure for the active site of rubisco to favor carbon dioxide over oxygen. Although in today's atmosphere such a change would be highly adaptive, apparently the necessary mutations have never occurred. Instead, over evolutionary time, flowering plants have evolved two different but related mechanisms to circumvent wasteful photorespiration: the C_4 pathway and crassulacean acid metabolism (CAM; named after the family of plants in which it was discovered). Each of these alternate pathways is found in roughly 5% of the families of flowering plants. Although both of these pathways involve several additional steps and consume more ATP than does the C_3 pathway alone, they confer an important advantage under hot, dry conditions.

C_4 Plants Capture Carbon and Synthesize Sugar in Different Cells

In typical plants, known as **C_3 plants,** the Calvin cycle occurs in mesophyll cells, where it both fixes carbon (via the C_3 pathway) and generates the G3P molecules used to synthesize the sugar glucose. Under dry, hot conditions, photorespiration causes photosynthesis in C_3 plants to slow dramatically. Some plants, called **C_4 plants,** avoid this by using a separate series of reactions, called the C_4 pathway, to selectively capture carbon in mesophyll cells. This fixed carbon is then shuttled into bundle sheath cells (see Fig. 7-1) where it enters the Calvin cycle with little competition from oxygen (**Fig. 7-11a**).

How is carbon captured and shuttled? C_3 and C_4 leaves have both structural and biochemical differences. Unlike C_3 plants (whose bundle sheath cells lack chloroplasts), C_4 plants have chloroplasts in both their bundle sheath cells and their mesophyll cells. Another difference is that the mesophyll chloroplasts of C_4 plants lack the enzymes used in the Calvin cycle; only the bundle sheath chloroplasts of C_4 plants contain Calvin cycle enzymes.

(a) C$_4$ plants   (b) CAM plants

▲ **FIGURE 7-11 The C$_4$ pathway and the CAM pathway** Some of the reactions illustrated here occur in the cytoplasm, whereas others, including all those of the Calvin cycle, occur in chloroplasts. If you compare parts **(a)** and **(b)**, you will see that both use the C$_4$ pathway, in which the three-carbon (3C) PEP molecule is combined (by the selective enzyme PEP carboxylase) with a one-carbon CO$_2$ molecule to become the four-carbon (4C) oxaloacetate. The oxaloacetate molecule is rearranged to generate the four-carbon malate molecule that will release CO$_2$ to be used in the Calvin cycle. After releasing its carbon as CO$_2$, the malate is transformed into a three-carbon pyruvate, which is eventually converted back to the three-carbon PEP. By creating a high level of CO$_2$ in **(a)** the bundle sheath cells of C$_4$ plants and **(b)** the mesophyll cells of CAM plants (during the day, when stomata are closed), each of these specialized photosynthetic pathways minimizes photorespiration.

QUESTION Why do C$_3$ plants have an advantage over C$_4$ plants under conditions that are *not* hot and dry?

In the **C$_4$ pathway,** mesophyll cells of C$_4$ plants fix carbon using an enzyme called PEP carboxylase that (unlike rubisco) is highly selective for CO$_2$ over O$_2$. PEP carboxylase catalyzes a reaction between CO$_2$ and a three-carbon molecule called phosphoenolpyruvate (PEP). This produces the four-carbon molecule oxaloacetate, from which the C$_4$ pathway gets its name. Oxaloacetate is rapidly converted into another four-carbon molecule, malate, which diffuses from the mesophyll cells into bundle sheath cells. The malate effectively acts as a shuttle for CO$_2$.

In the bundle sheath cells, malate is broken down, forming the three-carbon molecule pyruvate and releasing CO$_2$. This creates a high CO$_2$ concentration in the bundle sheath cells (up to 10 times higher than atmospheric CO$_2$). The high level of CO$_2$ allows rubisco in the C$_3$ pathway of the Calvin cycle to fix carbon, and thus generate sugar, with little competition from oxygen. The pyruvate is then actively transported back to the mesophyll cells. Here, more ATP energy is used to convert pyruvate back into PEP, allowing the cycle to continue.

CAM Plants Capture Carbon and Synthesize Sugar at Different Times

Like C$_4$ plants, CAM plants use the C$_4$ pathway to selectively capture CO$_2$ by combining it with PEP to form oxaloacetate. They also convert the oxaloacetate to malate, which breaks down, releasing CO$_2$ for use in the Calvin cycle to synthesize sugar. But in contrast to C$_4$ plants, CAM plants do not use different cell types to capture carbon and to synthesize sugar. Instead, they perform both of these activities in the same mesophyll cells, but at different times; carbon fixation occurs at night, and sugar synthesis occurs during the day (**Fig. 7-11b**).

At night, when temperatures are cooler and humidity is higher, the stomata of CAM plants open, allowing CO$_2$ to diffuse in, where it is captured in mesophyll cells using the C$_4$ pathway. The resulting oxaloacetate is converted to malate, which is then shuttled into the central vacuole where it is stored as malic acid until daytime. During the day, when stomata are closed to conserve water, the malic acid leaves the vacuole and re-enters the cytoplasm as

Earth Watch

Biofuels—Are Their Benefits Bogus?

When you drive your car, turn up the thermostat, or flick on your desk lamp, you are actually unleashing the energy of prehistoric sunlight trapped by photosynthetic organisms. Over hundreds of millions of years, heat and pressure converted their bodies—with their stored solar energy and carbon captured from ancient atmospheric CO_2—into coal, oil, and natural gas. Without human intervention, these fossil fuels would have remained trapped deep underground.

Global warming is big news, and a major contributor is a growing human population burning large amounts of fossil fuels that release CO_2 into the atmosphere. Carbon dioxide, a greenhouse gas, traps heat in the atmosphere that would otherwise radiate into space. Since the industrial revolution began in the mid-1800s, humans have increased the CO_2 content of the atmosphere by almost 37%, much of this by burning fossil fuels. As a result, Earth is growing warmer, and many biologists and climate scientists fear that a hotter future climate will place extraordinary stresses on Earth's inhabitants, including humans (see pp. 545–549).

To reduce CO_2 emissions and reliance on imported oil, governments throughout the world are promoting the use of biofuels. Bioethanol is produced by fermenting sugar- or starch-rich plants, such as sugar cane or corn, to produce alcohol (fermentation is described on pp. 136–139). Biodiesel fuel is made primarily from oil derived from plants such as soybeans, canola, or palms. Because the carbon stored in them was removed from the modern atmosphere by photosynthesis, burning biofuels simply restores CO_2 that was recently present in the atmosphere. Is this a solution to global warming?

The environmental and social benefits of burning food crops in our gas tanks are hotly debated. One concern is that this added demand will drive up food prices. In Nebraska, for example, ethanol refineries now consume about one-third of the state's corn production. But growing and converting this crop into ethanol uses up large quantities of fossil fuel, making it, at best, only slightly better than burning gasoline. The demand for corn as fuel has caused farmers to convert wheat and soybean fields to corn fields. In Indonesia, plans for enormous new palm plantations to make biodiesel threaten the rain forests of Borneo, home to endangered orangutans. In Brazil, soybean plantations are replacing large expanses of rain forest (Fig. E7-1). Ironically, clearing these forests for agriculture increases atmospheric CO_2 because rain forests trap far more carbon than the crops that replace them.

Biofuels would have far less environmental and social impact if they were not produced from food crops. Algae show great promise. These photosynthesizers can double their mass in a day or less. Some algae produce starch that can be fermented into ethanol; others produce oil that can become biodiesel. Another solution would be to cleave cellulose into its component sugars, which would allow ethanol to be generated from corn stalks, wood chips, or grasses. Several small cellulose biorefineries are now being brought online in the United States. Although the benefits of most biofuels produced today may not justify their environmental costs, there is hope that this will change as we develop better technologies to harness the energy captured by photosynthesis.

▲ **FIGURE E7-1 A Brazilian rain forest has been felled to make way for soybean fields**

malate. The malate is broken down, forming pyruvate and releasing CO_2, which enters the Calvin cycle to produce sugar. The pyruvate is then regenerated into PEP using ATP energy.

Alternate Pathways Adapt Plants to Different Environmental Conditions

Because they are so much more efficient at fixing carbon, you might think that C_4 plants and CAM plants should have taken over the world by now. However, plants using these pathways consume more energy than do C_3 plants. They only have the advantage when light energy is abundant but water is not. In environments where water is abundant or light levels are low, plants using the C_3 carbon fixation pathway dominate. These differing adaptations explain why your spring lawn of lush Kentucky bluegrass (a C_3 plant) may be taken over by spiky crabgrass (a C_4 plant) during a long, hot, dry summer. Plants using C_4 photosynthesis include corn, sugarcane, sorghum, some grasses, and some thistles. CAM plants include cacti, most succulents (such as the jade plant), and pineapples.

Case Study revisited
Did the Dinosaurs Die from Lack of Sunlight?

Paleontologists (scientists who study fossils) have cataloged the extinction of approximately 70% of the species existing at that time by the disappearance of their fossils at the end of the Cretaceous period. In sites from around the globe, researchers have found a thin layer of clay deposited around 65 million years ago; the clay has about 30 times the typical levels of a rare element called iridium, which is found in high concentrations in some meteorites. The clay also contains soot, such as would have been deposited in the aftermath of massive fires.

Did a meteorite wipe out the dinosaurs? Many scientists believe it did. Certainly, the evidence of an enormous meteorite impact, dated to 65 million years ago, is clear on the Yucatán Peninsula. But other scientists believe that more gradual climate changes, possibly triggered by intense volcanic activity, produced conditions that would no longer support the

enormous reptiles. Volcanoes also spew out soot and ash, and iridium is found in higher levels in Earth's molten mantle than on its surface, so furious volcanic activity could also explain the iridium layer.

Either scenario would significantly reduce the amount of sunlight and immediately impact the rate of photosynthesis. Large herbivores (plant eaters), such as *Triceratops*, which would have needed to consume hundreds of pounds of vegetation daily, would suffer if plant growth slowed significantly. Predators such as *Tyrannosaurus*, which fed on herbivores, would also be deprived of food. In the Cretaceous as now, interrupting this vital flow of energy would be catastrophic.

Consider This

Design an experiment to test the effects of light-blocking soot (such as may have filled Earth's atmosphere after a huge meteor strike) on photosynthesis. What might you measure to determine the relative amounts of photosynthesis that occurred under normal versus sooty conditions?

CHAPTER REVIEW

Summary of Key Concepts

7.1 What Is Photosynthesis?
Photosynthesis captures the energy of sunlight and uses it to convert the inorganic molecules of carbon dioxide and water into a high-energy sugar molecule, releasing oxygen as a by-product. In plants, photosynthesis takes place in the chloroplasts, using two major reaction sequences: the light reactions and the Calvin cycle.

7.2 Light Reactions: How Is Light Energy Converted to Chemical Energy?
The light reactions occur in the thylakoids of chloroplasts. Light excites electrons in chlorophyll molecules located in photosystems II and I. Energetic electrons jump to a primary electron acceptor, then move into adjacent electron transport chains. Energy lost as the electrons move through ETC II is used to pump hydrogen ions into the thylakoid space, creating an H^+ gradient across the thylakoid membrane. Hydrogen ions move down this concentration gradient through ATP synthase channels in the membrane, driving ATP synthesis. For every two energized electrons that pass through ETC I, one m olecule of the energy carrier NADPH is formed from $NADP^+$ and H^+. Electrons lost from photosystem II are replaced by electrons liberated by splitting water, which also generates H^+ and O_2.

7.3 The Calvin Cycle: How Is Chemical Energy Stored in Sugar Molecules?
The Calvin cycle, which occurs in the stroma of chloroplasts, uses energy from ATP and NADPH generated during the light reactions to drive the synthesis of G3P; two molecules of G3P combine to form glucose. The Calvin cycle has three major parts: (1) **Carbon fixation**: Carbon dioxide combines with ribulose

bisphosphate (RuBP) to form phosphoglyceric acid (PGA). (2) **Synthesis of G3P**: PGA is converted to glyceraldehyde-3-phosphate (G3P), using energy from ATP and NADPH. (3) **Regeneration of RuBP**: Five molecules of G3P are used to regenerate three molecules of RuBP, using ATP energy. One molecule of G3P exits the cycle; G3P may be used to synthesize glucose and other molecules.

BioFlix™ Photosynthesis

7.4 Why Do Some Plants Use Alternate Pathways for Carbon Fixation?
The enzyme rubisco, which catalyzes the reaction between RuBP and CO_2, can also catalyze a reaction, called photorespiration, between RuBP and O_2. Under hot, dry conditions, stomata remain closed, CO_2 concentrations fall, and O_2 concentrations rise, causing wasteful photorespiration, which prevents carbon fixation. C_4 and CAM plants minimize photorespiration. In the mesophyll cells of C_4 plants, CO_2 combines with phosphoenolpyruvic acid (PEP) to form a four-carbon oxaloacetate molecule, which is converted to malate and travels into adjacent bundle sheath cells. Here, the malate is broken down, releasing CO_2. This creates a high concentration of CO_2 in the bundle sheath cells. The CO_2 is then fixed using the Calvin cycle. Mesophyll cells of CAM plants open their stomata at night, and generate malate using the CO_2 that diffuses into the leaf. The mesophyll cells store the malate as malic acid in their central vacuoles. During the day, when stomata are closed, mesophyll cells break down the malate, releasing CO_2 for the Calvin cycle.

Key Terms

accessory pigment *116*	C_4 pathway *123*
ATP synthase *119*	C_4 plant *122*
bundle sheath cells *113*	Calvin cycle *114*
C_3 pathway *120*	carbon fixation *120*
C_3 plant *122*	carotenoids *116*

Thinking Through the Concepts

Fill-in-the-Blank

1. Plant leaves contain pores called _____ that allow the plant to release _____ and take in _____. In hot dry weather, these pores are closed to prevent _____. Photosynthesis occurs in organelles called _____ that are concentrated within the _____ cells of most plant leaves. In plants that use the C_4 pathway, these organelles are also found in _____ cells.

2. Chlorophyll captures wavelengths of light that correspond to which three colors? _____, _____, and _____ What color does chlorophyll reflect? _____ Accessory pigments that reflect yellow and orange are called _____.

3. During the first stage of photosynthesis, light is captured by pigment molecules clustered in _____ and funneled into the reaction center, a region containing special _____ molecules and a(n) _____ molecule. An electron energized by light passes through a series of molecules called the _____. Energy lost during transfers is used to create a gradient of _____. The process that uses this gradient to generate ATP is called _____.

4. The oxygen produced as a by-product of photosynthesis is derived from _____, and the carbons used to make glucose are derived from _____. The process of capturing carbon is called _____. In most plants, the enzyme that catalyzes carbon capture is _____, which is quite nonselective, binding _____ as well as CO_2.

5. Fill in the blanks with "C_4 plants," "CAM plants," or "both": Live in environments that are hot and dry: _____; capture carbon using the C_4 pathway: _____; carbon capture and the Calvin cycle occur in separate cell types: _____; carbon capture and the Calvin cycle occur in the same mesophyll cells: _____.

6. Light reactions generate the energy-carrier molecules _____ and _____, which are then used in the _____ cycle. Carbon fixation combines carbon dioxide with the five-carbon sugar _____. Two molecules of _____ can be combined to produce the six-carbon sugar _____.

Review Questions

1. Write the overall equation for photosynthesis. Does the overall equation differ between C_3 and C_4 plants?

2. Draw a simplified diagram of a chloroplast, and label it. Explain specifically how chloroplast structure is related to its function.

3. Summarize the light reactions and the Calvin cycle. In what part of the chloroplast does each occur?

4. What are the differences in carbon fixation among C_3, C_4, and CAM plants? Under what conditions does each mechanism of carbon fixation work most effectively?

5. Trace the flow of energy in chloroplasts from sunlight to ATP.

Applying the Concepts

1. Suppose an experiment is performed in which plant I is supplied with normal carbon dioxide but with water that contains radioactive oxygen atoms. Plant II is supplied with normal water but with carbon dioxide that contains radioactive oxygen atoms. Each plant is allowed to perform photosynthesis, and the oxygen gas and sugars produced are tested for radioactivity. Which plant would you expect to produce radioactive sugars, and which plant would you expect to produce radioactive oxygen gas? Why?

2. You continuously monitor the photosynthetic oxygen production from the leaf of a plant illuminated by white light. Explain how oxygen production will change—and why—if you place filters in front of the light source that transmit (a) red, (b) blue, and (c) green light onto the leaf.

3. Based on your knowledge of pH gleaned from Chapter 2, if you were to measure the pH in the space surrounded by the thylakoid membrane in an actively photosynthesizing plant, would you expect it to be acidic, basic, or neutral? Explain your answer.

4. You are called before the Ways and Means Committee of the House of Representatives to explain why the U.S. Department of Agriculture should continue to fund photosynthesis research. How would you justify the expense of using genetic engineering to modify the enzyme rubisco, making it selective for CO_2 and preventing it from reacting with O_2? Describe potential applied benefits of this research.

(MB) *Go to www.masteringbiology.com for practice quizzes, activities, eText, videos, current events, and more.*

Harvesting Energy: Glycolysis and Cellular Respiration

Case Study

When Athletes Boost Their Blood Counts: Do Cheaters Prosper?

JUST AN HOUR before the start of the 12th stage of the 2008 Tour de France, the Saunier-Duval team was in high spirits. Their star cyclist, Riccardo Riccò, had led the pack in two stages, including the grueling Stage 9, which crested two mountains over a 139-mile (224-km) course. But their optimism turned to consternation as they watched their top rider escorted away by police. Minutes later, the entire team withdrew from the race. Riccò's offense? Blood doping.

Blood doping packs more oxygen-carrying red blood cells into the bloodstream with the goal of enhancing athletic performance. Riccò accomplished this by injecting the drug CERA (continuous erythropoietin receptor activator), a synthetic version of erythropoietin. The natural hormone erythropoietin (EPO) stimulates bone marrow to produce red blood cells. A healthy body produces just enough EPO to ensure that red blood cells are replaced as they age and die. If a person moves to a higher altitude where each lungful of air provides less oxygen, the body compensates by increasing EPO and producing more red blood cells. An injection of synthetic EPO, however, can stimulate the production of a huge number of extra red blood cells, increasing the oxygen-carrying capacity of the blood beyond normal levels, and enhancing performance in sports that require endurance, such as cycling.

Why is endurance improved by extra oxygen molecules in the bloodstream? Think about this question as we examine the role of oxygen in supplying energy to muscle cells.

▲ Riccardo Riccò celebrates victory in Stage 6 of the 2008 Tour de France. He later admitted to taking a new drug that increased the oxygen-carrying capacity of his blood.

8.1 HOW DO CELLS OBTAIN ENERGY?

Cells require a continuous supply of energy to power the multitude of metabolic reactions that are essential just to stay alive. To drive a reaction, however, energy must be in a usable form. Most cellular energy is stored in the chemical bonds of energy-carrier molecules, especially **adenosine triphosphate (ATP).** In this chapter, we describe the cellular reactions that transfer energy from energy-storage molecules, particularly glucose, to energy-carrier molecules, such as ATP. Cells break down glucose in two stages: glycolysis, which liberates a small quantity of ATP, followed by cellular respiration, which produces far more ATP.

As you read this chapter, think back to the principles of energy use in cells explained in Chapter 6. As you may recall from our discussion of the second law of thermodynamics, every time a spontaneous reaction occurs, the amount of useful energy is decreased, and heat is generated. Cells are relatively efficient at capturing chemical energy during glucose breakdown, storing about 40% of the energy released by glucose in ATP molecules and releasing the rest as heat. If cells were as inefficient as most gasoline engines (25% or less), animals would need to eat far more voraciously to remain active.

You may also recall from Chapter 6 that enzymes are needed to promote biochemical reactions. Although for simplicity we do not show enzymes in the pathways illustrated here, each stage in the conversion of one molecule to another requires a specific enzyme to help overcome activation energy and allow the body to regulate the rate of the reaction.

Photosynthesis Is the Ultimate Source of Cellular Energy

Figure 8-1 illustrates the interrelationship between photosynthesis and the breakdown of glucose by glycolysis and

▲ FIGURE 8-1 **Photosynthesis captures the energy released by glycolysis and cellular respiration** Energy from sunlight is captured in glucose by photosynthesis, which occurs in the chloroplasts of green plants. Then glycolysis (which occurs in the cytoplasmic fluid) and cellular respiration (which occurs in the mitochondria) liberate the chemical energy stored in glucose. As indicated by the thickness of the red arrows, cellular respiration yields far more energy than does glycolysis. The products of photosynthesis are used in cellular respiration, which in turn releases molecules used in photosynthesis.

cellular respiration. Most organisms, whether or not they engage in photosynthesis, rely on this process to provide both high energy molecules and the oxygen used to break them down. As you learned in Chapter 7, photosynthesis, which occurs in chloroplasts, captures the energy of sunlight and uses it to form glucose ($C_6H_{12}O_6$) from the simple molecules CO_2 and H_2O. Oxygen is liberated as a by-product. In mitochondria, cells break down glucose to supply energy, which is captured in the energy-carrier molecule ATP. In forming ATP during cellular respiration, cells use oxygen and liberate both water and carbon dioxide—raw materials for photosynthesis.

The chemical equations for glucose formation by photosynthesis and the breakdown of glucose are almost perfectly symmetrical:

Photosynthesis:
$$6\,CO_2 + 6\,H_2O + \text{light energy} \rightarrow C_6H_{12}O_6 + 6\,O_2$$

Complete Glucose Breakdown:
$$C_6H_{12}O_6 + 6\,O_2 \rightarrow 6\,CO_2 + 6\,H_2O +$$
$$\text{chemical energy (ATP)} + \text{heat}$$

Glucose Is a Key Energy-Storage Molecule

Most cells can metabolize a variety of organic molecules to produce ATP. In this chapter, we focus on the breakdown of glucose, which all cells can use as an energy source. Humans and many other animals store energy in molecules such as glycogen (a carbohydrate consisting of long chains of glucose

molecules) and fat (see pp. 43–44). When cells use molecules such as glycogen, starch, or fat to produce ATP, they first convert the molecules to glucose or to other compounds that enter the metabolic pathway that is used to break down glucose (see "Health Watch: Why Can You Get Fat by Eating Sugar?" on p. 137).

An Overview of Glucose Breakdown

Glucose breakdown proceeds in stages, as summarized below and illustrated in **Figure 8-2:**

- The first stage is glycolysis (from the Greek, "glyco," meaning "sweet," and "lysis," meaning "to split apart"). **Glycolysis** begins the breakdown of glucose (a six-carbon sugar), producing two molecules of pyruvate (a three-carbon molecule). Some of the energy in glucose is used to generate two ATP molecules. Glycolysis does not require oxygen and proceeds in the same way under both **aerobic** (with oxygen) and **anaerobic** (without oxygen) conditions. The reactions of glycolysis occur in the cytoplasmic fluid and are described in section 8.2.
- If oxygen is available, the second stage of glucose breakdown is cellular respiration. During **cellular respiration,** the two pyruvate molecules produced by glycolysis are broken down into six carbon dioxide

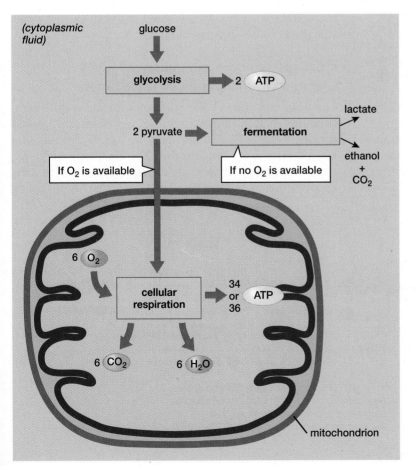

◀ FIGURE 8-2 **A summary of glucose breakdown**

molecules and six water molecules. Oxygen is used during the final stage of cellular respiration, which produces an additional 34 or 36 ATP molecules for every two pyruvate molecules that enter. In eukaryotic cells, the reactions of cellular respiration occur in **mitochondria,** organelles specialized for the aerobic breakdown of pyruvate. Cellular respiration is described in section 8.3.

- If oxygen is not available, the second stage of glucose breakdown is fermentation, which does not generate any additional chemical energy. During **fermentation,** pyruvate does not enter the mitochondria; it instead remains in the cytoplasmic fluid and is converted either into lactate, or into ethanol and CO_2. Fermentation is described in section 8.4.

8.2 WHAT HAPPENS DURING GLYCOLYSIS?

Glycolysis has two parts: glucose activation and energy harvesting, each with several steps (**Fig. 8-3**).

Before glucose can be broken down, it must be activated. Activating glucose uses up the energy from two molecules of ATP. When ATP energy is used, **adenosine diphosphate (ADP)** is formed (ADP is the energy-depleted form of ATP, with one fewer phosphate group). Glucose activation converts a stable glucose molecule into an "activated" molecule of fructose bisphosphate (**Fig. 8-3 ❶**). Fructose is a sugar molecule similar to glucose; "bisphosphate" ("bis" means "two") refers to the two phosphate groups acquired from the ATP molecules. Although the formation of fructose bisphosphate costs the cell two ATP molecules, this initial investment of energy is necessary to produce greater energy returns later. Because energy from ATP is now stored in the bonds linking the phosphate groups to the sugar, fructose bisphosphate is a highly unstable molecule.

Next, in the energy-harvesting steps, fructose bisphosphate is split apart into two, three-carbon molecules of glyceraldehyde-3-phosphate, or G3P (**Fig. 8-3 ❷**; you may recognize G3P from the Calvin cycle of photosynthesis in

Chapter 7). Each G3P molecule, which retains one phosphate with its high-energy bond, then undergoes a series of reactions that convert the G3P to pyruvate. During these reactions, two ATPs are generated for each G3P, for a total of four ATPs per glucose molecule. Because two ATPs were used up to activate the glucose molecule in the first place, there is a net gain of only two ATPs per glucose molecule. Along the pathway from G3P to pyruvate, two high-energy electrons and a hydrogen ion (H⁺) are added to the "empty" electron-carrier **nicotinamide adenine dinucleotide (NAD⁺)** to produce the high-energy electron-carrier molecule **NADH.** For more on glycolysis, see "A Closer Look at Glycolysis."

> **Summing Up**   Glycolysis
>
> - Each molecule of glucose is broken down into two molecules of pyruvate.
> - These reactions produce a net of two molecules of ATP and two molecules of NADH.

8.3 WHAT HAPPENS DURING CELLULAR RESPIRATION?

In most organisms, if oxygen is present, glycolysis is followed by the second stage of glucose breakdown, cellular respiration. In this series of reactions, the pyruvate produced by glycolysis is broken down, extracting a great deal more energy and also releasing carbon dioxide and water. As you read through the reactions, keep in mind that each glucose molecule produces two pyruvate molecules.

Cellular Respiration in Eukaryotic Cells Occurs in Mitochondria in Three Stages

In eukaryotic cells, cellular respiration occurs within mitochondria, organelles that are sometimes called the "powerhouses of the cell." A mitochondrion has two membranes that produce two compartments. The inner membrane encloses a central compartment containing the fluid **matrix,** and the outer membrane surrounds the organelle, producing

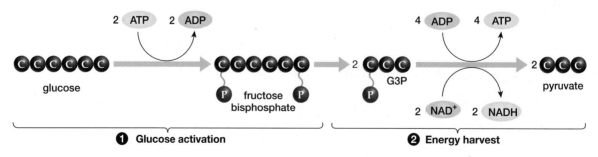

▲ FIGURE 8-3 **The essentials of glycolysis** ❶ Glucose activation: The energy of two ATP molecules is used to convert glucose to the highly reactive fructose bisphosphate, which splits into two reactive molecules of G3P. ❷ Energy harvest: The two G3P molecules undergo a series of reactions that generate four ATP and two NADH molecules. Glycolysis results in a net production of two ATP and two NADH molecules for each glucose molecule.

A Closer Look At *Glycolysis*

Glycolysis is a series of enzyme-catalyzed reactions that break down a single molecule of glucose into two molecules of pyruvate. To help you follow the reactions in **Figure E8-1,** we show only the "carbon skeletons" of glucose and the molecules produced during glycolysis. Each blue arrow represents a reaction catalyzed by at least one enzyme.

❶ A glucose molecule is energized by the addition of a high-energy phosphate from ATP.

❷ The molecule is slightly rearranged, forming fructose-6-phosphate.

❸ A second phosphate is added from another ATP.

❹ The resulting molecule, fructose-1,6-bisphosphate, is split into two three-carbon molecules, one DHAP (dihydroxyacetone phosphate) and one G3P. Each has one phosphate attached.

❺ DHAP rearranges into G3P. From now on, there are two molecules of G3P going through the same reactions.

❻ Each G3P undergoes two almost-simultaneous reactions. Two electrons and a hydrogen ion are donated to NAD^+ to make the energized carrier NADH, and an inorganic phosphate (P) is attached to the carbon skeleton with a high-energy bond. The resulting molecules of 1,3-bisphosphoglycerate have two high-energy phosphates.

❼ One phosphate from each bisphosphoglycerate is transferred to ADP to form ATP, for a net of two ATPs. This transfer compensates for the initial two ATPs used in glucose activation.

❽ After another rearrangement, the second phosphate from each phosphoenolpyruvate is transferred to ADP to form ATP, leaving pyruvate as the final product of glycolysis. There is a net profit of two ATPs from each glucose molecule.

▲ FIGURE E8-1 **Glycolysis**

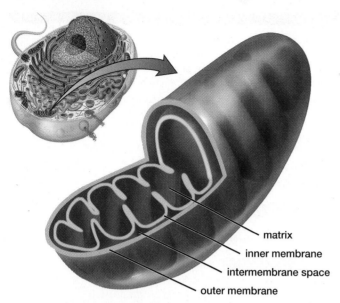

▲ **FIGURE 8-4 A mitochondrion** The double membrane of this organelle creates two spaces. The intermembrane space lies between the outer and inner membranes, and the matrix is enclosed by the inner membrane.

an **intermembrane space** between the inner and outer membranes (Fig. 8-4).

First, Pyruvate Is Broken Down in the Mitochondrial Matrix, Releasing Energy and CO_2

Pyruvate, the end product of glycolysis, is synthesized in the cytoplasmic fluid. Before cellular respiration can occur, the pyruvate must be transported from the cytoplasmic fluid into the mitochondrial matrix, where the necessary enzymes are located.

The reactions of the mitochondrial matrix, illustrated in **Figure 8-5**, occur in two stages: the formation of acetyl CoA

and the Krebs cycle. Acetyl CoA consists of a two-carbon acetyl group attached to a molecule called coenzyme A (CoA). To generate acetyl CoA, pyruvate is split, forming an acetyl group and releasing CO_2. The acetyl group reacts with CoA, forming acetyl CoA (**Fig. 8-5 ❶**). During this reaction, two high-energy electrons and a hydrogen ion are transferred to NAD^+, forming NADH.

The next set of mitochondrial matrix reactions forms a cyclic pathway known as the **Krebs cycle** (**Fig. 8-5 ❷**). (The cycle is named after its discoverer Hans Krebs, a biochemist who won a Nobel Prize for this work in 1953.) The Krebs cycle is also called the **citric acid cycle** because citrate (the dissolved, ionized form of citric acid) is the first molecule produced in the cycle.

The Krebs cycle begins by combining acetyl CoA with a four-carbon molecule to form the six-carbon citrate; coenzyme A is released. Like an enzyme, CoA is not permanently altered during these reactions and is reused many times. As the Krebs cycle proceeds, enzymes within the mitochondrial matrix break down the acetyl group, releasing two CO_2 molecules (whose carbons come from the acetyl group) and regenerating the four-carbon molecule for use in future cycles.

During the Krebs cycle, chemical energy released by breaking down each acetyl group (formed from pyruvate generated during glycolysis) is captured in energy-carrier molecules. Each acetyl group produces one ATP, three NADH, and one **$FADH_2$. FAD** is **flavin adenine dinucleotide,** a high-energy electron carrier similar to NAD^+. During the Krebs cycle, FAD picks up two energetic electrons along with two H^+, forming $FADH_2$. Remember that for each glucose molecule, two pyruvate molecules are formed, so the energy generated per glucose molecule is twice the energy generated for each pyruvate. These reactions are shown in more detail in "A Closer Look at the Mitochondrial Matrix Reactions."

▶ **FIGURE 8-5 Reactions in the mitochondrial matrix ❶** Pyruvate reacts with CoA, forming acetyl CoA and releasing CO_2. During this reaction, two high-energy electrons and a hydrogen ion are added to NAD^+, forming NADH. ❷ When acetyl CoA enters the Krebs cycle, CoA is released for reuse. The Krebs cycle produces one ATP, three NADH, one $FADH_2$, and two CO_2 from each acetyl CoA.

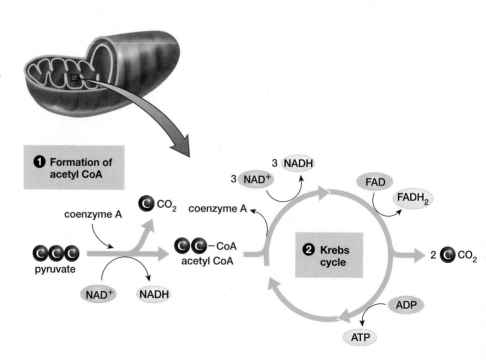

A Closer Look At *The Mitochondrial Matrix Reactions*

Mitochondrial matrix reactions occur in two stages: the formation of acetyl coenzyme A and the Krebs cycle (**Fig. E8-2**). Here we show only the carbon skeletons of the molecules. The blue arrows represent enzyme-catalyzed reactions. Recall that glycolysis produces two pyruvates from each glucose molecule, so each set of matrix reactions occurs twice during the breakdown of a single glucose molecule.

First Stage: Formation of Acetyl Coenzyme A

Pyruvate is split to form CO_2 and an acetyl group. The acetyl group attaches to CoA to form acetyl CoA. Simultaneously, NAD^+ receives two energized electrons and a hydrogen ion to make NADH. Acetyl CoA enters the Krebs cycle.

Second Stage: The Krebs Cycle

❶ Acetyl CoA donates its acetyl group to the four-carbon molecule oxaloacetate, forming citrate. CoA is released. Water donates hydrogen to the CoA molecule and oxygen to citrate.

❷ Citrate is rearranged to form isocitrate.

❸ Isocitrate forms α-ketoglutarate by releasing CO_2. Two energetic electrons and a H^+ are captured by NAD^+ to form NADH.

❹ Alpha-ketoglutarate forms succinate by releasing CO_2. Two energetic electrons and a H^+ are captured by NAD^+ to form NADH, and additional energy is captured in a molecule of ATP. At this point, all three carbons of the original pyruvate have been released as CO_2.

❺ Succinate is converted to fumarate. Two energetic electrons and two H^+ are captured by FAD, forming $FADH_2$.

❻ Fumarate is converted to malate, which contains two additional hydrogens and one additional oxygen, derived from water.

❼ Malate is converted to oxaloacetate. Two energetic electrons and a H^+ are captured by NAD^+ to form NADH.

For each acetyl CoA, the Krebs cycle produces two CO_2, one ATP, three NADH, and one $FADH_2$. The formation of each acetyl CoA prior to the Krebs cycle also generates one CO_2 and one NADH. So for each pyruvate molecule supplied by glycolysis, the mitochondrial matrix reactions produce three CO_2, one ATP, four NADH, and one $FADH_2$. Because each glucose molecule produces two pyruvates, the number of high-energy products and CO_2 per glucose molecule will be double that from a single pyruvate. The high-energy electron-carrier molecules NADH and $FADH_2$ will deliver their high-energy electrons to the electron transport chain, where their energy will be used to synthesize ATP by chemiosmosis.

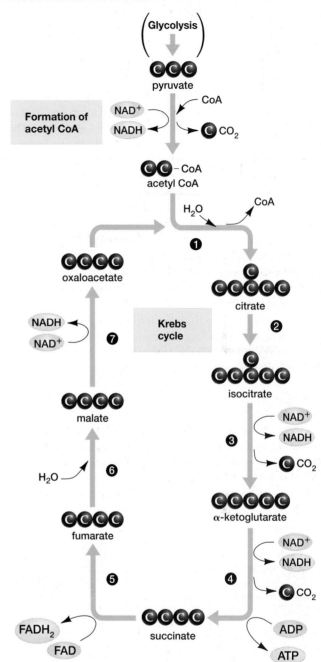

▲ FIGURE E8-2 **The mitochondrial matrix reactions**

During the mitochondrial matrix reactions, CO_2 is generated as a waste product. In your body, the CO_2 diffuses out of your cells and into your blood, which carries it to your lungs, where it is exhaled.

During the Second Stage of Cellular Respiration, High-Energy Electrons Travel Through the Electron Transport Chain

At the end of the mitochondrial matrix reactions, the cell has gained only four ATPs from the original glucose molecule (a net of two during glycolysis and two during the Krebs cycle). During glycolysis and the mitochondrial matrix reactions, however, the cell has captured many high-energy electrons in carrier molecules: a total of 10 NADH and two $FADH_2$ for every glucose molecule that is broken down. These carriers each release two high-energy electrons into an **electron transport chain (ETC),** many copies of which are embedded in the inner mitochondrial membrane (**Fig. 8-6 ❶**). The depleted carriers are then available for recharging by glycolysis and the Krebs cycle.

The ETCs within the mitochondrial membrane are very similar in function to the ETCs embedded in the thylakoid membrane of chloroplasts, described in Chapter 7. High-energy electrons jump from molecule to molecule along the ETC, losing small amounts of energy at each step. Although some energy is lost as heat, some is harnessed to pump H^+ from the matrix across the inner membrane and into the intermembrane space (**Fig. 8-6 ❷**). This produces a concentration gradient of H^+, which is used to generate ATP during chemiosmosis, as discussed in the next section.

Finally, at the end of the electron transport chain, the energy-depleted electrons are transferred to oxygen, which acts as an electron acceptor. This step clears out the transport chain, leaving it ready to accept more electrons. The energy-depleted electrons, oxygen, and hydrogen ions combine to form water. One water molecule is produced for every two electrons that traverse the ETC (**Fig. 8-6 ❸**).

Without oxygen, which we get from the air we breathe, electrons would be unable to move through the ETC, and H^+ would not be pumped across the inner membrane. The H^+ gradient would soon dissipate, and ATP synthesis by chemiosmosis would stop. Because our cells are so metabolically active, they cannot survive without a steady supply of oxygen to allow ATP generation to continue.

Case Study continued
When Athletes Boost Their Blood Counts: Do Cheaters Prosper?

When people and other animals exercise vigorously, they are unable to get enough air into their lungs, enough oxygen into their blood, and enough blood circulating to their muscles to allow cellular respiration to meet all their energy needs. As oxygen demand exceeds oxygen supply, muscles must rely on glycolysis (yielding far less ATP) for short periods of intense exercise. This is why athletes, desperate for a competitive edge, may turn to illegal blood doping to increase the ability of their blood to carry oxygen.

The Third Stage of Cellular Respiration Generates ATP by Chemiosmosis

Why pump hydrogen ions across a membrane? As you may recall from Chapter 7, **chemiosmosis** is the process by which

▶ FIGURE 8-6 **The electron transport chain** The electron transport chain is embedded in the inner membrane of the mitochondrion. ❶ NADH and $FADH_2$ donate their energetic electrons and hydrogen ions to the ETC. As the electrons pass along the chain (thick gray arrows), some of their energy is used to pump hydrogen ions from the matrix into the intermembrane space (thin red arrows). ❷ This creates a hydrogen ion gradient that is used to drive ATP synthesis. ❸ At the end of the electron transport chain, the energy-depleted electrons combine with hydrogen ions and oxygen and in the matrix to form water. ❹ The hydrogen ions flow down their concentration gradient from the inter-membrane space and into the matrix through ATP synthase channels, generating ATP from ADP and phosphate.

QUESTION How would the rate of ATP production be affected by the absence of oxygen?

energy is first used to generate a gradient of H^+, and then captured in the bonds of ATP as H^+ flows down its gradient. As the ETC pumps H^+ across the inner membrane, it produces a high concentration of H^+ in the intermembrane space and a low concentration in the matrix (see Fig. 8-6 ❷). According to the second law of thermodynamics, energy must be expended to produce this nonuniform distribution of H^+, sort of like charging a battery. This energy is released when hydrogen ions are allowed to flow down their concentration gradient, a process somewhat comparable to using the energy stored in a battery to light a bulb.

As in the thylakoid membranes of chloroplasts, the inner membranes of mitochondria are only permeable to H^+ at ATP synthase channels. As hydrogen ions flow from the intermembrane space into the matrix through these ATP-synthesizing enzymes, the flow of ions generates ATP from ADP and phosphate dissolved in the matrix, providing the energy to synthesize 32 or 34 molecules of ATP for each molecule of glucose (Fig. 8-6 ❹).

The ATP synthesized in the mitochondrial matrix during chemiosmosis enters the surrounding cytoplasmic fluid. These ATP molecules provide most of the energy needed by the cell. Simultaneously, ADP moves from the cytoplasmic fluid into the mitochondrial matrix, replenishing the supply of ADP and allowing more ATP synthesis.

Summing Up **Cellular Respiration**

- In the mitochondrial matrix, each pyruvate molecule is converted into acetyl CoA, producing one NADH per pyruvate molecule and releasing one CO_2.
- As each acetyl CoA passes through the Krebs cycle, its energy is captured in one ATP, three NADH, and one $FADH_2$. Its carbons are released in two CO_2 molecules.
- By the end of the matrix reactions, the two pyruvate molecules produced from each glucose molecule during glycolysis have been completely broken down, yielding a total of two ATP and 10 high-energy electron carriers: eight NADH and two $FADH_2$. Carbon atoms have been released in six molecules of CO_2.
- The NADH and $FADH_2$ release their energetic electrons into the ETC embedded in the inner mitochondrial membrane.
- As they pass through the ETC, energy from the high-energy electrons is harnessed to pump H^+ into the intermembrane space.
- As they leave the ETC, the energy-depleted electrons combine with hydrogen ions and oxygen to form water.
- During chemiosmosis, hydrogen ions in the intermembrane space flow down their concentration gradient through ATP synthase channels, which synthesize ATP.

Have you ever wondered

Why Cyanide Is So Deadly?

Cyanide is a common weapon in old murder mysteries, where its hapless victims fall dead almost instantly. Cyanide exerts its deadly effects by reacting with the final protein in the ETC, blocking oxygen from accepting electrons from this protein. If the energy-depleted electrons that emerge from the ETC are not carried away by oxygen, no new high-energy electrons can enter the chain, no hydrogen can be pumped across the membrane, and ATP production by chemiosmosis comes to a screeching halt. We are so dependent on the large numbers of ATP molecules produced by cellular respiration that blocking it with cyanide can kill a person within a few minutes.

A Summary of Glucose Breakdown in Eukaryotic Cells

Figure 8-7 summarizes the breakdown of one glucose molecule in a eukaryotic cell with oxygen present, showing the energy produced during each stage. Glycolysis occurs in the cytoplasmic fluid, producing two, three-carbon pyruvate molecules and releasing a small fraction of the chemical energy stored in glucose. Some of this energy is used to generate two ATP molecules, and some is captured in two NADH, which (if oxygen is present) will feed their electrons into the ETC during cellular respiration, generating more ATP.

During cellular respiration, the two pyruvate molecules enter a mitochondrion. First, each reacts with coenzyme A (CoA). This captures high-energy electrons in two NADH, produces two molecules of acetyl CoA, and liberates two molecules of carbon dioxide. The acetyl CoA molecules enter the Krebs cycle. The Krebs cycle releases four molecules of carbon dioxide, produces two ATP, and captures high-energy electrons in six NADH and two $FADH_2$. These electrons are passed into the ETC, where their energy is used during chemiosmosis to generate a gradient of H^+, yielding a net of 32 or 34 ATP. As energy-depleted electrons exit the ETC, they are picked up by the hydrogen ions released from the high-energy electron carriers NADH and $FADH_2$, and combine with oxygen to form water. The total energy captured from the breakdown of a single glucose molecule, starting with glycolysis and continuing through cellular respiration, is 36 or 38 ATP. The ATP enters the cytoplasmic fluid for use in cellular metabolic activities.

Why do we provide two different numbers for ATP? Glycolysis, which occurs in the cytoplasmic fluid, produces two NADH molecules, which must be actively transported into a mitochondrion to the ETC. In most body cells (including those of the brain and skeletal muscle) this transport uses up one ATP molecule per NADH (two ATPs per glucose molecule), so these cells generate a total of 36 ATPs during the breakdown of one glucose molecule. The heart and liver cells of mammals, however, use a more efficient transport mechanism that allows them to generate 38 ATPs per glucose molecule.

▶ FIGURE 8-7 **The energy sources and ATP harvest from glycolysis and cellular respiration** Here we follow the energy captured from one glucose molecule, which generates two molecules of pyruvate (during glycolysis) that then enter cellular respiration, which encompasses all of the reactions shown inside the mitochondrion. Notice that most of the ATP derived from glucose breakdown comes as a result of high-energy electrons donated by NADH and $FADH_2$ to the electron transport chain, which allows chemiosmosis to occur.

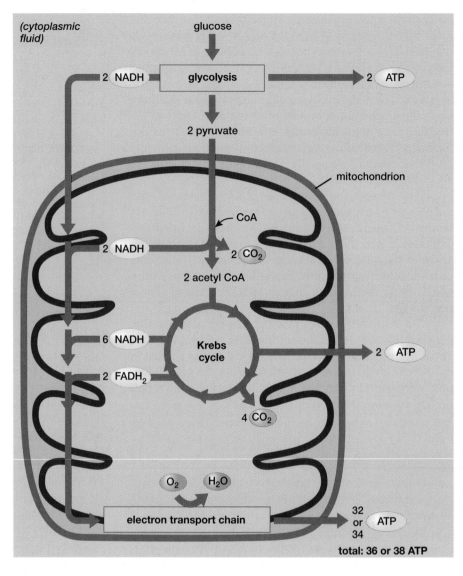

The breakdown of glucose is a multistep process with many intermediate molecules. By regulating enzymes (see pp. 105–107), cells can promote reactions that divert these intermediate molecules into other pathways. For example, if the cell has adequate supplies of ATP, it can use extra glucose and other sugars to generate fat, as described in "Health Watch: Why Can You Get Fat by Eating Sugar?"

BioFlix™ Cellular Respiration

8.4 WHAT HAPPENS DURING FERMENTATION?

Virtually every organism on Earth uses glycolysis, providing evidence that it is one of the most ancient of all biochemical pathways. Scientists hypothesize that the earliest forms of life appeared under anaerobic conditions (before the evolution of oxygen-liberating photosynthesis). These pioneering life-forms relied on glycolysis for energy production, breaking down the organic molecules formed under the conditions that existed on Earth before life appeared (see pp. 318–320).

Many microorganisms still thrive in places where oxygen is rare or absent, such as in the stomach and intestines of animals (including humans), deep in soil, or in bogs and marshes. Some microorganisms lack the enzymes for cellular respiration; these are unable to use oxygen even under aerobic conditions. A few types of bacteria, such as those that cause tetanus, are actually poisoned by oxygen.

Why Is Fermentation Necessary?

Following glycolysis, under anaerobic conditions, fermentation occurs. Fermentation does not produce more ATP, so why is it necessary? Fermentation is required to convert the NADH produced during glycolysis back to NAD⁺, which needs to be continuously recycled to allow glycolysis to continue.

Under aerobic conditions, most organisms use cellular respiration and regenerate NAD⁺ by donating the energetic electrons from NADH to the ETC. But under anaerobic conditions, with no oxygen to allow the ETC to function, the cell must regenerate the NAD⁺ using fermentation. During fermentation, the electrons from NADH (along with some

Health Watch

Why Can You Get Fat by Eating Sugar?

People fortunate enough to have access to abundant food often wonder why everything they eat seems to turn to fat. Why don't we just excrete excess high-energy molecules that we don't need? Why do we continue to feel hungry even if we are already carrying a great deal of excess weight?

From an evolutionary perspective, overeating during times of easy food availability is a highly adaptive behavior. During times of famine, which were common during our early history, heavier people are more likely to survive, while leaner individuals succumb to starvation. It is only recently (from an evolutionary vantage point) that many people have had continuous access to high-calorie food. Under these conditions, the drive to eat and the adaptation of storing excess food as fat leads to obesity, a growing health problem in the United States, Mexico, and many other countries throughout the world.

Why don't we simply store energy in glucose or ATP? As you may recall from Chapter 3, fats store twice as much energy per unit weight as do proteins or carbohydrates such as glucose. Because using fat as a storage molecule actually reduces the weight we must carry, this adaptation was important to our prehistoric ancestors who needed to move quickly to catch prey or to avoid becoming prey themselves. We don't use ATP for long-term energy storage because the amount of energy stored in its bonds makes ATP too unstable.

Gaining fat by eating sugar or other carbohydrates is common among animals. For example, a ruby-throated hummingbird weighs 0.035 to 0.07 of an ounce (2 to 3 grams; about as much as a penny). During late summer, it feeds voraciously on the sugary nectar of flowers (Fig. E8-3), storing enough fat to almost double its weight. The energy in this fat allows it to make its long migration from the eastern United States, across the Gulf of Mexico and into Mexico or Central America for the winter. If the hummingbird stored sugar instead of fat, it might be too heavy to fly.

Because fat storage is so important for survival, cells have metabolic pathways that can chemically transform a variety of foods into fat if the foods are consumed in excessive amounts. In addition to breaking down glucose, the biochemical pathways described in this chapter participate in producing fat as well. In Chapter 3 we described the structure of a fat: three fatty acids attached to a glycerol backbone (see Fig 3-12). When you eat a candy bar loaded with sucrose (table sugar), for example, this disaccharide is first broken down into its component simple sugars: glucose and fructose. Both enter glycolysis (the fructose enters a bit further along than glucose), and both are converted into G3P. If cells have plenty of ATP, some of this G3P is diverted and used to make the glycerol backbone of fat. As the sugars continue to be broken down, acetyl CoA is formed (see Fig. 8-5). Excess acetyl CoA molecules are used as raw materials to synthesize the fatty acids that will be linked to the glycerol to form a fat molecule. Starches, such as those in potatoes or bread, are actually long chains of glucose molecules, so you can now see how eating large amounts of starch, as well as sugar, can make you fat.

▲ FIGURE E8-3 **A ruby-throated hummingbird feeds on nectar**

---

hydrogen ions) are donated to pyruvate, changing it chemically. If the supply of NAD⁺ were to be exhausted—which would happen quickly without fermentation—glycolysis would stop, energy production would cease, and the organism would rapidly die.

Depending on which metabolic pathway they have evolved, organisms use one of two types of fermentation to regenerate NAD⁺: lactic acid fermentation, which produces lactic acid from pyruvate, or alcoholic fermentation, which generates alcohol and CO_2 from pyruvate. Because fermentation does not break down glucose completely and does not use the energy of NADH to produce more ATP, organisms that rely on fermentation must consume far more sugar to generate the same amount of ATP than do organisms using cellular respiration.

Some Cells Ferment Pyruvate to Form Lactate

Fermentation of pyruvate to lactate is called **lactic acid fermentation** (in the cytoplasmic fluid, lactic acid is dissolved and becomes ionized, forming lactate). Lactic acid fermentation happens in muscles that are working hard enough to use up all their available oxygen.

When deprived of adequate oxygen, muscles do not immediately stop working. After all, animals exercise most vigorously when fighting, fleeing, or pursuing prey. During these activities, the ability to continue just a little bit longer can make the difference between life and death. When muscles are sufficiently low on oxygen, glycolysis supplies its meager two ATPs per glucose molecule, which may provide the energy needed for a final, brief burst of speed. To regenerate NAD$^+$, muscle cells ferment pyruvate molecules to lactate, using electrons from NADH and hydrogen ions (**Fig. 8-8**).

▲ FIGURE 8-8 **Glycolysis followed by lactic acid fermentation**

For example, if you're breathing hard after sprinting to arrive at class on time, your muscles have been relying on glycolysis for part of their energy, and your lungs are working to restore the oxygen needed for cellular respiration. As oxygen is replenished, lactate is converted back into pyruvate both in muscle cells, where it will be used for cellular respiration, and in the liver, where the pyruvate is converted back into glucose. This glucose may then be released into the bloodstream to be used as an energy source by cells throughout the body.

A variety of microorganisms use lactic acid fermentation, including the bacteria that convert milk into yogurt, sour cream, and cheese. Because acids taste sour, the lactic acid contributes to the distinctive tastes of these foods. The acid also denatures milk protein, altering its three-dimensional structure. This causes the milk to thicken, so that sour cream and yogurt are semisolid in texture.

Some Cells Ferment Pyruvate to Form Alcohol and Carbon Dioxide

Many microorganisms, such as yeast (single-celled fungi), engage in **alcoholic fermentation** under anaerobic conditions. As in lactic acid fermentation, the NAD$^+$ must be regenerated

---

Case Study continued

When Athletes Boost Their Blood Counts: Do Cheaters Prosper?

Why is the average speed of the 5,000-meter run in the Olympics slower than that of the 100-meter dash? During the dash, runners' leg muscles use more ATP than cellular respiration can supply. But anaerobic fermentation can only provide ATP for a short dash. Longer runs must be aerobic, and thus slower, to prevent lactic acid buildup from causing extreme fatigue, muscle pain, and cramps.

---

to allow glycolysis to continue. During alcoholic fermentation, H$^+$ and electrons from NADH are used to convert pyruvate into ethanol and CO$_2$ (rather than lactate). This releases NAD$^+$, which is then available to accept more high-energy electrons during glycolysis (**Fig. 8-9**).

▲ FIGURE 8-9 **Glycolysis followed by alcoholic fermentation**

In sparkling wines, fermentation continues in the bottle, trapping CO$_2$ and producing the tiny bubbles for which champagne is noted (**Fig. 8-10**). See "Links to Everyday Life: A Jug of Wine, a Loaf of Bread, and a Nice Bowl of Sauerkraut" for more about how people put fermentation to use.

▲ FIGURE 8-10 **Fermentation in action** Sparkling wines rely on alcoholic fermentation for their alcohol; the CO$_2$ it releases can cause this explosive decompression.

QUESTION Some species of bacteria use aerobic respiration and other species use anaerobic (fermenting) respiration. In an oxygen-rich environment, would either type be at a competitive advantage? What about in an oxygen-poor environment?

Links to *Everyday Life*

A Jug of Wine, a Loaf of Bread, and a Nice Bowl of Sauerkraut

Life would be a little less interesting without fermentation. Persian poet Omar Khayyam (1048–1122) described his vision of paradise on Earth as "A Jug of Wine, a Loaf of Bread—and Thou Beside Me." People have long exploited yeast's ability to ferment the sugars in fruit to form alcohol; historical evidence suggests that wine and beer were commercially produced at least 5,000 years ago. Yeasts (single-celled fungi) are opportunists; they will engage in efficient cellular respiration if oxygen is available, but switch to alcoholic fermentation if they run out of oxygen. Thus, wine must be fermented in special containers that prevent air from entering (so cellular respiration doesn't occur) but allow carbon dioxide to escape (so the containers don't explode). Sparkling (fizzy) wines and champagne are made by adding more yeast and sugar just before the wine is bottled, so that final fermentation occurs in the sealed bottle, trapping carbon dioxide (see Fig. 8-10).

Fermentation also gives bread its airy texture. Bread contains yeast, flour, and water. Dry yeast cells are awakened from their dormant state by water, and the yeast cells multiply rapidly while metabolizing the sugars present in flour. The yeasts release CO_2 during cellular respiration while oxygen is present, and they also release CO_2 during alcoholic fermentation after they have used up the available oxygen. The CO_2 forms tiny pockets of gas in the bread dough. Kneading distributes the multiplying yeast cells evenly throughout the bread and makes the dough stretchy and resilient so it traps the gas, resulting in an evenly porous texture that is solidified by baking. Although both wine and bread are produced by alcoholic fermentation, bacteria that utilize lactic acid fermentation are responsible for other culinary staples.

For thousands of years, people have relied on microorganisms that produce lactic acid to convert milk into sour cream, yogurt, and a wide variety of cheeses (**Fig. E8-4**). In addition, lactate fermentation by salt-loving bacteria converts the sugars in cucumbers and cabbage to lactic acid. The result: dill pickles and sauerkraut, excellent partners for other fermented foods.

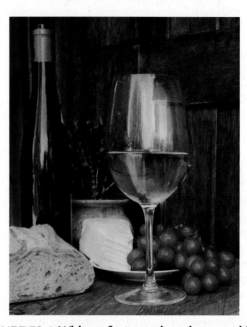

▲ FIGURE E8-4 **Without fermentation, there would be no wine, bread, or cheese**

Case Study revisited
When Athletes Boost Their Blood Counts: Do Cheaters Prosper?

Although runners can do a 100-meter dash without adequate oxygen, distance runners and other long-distance athletes, such as cross-country skiers and cyclists, must pace themselves. They must rely on aerobic cellular respiration for most of the race, saving the anaerobic sprint for the finish. Training for distance events focuses on increasing the capacity of the athletes' respiratory and circulatory systems to deliver enough oxygen to their muscles. For this reason, it is the distance athletes who most often resort to blood doping, to increase the oxygen-carrying capacity of their blood. This delivers more oxygen to their muscles so that cellular respiration can generate the maximum amount of ATP from glucose.

The EPO-mimicking drug CERA—that Riccò now admits taking—helped keep his muscles supplied with ATP by stimulating overproduction of oxygen-carrying red blood cells. In the particularly demanding mountain stages of the Tour de

France, which Riccò won, his "clean" competitors were at a disadvantage as their leg muscles became painfully laden with lactate from fermentation sooner than did Riccò's.

Because EPO is produced naturally in the human body, its abuse is hard to detect. CERA, intended for use by people with anemia (who have too few red blood cells), was new on the market at the time of the 2008 Tour de France, and Riccò may have assumed it would be undetectable. But CERA's manufacturer, the pharmaceutical firm Hoffman-La Roche, had provided samples of the drug to the World Anti-Doping Agency before it was marketed, allowing researchers to develop urine tests to identify users.

Consider This

BioEthics Some athletes move to high-altitude locations to train for races run at lower altitudes, because the low oxygen levels present at high altitudes stimulate increased production of red blood cells. Is this cheating? Explain your reasoning. Advances in gene therapy may one day make it possible to modify athletes' cells so that they have extra copies of the gene that produces EPO. Would this be cheating?

CHAPTER REVIEW

Summary of Key Concepts

8.1 How Do Cells Obtain Energy?
Cells produce chemical energy by breaking down glucose into lower-energy compounds and capturing some of the released energy as ATP. During glycolysis, glucose is broken down in the cytoplasmic fluid, forming pyruvate and generating a small quantity of ATP and the high-energy electron carrier NADH. If oxygen is available, pyruvate is broken down through cellular respiration in the mitochondria, generating much more ATP than does glycolysis.

8.2 What Happens During Glycolysis?
During glycolysis, a molecule of glucose is activated by adding high-energy phosphates from two ATP molecules to form fructose bisphosphate. Then, in a series of reactions, the fructose bisphosphate is broken down into two molecules of pyruvate. This produces a net yield of two ATP and two NADH.

8.3 What Happens During Cellular Respiration?
If oxygen is available, cellular respiration can occur. Pyruvate is transported into the matrix of the mitochondria. Here, it reacts with coenzyme A to form acetyl CoA plus CO_2. The acetyl CoA enters the Krebs cycle and releases the remaining two carbons as CO_2. One ATP, three NADH, and one $FADH_2$ are also formed for each acetyl group that goes through the cycle. During the reactions in the mitochondrial matrix, each molecule of glucose that originally entered glycolysis produces a total of two ATP, eight NADH, and two $FADH_2$ (see Fig. 8-7).

The NADH and $FADH_2$ deliver their high-energy electrons to the electron transport chain (ETC) embedded in the inner mitochondrial membrane. The energy of the electrons is used to pump hydrogen ions across the inner membrane from the matrix to the intermembrane space. At the end of the ETC, the depleted electrons combine with oxygen and hydrogen ions, forming water. This is the oxygen-requiring step of cellular respiration. During chemiosmosis, the hydrogen ion gradient created by the ETC is used to produce ATP, as the hydrogen ions diffuse back across the inner membrane through channels that contain ATP synthase. Electron transport and chemiosmosis yield 32 or 34 additional ATP, for a net yield of 36 or 38 ATP per glucose molecule during combined glycolysis and cellular respiration.

BioFlix™ Cellular Respiration

8.4 What Happens During Fermentation?
Glycolysis uses up NAD+ to produce NADH as glucose is broken down into pyruvate. For these reactions to continue, NAD must be continuously recycled. Under anaerobic conditions, NADH cannot release its high-energy electrons to the ETC, because there is no oxygen to accept them at the end of the chain. So, NAD is regenerated from NADH by fermenting pyruvate to ethanol and CO_2, or to lactate, depending on the organism. Yeast and certain other microorganisms generate ethanol and CO_2. Humans and other animals generate lactate.

Key Terms

adenosine diphosphate (ADP) *130*
adenosine triphosphate (ATP) *128*
aerobic *129*
alcoholic fermentation *138*
anaerobic *129*
cellular respiration *129*
chemiosmosis *134*
citric acid cycle *132*
electron transport chain (ETC) *134*
fermentation *130*
flavin adenine dinucleotide (FAD or $FADH_2$) *132*
glycolysis *129*
intermembrane space *132*
Krebs cycle *132*
lactic acid fermentation *137*
matrix *130*
mitochondrion *130*
nicotinamide adenine dinucleotide (NAD+ or NADH) *130*

Thinking Through the Concepts

Fill-in-the-Blank

1. The complete breakdown of glucose in the presence of oxygen occurs in two stages: _____ and _____. The first of these stages occurs in the _____ of the cell, and the second stage occurs in organelles called _____. Which stage generates the most ATP? _____

2. Conditions in which oxygen is absent are described as _____. In the absence of oxygen, some microorganisms break down glucose using _____, which generates only _____ molecules of ATP. This process is followed by_____, in which no more ATP is produced, but the electron-carrier molecule _____ is regenerated so it can be used in further glucose breakdown.

3. Yeast in bread dough and alcoholic beverages use a type of fermentation that generates _____ and _____. Muscles pushed to their limit use _____ fermentation. Which form of fermentation is used by microorganisms that produce yogurt, sour cream, and sauerkraut? _____

4. The hormone _____ causes production of extra _____ cells, which increase the ability of the blood to carry _____. This gives athletes a competitive edge because their muscle cells can engage in _____ for energy production for a longer time during vigorous exercise.

5. During cellular respiration, the electron transport chain pumps H+ out of the mitochondrial _____ into the _____, producing a large _____ of H+. The ATP produced by cellular respiration is generated by a process called _____. During this process, H+ travels through membrane channels linked to _____.

6. The cyclic portion of cellular respiration is called the _____ cycle, or the _____ cycle. The molecule that enters this cycle is _____. How many ATP molecules are generated by the cycle per molecule of glucose? _____ What two types of high-energy electron-carrier molecules are generated during the cycle? _____ and _____

Review Questions

1. Starting with glucose ($C_6H_{12}O_6$), write the overall reactions for aerobic respiration.

2. Draw and label a mitochondrion, and explain how its structure relates to its function.

3. What role do the following play in the breakdown of glucose: glycolysis, mitochondrial matrix, inner membrane of mitochondria, fermentation, and NAD^+?

4. Outline the two major stages of glycolysis. How many ATP molecules (overall) are generated per glucose molecule during glycolysis? Where in the cell does glycolysis occur?

5. Under what conditions does fermentation occur? What are its possible products? What is its function?

6. What molecule is the end product of glycolysis? How are the carbons of this molecule used during the Krebs cycle? In what form is most of the energy from the Krebs cycle captured?

7. Describe the mitochondrial electron transport chain and the process of chemiosmosis.

8. Why is oxygen necessary for cellular respiration to occur?

9. Compare the structure of chloroplasts (described in Chapter 7) to that of mitochondria, and describe how the similarities in structure relate to similarities in function. Also describe any differences in structure and function between chloroplasts and mitochondria.

Applying the Concepts

1. Some years ago a freight train overturned, spilling a load of grain. Because the grain was unusable, it was buried in the railroad embankment. Although there is no shortage of other food, the local bear population has become a nuisance by continually uncovering the grain. Yeasts are common in the soil. What do you think has happened to the grain to make the bears keep digging it up, and how is their behavior related to human cultural evolution?

2. Why can't a victim of cyanide poisoning survive by using anaerobic respiration?

3. Some species of bacteria that live at the surface of sediment on the bottom of lakes are capable of using either glycolysis plus fermentation or cellular respiration to generate ATP. There is very little circulation of water in lakes during the summer. Predict and explain what will happen to the bottommost water of lakes as the summer progresses, and describe how this situation will affect energy production by bacteria.

4. Dumping large amounts of raw sewage into rivers or lakes typically leads to massive fish kills, although sewage itself is not toxic to fish. Similar fish kills also occur in shallow lakes that become covered with ice during the winter. What kills the fish? How might you reduce fish mortality after raw sewage is accidentally released into a small pond?

5. Different types of cells respire at different rates. Explain why this is useful. How could you predict the relative respiratory rates of different tissues by examining cells through a microscope?

6. Imagine a hypothetical situation in which a starving cell reaches the stage where every bit of its ATP has been depleted and converted to ADP plus phosphate. If at this point you place the cell in a solution containing glucose, will it recover and survive? Explain your answer based on what you know about glucose breakdown.

(MB) *Go to www.masteringbiology.com for practice quizzes, activities, eText, videos, current events, and more.*

Inheritance

Inheritance provides for both
similarity and difference. All
dogs share many similarities
because their genes are nearly
identical. The enormous variety
of sizes, fur length and color,
and bodily proportions result
from tiny differences in their
genes.

The Continuity of Life: Cellular Reproduction

Chapter **9**

Case Study

Send in the Clones

IN FEBRUARY 2008, the Korean biotech company RNL Bio offered to clone your pet dog for a mere $150,000. But some people may have preferred to take their chances in the June online auction hosted by BioArts of Mill Valley, California, where the bidding for "Best Friends Again" dog cloning began at only $100,000 (the winning bids were $170,000, $155,000, and $140,000).

Cloning is the production of one or more individual organisms (**clones**) that are genetically identical to a preexisting individual. Frogs were the first animals to be cloned, back in the 1950s. Cloning pets got its start in 1997 when Joan Hawthorne and John Sperling, the founder of the University of Phoenix, decided that Hawthorne's aging dog, Missy, was special—so special that Sperling invested millions of dollars to clone her. Although the original "Missyplicity Project" at the wittily named Genetic Savings and Clone (GSC) cloned a few cats, GSC failed to clone Missy. In 2006, GSC shut down.

In 2005, however, researchers at the South Korean National University produced Snuppy—a cloned Afghan hound (see the photo to the left). About 2 years later, the Korean team successfully produced three clones of Missy. In 2008, BioArts, the successor company to GSC, announced the "Best Friends Again" auction.

Not all cloned dogs will be pets. For example, Korean teams have produced seven clones of South Korea's top drug-sniffing dog. No one knows if either the ability or the temperament to be superb sniffer dogs is genetically determined, but government officials believe that the expense of cloning will be more than worth it if the clones are as good as their "genetic parent."

Valuable livestock are another favorite subject for cloning. For example, in 2006 the Texas firm ViaGen cloned the 10-time world champion barrel-racing horse, Scamper. Why couldn't Scamper's owner, Charmayne James, just breed Scamper the old-fashioned way? By the time you've finished this chapter, you'll know why many famous horses don't sire offspring that are as athletic as they are. In any case, Scamper is a gelding—a castrated male—so he can't breed.

Why is a clone nearly identical to its genetic parent, while offspring produced by sexual reproduction are often so different from their biological parents and from each other? Keep that question in mind as we explore two types of cellular reproduction—mitotic and meiotic cell division—that provide for both constancy and variability in eukaryotic organisms.

▲ Snuppy (pronounced Snoopy; center), the first cloned dog, poses for a family portrait with his genetic donor, a male Afghan hound (left), and his surrogate mother, a Labrador retriever (right).

At a Glance

9.1 WHY DO CELLS DIVIDE?

"All cells come from cells." This insight, first stated by the German physician Rudolf Virchow in the mid-1800s, captures the critical importance of cellular reproduction for all living organisms. Cells reproduce by **cell division,** in which a parent cell normally gives rise to two **daughter cells.** In typical cell division, each daughter cell receives a complete set of hereditary information, usually identical to the hereditary information of the parent cell, and about half the cytoplasm.

Cell Division Transmits Hereditary Information to Each Daughter Cell

The hereditary information of all living cells is **deoxyribonucleic acid (DNA),** contained in one or more **chromosomes.** A single molecule of DNA consists of a long chain composed of smaller subunits called **nucleotides** (**Fig. 9-1a**; see also pp. 51 and 203). Each nucleotide consists of a phosphate, a sugar (deoxyribose), and one of four bases—adenine (A), thymine (T), guanine (G), or cytosine (C). The DNA in a chromosome consists of two long strands of nucleotides wound around each other, as a ladder would look if it were twisted into a corkscrew shape. This structure is called a double helix (**Fig. 9-1b**). The units of inheritance, called **genes,** are segments of DNA ranging from a few hundred to many thousands of nucleotides long. Like the letters of an alphabet, in a language with very long sentences, the specific sequences of nucleotides in genes spell out the instructions for making the proteins of a cell. We will see in Chapters 11 and 12 how DNA encodes genetic information and how a cell regulates which genes it uses at any given time.

For a cell to survive, it must have a complete set of genetic instructions. Therefore, when a cell divides, it cannot simply split its set of genes in half and give each daughter cell half a set. Rather, the cell must first replicate its DNA to make two identical copies, much like making a photocopy of an instruction manual. Each daughter cell then receives a complete "DNA manual" containing all the genes.

Cell Division Is Required for Growth and Development

The familiar form of cell division in eukaryotic cells, in which each daughter cell is genetically identical to the parent cell, is called mitotic cell division (see sections 9.4 and 9.5). Since your conception as a single fertilized egg, mitotic cell division has produced all the cells in your body, and continues every day in many organs. After cell division, the daughter cells may grow and divide again, or they may **differentiate,** becoming specialized for specific functions, such as contraction (muscle cells), fighting infections (white blood cells), or producing digestive enzymes (cells of the pancreas, stomach, and intestine). This repeating pattern of divide, grow, and (possibly) differentiate, then divide again, is called the **cell cycle** (see sections 9.2 and 9.4).

Most multicellular organisms have three categories of cells, based on their abilities to divide and differentiate:

- **Stem cells** Most of the daughter cells formed by the first few cell divisions of a fertilized egg, and a few cells in adults, including cells in the heart, skin, intestines, brain, and bone marrow, are **stem cells.** Stem cells have two important characteristics: self-renewal and the ability to differentiate into a variety of cell types. Stem cells self-renew because they retain the ability to divide, perhaps for the entire life of the organism. Usually, when a stem cell divides, one of its daughters remains a stem cell, maintaining the population of stem cells. The other daughter cell often undergoes several rounds of cell division, but the resulting cells eventually differentiate into specialized cell types. Some stem cells in early embryos can produce any of the specialized cell types of the entire body.
- **Other cells capable of dividing** Many cells of the bodies of embryos, juveniles, and adults can also divide, but typically differentiate into only one or two different cell types. Dividing cells in your liver, for example, can only become more liver cells.

▶ **FIGURE 9-1 The structure of DNA**
(a) A nucleotide consists of a phosphate, a sugar, and one of four bases—adenine (A), thymine (T), guanine (G), or cytosine (C). A single strand of DNA consists of a long chain of nucleotides held together by bonds between the phosphate of one nucleotide and the sugar of the next. **(b)** Two DNA strands twist around one another to form a double helix.

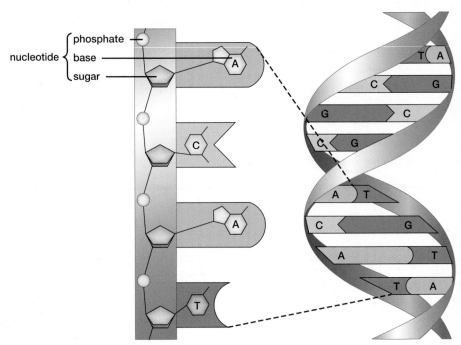

(a) A single strand of DNA   (b) The double helix

- **Permanently differentiated cells** Some cells differentiate and never divide again. For example, most of the cells in your heart and brain cannot divide.

Cell Division Is Required for Sexual and Asexual Reproduction

Sexual reproduction in eukaryotic organisms occurs when offspring are produced by the fusion of **gametes** (sperm and eggs) from two adults. Cells in the adult's reproductive system undergo a specialized type of cell division called meiotic cell division, which we will describe in section 9.8, to produce daughter cells with exactly half of the genetic information of their parent cells (and of the "ordinary" body cells of the rest of the adult organism). In animals, these cells become sperm or eggs. When a sperm fertilizes an egg, the resulting offspring

once again contain the full complement of hereditary information typical of that species.

Reproduction in which offspring are formed from a single parent, without having a sperm fertilize an egg, is called **asexual reproduction.** Asexual reproduction produces offspring that are genetically identical to the parent. Bacteria (**Fig. 9-2a**) and single-celled eukaryotic organisms, such as *Paramecium* commonly found in ponds (**Fig. 9-2b**), reproduce asexually by cell division, in which two new cells arise from each preexisting cell. Some multicellular organisms can also reproduce by asexual reproduction. A *Hydra* reproduces by growing a small replica of itself, called a bud, on its body (**Fig. 9-2c**). Eventually, the bud is able to live independently and separates from its parent. Many plants and fungi reproduce both asexually and sexually. The beautiful aspen groves of Colorado, Utah, and New Mexico develop asexually from

(a) Dividing bacteria

(b) Cell division in *Paramecium*

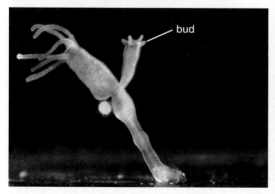

bud

(c) *Hydra* reproduces asexually by budding

The trees in this grove have already lost their leaves

The trees in this grove have begun to change color

The trees in this grove are still green

(d) A grove of aspens often consists of genetically identical trees produced by asexual reproduction

▲ FIGURE 9-2 **Cell division enables asexual reproduction (a)** Bacteria reproduce asexually by dividing in two. **(b)** In unicellular eukaryotic microorganisms, such as the protist *Paramecium*, cell division produces two new, independent organisms. **(c)** *Hydra*, a freshwater relative of the sea anemone, grows a miniature replica of itself (a bud) on its side. When fully developed, the bud breaks off and assumes independent life. **(d)** Trees in an aspen grove are often genetically identical. Each tree grows up from the roots of a single ancestral tree. This photo shows three separate groves near Aspen, Colorado. In fall, the timing of the changing color of their leaves shows the genetic identity within a grove and the genetic difference between groves.

shoots growing up from the root system of a single parent tree (**Fig. 9-2d**). Although a grove looks like a population of separate trees, it is often a single individual whose multiple trunks are interconnected by a common root system. Aspen can also reproduce by seeds, which result from sexual reproduction.

Both prokaryotic and eukaryotic cells have cell cycles that include growth, metabolic activity, DNA replication, and cell division. However, prokaryotic and eukaryotic cells have major structural and functional differences, including in the organization of their DNA—the structure, size, number, and location of their chromosomes. Therefore, we will first describe the organization of the prokaryotic chromosome and the prokaryotic cell cycle. We will then examine the eukaryotic chromosome and the essential processes of the eukaryotic cell cycle. Finally, we will describe the two types of cell division in eukaryotes, mitotic cell division and meiotic cell division.

9.2 WHAT OCCURS DURING THE PROKARYOTIC CELL CYCLE?

The DNA of a prokaryotic cell is contained in a single, circular chromosome about a millimeter or two in circumference. Unlike eukaryotic chromosomes, prokaryotic chromosomes are not contained in a membrane-bound nucleus (see pp. 65–67).

The prokaryotic cell cycle consists of a relatively long period of growth—during which the cell also replicates its DNA—followed by a type of cell division called **binary fission,** which means "splitting in two" (**Fig. 9-3a**). The prokaryotic chromosome is usually attached at one point to the plasma membrane of the cell (**Fig. 9-3b ❶**). During the growth phase of the prokaryotic cell cycle, the DNA is replicated, producing two identical chromosomes that become attached to the plasma membrane at nearby, but separate, sites (**Fig. 9-3b ❷**). As the cell grows, new plasma membrane is added between the attachment sites of the chromosomes, pushing them apart (**Fig. 9-3b ❸**). When the cell has approximately doubled in size, the plasma membrane around the middle of the cell grows inward between the two attachment sites (**Fig. 9-3b ❹**). Fusion of the plasma membrane along the equator of the cell completes binary fission, producing two daughter cells, each containing one of the chromosomes (**Fig. 9-3b ❺**). Because DNA replication produces two identical DNA molecules, the two daughter cells are genetically identical to one another and to the parent cell.

Under ideal conditions, binary fission in prokaryotes occurs rapidly. For example, the common intestinal bacterium *Escherichia coli* (usually called simply *E. coli*) can grow, replicate its DNA, and divide in about 20 minutes. Luckily, the environment in our intestines isn't ideal for bacterial growth; otherwise, the bacteria would soon outweigh the rest of our bodies!

▶ FIGURE 9-3 **The prokaryotic cell cycle (a)** The prokaryotic cell cycle consists of growth and DNA replication, followed by binary fission. **(b)** Binary fission in prokaryotic cells.

(a) The prokaryotic cell cycle

❶ The circular DNA double helix is attached to the plasma membrane at one point.

❷ The DNA replicates and the two DNA double helices attach to the plasma membrane at nearby points.

❸ New plasma membrane is added between the attachment points, pushing them farther apart.

❹ The plasma membrane grows inward at the middle of the cell.

❺ The parent cell divides into two daughter cells.

(b) Binary fission

9.3 HOW IS THE DNA IN EUKARYOTIC CHROMOSOMES ORGANIZED?

Eukaryotic chromosomes are separated from the cytoplasm in a membrane-bound nucleus. Further, eukaryotic cells always have multiple chromosomes—the smallest number, 2, is found in the cells of females of a species of ant, but most animals have dozens and some ferns have more than 1,200! Finally, eukaryotic chromosomes usually contain more DNA than do prokaryotic chromosomes. Human chromosomes, for example, are about 10 to 80 times longer than the typical prokaryotic chromosome, and contain 10 to 50 times more DNA. The complex events of eukaryotic cell division are largely an evolutionary solution to the problem of sorting out a large number of long chromosomes. Therefore, we will begin by taking a closer look at the structure of the eukaryotic chromosome.

The Eukaryotic Chromosome Consists of a Linear DNA Double Helix Bound to Proteins

Each human chromosome contains a single DNA double helix, about 50 million to 250 million nucleotides long. If their DNA were completely relaxed and extended, human chromosomes would be about 0.6 to 3.0 inches long (15 to 75 millimeters). Laid end to end, the total DNA in a single human cell would be about 6 feet long (1.8 meters).

Fitting this huge amount of DNA into a nucleus only a few micrometers in diameter is no trivial task. For most of a cell's life, the DNA in each chromosome is wound around proteins called histones. These DNA/histone beads further coil up and attach to other proteins, reducing the length of the DNA about 1,000-fold (Fig. 9-4). When a cell needs to read some of its genetic information, it temporarily frees specific regions of DNA from these proteins, but the DNA is soon repacked. However, even this enormous degree of compaction still leaves the chromosomes much too long to be sorted out and moved into the daughter nuclei during cell division. Just as thread is easier to organize when it is wound onto spools, sorting and transporting chromosomes is easier when they are condensed and shortened. During cell division, still more proteins fold up the DNA of each chromosome into compact structures that are about 10 times shorter than they are during the rest of the cell cycle, to about 4 micrometers in length (less than 2 ten-thousands of an inch; see Fig. 9-4).

Genes Are Segments of the DNA of a Chromosome

Genes are sequences of DNA from hundreds to thousands of nucleotides long. Each gene occupies a specific place, or **locus** (plural, **loci**), on a chromosome (Fig. 9-5a). Chromosomes vary in the number of genes they contain. The largest human chromosome, chromosome 1, contains more than 3,000 genes, whereas one of the smallest human chromosomes, chromosome 22, contains only about 600 genes.

In addition to genes, every chromosome has specialized regions that are crucial to its structure and function: two

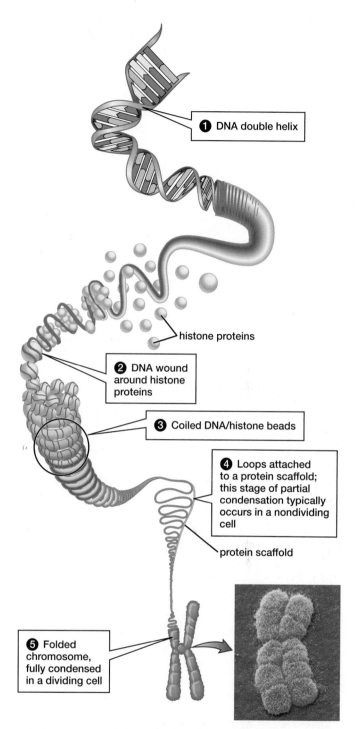

① DNA double helix

histone proteins

② DNA wound around histone proteins

③ Coiled DNA/histone beads

④ Loops attached to a protein scaffold; this stage of partial condensation typically occurs in a nondividing cell

protein scaffold

⑤ Folded chromosome, fully condensed in a dividing cell

▲ FIGURE 9-4 **Chromosome structure** ① A eukaryotic chromosome contains a single DNA double helix. ② The DNA is wound around proteins called histones, reducing the length by about a factor of 6. ③ Other proteins coil up the DNA/histone beads, much like a Slinky toy, reducing the length by another factor of 6 or 7. ④ These coils are attached in loops to protein "scaffolding" to complete the chromosome as it occurs during most of the life of a cell. The wrapping, coiling, and looping make the chromosome roughly 1,000 times shorter than the DNA molecule it contains. ⑤ During cell division, still other proteins fold up the chromosome, yielding about another 10-fold condensation. (Inset) The fuzzy edges visible in the electron micrograph are loops of folded chromosome.

gene loci

centromere

telomeres

(a) A eukaryotic chromosome before DNA replication

sister chromatids

duplicated chromosome (two DNA double helices)

centromere

(b) A eukaryotic chromosome after DNA replication

independent daughter chromosomes, each with one identical DNA double helix

(c) Separated sister chromatids become independent chromosomes

▲ **FIGURE 9-5 The principal features of a eukaryotic chromosome during cell division (a)** Before DNA replication, each chromosome consists of a single DNA double helix. Genes are segments of the DNA, usually hundreds to thousands of nucleotides in length. The ends of the chromosome are protected by telomeres. **(b)** The two sister chromatids of a duplicated chromosome are held together by the centromere. **(c)** The sister chromatids separate during cell division to become two independent, genetically identical, chromosomes.

telomeres and one centromere (see Fig. 9-5a). The two ends of a chromosome consist of repeated nucleotide sequences called **telomeres** ("end body" in Greek), which are essential for chromosome stability. Without telomeres, the ends of chromosomes might be removed by DNA repair enzymes, or the ends of two or more chromosomes might become connected, forming long, unwieldy structures that probably could not be distributed properly to the daughter cells during cell division. The second specialized region of the chromosome is the **centromere.** As we will see, the centromere has two principal functions: (1) It temporarily holds two daughter DNA double helices together after DNA replication, and (2) it is the attachment site for microtubules that move the chromosomes during cell division.

Duplicated Chromosomes Separate During Cell Division

Prior to cell division, the DNA within each chromosome is replicated, by a mechanism that we will describe in Chapter 11. At the end of DNA replication, a **duplicated chromosome** consists of two identical DNA double helices, now called sister **chromatids,** which are attached to each other at the centromere (**Fig. 9-5b**).

During mitotic cell division, the two sister chromatids separate, each becoming an independent chromosome that is delivered to one of the two daughter cells (**Fig. 9-5c**).

Eukaryotic Chromosomes Usually Occur in Pairs with Similar Genetic Information

The chromosomes of each eukaryotic species have characteristic shapes, sizes, and staining patterns. When we view an entire set of stained chromosomes from a single cell—its **karyotype**—we see that the nonreproductive cells of many organisms, including humans, contain pairs of chromosomes (**Fig. 9-6**). With one exception that we will discuss shortly, both members of each pair are the same length and have the same staining pattern. This similarity in size, shape, and staining occurs because each chromosome in a pair carries the same genes arranged in the same order. Chromosomes that contain the same genes are called **homologous chromosomes,** or **homologues,** from Greek words that mean "to say the same thing." Cells with pairs of homologous chromosomes are called **diploid,** meaning "double."

Homologous Chromosomes Are Usually Not Identical

Despite their name, homologues usually don't say exactly the "same thing." Why not? A cell might make a mistake when it

▲ **FIGURE 9-6 The karyotype of a human male** Staining and photographing the entire set of duplicated chromosomes within a single cell produces a karyotype. Pictures of the individual chromosomes are cut out and arranged in descending order of size. The chromosome pairs (homologues) are similar in both size and staining pattern and have similar genetic material. Chromosomes 1 through 22 are the autosomes; the X and Y chromosomes are the sex chromosomes. Note that the Y chromosome is much smaller than the X chromosome. If this were a female karyotype, it would have two X chromosomes.

copies the DNA of one homologue but not the other (see Chapter 11). Or, for example, a ray of ultraviolet light from the sun might zap the DNA of one homologue, thus changing it. These changes in the sequence of nucleotides in DNA are called **mutations,** and will make one homologue be a little different, genetically, than its pair. A given mutation might have happened yesterday, or perhaps 10,000 years ago and have been inherited ever since. If we think of the DNA as an instruction manual for building a cell or an organism, then mutations are like misspelled words in the manual. Although some misspellings might not matter much, others might have serious consequences. For example, single-letter misspellings in crucial genes cause genetic diseases such as sickle-cell anemia and cystic fibrosis. Occasionally, however, a mutation may actually improve the DNA manual and spread throughout a population, as the organisms carrying the mutation survive and reproduce better than other members of its species (see Unit 3).

As shown in Figure 9-6, a typical human cell has 23 pairs of chromosomes, for a total of 46. There are two copies of chromosome 1, two copies of chromosome 2, and so on, up through chromosome 22. These chromosomes—which have similar appearance, similar (but probably not identical) DNA sequences, and are paired in diploid cells of both sexes—are called **autosomes.** The cell also has two **sex chromosomes:** either two X chromosomes (in females) or an X and a Y chromosome (in males). The X and Y chromosomes are quite different in size (see Fig. 9-6) and in genetic composition. Thus, sex chromosomes are an exception to the rule that homologous chromosomes contain the same genes. However, in a male, the X and Y chromosomes behave as a pair during meiotic cell division.

Not All Cells Have Paired Chromosomes

Most cells in our bodies are diploid. However, during sexual reproduction, cells in the ovaries or testes undergo meiotic cell division (see section 9.8) to produce gametes (sperm or eggs). Gametes contain only one member of each pair of autosomes and one of the two sex chromosomes. Cells that contain only one of each type of chromosome are called **haploid** (meaning "half"). In humans, a haploid cell contains one each of the 22 autosomes, plus either an X or Y sex chromosome, for a total of 23 chromosomes. (Think of a haploid cell as one that contains half the diploid number of chromosomes, or one of each type of chromosome.)

When a sperm fertilizes an egg, fusion of the two haploid cells produces a diploid cell with two copies of each type of chromosome. Because one member of each pair of homologues was inherited from the mother (in her egg), these are usually called the maternal chromosomes. The chromosomes inherited from the father (in his sperm) are called paternal chromosomes.

In biological shorthand, the number of different types of chromosomes in a species is called the haploid number and is designated n. For humans, $n = 23$ because we have 23 different types of chromosomes (autosomes 1 to 22 plus one sex chromosome). Diploid cells contain $2n$ chromosomes. Thus, the body cells of humans have 46 (2×23) chromo-

somes. Every species has a specific number of chromosomes in its cells, from just a handful (e.g., 6 in mosquitoes) to hundreds (in shrimp and some plants).

Not all organisms are diploid. The bread mold *Neurospora*, for example, has haploid cells for most of its life cycle. Some plants, on the other hand, have more than two copies of each type of chromosome, with $4n$, $6n$, or even more chromosomes per cell.

9.4 WHAT OCCURS DURING THE EUKARYOTIC CELL CYCLE?

Newly formed cells usually acquire nutrients from their environment, synthesize additional cellular components, and grow larger. After a variable amount of time—depending on the organism, the type of cell, and the nutrients available—the cell may divide. Each daughter cell may then enter another cell cycle, producing additional cells. Many cells, however, divide only if they receive signals, such as growth hormones, that cause them to enter another cell cycle. Other cells may differentiate and never divide again.

The Eukaryotic Cell Cycle Consists of Interphase and Cell Division

The eukaryotic cell cycle is divided into two major phases: interphase and cell division (**Fig. 9-7**). During **interphase,** the cell acquires nutrients from its environment, grows, and

▲ FIGURE 9-7 **The eukaryotic cell cycle** The eukaryotic cell cycle consists of interphase and mitotic cell division.

duplicates its chromosomes. With the exception of meiotic cell division, cell division parcels one copy of each chromosome and usually about half the cytoplasm (including mitochondria, ribosomes, and other organelles) into each of the two daughter cells.

During Interphase, a Cell Grows in Size, Replicates Its DNA, and Often Differentiates

Most eukaryotic cells spend the majority of their time in interphase. For example, some cells in human skin, which divide about once a day, spend roughly 22 hours in interphase. Interphase itself contains three subphases: G_1 (the first gap in DNA synthesis and the first growth phase), S (DNA synthesis), and G_2 (the second gap in DNA synthesis and the second growth phase).

Immediately after it is formed by cell division, a newly formed daughter cell enters the G_1 portion of interphase. During G_1, a cell carries out one or more of three activities. First, it almost always grows in size. Second, it often specializes, or differentiates, to perform a specific function. For example, most nerve cells grow long strands, called axons, that allow them to connect with other cells, while liver cells produce bile, proteins such as clotting factors, and enzymes that detoxify many poisonous materials. Third, the cell is sensitive to internal and external signals that help it "decide" whether to divide. If that decision is positive, the cell enters the S phase, when DNA synthesis (replication) occurs. The cell then proceeds to the G_2 phase, during which it may grow some more and then synthesize the proteins needed for cell division.

Many cells, such as liver cells, can be recalled from the differentiated state back into the dividing state, whereas others, such as most heart muscle and nerve cells, never divide again. That is one reason why heart attacks and strokes are so devastating: The dead cells usually cannot be replaced. However, the heart and brain contain a few stem cells that *can* divide. Biomedical researchers hope that, one day, these stem cells can be coaxed into dividing rapidly and repairing the damaged organs.

The cell cycle is carefully controlled throughout the life of an organism. Without enough cell divisions at the right time and in the right organs, development falters or body parts fail to replace worn-out or damaged cells. With too many cell divisions, cancers may form. We will investigate how the cell cycle is controlled in section 9.6.

There Are Two Types of Cell Division in Eukaryotic Cells: Mitotic Cell Division and Meiotic Cell Division

Eukaryotic cells may undergo one of two evolutionarily related, but very different, types of cell division: mitotic cell division or meiotic cell division.

Mitotic Cell Division **Mitotic cell division** consists of nuclear division (called **mitosis**) followed by cytoplasmic division (called **cytokinesis**). The word "mitosis" comes from the Greek for "thread"; during mitosis, chromosomes condense and appear as thin, thread-like structures when viewed through a light microscope. Cytokinesis (from the Greek words for "cell movement") is the process by which the cytoplasm is divided between the two daughter cells. As we will see in section 9.5, mitosis gives each daughter nucleus one copy of the parent cell's replicated chromosomes, and cytokinesis usually places one of these nuclei into each daughter cell. Hence, mitotic cell division typically produces two daughter cells that are genetically identical to each other and to the parent cell, and usually contain about equal amounts of cytoplasm.

Mitotic cell division takes place in all types of eukaryotic organisms. It is the mechanism of asexual reproduction in eukaryotic cells, including unicellular organisms such as yeast, *Amoeba*, and *Paramecium*, and multicellular organisms such as *Hydra* and aspens. Mitotic cell division followed by differentiation of the daughter cells allows a fertilized egg to grow into an adult with perhaps trillions of specialized cells. Mitotic cell division also allows an organism to maintain its tissues, many of which require frequent replacement; to repair damaged parts of the body, for example, after a wound; and sometimes even to regenerate body parts. Mitotic cell division is also the mechanism whereby stem cells reproduce.

Meiotic Cell Division **Meiotic cell division** is a prerequisite for sexual reproduction in all eukaryotic organisms. In animals, meiotic cell division occurs only in ovaries and testes. The process of meiotic cell division involves a specialized nuclear division called **meiosis** and two rounds of cytokinesis to produce four daughter cells that can become gametes (eggs or sperm). Gametes carry half of the genetic material of the parent. As we shall see in section 9.8, the cells produced by meiotic cell division are not genetically identical to each other *or* to the original cell. During sexual reproduction, fusion of two gametes, one from each parent, reconstitutes a full complement of genetic material, forming a genetically unique offspring that is similar to both parents, but identical to neither.

9.5 HOW DOES MITOTIC CELL DIVISION PRODUCE GENETICALLY IDENTICAL DAUGHTER CELLS?

Mitotic cell division consists of mitosis (nuclear division) and cytokinesis (cytoplasmic division) (**Fig. 9-8**). After interphase (**Fig. 9-8a**), when the cell's chromosomes have been duplicated and all other necessary preparations for division have been made, mitotic cell division can occur. For convenience, biologists divide mitosis into four phases, based on the appearance and behavior of the chromosomes: prophase, metaphase, anaphase, and telophase. As with most biological processes, however, these phases are not really discrete events. Rather, they form a continuum, each phase merging into the next.

Cytokinesis usually occurs during telophase. However, mitosis sometimes occurs without cytokinesis, producing cells with multiple nuclei. This is fairly common in fungi and in certain stages of development in plants and flies.

During Prophase, the Chromosomes Condense, the Spindle Microtubules Form, and the Chromosomes Are Captured by the Spindle Microtubules

The first phase of mitosis is called **prophase** (meaning "the stage before" in Greek). During prophase, three major events occur: (1) The duplicated chromosomes condense, (2) the spindle microtubules form, and (3) the chromosomes are captured by the spindle microtubules (**Figs. 9-8b,c**).

Recall that chromosome duplication occurs during the S phase of interphase. Therefore, when mitosis begins, each chromosome already consists of two sister chromatids attached to one another at the centromere. During prophase, the duplicated chromosomes coil up and condense. In addition, the nucleolus, a structure within the nucleus where ribosomes assemble, disappears.

After the duplicated chromosomes condense, the **spindle microtubules** begin to assemble. In all eukaryotic cells, the proper movement of chromosomes during mitosis depends on these spindle microtubules. In animal cells, the spindle microtubules originate from a region in which a pair of microtubule-containing structures called **centrioles** is located. During interphase, a new pair of centrioles forms near the previously existing pair. During prophase, the centriole pairs migrate to opposite sides of the nucleus (see Fig. 9-8b). When the cell divides, each daughter cell will receive a pair of centrioles. Each centriole pair serves as a central point from which the spindle microtubules radiate, both inward toward the nucleus and outward toward the plasma membrane. These points are called spindle poles (see Fig. 9-8c). Although the cells of plants, fungi, many algae, and certain mutant fruit flies do not contain centrioles, they nevertheless form functional spindles during mitotic cell division, showing that centrioles are not required for spindle formation.

As the spindle microtubules form into a complete basket around the nucleus, the nuclear envelope disintegrates, releasing the duplicated chromosomes. Each sister chromatid has a protein-containing structure at its centromere called a **kinetochore.** In each duplicated chromosome, the kinetochores of the two sister chromatids are arranged back-to-back, facing away from one another. The kinetochore of one sister chromatid binds to the ends of spindle microtubules leading to one pole of the cell, while the kinetochore of the other sister chromatid binds to spindle microtubules leading to the opposite pole of the cell (see Fig. 9-8c). The microtubules that bind to kinetochores are called kinetochore microtubules, to distinguish them from microtubules that do not bind to a kinetochore (see below). When the sister chromatids separate later in mitosis, the newly independent chromosomes will move along the kinetochore microtubules to opposite poles.

Other spindle microtubules, called polar microtubules, do not attach to chromosomes; rather, they have free ends that overlap along the cell's equator. As we will see, the polar microtubules will push the two spindle poles apart later in mitosis.

During Metaphase, the Chromosomes Line Up Along the Equator of the Cell

At the end of prophase, the two kinetochores of each duplicated chromosome are connected to spindle microtubules leading to opposite poles of the cell. As a result, each duplicated chromosome is connected to both spindle poles. During **metaphase** (the "middle stage"), the two kinetochores on a duplicated chromosome engage in a "tug of war." During this process, the microtubules lengthen or shorten, until each chromosome lines up along the equator of the cell, with one kinetochore facing each pole (**Fig. 9-8d**).

During Anaphase, Sister Chromatids Separate and Are Pulled to Opposite Poles of the Cell

At the beginning of **anaphase** (**Fig. 9-8e**), the sister chromatids separate, becoming independent daughter chromosomes. This separation allows motor proteins in each kinetochore to pull the chromosome poleward, while simultaneously nibbling off the end of the attached microtubule, thereby shortening it (a mechanism appropriately called "Pac-Man" movement). One of the two daughter chromosomes derived from each original parental chromosome moves to each pole of the cell. Because the daughter chromosomes are identical copies of the parental chromosomes, each cluster of chromosomes that forms at opposite poles of the cell contains one copy of every chromosome that was in the parent cell.

At about the same time, the polar microtubules emanating from each pole grab onto one another where they overlap at the equator. These polar microtubules then simultaneously lengthen and push on one another, which forces the poles of the cell apart, so that the cell assumes an oval shape (see Fig. 9-8e).

During Telophase, Nuclear Envelopes Form Around Both Groups of Chromosomes

When the chromosomes reach the poles, **telophase** (the "end stage") begins (**Fig. 9-8f**). The spindle microtubules disintegrate and a nuclear envelope forms around each group of chromosomes. The chromosomes revert to their extended state, and nucleoli begin to form. In most cells, cytokinesis occurs during telophase, isolating each daughter nucleus in its own daughter cell (**Fig. 9-8g**).

During Cytokinesis, the Cytoplasm Is Divided Between Two Daughter Cells

In animal cells, microfilaments attached to the plasma membrane form a ring around the equator of the cell (see Fig. 9-8f). During cytokinesis, the ring contracts and constricts the cell's equator, much like the drawstring on a pair of sweatpants tightens the waist when pulled (see Fig. 9-8g). Eventually the "waist" constricts completely, dividing the cytoplasm into two new daughter cells (**Fig. 9-8h**).

INTERPHASE   MITOSIS

(a) Late Interphase
Duplicated chromosomes are in the relaxed uncondensed state; duplicated centrioles remain clustered.

(b) Early Prophase
Chromosomes condense and shorten; spindle microtubules begin to form between separating centriole pairs.

(c) Late Prophase
The nucleolus disappears; the nuclear envelope breaks down; some spindle microtubules attach to the kinetochore (blue) of each sister chromatid.

(d) Metaphase
Kinetochore microtubule line up the chromosome at the cell's equator.

▲ FIGURE 9-8 **Mitotic cell division in an animal cell**

QUESTION What would the consequences be if one set of sister chromatids failed to separate at anaphase?

Cytokinesis in plant cells is quite different, perhaps because their stiff cell walls make it impossible to divide one cell into two by pinching at the waist. Instead, carbohydrate-filled vesicles, which bud off the Golgi apparatus, line up along the cell's equator between the two nuclei (Fig. 9-9). The vesicles fuse, producing a structure called the **cell plate,** which is shaped like a flattened sac, surrounded by membrane and filled with sticky carbohydrates. When enough vesicles have fused, the edges of the cell plate merge with the plasma membrane around the circumference of the cell. The two sides of the cell plate membrane form new plasma membranes between the two daughter cells. The carbohydrates formerly contained in the vesicles remain between the plasma membranes as part of the cell wall.

Following cytokinesis, eukaryotic cells enter G_1 of interphase, thus completing the cell cycle.

Case Study continued
Send in the Clones

Mitotic cell division is essential for cloning, because mitosis produces daughter nuclei that are genetically identical to the parent nucleus. Therefore, nuclei taken from almost any of Missy's or Scamper's cells will produce clones that are genetically identical to their respective dog or horse "nuclear donor." Cloning is explored more thoroughly in "Scientific Inquiry: Carbon Copies—Cloning in Nature and the Lab" on pp. 156–157.

BioFlix ™ Mitosis

INTERPHASE

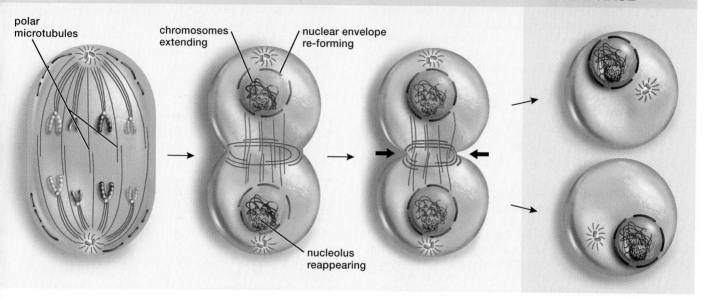

polar microtubules

chromosomes extending

nuclear envelope re-forming

nucleolus reappearing

(e) Anaphase
Sister chromatids separate and move to opposite poles of the cell; polar microtubules push the poles apart.

(f) Telophase
One set of chromosomes reaches each pole and begins to decondense; nuclear envelopes start to form; nucleoli begin to reappear; spindle microtubules begin to disappear; microfilaments form rings around the equator.

(g) Cytokinesis
The ring of microfilaments contracts, dividing the cell in two; each daughter cell receives one nucleus and about half of the cytoplasm.

(h) Interphase of daughter cells
Spindles disappear, intact nuclear envelopes form, and the chromosomes extend completely.

◀ FIGURE 9-9 Cytokinesis in a plant cell

cell plate forming a new cell wall

Golgi apparatus

cell wall

plasma membrane

carbohydrate-filled vesicles

❶ Carbohydrate-filled vesicles bud off the Golgi apparatus and move to the equator of the cell.

❷ The vesicles fuse to form a new cell wall (red) and plasma membrane (yellow) between the daughter cells.

❸ Complete separation of the daughter cells.

Scientific Inquiry

Carbon Copies—Cloning in Nature and the Lab

The word "cloning" usually brings to mind images of Dolly the sheep or even *Star Wars: Attack of the Clones*, but nature has been quietly cloning for hundreds of millions of years. How are clones produced, either in nature or in the lab? Why is cloning such a controversial topic? And why is cloning included in a chapter on cell division?

Cloning in Nature: The Role of Mitotic Cell Division

Let's address the last question first. As you know, there are two types of cell division: mitotic division and meiotic division. Sexual reproduction relies on meiotic cell division, the production of gametes, and fertilization, and usually produces genetically unique offspring. In contrast, asexual reproduction (see Fig. 9-2) relies on mitotic cell division. Because mitotic cell division creates daughter cells that are genetically identical to the parent cell, offspring produced by asexual reproduction are genetically identical to their parents—they are clones.

Cloning Plants: A Familiar Application in Agriculture

Humans have been in the cloning business a lot longer than you might think. For example, consider navel oranges, which don't produce seeds. Without seeds, how do they reproduce? Navel orange trees are propagated by cutting a piece of stem from an adult navel tree and grafting it onto the top of the root of a seedling orange tree. Therefore, the cells of the aboveground, fruit-bearing parts of the resulting tree are clones of the original navel orange stem. All navel oranges originated from a single mutant bud of an orange tree discovered in Brazil in the early 1800s, and propagated asexually ever since. Two navel orange trees were brought from Brazil to Riverside, California, in the 1870s—one of them is still there! All American navel orange trees are clones of these two trees.

Cloning Adult Mammals

In the 1950s, John Gurdon and his colleagues destroyed the nuclei of frog eggs, and then inserted new nuclei, taken from embryonic frog cells, into them. Some of the resulting cells developed into complete frogs. By the 1990s, several labs had cloned mammals using nuclei from embryos, but it wasn't until 1996 that Dr. Ian Wilmut of the Roslin Institute in Edinburgh, Scotland, cloned the first adult mammal, the famous Dolly (**Fig. E9-1**).

In agriculture, it is important to clone adults, because only in adults can we see the traits that we wish to propagate (such as milk production in cows, or speed and strength in horses). Any valuable traits of the adult that are genetically determined will also be expressed in all of its clones. Cloning of embryos would usually not be useful, because the embryonic cells would have been produced by sexual reproduction in the first place, and normally no one could tell if the embryo had any especially desirable traits.

For some medical applications, too, cloning adults is essential. Suppose that a pharmaceutical company genetically engineered (see Chapter 13) a cow that secreted a valuable molecule, such as an antibiotic, in its milk. These techniques are extremely expensive and somewhat hit or miss, so the company might successfully produce only one profitable cow. This cow could then be cloned, creating a whole herd of antibiotic-producing cows. Cloned cows that produce more milk or meat, and pigs tailored to be organ donors for humans, already exist.

Cloning might also help rescue critically endangered species, many of which don't reproduce well in zoos. As Richard Adams of Texas A&M University put it, "You could repopulate the world [with an endangered species] in a matter of a couple of years. Cloning is not a trivial pursuit."

Cloning: An Imperfect Technology

Unfortunately, cloning mammals is inefficient and beset with difficulties. An egg is subjected to severe trauma when its nucleus is sucked out or destroyed and a new nucleus is inserted (see Fig. E9-1). Often, the egg may simply die. Molecules in the cytoplasm that are needed to control development may be lost or moved to the wrong places, so that even if the egg survives and divides, it may not develop properly. If the eggs develop into viable embryos, the embryos must then be implanted into the uterus of a surrogate mother. Many clones die or are aborted during gestation, often with serious or fatal consequences for the surrogate mother. Even if the clone survives gestation and birth, it may have defects, commonly a deformed head, lungs, or heart. Given the high failure rate—it took 277 tries to produce Dolly, and more than 1,000 embryos implanted into 123 female dogs to produce Snuppy—cloning mammals is an expensive proposition.

To make things even more problematic, some "successful" clones may have hidden defects. Dolly, for example, developed arthritis when she was $5\frac{1}{2}$ and was euthanized with a serious lung disease when she was $6\frac{1}{2}$, so her problems occurred at a relatively young age (the typical life span of a sheep is 11 to 16 years), although no one knows if these health problems occurred because she was a clone.

The Future of Cloning

Modern cloning technology has now successfully cloned dogs, cows, cats, sheep, horses, and a variety of other animals. As the process becomes more routine, it also brings ethical questions. While hardly anyone objects to cloning navel oranges, and few would refuse antibiotics or other medicinal products from cloned livestock, some people think that cloning pets is a frivolous luxury—especially when you consider that almost 10 million unwanted dogs and cats are euthanized in the United States every year. We will briefly consider human cloning in the "Case Study Revisited: Send in the Clones" section at the end of this chapter.

Finn Dorset ewe

donor cell
from an udder

electric pulse   fused cells

1 Cells from the udder of a Finn Dorset ewe are grown in culture with low nutrient levels. The starved cells stop dividing.

Blackface ewe

egg
cell

nucleus is
removed

DNA

3 The egg cell without a nucleus and the nondividing udder cell are placed side by side in a culture dish. An electric pulse stimulates the cells to fuse and initiates mitotic cell division.

2 Meanwhile, the nucleus is sucked out of an unfertilized egg cell taken from a Scottish Blackface ewe. This egg will provide cytoplasm but no chromosomes.

4 The cell divides, forming an embryo that consists of a ball of cells.

5 The ball of cells is implanted into the uterus of another Blackface ewe.

6 The Blackface ewe gives birth to Dolly, a female Finn Dorset lamb, a genetic twin of the Finn Dorset ewe.

▲ FIGURE E9-1 **The making of Dolly**

9.6 HOW IS THE CELL CYCLE CONTROLLED?

Some cells, such as those of the stomach lining, divide frequently throughout the life of an organism. Others divide in response to specific stimuli such as tissue damage or infection. Still other cells—such as most cells in the brain, heart, and skeletal muscles—never divide in an adult. Cell division is regulated by a bewildering array of molecules, not all of which have been identified and studied. Nevertheless, some general principles apply to the cell cycles of most eukaryotic cells.

The Activities of Specific Enzymes Drive the Cell Cycle

The cell cycle is controlled by a family of proteins called cyclin-dependent kinases, or Cdks for short. These proteins get their name from two features: First, a kinase is an enzyme that phosphorylates (adds a phosphate group to) other proteins, stimulating or inhibiting the activity of the target protein. Second, these are "cyclin dependent" because they are active only when they bind still another protein, called a cyclin. The name "cyclin" tells you a lot about these proteins: Their abundance changes during the cell cycle, and in fact helps to regulate the cell cycle.

Normal cell-cycle control works like this. Most cells in your body are in the G_1 phase of the cell cycle, and a cell will usually divide only if it receives signals from hormone-like molecules called growth factors. For example, if you cut your skin, platelets (cell fragments in the blood that are involved in blood clotting) accumulate at the wound site and release growth factors, including platelet-derived growth factor and epidermal growth factor. These growth factors bind to receptors on the surfaces of cells deep in the skin (**Fig. 9-10 ❶**). When a cell in G_1 is stimulated by growth factors, it synthesizes cyclin proteins (**Fig. 9-10 ❷**) that bind to specific Cdks (**Fig. 9-10 ❸**). The cyclin–Cdk complexes then stimulate the synthesis and activity of proteins that are required for DNA synthesis to occur (**Fig. 9-10 ❹**). The cell thus enters the S phase and replicates its DNA. After DNA replication is complete, other Cdks become activated during G_2 and mitosis, causing chromosome condensation, breakdown of the nuclear envelope, formation of the spindle, and attachment of the chromosomes to the spindle microtubules. Finally, still other Cdks stimulate processes that allow the sister chromatids to separate into individual chromosomes and move to opposite poles of the cell during anaphase.

▶ FIGURE 9-10 **Growth factors stimulate cell division** Progress through the cell cycle is under the overall control of cyclin and cyclin-dependent kinases (Cdks). In most cases, growth factors stimulate synthesis of cyclin proteins, which activate Cdks, starting a cascade of events that lead to DNA replication and cell division.

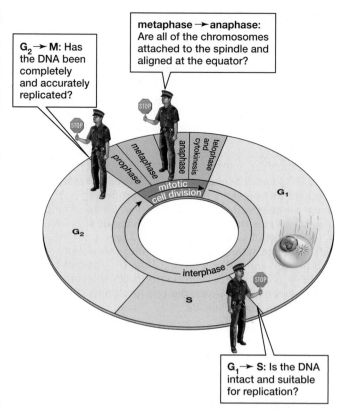

▲ FIGURE 9-11 Control of the cell cycle Three major checkpoints regulate a cell's transitions from one phase of the cell cycle to the next: (1) G_1 to S, (2) G_2 to mitosis (M), and (3) metaphase to anaphase.

Checkpoints Regulate Progress Through the Cell Cycle

When unregulated, cell division can be dangerous. If a cell contains mutations in its DNA or if daughter cells receive too many or too few chromosomes, the daughter cells may die, or they may become cancerous. To prevent this, the eukaryotic cell cycle has three major **checkpoints (Fig. 9-11)**. At each checkpoint, protein complexes in the cell determine whether the cell has successfully completed a specific phase of the cycle:

- **G_1 to S:** Is the cell's DNA intact and suitable for replication?
- **G_2 to mitosis:** Has the DNA been completely and accurately replicated?
- **Metaphase to anaphase:** Are all the chromosomes attached to the spindle and aligned properly at the equator of the cell?

The checkpoint proteins usually regulate the production of cyclins or the activity of cyclin-dependent kinases, or both, thereby regulating progression from one phase of the cell cycle to the next. Defective checkpoint control is a primary cause of cancer, as we explore in "A Closer Look at Control of the Cell Cycle and Its Role in Cancer" on pp. 160–161.

9.7 WHY DO SO MANY ORGANISMS REPRODUCE SEXUALLY?

There are a number of very successful organisms that routinely reproduce asexually. For example, the molds *Penicillium* (which synthesizes penicillin) and *Aspergillus niger* (used in the commercial manufacture of vitamin C) reproduce by "mitospores"—clouds of tiny cells produced by mitosis—and in fact have never been observed to reproduce sexually. Many of the grasses and weeds in your lawn can reproduce by sprouting whole new plants from their stems or roots. Some, like Kentucky bluegrass and dandelions, even bear flowers that can produce seeds without being fertilized! Clearly, asexual reproduction must work pretty well.

Why, then, do nearly all eukaryotic organisms, including bluegrass and dandelions, also reproduce sexually? As we have seen, mitosis can only produce clones of genetically identical offspring. In contrast, sexual reproduction shuffles genes to produce genetically unique offspring. The nearly universal presence of sexual reproduction provides evidence for the tremendous evolutionary advantage that DNA exchange among individuals confers on a species.

Case Study continued

Send in the Clones

Consider a dandelion producing seeds without using sexual reproduction. That dandelion, and all of its offspring, will be genetically identical to one another (except for mutations), probably genetically a little different from all other dandelions, and incapable of sharing genes with any other dandelion. You may have a few such "microspecies" clones in your own backyard!

Mutations in DNA Are the Ultimate Source of Genetic Variability

As we will see in Chapter 11, the fidelity of DNA replication minimizes errors as the DNA is duplicated, but changes in DNA do occur, producing mutations. Although most mutations are either neutral or harmful, they are also the raw material for evolution. Mutations in gametes may be passed to offspring and become a part of the genetic makeup of the species. Such mutations form **alleles,** alternate forms of a given gene that may produce differences in structure or function—such as black, brown, or blond hair in humans, or different mating calls in frogs. As we saw earlier, most eukaryotic organisms are diploid, containing pairs of homologous chromosomes. Homologous chromosomes have the same genes, but each homologue may have the same alleles of some genes and different alleles of other

A Closer Look At *Control of the Cell Cycle and Its Role in Cancer*

As we described in section 9.6, the cell cycle is tightly controlled. Both during embryonic development, and during maintenance and repair of the adult body, progression through the cell cycle is regulated primarily by two interacting processes: (1) production of, and responses to, growth factors that generally speed up the cell cycle; and (2) intracellular checkpoints that stop the cell cycle if problems such as mutations in DNA or misalignment of the chromosomes have occurred. Most cancers develop because one or both of these processes goes awry.

Many different molecules control the cell cycle; here, we will focus on the proteins produced from two important types of genes, called oncogenes and tumor suppressor genes. We will first examine their roles in normal cell cycle control, and then we will explore how defective oncogenes and tumor suppressor genes lead to cancer. Because of the importance of the G_1 to S checkpoint in cancer, we will discuss only their effects at this checkpoint.

Normal Control of the G_1 to S Checkpoint

Proto-oncogenes

Any gene whose protein product tends to promote mitotic cell division is called a proto-oncogene. The genes for growth factors, growth factor receptors, and some of the cyclins and Cdks are proto-oncogenes. In most cases, progress through the cell cycle begins when a growth-stimulating protein, such as epidermal growth factor (EGF), binds to a receptor on the surface of a cell (see Fig. 9-10). This stimulates the synthesis of cyclins, which bind to Cdks and activate them. Thus, these proto-oncogenes are essential to the normal control of the cell cycle. We will shortly examine what happens when a proto-oncogene mutates into an oncogene.

Tumor suppressor genes

The protein products of tumor suppressor genes prevent uncontrolled cell division and the production of daughter cells with mutated DNA, both of which are common in tumors. Let's examine the activity of the proteins produced by two important tumor suppressor genes, *Rb* and *p53*. (We will follow the usual convention of italicizing the gene [*Rb*] and using normal fonts for the protein [Rb].)

Recall that Cdks regulate the activity of other proteins by adding a phosphate group to them. One such protein is Rb. Normally, Rb inhibits transcription of several genes whose protein products are required for DNA synthesis. Phosphorylation of Rb by Cdks relieves this inhibition in the G_1 phase of the cell cycle, allowing the cell to proceed to the S phase and replicate its DNA (**Fig. E9-2a**). This chain of events, from growth factor stimulation to phosphorylation of Rb, ensures that the cell cycle starts up only when the body needs it to.

Another tumor suppressor protein, called p53 ("a **p**rotein with a molecular weight of **53**,000"), monitors the integrity of the cell's DNA and indirectly regulates Rb activity. Healthy cells, with intact DNA, contain little p53. However, when DNA has been damaged (for example, by ultraviolet rays in sunlight), p53 levels rise. The p53 protein then stimulates the expression of proteins that inhibit Cdks. If Cdks are inhibited, then Rb is not phosphorylated and DNA synthesis is blocked; this prevents the cell from producing daughter cells with damaged DNA (**Fig. E9-2b**). The p53 also stimulates the synthesis of DNA repair enzymes. After the DNA has been repaired, p53 levels decline, Cdks become active, Rb becomes phosphorylated, and the cell enters the S phase. If the DNA cannot be repaired, p53 triggers a special form of cell death called apoptosis, in which the cell cuts up its DNA and effectively commits suicide.

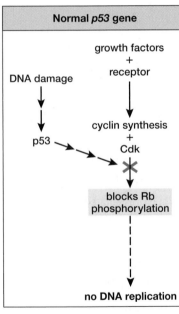

(a) Normal operation of the G_1 to S checkpoint

(b) DNA damage prevents progression through the G_1 to S checkpoint

▲ **FIGURE E9-2 Controlling the transition from G_1 to S** **(a)** The Rb protein inhibits DNA synthesis. Toward the end of the G_1 phase, cyclin levels rise. These activate Cdk, which then adds a phosphate group to the Rb protein. Phosphorylated Rb no longer inhibits DNA synthesis, so the cell enters the S phase. **(b)** Damaged DNA stimulates increased levels of the p53 protein, which triggers a cascade of events that inhibit Cdk, thereby preventing entry into the S phase until the DNA has been repaired.

Defective Control of the G₁ to S Checkpoint Can Produce Cancerous Cells

Oncogenes

A mutation may convert a harmless, indeed essential, proto-oncogene into a cancer-causing oncogene ("a gene that causes cancer"). For example, mutated receptors for growth factors may be "turned on" all the time, regardless of the presence or absence of a growth factor (**Fig. E9-3a**). Mutations in cyclin genes may cause cyclins to be continuously synthesized at a high rate, regardless of growth factor activity (see Fig. E9-3a). In either case, a cell may skip right through the G₁ to S checkpoint and divide much more frequently than it should. Rapid, uncontrolled cell division, of course, is one of the hallmarks of cancerous cells.

Inactive tumor suppressor genes

Many carcinogens mutate the *Rb* or *p53* genes, so that the proteins encoded by these genes can't do their jobs (**Fig. E9-3b**). Mutated Rb mimics phosphorylated Rb, which permits uncontrolled DNA synthesis. Mutated p53 is inactive, so Cdks remain active, phosphorylating Rb and allowing damaged DNA to be replicated (see Fig. E9-3b). With either mutation, replication proceeds, whether or not the DNA has been damaged. Not surprisingly, about half of all cancers—including tumors of the breast, lung, brain, pancreas, bladder, stomach, and colon—have mutations in

the *p53* gene. Many others, including tumors of the eye (retinoblastoma, hence the name *Rb*), lung, breast, and bladder, have a mutated *Rb* gene.

From Mutated Cell to Cancer

Do overactive oncogenes or inactive tumor suppressor genes, and the mutated DNA that usually accompanies them, doom a person to cancer? Not necessarily. Many mutations cause the surface of a cell to "look foreign" to the cells of the immune system, which then kills the mutated cell. Occasionally, however, a renegade cell survives and reproduces. Because mitotic cell division usually faithfully transmits genetic information from cell to cell, the descendants of the original cancerous cell will themselves be cancerous.

Why does medical science, which has conquered smallpox, measles, and a host of other diseases, have such a difficult time curing cancer? Both normal and cancerous cells use the same machinery for cell division, so treatments that slow down the multiplication of cancer cells also inhibit the maintenance of essential body parts, such as the stomach, intestine, and blood cells. Truly effective and selective treatments for cancer must target cell division only in cancerous cells. Although great strides have been made in the fight to cure cancer, much remains to be done.

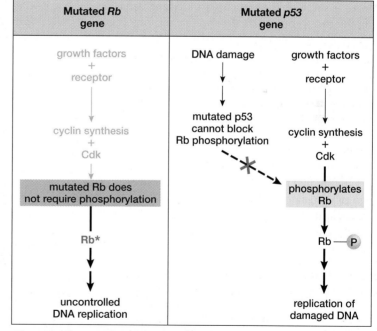

(a) Actions of oncogenes

(b) Actions of mutated tumor suppressor genes

▲ **FIGURE E9-3 Actions of oncogenes and tumor suppressor genes** **(a)** Oncogenes permit DNA replication and cell division without stimulation by growth factors. **(b)** Mutated *Rb* tumor suppressor genes (left) permit DNA replication without stimulation by growth factors. Mutated *p53* tumor suppressor genes (right) permit replication of damaged DNA.

▲ **FIGURE 9-12 Homologous chromosomes may have the same or different alleles of individual genes** The two homologues have the same genes at the same locations (loci). The homologues may have the same allele of a gene at certain loci (left) and different alleles of a gene at other loci (right).

genes (**Fig. 9-12**). We'll explore the consequences of having paired genes—and more than one allele of each gene—in Chapter 10.

Sexual Reproduction May Combine Different Parental Alleles in a Single Offspring

Let's consider a hypothetical evolutionary problem: Camouflage coloration can help an animal avoid predation only if it stays still when it sees a predator. Camouflaged animals that constantly jump around and brightly colored animals that "freeze" when a predator appears will probably both be eaten. How might a single animal combine camouflage coloration and freezing behavior? Let's suppose that a ground-nesting bird has better-than-average camouflage color, while another bird of the same species has more effective freezing behavior. Combining the two through sexual reproduction might produce offspring that are able to avoid predation better than either parent. Combining useful, genetically determined traits is probably one reason that sexual reproduction is so ubiquitous.

How does sexual reproduction combine traits from two parents in a single offspring? As we will see shortly, meiotic cell division produces haploid cells, each containing one copy of each chromosome. In animals, these haploid cells usually become gametes. A haploid sperm from animal A might contain alleles contributing to camouflage coloration, and a haploid egg from animal B might contain alleles that favor freezing at the first sign of a predator. Fusion of these gametes may produce an animal with camouflage coloration that also becomes motionless when a predator approaches.

9.8 HOW DOES MEIOTIC CELL DIVISION PRODUCE HAPLOID CELLS?

The key to sexual reproduction in eukaryotes is meiosis, the production of haploid nuclei with unpaired chromosomes from diploid parent nuclei with paired chromosomes.

Meiosis Separates Homologous Chromosomes, Producing Haploid Daughter Nuclei

In meiotic cell division (meiosis followed by cytokinesis), each daughter cell receives one member of each pair of homologous chromosomes. Therefore, meiosis (from a Greek

word meaning "to diminish") reduces the number of chromosomes in a diploid cell by half. For example, each diploid cell in your body contains 23 *pairs* of chromosomes; meiotic cell division produces sperm or eggs with 23 chromosomes, one from each pair.

Meiosis evolved from mitosis, so many of the structures and events of meiosis are similar or identical to those of mitosis. However, meiosis differs from mitosis in a major way: During meiosis, the cell undergoes *one* round of DNA replication followed by *two* nuclear divisions. One round of DNA replication produces two chromatids in each duplicated chromosome. Because diploid cells have pairs of homologous chromosomes—with two chromatids per homologue—a single round of DNA replication creates four chromatids for each type of chromosome (**Fig. 9-13a**).

The first division of meiosis (called meiosis I) separates the pairs of homologues and sends one of each pair into each of two daughter nuclei, producing two haploid nuclei. Each homologue, however, still consists of two chromatids (**Fig. 9-13b**).

A second division (called meiosis II) separates the chromatids and parcels one chromatid into each of two more daughter nuclei. Therefore, at the end of meiosis, there are four haploid daughter nuclei, each with one copy of each homologous chromosome. Because each nucleus is usually contained in a different cell, meiotic cell division normally produces four haploid cells from a single diploid parent cell (**Fig. 9-13c**).

We'll explore the stages of meiosis in more detail in the following sections.

Meiotic Cell Division Followed by Fusion of Gametes Keeps the Chromosome Number Constant from Generation to Generation

Why is meiotic cell division so important to sexual reproduction? Consider what would happen if the parent organisms' gametes were diploid, like the rest of the cells of the parents, with two copies of each homologous chromosome. Fertilization of diploid cells from the first-generation sperm and egg would result in a cell with four copies of each homologue, giving the offspring twice as many chromosomes as its parents. These offspring would produce gametes with four copies of each homologue, so their offspring would have eight copies. The next generation would have 16 copies, and so on. After a few generations, each cell would have enormous amounts of DNA. On the other hand, when a haploid sperm fuses with a haploid egg, the resulting offspring are diploid, just like their parents (**Fig. 9-14**).

Meiosis I Separates Homologous Chromosomes into Two Haploid Daughter Nuclei

The phases of meiosis have the same names as the roughly equivalent phases in mitosis, followed by I or II to distinguish the two nuclear divisions that occur in meiosis

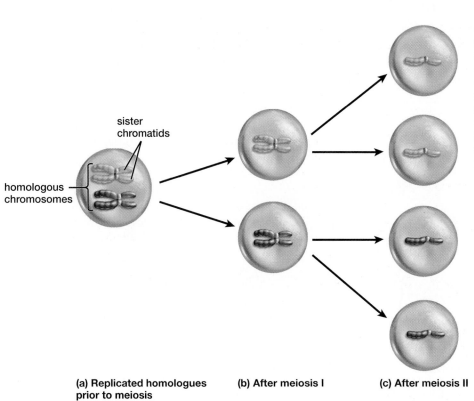

◄ **FIGURE 9-13 Meiosis halves the number of chromosomes (a)** Both members of a pair of homologous chromosomes are replicated prior to meiosis. **(b)** During meiosis I, each daughter cell receives one member of each pair of homologues. **(c)** During meiosis II, sister chromatids separate into independent chromosomes, and each daughter cell receives one of these chromosomes.

(a) Replicated homologues prior to meiosis

(b) After meiosis I

(c) After meiosis II

(Fig. 9-15). In the descriptions that follow, we assume that cytokinesis accompanies the nuclear divisions. As in mitosis, the chromosomes are duplicated during interphase prior to meiosis, and the sister chromatids of each chromosome are attached to one another at the centromere when meiosis begins.

During Prophase I, Homologous Chromosomes Pair Up and Exchange DNA

During mitosis, homologous chromosomes move completely independently of each other. In contrast, during prophase I of meiosis, homologous chromosomes line up

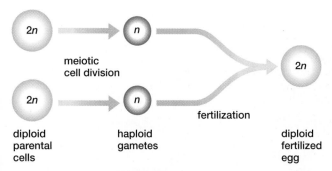

diploid parental cells

haploid gametes

diploid fertilized egg

▲ **FIGURE 9-14 Meiotic cell division is essential for sexual reproduction** In sexual reproduction, specialized reproductive cells undergo meiosis to produce haploid cells. In animals, these cells become gametes (sperm or eggs). When an egg is fertilized by a sperm, the resulting fertilized egg, or zygote, is once again diploid.

side by side and exchange segments of DNA (**Fig. 9-15a** and **Fig. 9-16**). We'll call one homologue the "maternal homologue" and the other the "paternal homologue," because one was originally inherited from the organism's mother and the other from the organism's father.

During prophase I, proteins bind the maternal and paternal homologues together so that they align precisely along their entire length. Enzymes then cut through the DNA of the paired homologues and graft the cut ends together, often joining part of one of the chromatids of the maternal homologue to part of one of the chromatids of the paternal homologue, and vice versa. The binding proteins and enzymes then depart, leaving crosses, or **chiasmata** (singular, **chiasma**), where the maternal and paternal chromosomes have exchanged parts (see Fig. 9-16). In human cells, each pair of homologues usually forms two or three chiasmata during prophase I. The mutual exchange of DNA between maternal and paternal chromosomes at chiasmata is called **crossing over.** If the chromosomes have different alleles, then crossing over creates genetic **recombination,** the formation of new combinations of alleles on a chromosome.

In addition to being the sites of crossing over, the arms of the homologues remain temporarily entangled at the chiasmata. This keeps the two homologues together until they are pulled apart during anaphase I.

As in mitosis, the spindle microtubules begin to assemble outside the nucleus during prophase I. Near the end of prophase I, the nuclear envelope breaks down and spindle microtubules invade the nuclear region, capturing the chromosomes by attaching to their kinetochores.

MEIOSIS I

(a) Prophase I
Duplicated chromosomes condense. Homologous chromosomes pair up and chiasmata occur as chromatids of homologues exchange parts by crossing over. The nuclear envelope disintegrates, and spindle microtubules form.

(b) Metaphase I
Paired homologous chromosomes line up along the equator of the cell. One homologue of each pair faces each pole of the cell and attaches to the spindle microtubules via the kinetochore (blue).

(c) Anaphase I
Homologues separate, one member of each pair going to each pole of the cell. Sister chromatids do not separate.

(d) Telophase I
Spindle microtubules disappear. Two clusters of chromosomes have formed, each containing one member of each pair of homologues. The daughter nuclei are therefore haploid. Cytokinesis commonly occurs at this stage. There is little or no interphase between meiosis I and meiosis II.

▲ **FIGURE 9-15** The homologous chromosomes of a diploid cell are separated, producing four haploid daughter cells. Two pairs of homologous chromosomes are shown. Yellow chromosomes are from one parent and violet chromosomes are from the other parent.

QUESTION What would be the consequences for the resulting gametes if one pair of homologues failed to separate at anaphase I?

During Metaphase I, Paired Homologous Chromosomes Line Up at the Equator of the Cell

During metaphase I, interactions between the kinetochores and the spindle microtubules move the paired homologues to the equator of the cell (**Fig. 9-15b**). Unlike in mitosis,

where *individual* duplicated chromosomes line up along the equator, in meiosis, *homologous pairs* of duplicated chromosomes, held together by chiasmata, line up along the equator during metaphase I. Which member of a pair of homologous chromosomes faces which pole of the cell is random—the

▲ **FIGURE 9-16 Crossing over** Nonsister chromatids of different members of a homologous pair of chromosomes exchange DNA at chiasmata.

MEIOSIS II

(e) Prophase II
If the chromosomes have decondensed after telophase I, they recondense. Spindle microtubules re-form and attach to the sister chromatids.

(f) Metaphase II
The chromosomes line up along the equator, with sister chromatids of each chromosome attached to kinetochore microtubules that lead to opposite poles.

(g) Anaphase II
The chromatids separate into independent daughter chromosomes, one former chromatid moving toward each pole.

(h) Telophase II
The chromosomes finish moving to opposite poles. Nuclear envelopes re-form, and the chromosomes decondense again (not shown here).

(i) Four haploid cells
Cytokinesis results in four haploid cells, each containing one member of each pair of homologous chromosomes (shown here in the condensed state).

maternal homologue may face "north" for some pairs and "south" for other pairs. This randomness (also called independent assortment), together with genetic recombination caused by crossing over, is responsible for the genetic diversity of the haploid cells produced by meiosis.

During Anaphase I, Homologous Chromosomes Separate

Anaphase in meiosis I differs considerably from anaphase in mitosis. In anaphase of mitosis, the *sister chromatids separate* and move to opposite poles. In contrast, in anaphase I of meiosis, the sister chromatids of each duplicated homologue remain attached to each other and move to the same pole, but the *homologues separate* as the chiasmata untangle, and move to opposite poles (**Fig. 9-15c**). One duplicated chromosome of each homologous pair (still consisting of two sister chromatids) moves to each pole of the dividing cell.

During Telophase I, Two Haploid Clusters of Duplicated Chromosomes Form

At the end of anaphase I, the cluster of chromosomes at each pole contains one member of each pair of homologous chromosomes. Therefore, each cluster contains the haploid number of chromosomes. In telophase I, the spindle microtubules disappear. Cytokinesis commonly occurs during telophase I (**Fig. 9-15d**). In many, but not all, organisms, nuclear envelopes re-form. Telophase I is usually followed immediately by meiosis II, with little or no intervening interphase. The chromosomes do not replicate between meiosis I and meiosis II, but they may temporarily decondense.

Meiosis II Separates Sister Chromatids into Four Daughter Nuclei

During meiosis II, the sister chromatids of each duplicated chromosome separate in a process that is virtually identical to mitosis, though it takes place in haploid cells. During prophase II, the spindle microtubules re-form (**Fig. 9-15e**). If the chromosomes decondensed at the end of meiosis I, they recondense. As in mitosis, the kinetochores of the sister chromatids of each duplicated chromosome attach to spindle microtubules extending to opposite poles of the cell. During metaphase II, the duplicated chromosomes line up at the cell's equator (**Fig. 9-15f**). During anaphase II, the sister chromatids separate and are towed to opposite poles (**Fig. 9-15g**). Telophase II and cytokinesis conclude meiosis II as nuclear envelopes re-form, the chromosomes decondense into their extended state, and the cytoplasm divides (**Fig. 9-15h**). Commonly, both daughter cells produced in meiosis I undergo meiosis II, producing a total of four haploid cells from the original parental diploid cell (**Fig. 9-15i**).

Now that we have covered all of the processes in detail, examine **Table 9-1** to review and compare mitotic and meiotic cell division.

BioFlix™ Meiosis

9.9 WHEN DO MITOTIC AND MEIOTIC CELL DIVISION OCCUR IN THE LIFE CYCLES OF EUKARYOTES?

The life cycles of almost all eukaryotic organisms have a common overall pattern (**Fig. 9-17**). First, two haploid cells fuse during the process of fertilization, bringing together genes from different parental organisms and endowing the resulting diploid cell with new gene combinations. Second, at some point in the life cycle, meiotic cell division occurs, re-creating haploid cells. Third, at some time in the life cycle, mitotic cell division of either haploid or diploid cells, or both, results in the growth of multicellular bodies, or in asexual reproduction.

Table 9-1 **A Comparison of Mitotic and Meiotic Cell Division in Animal Cells**

Feature	Mitotic Cell Division	Meiotic Cell Division
Cells in which it occurs	Body cells	Gamete-producing cells
Final chromosome number	Diploid—2n; two copies of each type of chromosome (homologous pairs)	Haploid—1n; one member of each homologous pair
Number of daughter cells	Two, identical to the parent cell and to each other	Four, containing recombined chromosomes due to crossing over
Number of cell divisions per DNA replication	One	Two
Function in animals	Development, growth, repair, and maintenance of tissues; asexual reproduction	Gamete production for sexual reproduction

In these diagrams, comparable phases are aligned. In both mitosis and meiosis, chromosomes are replicated during interphase. Meiosis I, with the pairing of homologous chromosomes, formation of chiasmata, exchange of chromosome parts, and separation of homologues to form haploid daughter nuclei, has no counterpart in mitosis. Meiosis II, however, is virtually identical to mitosis in a haploid cell.

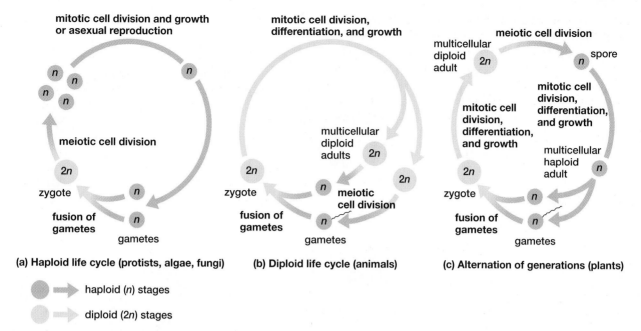

▲ FIGURE 9-17 **The three major types of eukaryotic life cycles** The lengths of the arrows correspond roughly to the proportion of the life cycle spent in each stage. **(a)** Almost all of a haploid life cycle is spent in the haploid state. Meiosis usually occurs soon after fertilization. **(b)** Almost all of a diploid life cycle is spent in the diploid state. Meiosis usually occurs just before fertilization. **(c)** In alternation of generations life cycles, significant portions of the cycle are spent in both haploid and diploid states. Meiosis occurs at the transition between diploid and haploid stages.

The seemingly vast differences between the life cycles of, say, ferns and humans are caused by variations in three aspects: (1) the interval between meiotic cell division and the fusion of haploid cells, (2) at what points in the life cycle mitotic and meiotic cell division occur, and (3) the relative proportions of the life cycle spent in the diploid and haploid states. These aspects of life cycles are interrelated, and we can conveniently label life cycles according to the relative dominance of diploid and haploid stages.

In Haploid Life Cycles, the Majority of the Cycle Consists of Haploid Cells

Some eukaryotes, such as many fungi and unicellular algae, spend most of their life cycles in the haploid state, with single copies of each type of chromosome (**Fig. 9-17a** and **Fig. 9-18**). Asexual reproduction by mitotic cell division produces a population of identical, haploid cells. Under certain environmental conditions, specialized reproductive haploid cells are produced. Two of these reproductive cells fuse, forming a diploid zygote. The zygote immediately undergoes meiosis, producing haploid cells again. In organisms with haploid life cycles, mitotic cell division never occurs in diploid cells.

In Diploid Life Cycles, the Majority of the Cycle Consists of Diploid Cells

Most animals have life cycles that are just the reverse of the haploid cycle. Virtually the entire animal life cycle is spent in the diploid state (**Fig. 9-17b** and **Fig. 9-19**). Haploid gametes (sperm in males, eggs in females) are formed by meiotic cell division. These fuse to form a diploid fertilized egg, called a zygote. Growth and development of the zygote to the adult organism result from mitotic cell division and differentiation of diploid cells.

In Alternation of Generations Life Cycles, There Are Both Diploid and Haploid Multicellular Stages

The life cycle of plants is called alternation of generations, because it alternates between multicellular diploid and multicellular haploid forms. In the typical pattern (**Fig. 9-17c** and **Fig. 9-20**), a multicellular diploid adult stage (the "diploid generation") gives rise to haploid cells, called spores, through meiotic cell division. These spores then undergo mitotic cell division and differentiation of the daughter cells to produce a multicellular haploid adult stage (the "haploid generation"). At some point, certain haploid cells differentiate into haploid gametes. Two gametes then fuse to form a diploid zygote. The zygote grows by mitotic cell division into another multicellular diploid adult stage.

In some plants, such as ferns, both the haploid and diploid stages are free-living, independent plants. Flowering plants, however, have reduced haploid stages, represented only by the pollen grain and a small cluster of cells in the ovary of the flower.

▶ **FIGURE 9-18 The life cycle of the unicellular alga *Chlamydomonas***
Chlamydomonas reproduces asexually by mitotic cell division of haploid cells. When nutrients are scarce, specialized haploid reproductive cells (usually from genetically different populations) fuse to form a diploid cell. Meiotic cell division then immediately produces four haploid cells, usually with different genetic compositions than either of the parental strains.

▶ **FIGURE 9-19 The human life cycle**
Through meiotic cell division, the two sexes produce gametes—sperm in males and eggs in females—that fuse to form a diploid zygote. Mitotic cell division and differentiation of the daughter cells produce an embryo, child, and ultimately a sexually mature adult. The haploid stages last only a few hours to a few days; the diploid stages may survive for a century.

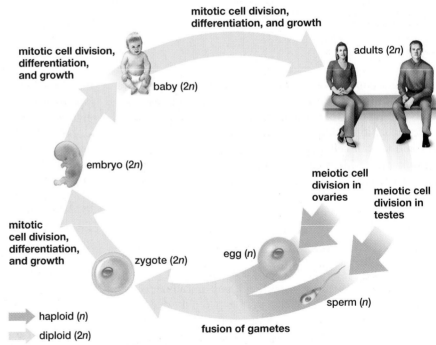

9.10 HOW DO MEIOSIS AND SEXUAL REPRODUCTION PRODUCE GENETIC VARIABILITY?

Genetic variability among organisms is essential for survival and reproduction in a changing environment and, therefore, for evolution. Mutations occurring randomly over millions of years are the original sources of genetic variability within the populations of organisms that exist today. However, mutations are rare events. Therefore, the genetic variability that occurs from one generation to the next results almost entirely from meiosis and sexual reproduction.

Shuffling of Homologues Creates Novel Combinations of Chromosomes

How does meiosis produce genetic diversity? One mechanism is the random distribution of maternal and paternal homologues to the daughter cells during meiosis I. Remember, at metaphase I the paired homologues line up at the cell's equator. In each pair of homologues, the maternal chromosome faces one pole and the paternal chromosome faces the opposite pole, but which homologue faces which pole is random, and is not affected by the distribution of the homologues of other chromosome pairs.

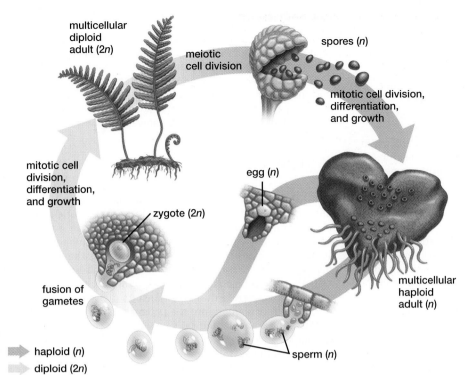

multicellular
diploid
adult (2n)

meiotic
cell division

spores (n)

mitotic cell division,
differentiation,
and growth

egg (n)

mitotic cell
division,
differentiation,
and growth

zygote (2n)

multicellular
haploid
adult (n)

fusion of
gametes

sperm (n)

➡ haploid (n)

➡ diploid (2n)

◀ **FIGURE 9-20 Alternation of generations in plants** In plants, such as this fern, specialized cells in the multicellular diploid adult stage undergo meiotic cell division to produce haploid spores. The spores undergo mitotic cell division and differentiation of the daughter cells to produce a multicellular haploid adult stage. Sometime later, perhaps many weeks later, some of these haploid cells differentiate into sperm and eggs. These fuse to form a diploid zygote. Mitotic cell division and differentiation once again give rise to a multicellular diploid adult stage.

Let's consider meiosis in mosquitoes, which have three pairs of homologous chromosomes ($n = 3$, $2n = 6$). At metaphase I, the chromosomes can align in four configurations (**Fig. 9-21a**). Therefore, anaphase I can produce eight possible sets of chromosomes ($2^3 = 8$; **Fig. 9-21b**).

When each of these chromosome clusters undergoes meiosis II, it produces two gametes. Therefore, a single mosquito, with three pairs of homologous chromosomes, can produce gametes with eight different chromosome sets. A single human, with 23 pairs of homologous chromosomes, can theoretically produce gametes with more than 8 million (2^{23}) different combinations of maternal and paternal chromosomes.

(a) The four possible chromosome arrangements at metaphase of meiosis I

(b) The eight possible sets of chromosomes after meiosis I

▲ **FIGURE 9-21 Random separation of homologous pairs of chromosomes produces genetic variability** For clarity, the chromosomes are depicted as large, medium, and small. The paternal chromosomes are colored yellow and the maternal chromosomes are colored violet.

Crossing Over Creates Chromosomes with Novel Combinations of Genes

In addition to the genetic variation resulting from the random assortment of parental chromosomes, crossing over during meiosis produces chromosomes with combinations of alleles that differ from those of either parent. In fact, some of these new combinations may never have existed before, because homologous chromosomes cross over in new and different places at each meiotic division. In humans, although 1 in 8 million gametes could have the same combination of maternal and paternal chromosomes, in reality, none of those chromosomes will be purely maternal or purely paternal. Even though a man produces about 100 million sperm each day, he may never produce two that carry exactly the same combinations of alleles. In all probability, every sperm and every egg is genetically unique.

Fusion of Gametes Adds Further Genetic Variability to the Offspring

At fertilization, two gametes, each containing a unique combination of alleles, fuse to form a diploid offspring. Even if we ignore crossing over, every human can theoretically produce about 8 million different gametes based solely on the random separation of the homologues. Therefore, fusion of gametes from just two people could produce 8 million × 8 million, or 64 trillion, genetically different children, which is far more people than have ever existed on Earth! Put another way, the chances that your parents could produce another child that is genetically the same as you are about $\frac{1}{8,000,000} \times \frac{1}{8,000,000}$, or about 1 in 64 trillion! When we factor in the almost endless variability produced by crossing over, we can confidently say that (except for identical twins) there never has been, and never will be, anyone just like you.

Case Study revisited
Send in the Clones

Why are clones genetically identical to their nuclear donors, while children are so different from their parents and from one another? As you've learned, barring the occasional mutation, mitotic cell division produces daughter cells that are genetically identical to the parent cell. Meiotic cell division, in contrast, produces haploid cells that have a random sampling of one member of each pair of homologous chromosomes. Crossing over further shuffles the genes. Thus, when a sperm fertilizes an egg, the offspring receive half their genes from the mother and half from the father. Two children of the same parents will never be genetically the same as either parent or as one another (except for identical twins). Genetic variability produced by sexual reproduction is the reason why many famous racehorses—including Seabiscuit, War Admiral, and Secretariat—never sired any offspring who could run as fast as they could.

During cloning, the nucleus is removed from a donor cell and implanted into an egg from which the nucleus has been removed or destroyed. The resulting cell divides by mitotic cell division to form a clone, so all of the cells of the clone have the same nuclear genes as the donor did.

However, everything about an organism—structure, metabolism, personality, learning ability, and other aspects of behavior—are influenced by both genes and environment. The uterus in which the cloned fetus develops, the rearrangement of cells as the embryo progresses from fertilized egg to complex newborn, and the conditions in which the organism lives (nutrition, family conditions, friends, world events, etc.) are important in ways that we have barely begun to understand. Further, in mammals all of a cell's mitochondria are inherited from the mother, in the cytoplasm of her egg cell. Mitochondria possess their own small supply of DNA (see pp. 70–71 and pp. 325–326), and mitochondrial DNA affects how well a mitochondrion functions. Therefore, a clone will usually have different mitochondrial genes than its nuclear donor. Nevertheless, clones are likely to resemble their nuclear donors, both in appearance and behavior, far more than any child resembles a parent, a brother, or a sister. For example, although the Missy clones don't look exactly like Missy, all three share her taste for broccoli!

Should animals be cloned? Does it depend on the animal and the reason it's being cloned? People will probably be debating about this for many years. One thing is certain: Send in the clones? In the words of Broadway songwriter Stephen Sondheim, "Don't bother, they're here."

BioEthics Consider This

Most people agree that human reproductive cloning—trying to make a duplicate human being—should not be allowed. But what about "therapeutic cloning"? In therapeutic cloning, the nucleus from a cell of a person with a disease, say Parkinson's disease, would be inserted into a human egg from which the nucleus has been removed. As the egg divides, some of its daughter cells will be embryonic stem cells that could be coaxed to develop into the type of brain cells that degenerate during Parkinson's disease. These cells might be transplanted into the patient to cure the disease. Because the transplanted cells would be genetically identical to the patient's own cells, there would be no risk of rejection by his immune system and no need for the patient to take drugs to suppress his immune response (which would make him more susceptible to diseases). Some people are fervent supporters of therapeutic cloning for medical treatments, whereas others are equally fervently opposed, on the grounds that a human embryo would be created, and destroyed, for each patient's treatment.

In late 2007, researchers may have discovered a way around this dilemma. They reported inserting just the right mix of genes into adult cells, causing them to become "induced pluripotent stem cells"; that is, stem cells that could be forced to differentiate into any type of cell of the entire body. But what if induced pluripotent stem cells turn out not to be as versatile as embryonic stem cells? Or what if pluripotent stem cells are found to be dangerous, for example, if the procedure might make them cancerous? Should therapeutic cloning of human embryos then be pursued as an option?

CHAPTER REVIEW

Summary of Key Concepts

9.1 Why Do Cells Divide?
Growth of multicellular eukaryotic organisms and replacement of cells that die during an organism's life occur through cell division and differentiation of the daughter cells. Asexual reproduction also occurs through cell division. A specialized type of cell division, called meiotic cell division, is required for sexual reproduction in eukaryotes.

9.2 What Occurs During the Prokaryotic Cell Cycle?
The prokaryotic cell cycle consists of growth, replication of the DNA of its single, circular chromosome, and division by binary fission. The two resulting daughter cells are genetically identical to the parent cell.

9.3 How Is the DNA in Eukaryotic Chromosomes Organized?
Each chromosome in a eukaryotic cell consists of a single DNA double helix and proteins that organize the DNA. Genes are segments of DNA found at specific locations on a chromosome. During cell growth, the chromosomes are extended and accessible for use by enzymes that read their genetic instructions. During cell division, the chromosomes are duplicated and condense into short, thick structures. Eukaryotic cells typically contain pairs of chromosomes, called homologues, that appear virtually identical because they carry the same genes with similar, although usually not identical, nucleotide sequences. Cells with pairs of homologous chromosomes are diploid. Cells with only one member of each chromosome pair are haploid.

9.4 What Occurs During the Eukaryotic Cell Cycle?

The eukaryotic cell cycle consists of interphase and cell division. During interphase, the cell grows and duplicates its chromosomes. Interphase is divided into G_1 (growth phase 1), S (DNA synthesis), and G_2 (growth phase 2). During G_1, many cells differentiate to perform a specific function. Some differentiated cells can reenter the dividing state; other cells stay differentiated for the life of the organism and never divide again. Most eukaryotic cells divide by mitotic cell division, which produces two daughter cells that are genetically identical to their parent cell. Specialized reproductive cells undergo meiotic cell division, each producing four haploid daughter cells.

9.5 How Does Mitotic Cell Division Produce Genetically Identical Daughter Cells?

The chromosomes are duplicated during interphase, prior to mitosis. A replicated chromosome consists of two identical sister chromatids that remain attached to one another at the centromere during the early stages of mitosis. Mitosis (nuclear division) consists of four phases, usually accompanied by cytokinesis (cytoplasmic division) during the last phase (see Fig. 9-8):

- **Prophase** The chromosomes condense and their kinetochores attach to spindle microtubules, called kinetochore microtubules, that form at this time.
- **Metaphase** Kinetochore microtubules move the chromosomes to the equator of the cell.
- **Anaphase** The two chromatids of each duplicated chromosome separate. The kinetochore microtubules move them to opposite poles of the cell. Meanwhile, polar microtubules force the cell to elongate.
- **Telophase** The chromosomes decondense, and nuclear envelopes re-form around each new daughter nucleus.
- **Cytokinesis** Cytokinesis normally occurs at the end of telophase and divides the cytoplasm into approximately equal halves, each containing a nucleus. In animal cells, a ring of microfilaments pinches the plasma membrane in along the equator. In plant cells, new plasma membrane forms along the equator by the fusion of vesicles produced by the Golgi apparatus.

BioFlix™ Mitosis

9.6 How Is the Cell Cycle Controlled?

Complex interactions among many proteins, particularly cyclins and cyclin-dependent protein kinases, drive the cell cycle. There are three major checkpoints at which progress through the cell cycle is regulated: between G_1 and S, between G_2 and mitosis, and between metaphase and anaphase. These checkpoints ensure that the DNA is intact and replicated accurately and that the chromosomes are properly arranged for mitosis before the cell divides.

9.7 Why Do So Many Organisms Reproduce Sexually?

Genetic differences among organisms originate as mutations, which, when preserved within a species, produce alternate forms of genes, called alleles. Alleles in different individuals of a species may be combined in offspring through sexual reproduction, creating variation among the offspring and potentially improving their likelihood of surviving and reproducing in their turn.

9.8 How Does Meiotic Cell Division Produce Haploid Cells?

Meiosis separates homologous chromosomes and produces haploid cells with only one homologue from each pair. During interphase before meiosis, chromosomes are duplicated. The cell then undergoes two specialized cell divisions—meiosis I and meiosis II—to produce four haploid daughter cells (see Fig. 9-15).

Meiosis I

During prophase I, homologous duplicated chromosomes, each consisting of two chromatids, pair up and exchange parts by crossing over. During metaphase I, homologues move together as pairs to the cell's equator, one member of each pair facing opposite poles of the cell. Homologous chromosomes separate during anaphase I, and two nuclei form during telophase I. Cytokinesis also usually occurs during telophase I. Each daughter nucleus receives only one member of each pair of homologues and, therefore, is haploid. The sister chromatids remain attached to each other throughout meiosis I.

Meiosis II

Meiosis II usually occurs in both daughter nuclei and resembles mitosis in a haploid cell. The duplicated chromosomes move to the cell's equator during metaphase II. The two chromatids of each chromosome separate and move to opposite poles of the cell during anaphase II. This second division produces four haploid nuclei. Cytokinesis normally occurs during or shortly after telophase II, producing four haploid cells.

BioFlix™ Meiosis

9.9 When Do Mitotic and Meiotic Cell Division Occur in the Life Cycles of Eukaryotes?

Most eukaryotic life cycles have three parts: (1) Sexual reproduction combines haploid gametes to form a diploid cell. (2) At some point in the life cycle, diploid cells undergo meiotic cell division to produce haploid cells. (3) At some point in the life cycle, mitosis of either a haploid cell, or a diploid cell, or both, results in the growth of multicellular bodies. When these stages occur, and what proportion of the life cycle is occupied by each stage, varies greatly among different species.

9.10 How Do Meiosis and Sexual Reproduction Produce Genetic Variability?

The random shuffling of homologous maternal and paternal chromosomes creates new chromosome combinations. Crossing over creates chromosomes with allele combinations that may never have occurred before on single chromosomes. Because of the separation of homologues and crossing over, a parent probably never produces any two gametes that are completely identical. The fusion of two such genetically unique gametes adds further genetic variability to the offspring.

Key Terms

allele *159*
anaphase *153*
asexual reproduction *147*
autosome *151*
binary fission *148*
cell cycle *146*
cell division *145*
cell plate *154*
centriole *153*
centromere *150*
checkpoint *159*
chiasma (plural, chiasmata) *163*
chromatid *150*
chromosome *146*
clone *144*
cloning *144*
crossing over *163*
cytokinesis *152*
daughter cell *145*
deoxyribonucleic acid (DNA) *146*
differentiate *146*
diploid *150*
duplicated chromosome *150*

gamete *147*
gene *146*
haploid *151*
homologous chromosome *150*
homologue *150*
interphase *151*
karyotype *150*
kinetochore *153*
locus (plural, loci) *149*
meiosis *152*
meiotic cell division *152*
metaphase *153*
mitosis *152*
mitotic cell division *152*
mutation *151*
nucleotide *146*
prophase *153*
recombination *163*
sex chromosome *151*
sexual reproduction *147*
spindle microtubule *153*
stem cell *146*
telomere *150*
telophase *153*

Thinking Through the Concepts

Fill-in-the-Blank

1. Prokaryotic cells divide by a process called _____.

2. Growth and development of eukaryotic organisms occur through _____ cell division and _____ of the resulting daughter cells.

3. Most plants and animals have pairs of chromosomes that have similar appearance and genetic composition. These pairs are called _____. Pairs of chromosomes that are the same in both males and females are called _____. Pairs that are different in males and females are called _____.

4. The four phases of mitosis are _____, _____, _____, and _____. Division of the cytoplasm into two cells, called _____, usually occurs during which phase? _____

5. Chromosomes attach to spindle microtubules at structures called _____. Some spindle microtubules, called _____ microtubules, do not bind to chromosomes, but have free ends that overlap along the equator of the cell. These microtubules push the poles of the cell apart.

6. Meiotic cell division produces _____haploid daughter cells from each diploid parental cell. The first haploid nuclei are produced at the end of _____. In animals, the haploid daughter cells produced by meiotic cell division are called _____.

7. During _____ of meiosis I, homologous chromosomes intertwine, forming structures called _____. These structures are the sites of what event? _____

8. Three processes that promote genetic variability of offspring during sexual reproduction are _____, _____, and _____.

Review Questions

1. Diagram and describe the eukaryotic cell cycle. Name the various phases, and briefly describe the events that occur during each.

2. Define mitosis and cytokinesis. What changes in cell structure would result if cytokinesis does not occur after mitosis?

3. Diagram the stages of mitosis. How does mitosis ensure that each daughter nucleus receives a full set of chromosomes?

4. Define the following terms: *homologous chromosome* (*homologue*), *centromere, kinetochore, chromatid, diploid,* and *haploid.*

5. Describe and compare the process of cytokinesis in animal cells and in plant cells.

6. How is the cell cycle controlled? Why must the progression of cells through the cell cycle be regulated?

7. Diagram the events of meiosis. At which stage do homologous chromosomes separate?

8. Describe crossing over. At which stage of meiosis does it occur? Name two functions of chiasmata.

9. In what ways are mitosis and meiosis similar? In what ways are they different?

10. Describe or diagram the three main types of eukaryotic life cycles. When do meiotic cell division and mitotic cell division occur in each?

11. Describe how meiosis provides for genetic variability. If an animal had a haploid number of two (no sex chromosomes), how many genetically different gametes could it produce? (Assume no crossing over.) If it had a haploid number of five?

Applying the Concepts

1. Most nerve cells in the adult human central nervous system, as well as heart muscle cells, do not divide. In contrast, cells lining the inside of the small intestine divide frequently. Discuss this difference in terms of why damage to the nervous system and heart muscle cells (such as damage caused by a stroke or heart attack) is so dangerous. What do you think might happen to tissues such as the intestinal lining if some disorder blocked mitotic cell division in all cells of the body?

2. Cancer cells divide out of control. Side effects of chemotherapy and radiation therapy that fight cancers include loss of hair and of the intestinal lining, producing severe nausea. Note that cells in hair follicles and intestinal lining divide frequently. What can you infer about the mechanisms of these treatments? What would you look for in an improved cancer therapy?

3. Some animal species can reproduce either asexually or sexually, depending on the state of the environment. Asexual reproduction tends to occur in stable, favorable environments; sexual reproduction is more common in unstable or unfavorable circumstances. Discuss the advantages and disadvantages of sexual and asexual reproduction.

(MB) *Go to www.masteringbiology.com for practice quizzes, activities, eText, videos, current events, and more.*

Patterns of Inheritance

Case Study

Sudden Death on the Court

FLO HYMAN, over 6 feet tall, graceful and athletic, was one of the best woman volleyball players of all time. Star of the 1984 silver medal American Olympic volleyball team, Hyman later joined a professional Japanese team. In 1986, taken out of a game for a short breather, she died at the age of 31, sitting quietly on the bench. How could this happen to someone so young and fit?

Flo Hyman had a genetic disorder called Marfan syndrome, which affects about 1 in 5,000 to 10,000 people, possibly including Abraham Lincoln, the classical composer and pianist Sergei Rachmaninoff, and the Egyptian pharaoh Akhenaten. People with Marfan syndrome are typically tall and slender, with unusually long limbs and large hands and feet. For some people with Marfan syndrome, these characteristics lead to fame and fortune. Unfortunately, Marfan syndrome can also be deadly.

Hyman died from a ruptured aorta, the massive artery that carries blood from the heart to most of the body. Why did Hyman's aorta break? What does a weak aorta have in common with tallness and large hands? Marfan syndrome is caused by a mutation in the gene that encodes a protein called fibrillin, an essential component of connective tissue. Many parts of your body contain connective tissue, including the tendons that attach muscles to bones, ligaments (such as the fibers that hold the lens in place in your eye), and the tough walls of arteries. Fibrillin forms long fibers that give strength to connective tissue. Normal fibrillin also "traps" certain types of growth factors, keeping them from excessively stimulating cell division (see p. 158) in, for example, bone-forming cells. Defective fibrillin cannot trap these growth factors, with the result that the arms, legs, hands, and feet of people with Marfan syndrome tend to become unusually long. The combination of defective fibrillin and high concentrations of growth factors also weakens bone, cartilage, and artery walls.

As we described in p. 158, diploid organisms, including people, generally have two copies of each gene, one on each homologous chromosome. One defective copy of the fibrillin gene is enough to cause Marfan syndrome. What does this tell us about the inheritance of Marfan syndrome? Are all inherited diseases caused by a single defective copy of a gene? To find out, we must go back in time to a monastery in Moravia and visit the garden of Gregor Mendel.

▲ Olympic volleyball silver medalist Flo Hyman was struck down by Marfan syndrome at the height of her career.

10.1 WHAT IS THE PHYSICAL BASIS OF INHERITANCE?

Inheritance is the process by which the characteristics of individuals are passed to their offspring. We will begin our exploration of inheritance with a brief overview of the structures—genes and chromosomes—that form its physical basis. In this chapter, we will confine our discussion to diploid organisms, including most plants and animals, that reproduce sexually by the fusion of haploid gametes.

Genes Are Sequences of Nucleotides at Specific Locations on Chromosomes

A chromosome consists of a single double helix of DNA, packaged with a variety of proteins. Segments of DNA ranging from a few hundred to many thousands of nucleotides in length are the units of inheritance—the **genes**—that encode the information needed to produce proteins, cells, and entire organisms. Therefore, genes are parts of chromosomes. A gene's physical location on a chromosome is called its **locus** (plural, **loci**). The chromosomes of diploid organisms occur in pairs called homologues. Both members of a pair of homologues carry the same genes, located at the same loci (**Fig. 10-1**). However, the nucleotide sequences of a given gene may differ in different members of a species, or even on the two homologues of a single individual. These different versions of a gene at a given locus are called **alleles** (see Fig. 10-1).

Mutations Are the Source of Alleles

Think of genes as very long sentences, written in an alphabet of nucleotides instead of letters. Alleles arise as mutations

a pair of homologous chromosomes

gene loci

Both chromosomes carry the same allele of the gene at this locus; the organism is homozygous at this locus

This locus contains another gene for which the organism is homozygous

Each chromosome carries a different allele of this gene, so the organism is heterozygous at this locus

the chromosome from the male parent

the chromosome from the female parent

◄ FIGURE 10-1 **The relationships among genes, alleles, and chromosomes** Each homologous chromosome carries the same set of genes. Each gene is located at the same position, or locus, on its chromosome. Differences in nucleotide sequences at the same gene locus produce different alleles of the gene. Diploid organisms have two alleles of each gene, one on each homologue. The alleles on the two homologues may be the same or different.

that slightly change the spelling of these nucleotide sentences. If a mutation occurs in the cells that become sperm or eggs, it can be passed on from parent to offspring.

Most of the alleles in an organism's DNA first appeared as mutations in the reproductive cells of the organism's ancestors, perhaps hundreds or even millions of years ago, and have been inherited, generation after generation, ever since. A few alleles, which we will call "new mutations," may have occurred in the reproductive cells of the organism's own parents.

An Organism's Two Alleles May Be the Same or Different

Because a diploid organism has pairs of homologous chromosomes, and both members of a pair contain the same gene loci, the organism has two copies of each gene. If both homologues have the same allele at a given gene locus, the organism is said to be **homozygous** at that locus. ("Homozygous" comes from Greek words meaning "same pair.") For example, the chromosomes shown in Figure 10-1 are homozygous at two loci. If two homologous chromosomes have different alleles at a locus, the organism is **heterozygous** ("different pair") at that locus. The chromosomes in Figure 10-1 are heterozygous at one locus. Organisms that are heterozygous at a specific locus are often called **hybrids.**

10.2 HOW WERE THE PRINCIPLES OF INHERITANCE DISCOVERED?

The common patterns of inheritance and many essential facts about genes, alleles, and the distribution of alleles in gametes and zygotes during sexual reproduction were discovered by an Austrian monk, Gregor Mendel (**Fig. 10-2**), in the mid-1800s. This was long before DNA, chromosomes, or meiosis had been discovered. Because his experiments are succinct, elegant examples of science in action, let's follow Mendel's paths of discovery.

Doing It Right: The Secrets of Mendel's Success

There are three key steps to any successful experiment in biology: choosing the right organism with which to work, designing and performing the experiment correctly, and analyzing the data properly. Mendel was the first geneticist to complete all three steps.

Mendel chose the edible pea as the subject for his experiments on inheritance (**Fig. 10-3**). Stamens, the male reproductive structures of a flower, produce pollen. Each pollen grain contains sperm. Pollination allows sperm to fertilize the female gamete, or egg, located within the ovary at the base of

▲ FIGURE 10-2 **Gregor Mendel**

intact pea flower

flower dissected to show
its reproductive structures

Carpel (female,
produces eggs)

Stamen (male, produces
pollen that contain sperm)

▲ **FIGURE 10-3 Flowers of the edible pea** In the intact pea
flower (left), the lower petals form a container enclosing the
reproductive structures—the stamens (male) and carpel (female).
Pollen normally cannot enter the flower from outside, so peas
usually self-pollinate and, hence, self-fertilize. If the flower is
opened (right), it can be cross-pollinated by hand.

the flower's female reproductive structure, called the carpel.
In pea flowers, the petals enclose all of the reproductive structures, preventing another flower's pollen from entering (see
Fig. 10-3). Therefore, the egg cells in a pea flower must be fertilized by sperm from the pollen of the same flower. When an
organism's sperm fertilize its own eggs, the process is called
self-fertilization.

Mendel, however, often wanted to mate two different
pea plants to see what types of offspring they would produce.
To do this, he opened one pea flower and removed its stamens, preventing self-fertilization. Then, he dusted the sticky
tip of the carpel with pollen from the flower of another plant.
When sperm from one organism fertilize eggs from a different organism, the process is called **cross-fertilization.**

Mendel's experimental design was simple, but brilliant.
Earlier researchers had generally tried to study inheritance by
simultaneously considering all of the features of entire organisms, including features that differed only slightly between organisms. Not surprisingly, the investigators were often
confused rather than enlightened. Mendel, however, chose to
study individual characteristics (called traits) that had unmis-
takably different forms, such as white versus purple flowers.
He also started out by studying only one trait at a time.

Mendel followed the inheritance of these traits for several generations, counting the numbers of offspring with each
type of trait. By analyzing these numbers, the basic patterns
of inheritance became clear. Today, quantifying experimental
results and applying statistical analysis are essential tools in
virtually every field of biology, but in Mendel's time, numer-
ical analysis was an innovation.

10.3 HOW ARE SINGLE TRAITS INHERITED?

To study inheritance, a researcher needs to begin with parental
organisms with easily identified traits that are inherited consistently from generation to generation. Organisms are called
true-breeding when they possess a trait, such as purple flowers, that is always inherited unchanged by all of its offspring

that are produced by self-fertilization. Even in the mid-1800s,
commercial seed dealers sold many types of peas that were
true-breeding for different forms of a single trait. In his first set
of experiments, Mendel cross-fertilized pea plants that were
true-breeding for different forms of a single trait, such as
flower color. He saved the resulting seeds and grew them the
following year to determine the traits of the offspring.

In one of these experiments, Mendel cross-fertilized true-
breeding, white-flowered plants with true-breeding, purple-
flowered plants. This was the parental generation, denoted by
the letter P. When he grew the resulting seeds, he found that all
the first-generation offspring (the "first filial," or F_1 generation)
produced purple flowers (**Fig. 10-4**). What had happened to
the white color? The flowers of the F_1 hybrids were just as purple as their parents. The white color seemed to have disappeared in the F_1 generation.

Mendel then allowed the F_1 flowers to self-fertilize,
collected the seeds, and planted them the next spring. In the
second generation (F_2), Mendel counted 705 plants with
purple flowers and 224 plants with white flowers. These
numbers are approximately three-fourths purple flowers
and one-fourth white flowers, or a ratio of about 3 purple to
1 white (**Fig. 10-5**). This result showed that the capacity to
produce white flowers had not disappeared in the F_1 plants,
but had only been "hidden."

Mendel allowed the F_2 plants to self-fertilize and produce yet a third (F_3) generation. He found that all the white-
flowered F_2 plants produced white-flowered offspring; that is,
they were true-breeding. For as many generations as he had
time and patience to raise, white-flowered parents always
gave rise only to white-flowered offspring. In contrast, when
purple-flowered F_2 plants self-fertilized, their offspring were
of two types. About one-third were true-breeding for purple,
but the other two-thirds were hybrids that produced both
purple- and white-flowered offspring, again in the ratio of 3
purple to 1 white. Therefore, the F_2 generation included one-
quarter true-breeding purple plants, one-half hybrid purple,
and one-quarter true-breeding white.

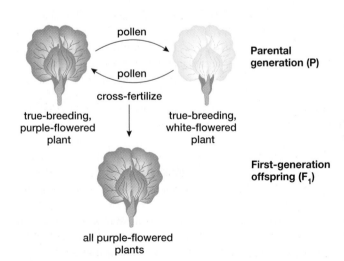

true-breeding,
purple-flowered
plant

pollen

cross-fertilize

pollen

true-breeding,
white-flowered
plant

Parental
generation (P)

First-generation
offspring (F_1)

all purple-flowered
plants

▲ **FIGURE 10-4 Cross of pea plants true-breeding for white
or purple flowers** All of the offspring bear purple flowers.

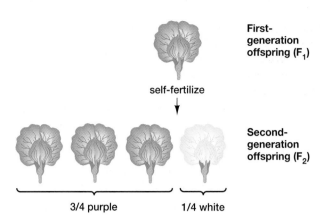

First-generation offspring (F₁)

self-fertilize

Second-generation offspring (F₂)

3/4 purple | 1/4 white

▲ FIGURE 10-5 **Self-fertilization of F₁ pea plants with purple flowers** Three-quarters of the offspring bear purple flowers and one-quarter bear white flowers.

The Inheritance of Dominant and Recessive Alleles on Homologous Chromosomes Can Explain the Results of Mendel's Crosses

Mendel's results, supplemented by modern knowledge of genes and homologous chromosomes, allow us to develop a five-part hypothesis to explain the inheritance of single traits:

- Each trait is determined by pairs of discrete physical units called genes. Each organism has two alleles for each gene, one on each homologous chromosome. True-breeding, white-flowered peas have different alleles of the flower-color gene than true-breeding, purple-flowered peas do.
- When two different alleles are present in an organism, one—the **dominant** allele—may mask the expression of the other—the **recessive** allele. The recessive allele, however, is still present. In the edible pea, the allele for purple flowers is dominant, and the allele for white flowers is recessive.
- The pairs of alleles on homologous chromosomes separate, or segregate, from each other during meiosis. This is known as Mendel's **law of segregation.** As a result, each gamete receives only one allele of each pair. (Unlike in animals, in plants, the gametes do not form immediately following meiosis [see Figs. 9-17c and 9-20]; however, later in its life cycle, the plant eventually does produce gametes containing one allele of each pair.) When a sperm fertilizes an egg, the resulting offspring receives one allele from the father (in his sperm) and one from the mother (in her egg).
- Chance determines which allele is included in a given gamete. Because homologous chromosomes separate at random during meiosis, the distribution of alleles to the gametes is also random.
- True-breeding organisms have two copies of the same allele for a given gene, and are therefore homozygous for that gene. All of the gametes from a homozygous individual receive the same allele for that gene (**Fig. 10-6a**). Hybrid organisms have two different alleles for a given gene and

are, therefore, heterozygous for that gene. Half of a heterozygote's gametes will contain one allele for that gene and half will contain the other allele (**Fig. 10-6b**).

Let's see how this hypothesis explains the results of Mendel's experiments with flower color (**Fig. 10-7**). Using letters to represent the different alleles, we will assign the uppercase letter P to the dominant allele for purple flower color and the lowercase letter p to the recessive allele for white flower color. A homozygous purple-flowered plant has two alleles for purple flower color (PP), whereas a homozygous white-flowered plant has two alleles for white flower color (pp). All the sperm and eggs produced by a PP plant carry the P allele; all the sperm and eggs of a pp plant carry the p allele (**Fig. 10-7a**).

The F₁ offspring were produced when P sperm fertilized p eggs or when p sperm fertilized P eggs. In both cases, the F₁ offspring were Pp. Because P is dominant over p, all of the offspring were purple (**Fig. 10-7b**).

For the F₂ generation, Mendel allowed the heterozygous F₁ plants to self-fertilize. Each gamete produced by a heterozygous Pp plant has an equal chance of receiving either the P allele or the p allele. That is, a heterozygous plant produces equal numbers of P and p sperm and equal numbers of P and p eggs. When a Pp plant self-fertilizes, each type of sperm has an equal chance of fertilizing each type of egg (**Fig. 10-7c**). Therefore, the F₂ generation contained three types of offspring: PP, Pp, and pp. The three types occurred in the approximate proportions of one-quarter PP (homozygous purple), one-half Pp (heterozygous purple), and one-quarter pp (homozygous white).

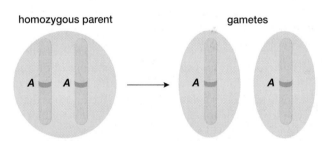

homozygous parent | gametes

A   A → A | A

(a) Gametes produced by a homozygous parent

heterozygous parent | gametes

A   a → A | a

(b) Gametes produced by a heterozygous parent

▲ FIGURE 10-6 **The distribution of alleles in gametes** **(a)** All of the gametes produced by homozygous organisms contain the same allele. **(b)** Half of the gametes produced by heterozygous organisms contain one allele, and half of the gametes contain the other allele.

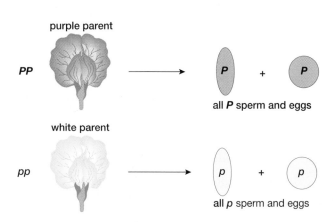

(a) Gametes produced by homozygous parents

Two organisms that look alike may actually carry different combinations of alleles. The actual combination of alleles carried by an organism (for example, *PP* or *Pp*) is its **genotype.** The organism's traits, including its outward appearance, behavior, digestive enzymes, blood type, or any other observable or measurable feature, make up its **phenotype.** As we have seen, plants with either the *PP* or the *Pp* genotype have the phenotype of purple flowers. Therefore, the F_2 generation of Mendel's peas consisted of three genotypes (one-quarter *PP*, one-half *Pp*, and one-quarter *pp*) but only two phenotypes (three-quarters purple and one-quarter white).

Simple "Genetic Bookkeeping" Can Predict Genotypes and Phenotypes of Offspring

The **Punnett square method,** named after R. C. Punnett, a famous geneticist of the early 1900s, is a convenient way to predict the genotypes and phenotypes of offspring. **Figure 10-8** shows how to use a Punnett square to determine the proportions of offspring that arise from the self-fertilization of a flower that is heterozygous for color (or the proportions of offspring produced by breeding any two organisms that are heterozygous for a single trait). This figure also provides the fractions that allow you to calculate the outcomes using the probabilities that each type of sperm will fertilize each type of egg.

As you use these "genetic bookkeeping" techniques, keep in mind that in a real experiment, the offspring will occur only in *approximately* the predicted proportions, because

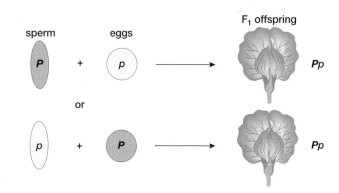

(b) Fusion of gametes produces F_1 offspring

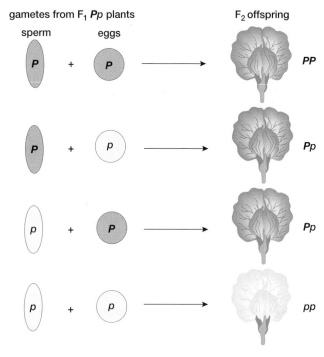

(c) Fusion of gametes from the F_1 generation produces F_2 offspring

▶ FIGURE 10-7 **Segregation of alleles and fusion of gametes predict the distribution of alleles and traits in Mendel's experiment with flower color in peas (a)** The parental generation. All of the gametes of the homozygous parents contain the same allele: only *P* alleles in the gametes of *PP* parents and only *p* alleles in the gametes of *pp* parents. **(b)** The F_1 generation: Fusion of gametes containing the *P* allele with gametes containing the *p* allele produces only *Pp* offspring. **(c)** The F_2 generation: Half of the gametes of heterozygous *Pp* parents contain the *P* allele and half contain the *p* allele. Fusion of these gametes produces *PP*, *Pp*, and *pp* offspring.

sperm and eggs with different alleles encounter one another randomly. Let's consider an example. Each time a baby is conceived, it has a 50:50 chance of becoming a boy or a girl. However, many families with two children do not have one girl and one boy. The 50:50 ratio of girls to boys occurs only if we average the genders of the children in many families.

Mendel's Hypothesis Can Be Used to Predict the Outcome of New Types of Single-Trait Crosses

You have probably recognized that Mendel used the scientific method: making an observation and using it to formulate a hypothesis. But does Mendel's hypothesis accurately predict the results of further experiments? Based on the hypothesis that the heterozygous F_1 plants had one allele for purple flowers and one for white (that is, they had the Pp genotype), Mendel predicted the outcome of cross-fertilizing Pp plants with homozygous recessive white plants (pp): There should be equal numbers of Pp (purple) and pp (white) offspring. This is indeed what he found.

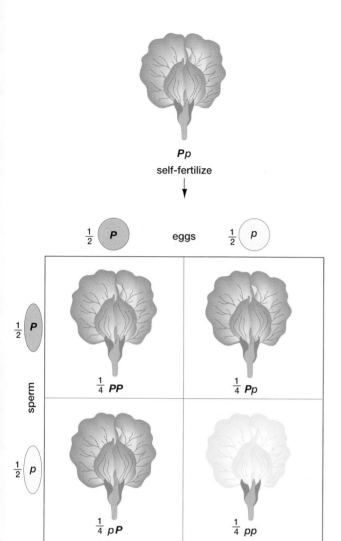

(a) Punnett square of a single-trait cross

◀ **FIGURE 10-8 Determining the outcome of a single-trait cross (a)** The Punnett square allows you to predict both genotypes and phenotypes of specific crosses; here we use it for a cross between pea plants that are heterozygous for a single trait—flower color.

(1) Assign letters to the different alleles; use uppercase for dominant alleles and lowercase for recessive alleles.
(2) Determine all the types of genetically different gametes that can be produced by the male and female parents.
(3) Draw the Punnett square, with the columns labeled with possible genotypes of the eggs and the rows labeled with possible genotypes of the sperm. (We have included the fractions of these genotypes with each label.)
(4) Fill in the genotype of the offspring in each box by combining the genotype of the sperm in its row with the genotype of the egg in its column. (Multiply the fraction of sperm of each type in the row headers by the fraction of eggs of each type in the column headers.)
(5) Count the number of offspring with each genotype. Note that Pp is the same as pP.
(6) Convert the number of offspring of each genotype to a fraction of the total number of offspring. In this example, out of four fertilizations, only one is predicted to produce the pp genotype, so one-quarter of the total number of offspring produced by this cross is predicted to be white. To determine phenotypic fractions, add the fractions of genotypes that would produce a given phenotype. For example, purple flowers are produced by $\frac{1}{4}PP + \frac{1}{4}Pp + \frac{1}{4}pP$, for a total of three-quarters of the offspring.

(b) Probabilities may also be used to predict the outcome of a single-trait cross. Determine the fractions of eggs and sperm of each genotype, and multiply these fractions together to calculate the fraction of offspring of each genotype. When two genotypes produce the same phenotype (e.g., Pp and pP), add the fractions of each genotype to determine the phenotypic fraction.

QUESTION If you crossed a heterozygous Pp plant with a homozygous recessive pp plant, what would be the expected ratio of offspring? How does this differ from the offspring of a $PP \times pp$ cross? Try working this out before you read further in the text.

(b) Using probabilities to determine the offspring of a single-trait cross

dominant (*Pp*) yields offspring with both dominant and recessive phenotypes in a 1:1 ratio.

10.4 HOW ARE MULTIPLE TRAITS INHERITED?

Having determined the inheritance modes for single traits, Mendel then turned to the more complex question of the inheritance of multiple traits in peas (**Fig. 10-10**). He began by crossbreeding plants that differed in two traits—for example, seed color (yellow or green) and seed shape (smooth or wrinkled). From other crosses of plants with these traits, Mendel already knew that the smooth allele of the seed shape gene (*S*) is dominant to the wrinkled allele (*s*), and that the yellow allele of the seed color gene (*Y*) is dominant to the green allele (*y*). He crossed a true-breeding plant with smooth, yellow seeds (*SSYY*) to a true-breeding plant with wrinkled, green seeds (*ssyy*). The *SSYY* plant produced only *SY* gametes, and the *ssyy* plant produced only *sy* gametes. Therefore, all the F_1 offspring were heterozygotes: genotypically *SsYy* with the phenotype of smooth, yellow seeds.

Allowing these heterozygous F_1 plants to self-fertilize, Mendel found that the F_2 generation consisted of 315 plants with smooth, yellow seeds; 101 with wrinkled, yellow seeds; 108 with smooth, green seeds; and 32 with wrinkled, green seeds—a ratio of about 9:3:3:1. The offspring produced from

Case Study continued
Sudden Death on the Court

When a person with Marfan syndrome has children with a person without the syndrome, those children have a 50% chance of inheriting the condition. Do you think that Marfan is inherited as a dominant or a recessive allele? Why? Check your reasoning in "Case Study Revisited: Sudden Death on the Court" at the end of the chapter.

This type of experiment also has practical uses. Cross-fertilization of an organism with a dominant phenotype (in this case, a purple flower) but an unknown genotype with a homozygous recessive organism (a white flower) tests whether the organism with the dominant phenotype is homozygous or heterozygous; logically enough, this is called a **test cross** (Fig. 10-9). When crossed with a homozygous recessive (*pp*), a homozygous dominant (*PP*) produces all phenotypically dominant offspring, whereas a heterozygous

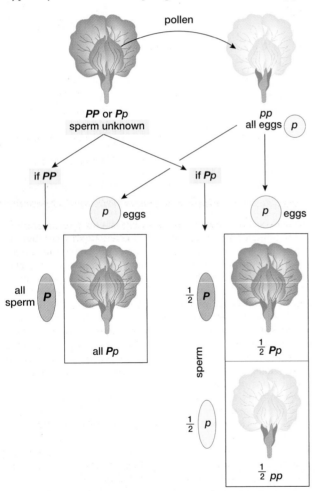

▲ FIGURE 10-9 **Punnett square of a test cross** An organism with a dominant phenotype may be either homozygous or heterozygous. Crossing such an organism with a homozygous recessive organism can determine whether the dominant organism was homozygous (left) or heterozygous (right).

Trait	Dominant form		Recessive form	
Seed shape		smooth		wrinkled
Seed color		yellow		green
Pod shape		inflated		constricted
Pod color		green		yellow
Flower color		purple		white
Flower location		at leaf junctions		at tips of branches
Plant size		tall (about 6 feet)		dwarf (about 8 to 16 inches)

▲ FIGURE 10-10 **Traits of pea plants studied by Gregor Mendel** other crosses of plants that were heterozygous for two traits also had phenotypic ratios of about 9:3:3:1.

Mendel Hypothesized That Traits Are Inherited Independently

Mendel realized that these results could be explained if the genes for seed color and seed shape were inherited independently of each other and did not influence each other during gamete formation. If so, then for each trait, three-quarters of the offspring should show the dominant phenotype and one-quarter should show the recessive phenotype. This result is just what Mendel observed. He found 423 plants with smooth seeds (of either color) and 133 with wrinkled seeds (a ratio of about 3:1); in this same group of plants, 416 produced yellow seeds (of either shape) and 140 produced green seeds (also about 3:1). **Figure 10-11** shows how a Punnett square or probability calculation can be used to determine the outcome of a cross between organisms that are heterozygous for two traits.

The independent inheritance of two or more traits is called the **law of independent assortment.** Multiple traits are inherited independently if the alleles of one gene are distributed to gametes independently of the alleles for other genes. Independent assortment will occur when the traits being studied are controlled by genes on different pairs of homologous chromosomes. Why? From Chapter 9, recall the movement of chromosomes during meiosis. When paired homologous chromosomes line up during metaphase I, which homologue faces which pole of the cell is random, and the orientation of one homologous pair does not influence other pairs. Therefore, when the homologues separate during anaphase I, which allele of a gene on homologous pair 1 moves "north" does not affect which allele of a gene on homologous pair 2 moves "north"; that is, the alleles of genes on different chromosomes are distributed, or assorted, independently (**Fig. 10-12**).

In an Unprepared World, Genius May Go Unrecognized

In 1865, Gregor Mendel presented the results of his experiments on inheritance to the Brünn Society for the Study of Natural Science, and they were published the following year. His paper did not mark the beginning of genetics. In fact, it didn't make any impression at all on the study of biology during his lifetime. Mendel's experiments, which eventually spawned one of the most important scientific theories in all of biology, simply vanished from the scene. Apparently, very few biologists read his paper, and those who did failed to recognize its significance.

It was not until 1900 that three biologists—Carl Correns, Hugo de Vries, and Erich Tschermak—working independently of one another and knowing nothing of Mendel's work, rediscovered the principles of inheritance. No doubt to their intense disappointment, when they searched the scientific literature

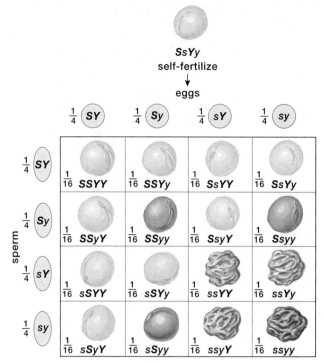

(a) Punnett square of a two-trait cross

seed shape	seed color	phenotypic ratio (9:3:3:1)
$\frac{3}{4}$ smooth ×	$\frac{3}{4}$ yellow =	$\frac{9}{16}$ smooth yellow
$\frac{3}{4}$ smooth ×	$\frac{1}{4}$ green =	$\frac{3}{16}$ smooth green
$\frac{1}{4}$ wrinkled ×	$\frac{3}{4}$ yellow =	$\frac{3}{16}$ wrinkled yellow
$\frac{1}{4}$ wrinkled ×	$\frac{1}{4}$ green =	$\frac{1}{16}$ wrinkled green

(b) Using probabilities to determine the offspring of a two-trait cross

▲ **FIGURE 10-11 Predicting genotypes and phenotypes for a cross between parents that are heterozygous for two traits** In pea seeds, yellow color (Y) is dominant to green (y), and smooth shape (S) is dominant to wrinkled (s). **(a)** Punnett square analysis. In this cross, an individual heterozygous for both traits self-fertilizes. In a cross involving two independent genes, the gamete types consist of all of the possible combinations of alleles of the two genes—S with Y, S with y, s with Y, and s with y. Place these gamete combinations as the labels for the rows and columns in the Punnett square, and then calculate the offspring as explained in Figure 10-8. Note that the Punnett square predicts both the frequencies of combinations of traits ($\frac{9}{16}$ smooth yellow, $\frac{3}{16}$ smooth green, $\frac{3}{16}$ wrinkled yellow, and $\frac{1}{16}$ wrinkled green) and the frequencies of individual traits ($\frac{3}{4}$ yellow, $\frac{1}{4}$ green, $\frac{3}{4}$ smooth, and $\frac{1}{4}$ wrinkled). **(b)** Probability theory states that the probability of two independent events is the product (multiplication) of their individual probabilities. Seed *shape* is independent of seed *color*. Therefore, multiplying the independent probabilities of the genotypes or phenotypes for each trait produces the predicted frequencies for the combined genotypes or phenotypes of the offspring. These ratios are identical to those generated by the Punnett square.

QUESTION Can the genotype of a plant bearing smooth yellow seeds be revealed by a test cross with a plant bearing wrinkled green seeds?

▶ **FIGURE 10-12 Independent assortment of alleles** Chromosome movements during meiosis produce independent assortment of alleles, shown here for two genes. Each combination of alleles is equally likely to occur, producing gametes in the predicted proportions one-quarter *SY*, one-quarter *sy*, one-quarter *Sy*, and one-quarter *sY*.

QUESTION If the genes for seed color and seed shape were on the same chromosome rather than on different chromosomes, would their alleles assort independently? Why or why not?

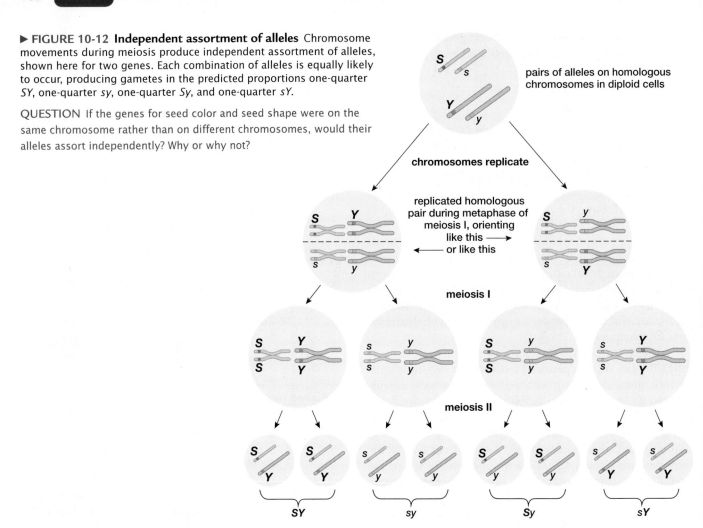

pairs of alleles on homologous chromosomes in diploid cells

chromosomes replicate

replicated homologous pair during metaphase of meiosis I, orienting like this ⟶ or like this ⟵

meiosis I

meiosis II

independent assortment produces four equally likely allele combinations during meiosis

before publishing their results, they found that Mendel had scooped them more than 30 years earlier. To their credit, they graciously acknowledged the important work of the Austrian monk, who had died in 1884.

10.5 HOW ARE GENES LOCATED ON THE SAME CHROMOSOME INHERITED?

Gregor Mendel knew nothing about the physical nature of genes or chromosomes. Much later, when scientists discovered that chromosomes are the vehicles of inheritance, it became obvious that there are many more traits (and therefore many more genes) than there are chromosomes. We now know that genes are parts of chromosomes, and that each chromosome contains many genes, up to several thousand in a really large chromosome. These facts have important implications for inheritance.

Genes on the Same Chromosome Tend to Be Inherited Together

We now know that chromosomes, not individual genes, assort independently during meiosis I. Therefore, genes located on *different chromosomes* assort independently into gametes. In contrast, genes on the *same chromosome* tend to be inherited together, a phenomenon called gene **linkage.** One of the first pairs of linked genes to be discovered was found in the sweet pea, a different species from Mendel's edible pea. In sweet peas, the gene for flower color (purple vs. red) and the gene for pollen grain shape (round vs. long) are carried on the same chromosome. Thus, the alleles for these genes normally assort together into gametes during meiosis and are inherited together.

Consider a heterozygous sweet pea plant with purple flowers and long pollen (**Fig. 10-13**). Note that the dominant purple allele of the flower-color gene and the dominant long allele of the pollen-shape gene are located on one homologous chromosome (see Fig. 10-13, top). The recessive red allele of the flower-color gene and the recessive round allele of the pollen-shape gene are located on the other homologue (see Fig. 10-13, bottom). Therefore, the gametes produced by this plant are likely to have either purple and long alleles or red and round alleles. This pattern of inheritance does not conform to the law of independent assortment, because the alleles for flower color and pollen shape do not segregate independently of one another, but tend to stay together during meiosis.

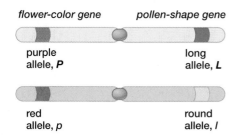

▲ **FIGURE 10-13 Linked genes on homologous chromosomes in the sweet pea** The genes for flower color and pollen shape are on the same chromosome, so they tend to be inherited together.

Crossing Over Creates New Combinations of Linked Alleles

Although they *tend* to be inherited together, genes on the same chromosome do not *always* stay together. If you cross-fertilized two sweet peas with the chromosomes shown in Figure 10-13, you might expect that all of the offspring would have either purple flowers with long pollen grains, or red flowers with round pollen grains. (Try working this out with a Punnett square.) However, in reality you would usually find a few plants in which the genes for flower color and pollen shape have been inherited as if they were not linked. That is, some of the offspring will have purple flowers and round pollen, and some will have red flowers and long pollen. How can this be?

As you learned in Chapter 9, during prophase I of meiosis, homologous chromosomes sometimes exchange parts, a process called crossing over (see Fig. 9-16). In most chromosomes, at least one exchange between each homologous pair occurs during each meiotic cell division. The exchange of corresponding segments of DNA during crossing over produces new allele combinations on both homologous chromosomes. Then, when homologues separate at anaphase I, the chromosomes that the haploid daughter cells receive will have different sets of alleles than the chromosomes of the parent cell did.

Crossing over during meiosis explains **genetic recombination:** the appearance of new combinations of alleles that were previously linked. Let's revisit the sweet pea during meiosis. During prophase I, the replicated, homologous chromosomes pair up (**Fig. 10-14a**). Each homologue will have one or more regions where crossing over will occur. Imagine that crossing over exchanges the alleles for flower color between nonsister chromatids of the two homologues (**Fig. 10-14b**). At anaphase I, the separated homologues will each now have one chromatid bearing a piece of DNA from a chromatid of the other homologue (**Fig. 10-14c**). During meiosis II, four types of chromosomes will be distributed to the four daughter cells: two unchanged chromosomes and two recombined chromosomes (**Fig. 10-14d**).

Therefore, some gametes will be produced with each of four chromosome configurations: *PL* and *pl* (the original parental types), and *Pl* and *pL* (the recombined chromosomes). If a sperm with a *Pl* chromosome fertilizes an egg with a *pl* chromosome, the offspring plant will have purple flowers (*Pp*) and round pollen (*ll*). If a sperm with a *pL*

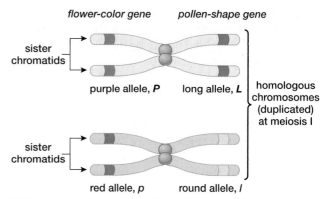

(a) Replicated chromosomes in prophase of meiosis I

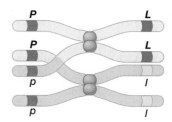

(b) Crossing over during prophase I

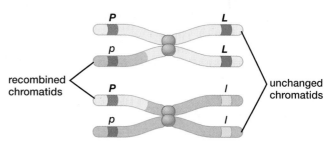

(c) Homologous chromosomes separate at anaphase I

(d) Unchanged and recombined chromosomes after meiosis II

▲ **FIGURE 10-14 Crossing over recombines alleles on homologous chromosomes** **(a)** During prophase of meiosis I, replicated homologous chromosomes pair up. **(b)** Nonsister chromatids of the two homologues exchange parts by crossing over. **(c)** When the homologous chromosomes separate during anaphase of meiosis I, one chromatid of each of the homologues now contains a piece of DNA from a chromatid of the other homologue. **(d)** After meiosis II, two of the haploid daughter cells receive unchanged chromosomes, and two receive recombined chromosomes. The recombined chromosomes contain allele arrangements that did not occur in the original parental chromosomes.

chromosome fertilizes an egg with a *pl* chromosome, then the offspring will have red flowers (*pp*) and long pollen (*Ll*).

Not surprisingly, the farther apart the genes are on a chromosome, the more likely it is that crossing over will occur between them. Two genes close together on a chromosome will rarely be separated by a crossover, but if two genes are very far apart, crossing over between the genes occurs so often that they seem to be independently assorted, just as if they were on different chromosomes. When Gregor Mendel discovered independent assortment, he was not only clever and careful, he was also lucky. The seven traits that he studied were controlled by genes on only four different chromosomes. He observed independent assortment because the genes that were on the same chromosome were far apart.

10.6 HOW IS SEX DETERMINED?

In mammals, an individual's sex is determined by a special pair of chromosomes, the **sex chromosomes.** Females have two identical sex chromosomes, called **X chromosomes,** whereas males have one X chromosome and one **Y chromosome (Fig. 10-15).** Although the Y chromosome is much smaller than the X chromosome, a small part of both sex chromosomes is homologous. As a result, the X and Y chromosomes pair up during prophase of meiosis I and separate during anaphase I. The other chromosomes, which occur in pairs that have identical appearance in both males and females, are called **autosomes.**

For organisms in which males are XY and females are XX, the sex chromosome carried by the sperm determines the sex of the offspring (**Fig. 10-16**). During sperm formation, the sex chromosomes segregate, and each sperm receives either

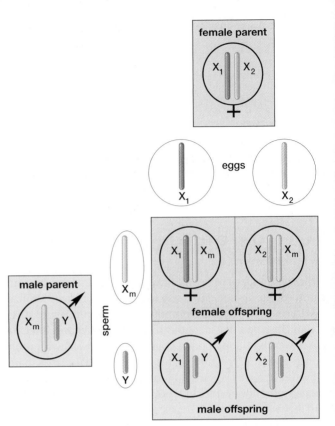

▲ FIGURE 10-16 **Sex determination in mammals** Male offspring receive their Y chromosome from their father; female offspring receive the father's X chromosome (labeled X_m). Both male and female offspring receive an X chromosome (either X_1 or X_2) from their mother.

▲ FIGURE 10-15 **Photomicrograph of human sex chromosomes** The Y chromosome (right), which carries relatively few genes, is much smaller than the X chromosome (left).
Image courtesy of Indigo® Instruments: http://www.indigo.com.

the X or the Y chromosome (plus one member of each pair of autosomes). The sex chromosomes also segregate during egg formation, but because females have two X chromosomes, every egg receives one X chromosome (along with one member of each pair of autosomes). Thus, a male offspring is produced if an egg is fertilized by a Y-bearing sperm, and a female offspring is produced if an egg is fertilized by an X-bearing sperm.

10.7 HOW ARE SEX-LINKED GENES INHERITED?

Sex-Linked Genes Are Found Only on the X or Only on the Y Chromosome

Genes that are on one sex chromosome but not on the other are said to be **sex-linked.** In many animal species, the Y chromosome carries only a few genes. In humans, the Y chromosome contains a few dozen genes (probably less than 80), many of which play a role in male reproduction. The most well-known Y-linked gene is *SRY*, the sex-determining region on the Y chromosome, discovered in 1990. During embryonic life, the action of this gene sets in motion the entire male developmental pathway. Under normal conditions, *SRY* causes the male gender to be 100% linked to the Y chromosome.

In contrast to the small Y chromosome, the human X chromosome contains more than 1,000 genes, few of which have a specific role in female reproduction. Most of the genes on the X chromosome have no counterpart on the Y chromosome, including traits that are important in both sexes, such as color vision, blood clotting, and certain structural proteins in muscles.

How does linkage of genes on the X chromosome affect inheritance? Because they have two X chromosomes, females can be either homozygous or heterozygous for genes on the X chromosome, and dominant versus recessive relationships among alleles will be expressed. Males, in contrast, fully express all the alleles they have on their single X chromosome, whether those alleles are otherwise dominant or recessive.

Let's look at a familiar example: red-green color blindness (**Fig. 10-17**). Color blindness is caused by recessive alleles of either of two genes located on the X chromosome. The normal, dominant alleles of these genes (we will call them *C*) encode proteins that allow one set of color-vision cells in the eye, called cones, to be most sensitive to red light and another set to be most sensitive to green light (**Fig. 10-17a**). There are several defective recessive alleles of these genes (we will call them *c*). In the most extreme cases, one of the genes will actually be missing from an X chromosome, or the defective alleles will encode proteins that make both sets of cones equally sensitive to both red and green light. Therefore, the affected person cannot distinguish red from green (**Fig. 10-17b**).

How is color blindness inherited? A man can have the genotype *CY* or *cY*, meaning that he has a color-vision allele *C* or *c* on his X chromosome and no corresponding gene on his Y chromosome. He will therefore have normal color vision if his X chromosome bears the *C* allele, or be color-blind if it bears the *c* allele. A woman may be *CC*, *Cc*, or *cc*. Women with *CC* or *Cc* genotypes will have normal color vision; only women with *cc* genotypes will be color-blind. Roughly 7% of men have defective color vision. Among women, about 93% are homozygous normal *CC*, 7% are heterozygous normal *Cc*, and less than 0.5% are color-blind *cc*.

A color-blind man (*cY*) will pass his defective allele only to his daughters, because only his daughters inherit his X chromosome. Usually, however, the daughters will have normal color vision, because they will also inherit a normal *C* allele from their mother, who is very likely homozygous normal *CC*.

A heterozygous woman (*Cc*), although she has normal color vision, will pass her defective allele to half of her sons (**Fig. 10-17c**). These sons will be color-blind (*cY*). The other half of her sons will inherit her functional allele and have normal color vision (*CY*).

▶ **FIGURE 10-17 Sex-linked inheritance of color blindness** Color grids help people compare **(a)** normal color vision to **(b)** red-green color deficiency. Usually, an affected person isn't really color "blind"—he sees most of the colors that normal people see, but not as well. **(c)** A Punnett square showing the inheritance of color blindness from a heterozygous woman (*Cc*) to her sons.

(a) Normal color vision

The individual cannot distinguish red from green

(b) Red-green color blindness

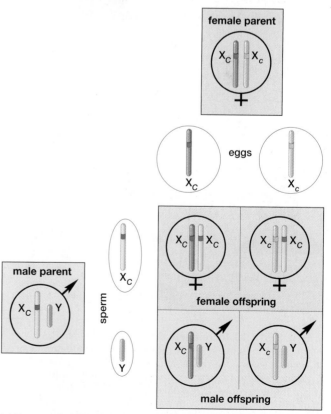

(c) Expected children of a man with normal color vision (*CY*), and a heterozygous woman (*Cc*)

10.8 DO THE MENDELIAN RULES OF INHERITANCE APPLY TO ALL TRAITS?

In our discussion of inheritance thus far, we have made some major simplifying assumptions: that each trait is completely controlled by a single gene, that there are only two possible alleles of each gene, and that one allele is completely dominant to the other, recessive, allele. Most traits, however, are influenced in more varied and subtle ways.

Incomplete Dominance: The Phenotype of Heterozygotes Is Intermediate Between the Phenotypes of the Homozygotes

When one allele is completely dominant over a second allele, heterozygotes with one dominant allele have the same phenotype as homozygotes with two dominant alleles (see Figs. 10-8 and 10-9). However, relationships between alleles are not always this simple. When the heterozygous phenotype is intermediate between the two homozygous phenotypes, the pattern of inheritance is called **incomplete dominance.** In humans, hair texture is influenced by a gene with two incompletely dominant alleles, which we will call C_1 and C_2 (**Fig. 10-18**). A person with two copies of the C_1 allele has curly hair; two copies of the C_2

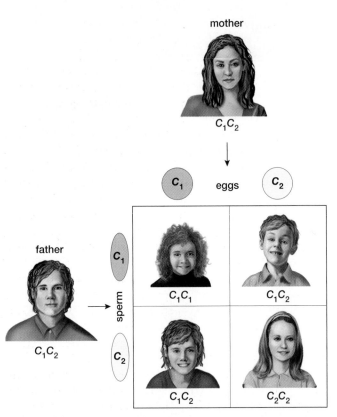

▲ **FIGURE 10-18 Incomplete dominance** The inheritance of hair texture in humans is an example of incomplete dominance. In such cases, we use capital letters for both alleles, here C_1 and C_2. Homozygotes may have curly hair (C_1C_1) or straight hair (C_2C_2). Heterozygotes (C_1C_2) have wavy hair. The children of a man and a woman, both with wavy hair, may have curly, straight, or wavy hair, in the approximate ratio of $\frac{1}{4}$ curly: $\frac{1}{2}$ wavy: $\frac{1}{4}$ straight.

allele produce straight hair. Heterozygotes, with the C_1C_2 genotype, have wavy hair. If two wavy-haired people marry, they might have children with any of the three hair types, with probabilities of one-quarter curly (C_1C_1), one-half wavy (C_1C_2), and one-quarter straight (C_2C_2).

A Single Gene May Have Multiple Alleles

Alleles arise through mutation, and the same gene in different individuals may have different mutations, each producing a new allele. Therefore, although an *individual* can have at most two different alleles, a *species* may have **multiple alleles** of many of its genes. There are multiple alleles for many human genetic disorders, including Marfan syndrome, Duchenne muscular dystrophy (see the "Health Watch: Muscular Dystrophy" on pp. 194–195), and cystic fibrosis (see the Case Study for Chapter 12).

The human blood types are an example of multiple alleles of a single gene, with an added twist to the pattern of inheritance. The blood types A, B, AB, and O arise as a result of three different alleles of a single gene on chromosome 9 (for simplicity, we will designate the alleles *A*, *B*, and *o*). This gene codes for an enzyme that adds sugar molecules to the ends of glycoproteins that protrude from the surfaces of red blood cells. Alleles *A* and *B* code for enzymes that add different sugars to the glycoproteins (we'll call the resulting molecules glycoproteins *A* and *B*, respectively). Allele *o* codes for a nonfunctional enzyme that doesn't add any sugar molecule.

A person may have one of six genotypes: *AA, BB, AB, Ao, Bo,* or *oo* (**Table 10-1**). Alleles *A* and *B* are dominant to *o*. Therefore, people with genotypes *AA* or *Ao* have only type A glycoproteins and have type A blood. Those with genotypes *BB* or *Bo* synthesize only type B glycoproteins and have type B blood. Homozygous recessive *oo* individuals lack both types of glycoproteins and have type O blood. In people with type AB blood, both enzymes are present, so the plasma membranes of their red blood cells have both A and B glycoproteins. When heterozygotes express phenotypes of *both* of the homozygotes (in this case, both A and B glycoproteins), the pattern of inheritance is called **codominance,** and the alleles are said to be codominant to one another.

People make antibodies to the type of glycoprotein(s) that they lack. These antibodies are proteins in blood plasma that bind to foreign glycoproteins by recognizing different sugar molecules. The antibodies cause red blood cells that bear foreign glycoproteins to clump together and rupture. The resulting clumps and fragments can clog small blood vessels and damage vital organs such as the brain, heart, lungs, or kidneys. This means that blood type must be determined and matched carefully before a blood transfusion is made.

Type O blood, lacking any sugars, is not attacked by antibodies in A, B, or AB blood, so it can be transfused safely to all other blood types. (The antibodies present in transfused blood become too diluted to cause problems.) People with type O blood are called "universal donors." But O blood carries antibodies to both A and B glycoproteins, so type O individuals can receive transfusions of only type O blood. Table 10-1 summarizes blood types and transfusion characteristics.

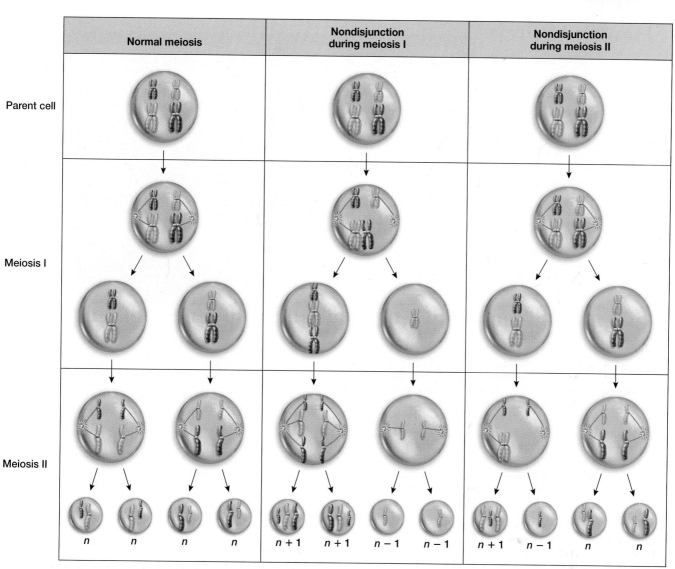

▲ **FIGURE 10-25 Nondisjunction during meiosis** Nondisjunction may occur either during meiosis I or meiosis II, resulting in gametes with too many ($n + 1$) or too few ($n - 1$) chromosomes.

Table 10-2   Effects of Nondisjunction of the Sex Chromosomes During Meiosis

	Nondisjunction in Father		
Sex Chromosomes of Defective Sperm	Sex Chromosomes of Normal Egg	Sex Chromosomes of Offspring	Phenotype
O (none)	X	XO	Female—Turner syndrome
XX	X	XXX	Female—Trisomy X
XY	X	XXY	Male—Klinefelter syndrome
YY	X	XYY	Male—Jacob syndrome
	Nondisjunction in Mother		
Sex Chromosomes of Normal Sperm	Sex Chromosomes of Defective Egg	Sex Chromosomes of Offspring	Phenotype
X	O (none)	XO	Female—Turner syndrome
Y	O (none)	YO	Dies as embryo
X	XX	XXX	Female—Trisomy X
Y	XX	XXY	Male—Klinefelter syndrome

Health Watch

Muscular Dystrophy

When Olympic weightlifter Matthias Steiner of Germany won the gold medal in 2008 with a "clean and jerk" lift of almost 569 pounds (258 kilograms), he exerted tremendous forces on his own body (Fig. E10-1). How could his muscles withstand these stresses? For that matter, why don't the muscles in your body rip apart when you climb a flight of stairs?

Muscle cells are firmly tied together by a very long protein called dystrophin. The almost 3,700 amino acids of dystrophin form a supple yet strong rod that connects the cytoskeleton inside a muscle cell to proteins in its plasma membrane, which in turn attach to proteins that form a fibrous support surrounding each muscle. Thus, when a muscle contracts, the muscle cells remain intact because the forces are distributed fairly evenly throughout each cell in the muscle and to the extracellular support proteins.

Unfortunately, about 1 in 3,500 boys synthesizes seriously defective dystrophin proteins. As these boys use their muscles, the lack of functioning dystrophin means that ordinary muscle contraction tears the muscle cells. The cells die and are replaced by fat and connective tissue (Fig. E10-2). By the age of 7 or 8, the boys can no longer walk. Death usually occurs in the early 20s because of heart and respiratory difficulties.

These boys suffer from **muscular dystrophy,** which literally means "degeneration of the muscles." The most severe form is called Duchenne muscular dystrophy; a less severe, but eventually still fatal, form is called Becker muscular dystrophy, after the physicians who first described these disorders. Muscular dystrophy is caused by a defective allele of the dystrophin gene (usually called the *DMD* gene because of its involvement in **D**uchenne **M**uscular **D**ystrophy).

Girls almost never have muscular dystrophy. Why not? Because the dystrophin gene is on the X chromosome, and muscular dystrophy alleles are recessive. Therefore, a boy will suffer muscular dystrophy if he has a defective

▲ FIGURE E10-1 Matthias Steiner wins the gold with a lift of 569 pounds

dystrophin allele on his single X chromosome, but a girl, with two X chromosomes, would need two defective copies to suffer the disorder. This virtually never happens, because a girl would have to receive a defective dystrophin allele from both her mother, on one of her X chromosomes, and from her father, on his X chromosome. With their early disability and death, boys with muscular dystrophy almost never reproduce.

This scenario makes genetic sense, but it may seem to defy the concept of evolution by natural selection. How can a lethal allele be so common? Shouldn't natural selection have almost completely eliminated the defective

are essential to survival, so any embryo without at least one X chromosome spontaneously aborts very early in development.)

Turner Syndrome (XO)

About 1 in every 3,000 phenotypically female babies has only one X chromosome, a condition known as **Turner syndrome.** At puberty, hormone deficiencies prevent XO females from menstruating or developing secondary sexual characteristics, such as enlarged breasts. Treatment with estrogen promotes physical development. However, because most women with Turner syndrome lack mature eggs, hormone treatment does not make it possible for them to bear children. Additional characteristics of women with Turner syndrome include short stature, folds of skin around the neck, and increased risk of cardiovascular disease, kidney defects, and hearing loss. Because women with Turner syndrome have only one X chromosome, they display X-linked recessive disorders, such as hemophilia and color blindness, much more frequently than do XX women.

Trisomy X (XXX)

About 1 in every 1,000 women has three X chromosomes, a condition known as **trisomy X,** or triple X. Most such women have no detectable defects, except for a tendency to be tall and a higher incidence of learning disabilities. Unlike women with Turner syndrome, most trisomy X women are fertile and, interestingly enough, almost always bear normal XX and XY children. Some unknown mechanism must operate during meiosis to prevent an extra X chromosome from being included in their eggs.

Klinefelter Syndrome (XXY)

About 1 male in every 1,000 is born with two X chromosomes and one Y chromosome. Most of these men go through life never realizing that they have an extra X chromosome. However, at puberty, some show mixed secondary sexual characteristics, including partial breast development, broadening of the hips, and small testes. These symptoms are known as **Klinefelter syndrome.** XXY men are often infertile because of low sperm count but are not impotent. They are usually diagnosed when

(a) Normal muscle

(b) Degenerating muscle in muscular dystrophy

▲ **FIGURE E10-2 Defective dystrophin proteins cause muscle degeneration (a)** A normal muscle is packed with specialized muscle cells, with very little space between the cells. **(b)** In muscular dystrophy, the individual cells are scattered in the midst of fat, white blood cells, and connective tissue.

dystrophin alleles? Actually, natural selection *does* rapidly eliminate the defective alleles. However, the dystrophin gene is enormous—about 2.2 *million* nucleotides long, compared to about 27 *thousand* nucleotides for the average human gene. In fact, the dystrophin gene occupies about 2% of the entire X chromosome.

Why does this matter? Remember, alleles arise as mutations in DNA. The longer the gene, the greater the chances for a mistake during DNA replication. It is a tribute to the astounding accuracy of DNA copying that we don't all suffer from muscular dystrophy, and you shouldn't be surprised to learn that the mutation rate for the dystrophin gene is a hundred times greater than average. Therefore, about one-third of the boys with muscular dystrophy receive a new mutation that occurred in an X chromosome of a reproductive cell of their mother, and two-thirds inherit a preexisting allele in one of their mother's X chromosomes. The new mutations counterbalance natural

selection, resulting in the steady incidence of about 1 in 3,500 boys.

Is muscular dystrophy hopeless, then? Right now, there are no cures, although several treatments are available that slow the progress of the disorder, prolong life, and make the affected boys more comfortable. An exciting possibility based on stem cells, however, has been discovered in dogs with a genetic disorder very similar to Duchenne muscular dystrophy. As we described in Chapter 9, stem cells can differentiate into many different types of mature cells. Giulio Cossu and colleagues at the San Raffaele Scientific Institute in Milan, Italy, found that injecting these dogs with stem cells taken from the blood vessels of healthy dogs allows them to synthesize normal dystrophin and retain muscle function long after the dogs would normally be unable to walk. The Muscular Dystrophy Association is funding research in similar human stem cells, with the goal of eventually treating human patients.

an XXY man and his partner seek medical help because they are unable to have children.

Jacob Syndrome (XYY)

Jacob syndrome (XYY) occurs in about 1 male in every 1,000. You might expect that an extra Y chromosome, which has few active genes, would not make very much difference, and this seems to be true in most cases. However, XYY males often have high levels of testosterone, develop severe acne, and are tall (about two-thirds of XYY males are over 6 feet tall, compared with the average male height of 5 feet 9 inches).

Some Genetic Disorders Are Caused by Abnormal Numbers of Autosomes

Nondisjunction of the autosomes may also occur, producing eggs or sperm missing an autosome or with two copies of an autosome. Fusion with a normal gamete (bearing one copy of each autosome) leads to an embryo with either one

or three copies of the affected autosome. Embryos that have only one copy of any of the autosomes abort so early in development that the woman never knows she was pregnant. Embryos with three copies of an autosome (trisomy) also usually spontaneously abort. However, a small fraction of embryos with three copies of chromosomes 13, 18, or 21 survive to birth. In the case of trisomy 21, the child may live into adulthood.

Trisomy 21 (Down Syndrome)

In about 1 of every 900 births, the child inherits an extra copy of chromosome 21, a condition called **trisomy 21,** or **Down syndrome.** Children with Down syndrome have several distinctive physical characteristics, including weak muscle tone, a small mouth held partially open because it cannot accommodate the tongue, and distinctively shaped eyelids (**Fig. 10-26**). Much more serious defects include low resistance to infectious diseases, heart malformations, and varying degrees of mental retardation, often severe.

(a) Karyotype showing three copies of chromosome 21   (b) Girl with Down syndrome

▲ FIGURE 10-26 **Trisomy 21, or Down syndrome (a)** This karyotype of a Down syndrome child reveals three copies of chromosome 21 (arrow). **(b)** The younger of these two sisters shows the facial features common in people with Down syndrome.

The frequency of nondisjunction increases with the age of the parents, especially the mother; more than 3% of children born to women over 45 years of age have Down syndrome. Nondisjunction in sperm accounts for about 10% of the cases of Down syndrome, and there is only a small increase in defective sperm with increasing age of the father.

Since the 1970s, it has become more common for couples to delay having children, increasing the probability of trisomy 21. Trisomy can be diagnosed before birth by examining the chromosomes of fetal cells and, with less certainty, by biochemical tests and ultrasound examination of the fetus (see "Health Watch: Prenatal Genetic Screening" in pp. 258–259).

Case Study revisited
Sudden Death on the Court

Medical examinations revealed that Flo Hyman's father and sister have Marfan syndrome, but her mother and brother do not. Does this prove that Hyman inherited the defective allele from her father? As you learned in this chapter, diploid organisms, including people, generally have two alleles of each gene, one on each homologous chromosome. One defective fibrillin allele is enough to cause Marfan syndrome. What can we conclude from these data?

First, if even one defective fibrillin allele produces Marfan syndrome, then Hyman's mother must carry two normal alleles, because she does not have Marfan syndrome. Second, because Hyman's father has Marfan syndrome, it is very likely that Hyman inherited a defective fibrillin allele from him. The fact that her sister also has Marfan syndrome makes this virtually certain. Third, is Marfan syndrome inherited as a dominant or a recessive condition? Once again, if only one defective allele is enough to cause Marfan, then this allele must be dominant and the normal allele must be recessive. Finally, if Hyman had borne children, could they have inherited Marfan syndrome from her? For a dominant disorder, any children who inherited her defective allele would develop Marfan syndrome. Therefore, on average, half of her children would have had Marfan syndrome. (Try working this out with a Punnett square.)

At the beginning of this chapter, we suggested that Lincoln, Rachmaninoff, and Akhenaten also had Marfan syndrome. You may wonder how anyone could be sure if they actually had the disorder. Well, you're right—nobody really knows. The "diagnosis" is based on photographs and descriptions. For example, Rachmaninoff's hands could span 13 white keys on a piano (try it for yourself!); most modern pianists cannot play some of Rachmaninoff's music as it was originally written, because the chords are too large. As for Lincoln, one visitor to the White House is said to have remarked, "Mr. President, what long legs you have!" To which Lincoln reportedly replied, "Just long enough to reach the ground, Madam." Although other genetic conditions can contribute to tall stature, long limbs and large hands, the fact that these men were otherwise healthy, successful, and fertile points to Marfan syndrome.

BioEthics **Consider This**

At this time, Marfan syndrome cannot be detected in an embryo, although researchers are working on it. Some other genetic disorders, such as cystic fibrosis and sickle-cell anemia, can easily be detected, in adults, children, and embryos. In these recessive diseases, if two heterozygotes have children together, each of their children has a 25% chance of having the disorder. Although there is no cure, there will probably be better treatments within a few years. If you and your spouse were both heterozygotes, would you seek prenatal diagnosis of an embryo? What would you do if your embryo were destined to be born with Marfan syndrome?

CHAPTER REVIEW

Summary of Key Concepts

10.1 What Is the Physical Basis of Inheritance?

The units of inheritance are genes, which are segments of DNA found at specific locations (loci) on chromosomes. Genes may exist in two or more slightly different, alternative forms, called alleles. When both homologous chromosomes carry the same allele at a given locus, the organism is homozygous for that particular gene. When the two homologous chromosomes have different alleles at a given locus, the organism is heterozygous for that gene.

10.2 How Were the Principles of Inheritance Discovered?

Gregor Mendel deduced many principles of inheritance in the mid-1800s, before the discovery of DNA, genes, chromosomes, or meiosis. He did this by choosing an appropriate experimental subject, designing his experiments carefully, following progeny for several generations, and analyzing his data statistically.

10.3 How Are Single Traits Inherited?

A trait is an observable or measurable feature of the organism's phenotype, such as hair texture or blood type. Traits are inherited in particular patterns that depend on the alleles that parents pass on to their offspring. Each parent provides its offspring with one allele of every gene, so that the offspring inherits a pair of alleles for every gene. The combination of alleles in the offspring determines whether it displays a particular phenotype. Dominant alleles mask the expression of recessive alleles. The masking of recessive alleles can result in organisms with the same phenotype but different genotypes. Organisms with two dominant alleles (homozygous dominant) have the same phenotype as do organisms with one dominant and one recessive allele (heterozygous). Because each allele segregates randomly during meiosis, we can predict the relative proportions of offspring with a particular trait, using Punnett squares or probability.

10.4 How Are Multiple Traits Inherited?

If the genes for two traits are located on separate chromosomes, their alleles assort independently of one another into the egg or sperm; that is, the distribution of alleles of one gene into the gametes does not affect the distribution of the alleles of the other gene. Thus, crossing two organisms that are heterozygous at two loci on separate chromosomes produces offspring with nine different genotypes. If the alleles are typical dominant and recessive alleles, these progeny will display only four different phenotypes (see Fig. 10-11).

10.5 How Are Genes Located on the Same Chromosome Inherited?

Genes on the same chromosome (encoded on the same DNA double helix) are linked to one another and therefore tend to be inherited together. However, crossing over will result in some recombination of alleles on each chromosome. Crossing over will occur more often the farther apart on a chromosome the genes lie.

10.6 How Is Sex Determined?

In many animals, sex is determined by sex chromosomes, often designated X and Y. In mammals, females have two X chromosomes, whereas males have one X and one Y chromosome. The rest of the chromosomes, identical in the two sexes, are called autosomes. Males include either an X or a Y chromosome in their sperm, whereas females always include an X chromosome in their eggs. Therefore, gender is determined by the sex chromosome in the sperm that fertilizes an egg.

10.7 How Are Sex-Linked Genes Inherited?

Sex-linked genes are genes found on the X or Y chromosome. In mammals, the Y chromosome has many fewer genes than the X chromosome, so most sex-linked genes are found on the X chromosome. Because males have only one copy of X chromosome genes, recessive traits on the X chromosome are more likely to be phenotypically expressed in males.

10.8 Do the Mendelian Rules of Inheritance Apply to All Traits?

Not all inheritance follows the simple dominant-recessive pattern:

- In incomplete dominance, heterozygotes have a phenotype that is intermediate between the two homozygous phenotypes.
- If we examine the genes of many members of a given species, we find that many genes have more than two alleles; that is, there are multiple alleles of the gene.
- Codominance is a relationship among the alleles of a single gene in which two alleles independently contribute to the observed phenotype.
- Many traits are determined by several different genes that all contribute to the phenotype, a phenomenon called polygenic inheritance.
- Pleiotropy occurs when a single gene has multiple effects on an organism's phenotype.
- The environment influences the phenotypic expression of all traits.

10.9 How Are Human Genetic Disorders Investigated?

The genetics of humans is similar to the genetics of other animals, but is more difficult to study because experimental crosses are not feasible. Analysis of family pedigrees and, more recently, molecular genetic techniques are used to determine the mode of inheritance of human traits.

10.10 How Are Human Disorders Caused by Single Genes Inherited?

Some genetic disorders are inherited as recessive traits; therefore, only homozygous recessive persons show symptoms of the disease. Heterozygotes are called carriers; they carry the recessive allele but do not express the trait. Some other diseases are inherited as simple dominant traits. In such cases, only one copy of the dominant allele is needed to cause disease symptoms. Some human genetic disorders are sex-linked.

10.11 How Do Errors in Chromosome Number Affect Humans?

Errors in meiosis can result in gametes with abnormal numbers of sex chromosomes or autosomes. Many people with abnormal numbers of sex chromosomes have distinguishing physical characteristics. Abnormal numbers of autosomes typically lead to spontaneous abortion early in pregnancy. In rare instances, the fetus may survive to birth, but mental and physical deficiencies always occur, as is the case with Down syndrome (trisomy 21). The likelihood of abnormal numbers of chromosomes increases with increasing age of the mother and, to a lesser extent, the father.

Key Terms

albinism *190*	linkage *182*
allele *174*	locus (plural, **loci**) *174*
autosome *184*	multiple alleles *186*
carrier *190*	muscular dystrophy *194*
codominance *186*	nondisjunction *192*
cross-fertilization *176*	pedigree *189*
dominant *177*	phenotype *178*
Down syndrome *195*	pleiotropy *187*
gene *174*	polygenic inheritance *187*
genetic recombination *183*	Punnett square method *178*
genotype *178*	recessive *177*
hemophilia *191*	self-fertilization *176*
heterozygous *175*	sex chromosome *184*
homozygous *175*	sex-linked *184*
Huntington disease *191*	sickle-cell anemia *190*
hybrid *175*	test cross *180*
incomplete dominance *186*	trisomy 21 *195*
inheritance *174*	trisomy X *194*
Jacob syndrome *195*	true-breeding *176*
Klinefelter syndrome *194*	Turner syndrome *194*
law of independent	X chromosome *184*
assortment *181*	Y chromosome *184*
law of segregation *177*	

Thinking Through the Concepts

Fill-in-the-Blank

1. The physical position of a gene on a chromosome is called its _____. Alternative forms of a gene are called _____. These alternative forms of genes arise as _____, which are changes in the nucleotide sequence of a gene.

2. An organism is described as *Rr*: red. *Rr* is the organism's _____, while red color is its _____. This organism would be (homozygous/heterozygous) for this color gene.

3. The inheritance of multiple traits depends on the locations of the genes that control the traits. If the genes are on different chromosomes, then the traits are inherited (as a group/independently). If the genes are located close together on a single chromosome, then the traits tend to be inherited (as a group/independently). Genes on the same chromosome are said to be _____.

4. Many organisms, including mammals, have both autosomes and sex chromosomes. In mammals, males have _____ sex chromosomes and females have _____ chromosomes. The sex of offspring depends on which chromosome is present in the (sperm/egg).

5. Genes that are present on one sex chromosome but not the other are called _____.

6. If the phenotype of heterozygotes is intermediate between the phenotypes of the two homozygotes, this pattern of inheritance is called _____. If heterozygotes express phenotypes of both homozygotes (not intermediate, but showing both traits), this is called _____. In _____, many genes, usually with similar effects on phenotype, control the inheritance of a trait.

Review Questions

1. Define the following terms: *gene, allele, dominant, recessive, true-breeding, homozygous, heterozygous, cross-fertilization,* and *self-fertilization.*

2. Explain why genes located on the same chromosome are said to be linked. Why do alleles of linked genes sometimes separate during meiosis?

3. Define *polygenic inheritance.* Why does polygenic inheritance sometimes allow parents to produce offspring that are notably different in skin color than either parent?

4. What is sex linkage? In mammals, which sex would be most likely to show recessive sex-linked traits?

5. What is the difference between a phenotype and a genotype? Does knowledge of an organism's phenotype always allow you to determine the genotype? What type of experiment would you perform to determine the genotype of a phenotypically dominant individual?

6. In the pedigree of part (a) of Figure 10-21, do you think that the individuals showing the trait are homozygous or heterozygous? How can you tell from the pedigree?

7. Define *nondisjunction,* and describe the common syndromes caused by nondisjunction of sex chromosomes and autosomes.

Applying the Concepts

1. Sometimes the term *gene* is used rather casually. Compare the terms *allele* and *gene.*

2. **BioEthics** Mendel's numbers seemed almost too perfect to be real; some believe he may have cheated a bit on his data. Perhaps he continued to collect data until the numbers matched his predicted ratios, then stopped. Recently, there has been much publicity over violations of scientific ethics, including researchers plagiarizing others' work, using other scientists' methods to develop lucrative patents, or just plain fabricating data. How important is this issue for society? What are the boundaries of ethical scientific behavior? How should the scientific community or society "police" scientists? What punishments would be appropriate for violations of scientific ethics?

3. Although American society has been described as a "melting pot," people often engage in "assortative mating," in which they marry others of similar height, socioeconomic status, race, and IQ. Discuss the consequences to society of assortative mating among humans. Would society be better off if people mated more randomly? Explain.

Genetics Problems

1. In certain cattle, hair color can be red (homozygous R_1R_1), white (homozygous R_2R_2), or roan (a mixture of red and white hairs, heterozygous R_1R_2).

   a. When a red bull is mated to a white cow, what genotypes and phenotypes of offspring could be obtained?

   b. If one of the offspring bulls in part (a) were mated to a white cow, what genotypes and phenotypes of offspring could be produced? In what proportion?

2. The palomino horse is golden in color. Unfortunately for horse fanciers, palominos do not breed true. In a series of matings between palominos, the following offspring were obtained:

   65 palominos
   32 cream-colored
   34 chestnut (reddish brown)

   What is the probable mode of inheritance of palomino coloration?

3. In the edible pea, tall (T) is dominant to short (t), and green pods (G) are dominant to yellow pods (g). List the types of gametes and offspring that would be produced in the following crosses:

   a. $TtGg \times TtGg$
   b. $TtGg \times TTGG$
   c. $TtGg \times Ttgg$

4. In tomatoes, round fruit (R) is dominant to long fruit (r), and smooth skin (S) is dominant to fuzzy skin (s). A true-breeding round, smooth tomato ($RRSS$) was crossbred with a true-breeding long, fuzzy tomato ($rrss$). All the F_1 offspring were round and smooth ($RrSs$). When these F_1 plants were bred, the following F_2 generation was obtained:

   Round, smooth: 43
   Long, fuzzy: 13

   Are the genes for skin texture and fruit shape likely to be on the same chromosome or on different chromosomes? Explain your answer.

5. In the tomatoes of Problem 4, an F_1 offspring ($RrSs$) was mated with a homozygous recessive ($rrss$). The following offspring were obtained:

   | Round, smooth: 583 | Long, fuzzy: 602 |
   | Round, fuzzy: 21 | Long, smooth: 16 |

   What is the most likely explanation for this distribution of phenotypes?

6. In humans, hair color is controlled by two interacting genes. The same pigment, melanin, is present in both brown-haired and blond-haired people, but brown hair has much more of it. Brown hair (B) is dominant to blond (b). Whether any melanin can be synthesized depends on another gene. The dominant form of this second gene (M) allows melanin synthesis; the recessive form (m) prevents melanin synthesis. Homozygous recessives (mm) are albino. What will be the expected proportions of phenotypes in the children of the following parents?

   a. $BBMM \times BbMm$
   b. $BbMm \times BbMm$
   c. $BbMm \times bbmm$

7. In humans, one of the genes determining color vision is located on the X chromosome. The dominant form (C) produces normal color vision; red-green color blindness (c) is recessive. If a man with normal color vision marries a color-blind woman, what is the probability of them having a color-blind son? A color-blind daughter?

8. In the couple described in Problem 7, the woman gives birth to a color-blind but otherwise normal daughter. The husband sues for a divorce on the grounds of adultery. Will his case stand up in court? Explain your answer.

(MB) *Go to www.masteringbiology.com for practice quizzes, activities, eText, videos, current events, and more.*

DNA: The Molecule of Heredity

Case Study

Muscles, Mutations, and Myostatin

NO, THE BULL in the top photo hasn't been pumping iron—he's a Belgian Blue, and they always have bulging muscles. What makes a Belgian Blue look like a bodybuilder, compared to an ordinary bull, such as the Hereford in the bottom photo?

When any mammal develops, its cells divide many times, enlarge, and become specialized for a specific function. The size, shape, and cell types in any organ are precisely regulated during development, so that you don't wind up with a head the size of a basketball, or have hair growing on your liver. Muscle development is no exception. When you were very young, cells destined to form your muscles multiplied, fused together to form long, relatively thick cells with multiple nuclei, and synthesized the specialized proteins that cause muscles to contract and thereby move your skeleton. A protein called myostatin, found in all mammals, puts the brakes on this process. The word "myostatin" literally means "to make muscles stay the same," and that is exactly what myostatin does. As muscles develop, myostatin slows down—and eventually stops—the multiplication of these pre-muscle cells. Myostatin also regulates the ultimate size of muscle cells and, therefore, their strength. A bodybuilder can bulk up by lifting weights, which *enlarges* the muscle cells, but doesn't usually add many *more* cells.

Belgian Blues have more, and larger, muscle cells than ordinary cattle do. Why? You may already have guessed—they don't produce normal myostatin. And why not? As you will learn in this chapter, proteins are synthesized from the genetic directions contained in **deoxyribonucleic acid (DNA).** The DNA of a Belgian Blue is very slightly different from the DNA of normal cattle—it has a change, or mutation, in the DNA of its myostatin gene. As a result, it produces defective myostatin. Belgian Blue pre-muscle cells multiply more than normal, and the cells become extra large as they differentiate, thereby producing remarkably buff cattle.

How does DNA contain the instructions for traits such as muscle size, flower color, or gender? How are these instructions usually passed unchanged from generation to generation? And why do the instructions sometimes change? The answers to these questions lie in the structure and function of DNA.

▲ Ordinary bull or incredible hulk? A tiny change in DNA makes all the difference.

At a Glance

11.1 HOW DID SCIENTISTS DISCOVER THAT GENES ARE MADE OF DNA?

By the late 1800s, scientists had learned that genetic information exists in discrete units that they called genes. However, they didn't know what a gene was. Scientists merely knew that genes determine many of the heritable differences among individuals within a species. For example, genes for flower color determine whether roses are red, pink, yellow, or white. By the early 1900s, studies of dividing cells provided strong evidence that genes are parts of chromosomes (see pp. 149–150, 174–175). Soon, biochemists found that eukaryotic chromosomes are composed only of protein and DNA. One of these substances must carry the cell's hereditary blueprint, but which one?

Transformed Bacteria Revealed the Link Between Genes and DNA

In the late 1920s, a British researcher named Frederick Griffith was trying to make a vaccine to prevent bacterial pneumonia, a major cause of death at that time. Making a vaccine against some types of infectious bacteria is very difficult (for example, modern vaccines against anthrax are neither completely safe nor completely effective), but this was not known back in the 1920s. Some antibacterial vaccines consist of a weakened strain of the bacteria, which can't cause illness. Injecting this weakened but living strain into an animal may stimulate immunity against the disease-causing strains. Other vaccines use disease-causing (virulent) bacteria that have been killed by exposure to heat or chemicals.

Griffith was trying to make a vaccine using two strains of the *Streptococcus pneumoniae* bacterium. One strain, R, did not cause pneumonia when injected into mice (**Fig. 11-1a**). The other strain, S, was deadly when injected, causing pneumonia and killing the mice in a day or two (**Fig. 11-1b**). As expected, when the S-strain was killed and injected into mice, it did not cause disease (**Fig. 11-1c**). Unfortunately, neither the live R-strain nor the killed S-strain provided immunity against live S-strain bacteria.

Griffith also tried mixing living R-strain bacteria together with heat-killed S-strain bacteria and injecting the mixture into mice (**Fig. 11-1d**). Because neither of these bacterial strains causes pneumonia on its own, he expected the mice to remain healthy. To his surprise, the mice sickened and died. When he autopsied the mice, he recovered *living* S-strain bacteria from them. Griffith hypothesized that some substance in the heat-killed S-strain changed the living, harmless R-strain bacteria into the deadly S-strain, a process he called transformation. The transformed S-strain cells then multiplied and caused pneumonia.

Griffith never discovered an effective pneumonia vaccine, so in that sense his experiments were a failure (in fact, an effective and safe vaccine against most forms of *Streptococcus pneumoniae* was not developed until the late 1970s). However, Griffith's experiments marked a turning point in our understanding of genetics, because other researchers suspected that the substance that causes transformation might be the long-sought molecule of heredity.

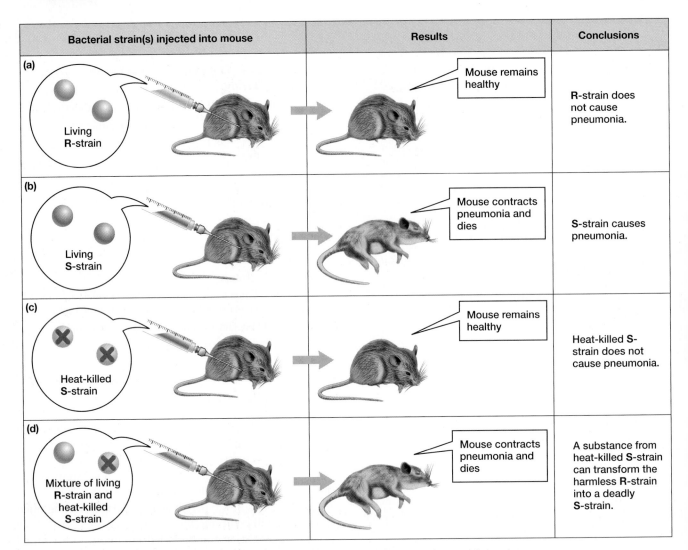

Bacterial strain(s) injected into mouse	Results	Conclusions
(a) Living **R-strain**	Mouse remains healthy	**R-strain** does not cause pneumonia.
(b) Living **S-strain**	Mouse contracts pneumonia and dies	**S-strain** causes pneumonia.
(c) Heat-killed **S-strain**	Mouse remains healthy	Heat-killed **S-strain** does not cause pneumonia.
(d) Mixture of living **R-strain** and heat-killed **S-strain**	Mouse contracts pneumonia and dies	A substance from heat-killed **S-strain** can transform the harmless **R-strain** into a deadly **S-strain**.

▲ FIGURE 11-1 **Transformation in bacteria** Griffith's discovery that bacteria can be transformed from harmless to deadly laid the groundwork for the discovery that genes are composed of DNA.

The Transforming Molecule Is DNA

In 1933, J. L. Alloway discovered that the mice played no role in transformation, which occurred just as well when live R-strain bacteria were mixed with dead S-strain bacteria in culture dishes. A decade later, Oswald Avery, Colin MacLeod, and Maclyn McCarty discovered that the transforming molecule is DNA. Avery, MacLeod, and McCarty isolated DNA from S-strain bacteria, mixed it with live R-strain bacteria, and produced live S-strain bacteria. To show that transformation was caused by DNA, and not by traces of protein contaminating the DNA, they treated some samples with protein-destroying enzymes. These enzymes did not prevent transformation. However, treating samples with DNA-destroying enzymes did prevent transformation.

This discovery helps us to interpret the results of Griffith's experiments. Heating S-strain cells killed them but did not completely destroy their DNA. When killed S-strain bacteria were mixed with living R-strain bacteria, fragments of DNA from the dead S-strain cells entered into some of the R-strain cells and be-

came incorporated into the chromosome of the R-strain bacteria (**Fig. 11-2**). If these fragments of DNA contained the genes needed to cause disease, an R-strain cell would be transformed into an S-strain cell. Thus, Avery, MacLeod, and McCarty concluded that genes are made of DNA.

DNA, Not Protein, Is the Molecule of Heredity

Nevertheless, not everyone was persuaded. Some still thought that genes are made of protein, and that the transforming DNA molecules from S-strain bacteria caused a mutation in the genes of R-strain bacteria. Others hypothesized that DNA might be the hereditary molecule of bacteria, but not of other organisms. However, evidence continued to accumulate that DNA is the genetic material in many, or perhaps all, organisms. For example, before dividing, a eukaryotic cell duplicates its chromosomes (see pp. 151–152) and exactly doubles its DNA content—just what would be expected if genes are made of DNA. Finally, virtually all of the remaining skeptics were convinced by a superb set of experiments by Alfred Hershey

bacterial chromosome

DNA fragments are transported into the bacterium

A DNA fragment is incorporated into the chromosome

▲ **FIGURE 11-2 Molecular mechanism of transformation** Most bacteria have a single circular chromosome made of DNA. Transformation may occur when a living bacterium takes up pieces of DNA from its environment and incorporates those fragments into its chromosome.

and Martha Chase, conclusively showing that DNA is the hereditary molecule of certain viruses (see "Scientific Inquiry: DNA Is the Hereditary Molecule of Bacteriophages" on pp. 204–205).

11.2 WHAT IS THE STRUCTURE OF DNA?

Knowing that genes are made of DNA does not answer critical questions about inheritance: How does DNA encode genetic information? How is DNA replicated so that a cell can pass its hereditary information to its daughter cells? The secrets of DNA function and, therefore, of heredity itself, are found in the three-dimensional structure of the DNA molecule.

DNA Is Composed of Four Nucleotides

As you learned in Chapter 3, DNA consists of four small subunits called **nucleotides.** Each nucleotide in DNA has three parts: a phosphate group, a sugar called deoxyribose, and one of four nitrogen-containing **bases: adenine (A), guanine (G), thymine (T),** or **cytosine (C) (Fig. 11-3).**

In the 1940s, when biochemist Erwin Chargaff of Columbia University analyzed the amounts of the four bases in DNA from organisms as diverse as bacteria, sea urchins, fish, and humans, he found a curious consistency. The DNA of any given species contains equal amounts of adenine and thymine, as well as equal amounts of guanine and cytosine.

phosphate — sugar — base = **adenine**

phosphate — sugar — base = **guanine**

phosphate — sugar — base = **thymine**

phosphate — sugar — base = **cytosine**

▲ **FIGURE 11-3 DNA nucleotides**

This consistency, often called "Chargaff's rule," certainly seemed significant, but it would be almost another decade before anyone figured out what it meant about DNA structure.

DNA Is a Double Helix of Two Nucleotide Strands

Determining the structure of any biological molecule is no simple task, even for scientists today. Nevertheless, in the late 1940s, several scientists began to investigate the structure of DNA. British scientists Maurice Wilkins and Rosalind Franklin used X-ray diffraction to study the DNA molecule. They bombarded crystals of purified DNA with X-rays and

Scientific Inquiry

DNA Is the Hereditary Molecule of Bacteriophages

Certain viruses infect only bacteria and are aptly called **bacteriophages,** meaning "bacteria eaters" (**Fig. E11-1**). A bacteriophage ("phage" for short) depends on its host bacterium for every aspect of its life cycle (**Fig. E11-1b**). When a phage encounters a bacterium, it attaches to the bacterial cell wall and injects its genetic material into the bacterium. The outer coat of the phage remains outside. The bacterium cannot distinguish phage genes from its own genes, so it "reads" the phage genes and uses that information to produce more phages. Finally, one of the phage genes directs the synthesis of an enzyme that ruptures the bacterium, freeing the newly manufactured phages.

Even though many bacteriophages have intricate structures (see **Fig. E11-1a**), they are chemically very simple, containing only DNA and protein. Therefore, one of these two molecules must be the phage genetic material. In the early 1950s, Alfred Hershey and Martha Chase used the chemical simplicity of bacteriophages to deduce that their genetic material is DNA.

Hershey and Chase knew that infected bacteria should contain phage genetic material, so if they could "label" phage DNA and protein, and separate the infected bacteria from the phage coats left outside, they could see which molecule entered the bacteria (**Fig. E11-2**). As you learned in Chapter 3, DNA and protein both contain carbon, oxygen, hydrogen, and nitrogen. DNA also contains phosphorus but not sulfur, whereas proteins contain sulfur (in the amino acids methionine and cysteine) but not phosphorus.

Hershey and Chase forced one population of phages to synthesize DNA using radioactive phosphorus, thereby labeling their DNA. Another population was forced to synthesize protein using radioactive sulfur, labeling their protein. When bacteria were infected by phages containing radioactively labeled protein, the bacteria did not become radioactive. However, when bacteria were infected by phages containing radioactive DNA, the bacteria did become radioactive. Hershey and Chase concluded that DNA, and not protein, was the genetic material of phages.

Hershey and Chase also reasoned that some of the labeled genetic material from the "parental" phages might be incorporated into the genetic material of the "offspring" phages. (You will learn more about this in section 11.4.) In a second set of experiments, the researchers again labeled DNA in one phage population and protein in another phage population, and allowed the phages to infect bacteria. After enough time had passed so that the phages had reproduced, the bacteria were broken open, and the offspring phages were separated from the bacterial debris. Radioactive DNA, but not radioactive protein, was found in the offspring phages. This second experiment confirmed the results of the first: DNA is the hereditary molecule.

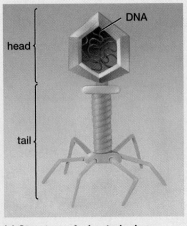

(a) Structure of a bacteriophage

❻ The bacterial wall is destroyed; phages are released

❶ The phage attaches to a bacterium

bacterium

❷ The phage injects its DNA into the bacterium

bacterial chromosome

❸ The phage DNA is replicated

❺ Complete phages are assembled

❹ Phage parts are synthesized, using the bacterium's metabolism

phage   phage DNA

DNA

head

tail

▲ **FIGURE E11-1 Bacteriophages (a)** Many bacteriophages have complex structures, including a head containing genetic material, tail fibers that attach to the surface of a bacterium, and an elaborate apparatus for injecting their genetic material into the bacterium. **(b)** The life cycle of a bacteriophage. The bacteriophage uses the metabolism of the bacterium to produce more phages.

(b) Bacteriophage life cycle

Observations:
1. Bacteriophage viruses consist of only DNA and protein.
2. Bacteriophages inject their genetic material into bacteria, forcing the bacteria to synthesize more phages.
3. The outer coat of bacteriophages stays outside of the bacteria.
4. DNA contains phosphorus but not sulfur.
   a. DNA can be "labeled" with radioactive phosphorus.
5. Protein contains sulfur but not phosphorus.
   a. Protein can be "labeled" with radioactive sulfur.

Question: Is DNA or protein the genetic material of bacteriophages?

Hypothesis: DNA is the genetic material.

Prediction:
1. If bacteria are infected with bacteriophages containing radioactively labeled DNA, the bacteria will be radioactive.
2. If bacteria are infected with bacteriophages containing radioactively labeled protein, the bacteria will not be radioactive.

Experiment:

Radioactive phosphorus (^{32}P)   Radioactive sulfur (^{35}S)

 Radioactive DNA (blue)   Radioactive protein (gold)

❶ Label the phages with ^{32}P or ^{35}S.

 ❷ Infect the bacteria with the labeled phages; the phages inject their genetic material into the bacteria.

 ❸ Whirl in a blender to break off the phage coats from the bacteria.

 ❹ Centrifuge to separate the phage coats (low density: stay in the liquid) from the bacteria (high density: sink to the bottom as a "pellet")

Results: Bacteria are radioactive; phage coats are not.   ❺ Measure the radioactivity of the phage coats and bacteria.   Results: Phage coats are radioactive; bacteria are not.

Conclusion: Infected bacteria are labeled with radioactive phosphorus but not with radioactive sulfur, supporting the hypothesis that the genetic material of bacteriophages is DNA, not protein.

▲ FIGURE E11-2 **The Hershey-Chase experiment** By radioactively labeling either the DNA or the protein of bacteriophages, Hershey and Chase tested whether the genetic material of phages is DNA (left side of the experiment) or protein (right side).

recorded how the X-rays bounced off the DNA molecules (**Fig. 11-4a**). As you can see, the resulting "diffraction" pattern does not provide a direct picture of DNA structure. However, experts like Wilkins and Franklin (**Figs. 11-4b,c**) could extract a lot of information about DNA from the pattern. First, a molecule of DNA is long and thin, with a uniform diameter of 2 nanometers (2 billionths of a meter). Second, DNA is helical; that is, it is twisted like a corkscrew or a spiral staircase. Third, the DNA molecule consists of repeating subunits.

The chemical and X-ray diffraction data did not provide enough information for researchers to work out the structure of DNA; some good guesses were also needed. Combining Wilkins and Franklin's data with a knowledge of how complex organic molecules bond together and an intuition that "important biological objects come in pairs," James Watson and Francis Crick proposed a model for the structure of DNA (see "Scientific Inquiry: The Discovery of the Double Helix" on p. 208). They suggested that the DNA molecule consists of two separate DNA polymers of linked nucleotides, called **strands** (**Fig. 11-5**). Within each DNA strand, the phosphate group of one nucleotide bonds to the sugar of the next nucleotide in the same strand. This bonding pattern produces a "backbone" of alternating, covalently bonded sugars and phosphates. The nucleotide bases protrude from this **sugar-phosphate backbone.**

All of the nucleotides within a single DNA strand are oriented in the same direction. Therefore, the two ends of a DNA strand differ; one end has a "free" or unbonded sugar, and the other end has a "free" or unbonded phosphate (see **Fig. 11-5a**). Picture a long line of cars stopped on a crowded one-way street at night; the cars' headlights (free phosphates) always point forward and their taillights (free sugars) always point backward. If the cars are jammed tightly together, a pedestrian standing in front of the line of cars will see only the headlights on the first car; a pedestrian at the back of the line will see only the taillights of the last car.

Hydrogen Bonds Between Complementary Bases Hold Two DNA Strands Together in a Double Helix

Watson and Crick proposed that two DNA strands are held together by hydrogen bonds that form between the bases protruding from the sugar-phosphate backbones of each strand (see Fig. 11-5a). These bonds give DNA a ladder-like structure, with the sugar-phosphate backbones on the outside (forming the uprights of the ladder) and the nucleotide bases on the inside (forming the rungs of the ladder). However, the DNA strands are not straight. Instead, they are twisted about each other to form a **double helix,** resembling a ladder twisted lengthwise into the shape of a circular staircase (see **Fig. 11-5b**). Further, the two strands in a DNA double helix are oriented in opposite directions, or are antiparallel. In the diagram of Figure 11-5a, note that the left-hand DNA strand has a free phosphate group at the top and a free sugar on the bottom, while these are reversed in the right-hand DNA strand. Again imagine an evening traffic jam, this time on a crowded two-lane highway. A traffic helicopter pilot overhead would see only the headlights on cars in one lane, and only the taillights of cars in the other lane.

Take a closer look at the pairs of bases that form each rung of the double helix ladder. Adenine forms hydrogen bonds only with thymine, and guanine forms hydrogen bonds only with cytosine (see Figs. 11-5a,b). These A–T and G–C pairs are called **complementary base pairs.** All of the bases of the two strands of a DNA double helix are complementary to each other. For example, if one strand reads A-T-T-C-C-A-G-G-C-T, then the other strand must read T-A-A-G-G-T-C-C-G-A.

(a) Diffraction pattern of DNA

(b) Maurice Wilkins

(c) Rosalind Franklin

▲ **FIGURE 11-4 X-ray diffraction studies of DNA (a)** The X formed of dark spots is characteristic of helical molecules such as DNA. Measurements of various aspects of the pattern indicate the dimensions of the DNA helix; for example, the distance between the dark spots corresponds to the distance between turns of the helix. **(b)** Maurice Wilkins and **(c)** Rosalind Franklin discovered many of the features of DNA by carefully examining such X-ray diffraction patterns. Wilkins shared the Nobel Prize in Physiology or Medicine with Watson and Crick in 1962. Franklin died in 1958; because Nobel Prizes are not awarded posthumously, her contributions often do not receive the recognition they deserve.

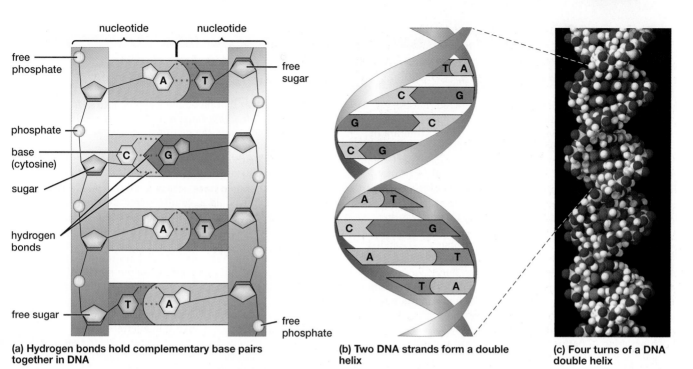

(a) **Hydrogen bonds hold complementary base pairs together in DNA**

(b) **Two DNA strands form a double helix**

(c) **Four turns of a DNA double helix**

▲ FIGURE 11-5 **The Watson-Crick model of DNA structure (a)** Hydrogen bonding between complementary base pairs holds the two strands of DNA together. Three hydrogen bonds hold guanine to cytosine, and two hydrogen bonds hold adenine to thymine. Note that each strand has a free phosphate on one end and a free sugar on the opposite end. Further, the two strands run in opposite directions. **(b)** Strands of DNA wind about each other in a double helix, like a twisted ladder, with the sugar-phosphate backbone forming the uprights and the complementary base pairs forming the rungs. **(c)** A space-filling model of DNA structure.

QUESTION Which do you think would be more difficult to break apart: an A–T base pair or a C–G base pair?

Complementary base pairs explain "Chargaff's rule"—that the DNA of a given species contains equal amounts of adenine and thymine, as well as equal amounts of cytosine and guanine. Because an A in one DNA strand always pairs with a T in the other strand, the amount of A always equals the amount of T. Similarly, because a G in one strand always pairs with a C in the other DNA strand, the amount of G always equals the amount of C.

Finally, look at the sizes of the bases: Because adenine and guanine consist of two fused rings, they are large, whereas thymine and cytosine, composed of only a single ring, are small. Because the double helix has only A–T and G–C pairs, all the rungs of the DNA ladder are the same width. Therefore, the double helix has a constant diameter, just as the X-ray diffraction pattern predicted.

The structure of DNA was solved. On March 7, 1953, at the Eagle Pub in Cambridge, England, Francis Crick proclaimed to the lunchtime crowd, "We have discovered the secret of life." This claim was not far from the truth. Although further data would be needed to confirm the details, within just a few years, their DNA model revolutionized biology, including genetics, evolution, and medicine. As we will see in later chapters, the revolution continues today.

11.3 HOW DOES DNA ENCODE INFORMATION?

Look again at the structure of DNA shown in Figure 11-5. Can you see why many scientists had trouble believing that DNA could be the carrier of genetic information? Consider the many characteristics of just one organism. How can the color of a bird's feathers, the size and shape of its beak, its ability to make a nest, its song, and its ability to migrate all be determined by a molecule with just four simple subunits?

The answer is that it's not the *number* of different subunits but their *sequence* that's important. Within a DNA strand, the four types of bases can be arranged in any order, and each unique sequence of bases represents a unique set of genetic instructions. An analogy might help: You don't need a lot of unique letters to make up a language. English has 26 letters, but Hawaiian has only 12, and the binary language of computers uses only two "letters" (0 and 1, or "off" and "on"). Nevertheless, all three languages can spell out thousands of different words. A stretch of DNA that is just 10 nucleotides long can have more than a million possible sequences of the four bases. Because an organism has millions (in bacteria) to billions (in plants or animals) of nucleotides, DNA molecules can encode a staggering amount of information.

Scientific Inquiry

The Discovery of the Double Helix

In the early 1950s, many biologists realized that the key to understanding inheritance lay in the structure of DNA. They also knew that whoever deduced the correct structure of DNA would receive recognition, probably including a Nobel Prize. Linus Pauling of the California Institute of Technology was the person most likely to solve the mystery of DNA structure. Pauling probably knew more about the chemistry of large organic molecules than any person alive. Like Rosalind Franklin and Maurice Wilkins, Pauling was an expert in X-ray diffraction techniques. In 1950, he used these techniques to show that many proteins were coiled into single-stranded helices (see Fig. 3-20b). Pauling, however, had two important handicaps. First, for years he had concentrated on protein research and, therefore, had little data about DNA. Second, he was active in the peace movement. At that time, some government officials considered such activity to be potentially subversive and threatening to national security. This latter handicap may have proved decisive.

The second most likely competitors were Wilkins and Franklin, the British scientists who had set out to determine the structure of DNA by using X-ray diffraction patterns. In fact, they were the only scientists who had good data about the general shape of the DNA molecule. Unfortunately for them, their methodical approach was slow.

The door was open for the eventual discoverers of the double helix—James Watson and Francis Crick, two scientists with neither Pauling's tremendous understanding of chemical bonds nor Franklin and Wilkins' expertise in X-ray analysis. Watson and Crick did no experiments in the ordinary sense of the word. Instead, they spent their time thinking about DNA, trying to construct a molecular model that made sense and fit the data. Because they were working in England and because Wilkins shared Franklin's data with them (perhaps against her wishes), Watson and Crick were familiar with all the X-ray information relating to DNA.

The X-ray data were just what Pauling lacked. Because of his presumed subversive tendencies, the U.S. State Department refused to issue Pauling a passport to leave the United States, so he could neither attend meetings at which Wilkins presented the X-ray data nor visit England to talk with Franklin and Wilkins directly. Watson and Crick knew that Pauling was working on DNA structure and were driven by the fear that he would beat them to it. In his book, *The Double Helix,* Watson recounts his belief that, had Pauling seen the X-ray pictures, "in a week at most, Linus would have [had] the structure."

You might be thinking, "But wait just a minute! That's not fair. If the goal of science is to advance knowledge, then everyone should have access to all the data. If Pauling was the best, he should have discovered the double helix first." Perhaps so. But after all, scientists are people, too. Although virtually all scientists want to see the progress of science and benefits for humanity, each individual also wants to be the one responsible for that progress and to receive the credit and glory. Linus Pauling remained in the dark about the X-ray data and was beaten to the correct structure.

Soon after Watson and Crick proposed the double helix (**Fig. E11-3**), Watson described it in a letter to Max Delbruck, a friend and adviser at Caltech. When Delbruck told Pauling about the double helix model for DNA, Pauling graciously congratulated Watson and Crick on their brilliant solution. The race was over.

▲ FIGURE E11-3 **The discovery of DNA** James Watson and Francis Crick with a model of DNA structure.

Of course, to make sense, the letters of a language must be in the correct order. Similarly, a gene must have the right bases in the right sequence. Just as "friend" and "fiend" mean different things, and "fliend" doesn't mean anything, different sequences of bases in DNA may encode very different pieces of information, or no information at all.

In Chapter 12, we will describe how the information in DNA is used to produce the structures of living cells. In the remainder of this chapter, we will examine how DNA is replicated during cell division to ensure accurate copying of this genetic information.

Case Study continued
Muscles, Mutations, and Myostatin

All "normal" mammals have a DNA sequence that encodes a functional myostatin protein, which limits their muscle growth. Belgian Blue cattle have a mutation that changes a "friendly" gene to a nonsensical "fliendly" one that no longer codes for a functional protein, so they have excessive muscle development.

11.4 HOW DOES DNA REPLICATION ENSURE GENETIC CONSTANCY DURING CELL DIVISION?

Replication of DNA Is a Critical Event in the Cell Cycle

In the 1850s, Austrian pathologist Rudolf Virchow realized that "all cells come from [preexisting] cells." All of the trillions of cells of your body are the offspring of other cells, going all the way back to when you were a fertilized egg. Moreover, almost every cell of your body contains identical genetic information—the same genetic information present in that fertilized egg. When cells reproduce by mitotic cell division, each daughter cell receives a nearly perfect copy of the parent cell's genetic information. Consequently, before cell division, the parent cell must synthesize two exact copies of its DNA. A process called **DNA replication** produces these two identical DNA double helices.

DNA Replication Produces Two DNA Double Helices, Each with One Original Strand and One New Strand

How does a cell accurately copy its DNA? In their paper describing DNA structure, Watson and Crick included one of the greatest understatements in all of science: "It has not escaped our notice that the specific [base] pairing we have postulated immediately suggests a possible copying mechanism for the genetic material." In fact, base pairing is the foundation of DNA replication. Remember, the rules for base pairing are that an adenine on one strand must pair with a thymine on the other strand, and a cytosine must pair with a guanine. If one strand reads A–T–G, for example, then the other strand must read T–A–C. Therefore, the base sequence of each strand contains all the information needed to replicate the other strand.

Conceptually, DNA replication is quite simple (**Fig. 11-6**). The essential ingredients are (1) the parental DNA strands, (2) **free nucleotides** that were previously synthesized in the cytoplasm and imported into the nucleus, and (3) a variety of enzymes that unwind the parental DNA double helix and synthesize new DNA strands.

First, enzymes called **DNA helicases** (meaning "enzymes that break apart the double helix") pull apart the parental DNA

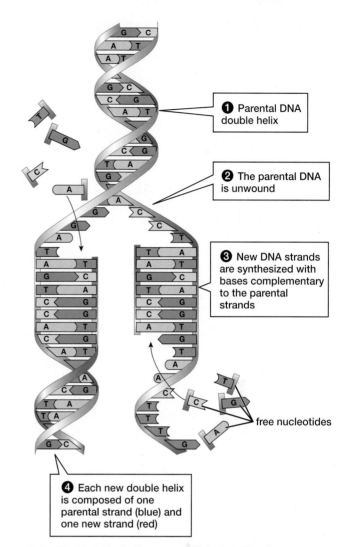

① Parental DNA double helix

② The parental DNA is unwound

③ New DNA strands are synthesized with bases complementary to the parental strands

free nucleotides

④ Each new double helix is composed of one parental strand (blue) and one new strand (red)

▲ **FIGURE 11-6 Basic features of DNA replication** During replication, the two strands of the parental DNA double helix separate. Free nucleotides that are complementary to those in each strand are joined to make new daughter strands. Each parental strand and its new daughter strand then form a new double helix.

Case Study c o n t i n u e d

Muscles, Mutations, and Myostatin

Through a complex mechanism involving many other molecules, myostatin prevents pre-muscle cells from replicating their DNA. Therefore, the cells stop dividing, and the number of mature muscle cells is limited. The mutated myostatin of Belgian Blue cattle fails to inhibit DNA replication, so the pre-muscle cells continue to divide, producing more muscle cells.

---

double helix, so that the bases of the two DNA strands no longer form base pairs with one another. Now DNA strands complementary to the two parental strands must be synthesized. Other enzymes, called **DNA polymerases** ("enzymes that synthesize a DNA polymer"), move along each separated parental DNA strand, matching bases on the strand with complementary free nucleotides. For example, DNA polymerase pairs an exposed adenine in the parental strand with a thymine. DNA polymerase also connects these free nucleotides with one another to form two new DNA strands, each complementary to one of the parental DNA strands. Thus, if a parental DNA strand reads T–A–G, DNA polymerase will synthesize a new DNA strand with the complementary sequence A–T–C. For more information on how DNA is replicated, refer to "A Closer Look at DNA Structure and Replication" on pp. 210–212.

When replication is complete, one parental DNA strand and its newly synthesized, complementary daughter

A Closer Look At *DNA Structure and Replication*

DNA Structure

To understand DNA replication, we must return to the structure of DNA. Biochemists keep track of the atoms in a complex molecule by numbering them. In the case of a nucleotide, the atoms that form the "corners" of the base are numbered 1 through 6 for the single-ringed cytosine and thymine, or 1 through 9 for the double-ringed adenine and guanine. The carbon atoms of the sugar are numbered 1′ through 5′. The prime symbol (′) is used to distinguish atoms in the sugar from atoms in the base. The carbons in the sugar are called "1-prime" through "5-prime" (**Fig. E11-4**).

The sugar of a nucleotide has two "ends" that can be involved in synthesizing the sugar-phosphate backbone of a DNA strand: a 3′ end, which has a free —OH (hydroxyl) group attached to the 3′ carbon of the sugar, and a 5′ end, which has a phosphate group attached to the 5′ carbon. When a DNA strand is synthesized, the phosphate of one nucleotide bonds with the hydroxyl group on the sugar of the next nucleotide (**Fig. E11-5**).

This still leaves a free hydroxyl group on the 3′ end of one nucleotide, and a free phosphate group on the 5′ end of the other nucleotide. No matter how many nucleotides are joined, there is always a free hydroxyl on the 3′ end of the strand and a free phosphate on the 5′ end.

The sugar-phosphate backbones of the two strands of a double helix are antiparallel, meaning that they run in opposite directions. Therefore, at one end of a double helix, one strand has a free hydroxyl on the sugar (the 3′ end), whereas the other strand has a free phosphate (the 5′ end). At the other end of the double helix, the strand ends are reversed (**Fig. E11-6**).

DNA Replication

DNA replication involves three major actions (**Fig. E11-7**). First, the DNA double helix must be opened up so that the base sequence can be read. Then, new DNA strands with base sequences complementary to the two original strands must be synthesized. In eukaryotic cells, these new DNA strands are synthesized in fairly short pieces. Therefore, the third step in DNA replication is to stitch the pieces together to form a continuous new strand of DNA. Each step is carried out by a distinct set of enzymes.

DNA helicase separates the parental DNA strands

Acting in concert with several other enzymes, DNA helicase breaks the hydrogen bonds between complementary base pairs that hold the two parental DNA strands together. This separates and unwinds the parental double helix, forming a replication "bubble" (**Fig. E11-7 ❶** and **❷**). Each replication bubble contains a replication "fork" at each end, where the two parental DNA strands are just beginning to be unwound. Within the replication bubble, the bases of the parental DNA strands are no longer paired with one another.

DNA polymerase synthesizes new DNA strands

Replication bubbles are essential because they allow a second enzyme, DNA polymerase, to gain access to the bases of each DNA strand (**Fig. E11-7 ❸**). At each replication fork, a complex of DNA polymerase and other proteins binds to each parental strand. Therefore, there will be two DNA polymerase complexes, one on each parental strand. DNA polymerase recognizes an unpaired base in the parental strand and matches it up with a complementary base in a free nucleotide. Then, DNA polymerase catalyzes the formation of new covalent bonds, linking the phosphate of the incoming free nucleotide (the 5′ end) to the sugar of the most recently added nucleotide (the 3′ end) of the growing daughter strand. In this way, DNA polymerase synthesizes the sugar-phosphate backbone of the daughter strand.

Why make replication bubbles, rather than simply starting at one end of a double helix and letting one DNA polymerase molecule copy the DNA in one continuous

▲ FIGURE E11-4 **Numbering of carbon atoms in a nucleotide**

▲ FIGURE E11-5 **Numbering of carbon atoms in a dinucleotide**

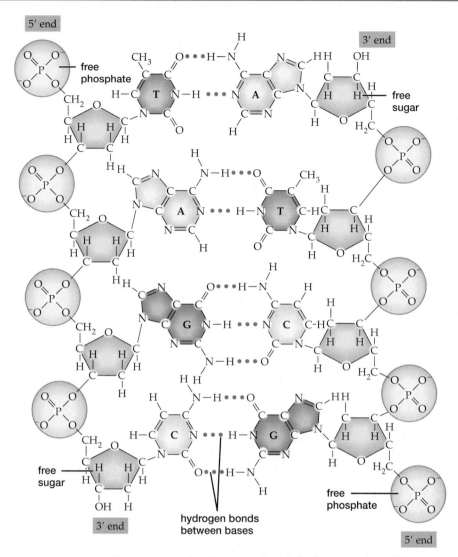

5′ end
free phosphate

free sugar
3′ end

free sugar

free phosphate

hydrogen bonds between bases

3′ end

5′ end

▲ FIGURE E11-6 **The two strands of a DNA double helix are antiparallel**

simultaneously moves 5′ → 3′ on the daughter strand. Finally, because the two strands of the parental DNA double helix are oriented in opposite directions, the DNA polymerase molecules move in opposite directions on the two parental strands (see Fig. E11-7 ❸).

DNA helicase and DNA polymerase work together (**Fig. E11-7 ❹**). A DNA helicase "lands" on the double helix and moves along, unwinding the double helix and separating the strands. Because the two DNA strands run in opposite directions, as a DNA helicase enzyme moves toward the 5′ end of one parental strand, it is simultaneously moving toward the 3′ end of the other parental strand. Now visualize two DNA polymerases landing on the two separated strands of DNA. One DNA polymerase (call it polymerase #1) can follow behind the helicase toward the 5′ end of the parental strand and can synthesize a continuous daughter DNA strand, until it runs into another replication bubble. This continuous daughter DNA strand is called the leading strand. On the other parental strand, however, DNA polymerase #2 moves *away from* the helicase: in ❸ of Figure E11-7, note that the helicase moves to the left, whereas DNA polymerase #2 moves to the right. Therefore, DNA synthesis on this strand will be discontinuous: DNA polymerase #2 will synthesize a short new DNA strand, called the lagging strand, but meanwhile, the helicase continues to move to the left, unwinding more of the double helix (see Fig. E11-7 ❹ and ❺). Additional DNA polymerases (#3, #4, and so on) must land on this strand and synthesize more short lagging strands.

DNA ligase joins segments of DNA

Multiple DNA polymerases synthesize pieces of DNA of varying lengths. Each chromosome may form hundreds of replication bubbles. Within each bubble, there will be one leading strand, tens to hundreds of thousands of nucleotide pairs long, and dozens to thousands of lagging strands, each about 100 to 200 nucleotide pairs long. Therefore, a cell might synthesize millions of pieces of DNA while replicating a single chromosome. How are all of these pieces sewn together? This is the job of the third major enzyme, **DNA ligase** ("an enzyme that ties DNA together"; **Fig. E11-7 ❺**). Many DNA ligase enzymes stitch the fragments of DNA together until each daughter strand consists of one long, continuous DNA polymer.

piece all the way to the other end? Well, eukaryotic chromosomes are *very* long: Human chromosomes range from about 23 million bases in the relatively tiny Y chromosome, to about 246 million bases in chromosome 1. Eukaryotic DNA is copied at a rate of about 50 nucleotides per second, so it would take about 5 to 57 days to copy human chromosomes in one continuous piece. To replicate an entire chromosome in a reasonable time, many DNA helicase enzymes open up many replication bubbles, allowing many DNA polymerase enzymes to copy the parental strands in fairly small pieces. The bubbles grow as DNA replication progresses, and they merge when they contact one another.

DNA polymerase always moves away from the 3′ end of a parental DNA strand (this is the end with the free hydroxyl group of the sugar) toward the 5′ end (with a free phosphate group). New nucleotides are always added to the 3′ end of the daughter strand. In other words, DNA polymerase moves 3′ → 5′ on a parental strand, and

(continued)

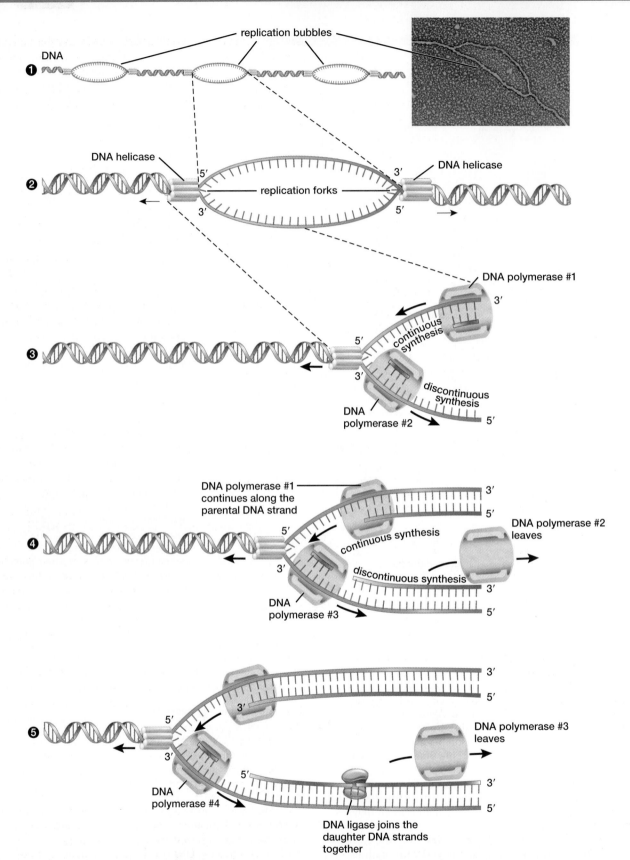

▲ FIGURE E11-7 DNA replication ❶ DNA helicase enzymes separate the parental strands of a chromosome to form replication bubbles. ❷ Each replication bubble consists of two replication forks, with unwound DNA strands between the forks. ❸ DNA polymerase enzymes synthesize new pieces of DNA. ❹ DNA helicase moves along the parental DNA double helix, unwinding it and enlarging the replication bubble. DNA polymerases in the replication bubble synthesize daughter DNA strands. ❺ DNA ligase joins the small DNA segments into a single daughter strand.

QUESTION During synthesis, why doesn't DNA polymerase move away from the replication fork on both strands?

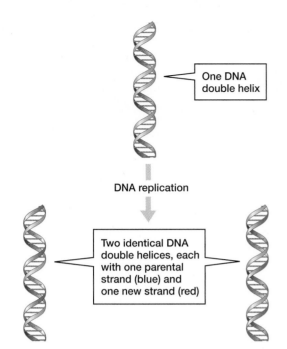

▲ FIGURE 11-7 Semiconservative replication of DNA

DNA strand wind together into one double helix. At the same time, the other parental strand and its daughter strand wind together into a second double helix. In forming a new double helix, the process of DNA replication conserves one parental DNA strand and produces one newly synthesized strand. Hence, the process is called **semiconservative replication** (Fig. 11-7).

If no mistakes have been made, the base sequences of both new DNA double helices are identical to the base sequence of the parental DNA double helix and, of course, to each other.

BioFlix ™ DNA Replication

11.5 HOW DO MUTATIONS OCCUR?

Nothing is perfect, including the DNA in your cells. Changes in the sequence of bases in DNA, often resulting in a defective gene, are called **mutations.** In most cells, mutations are minimized by highly accurate DNA replication, "proofreading" of the newly synthesized DNA, and the repair of any changes in DNA that may occur even when the DNA is not being replicated.

Accurate Replication and Proofreading Produce Almost Error-Free DNA

The specificity of hydrogen bonding between complementary base pairs makes DNA replication highly accurate. DNA polymerase incorporates incorrect bases about once in every 1,000 to 100,000 base pairs. However, completed DNA strands contain only about one mistake in every 100 million to 1 billion base pairs (in humans, usually less than one per chromosome per replication). This phenomenally low error rate is ensured by a variety of DNA repair enzymes that proofread each daughter strand during and after its synthesis. For example, some forms of DNA polymerase recognize a base pairing mistake as it is made. This type of DNA polymerase will pause, fix the mistake, and then continue synthesizing more DNA.

Mistakes Do Happen

Despite this amazing accuracy, neither humans nor any other organisms have error-free DNA. In addition to rare mistakes made during normal DNA replication, a variety of environmental conditions can damage DNA. For example, certain chemicals (such as components of cigarette smoke) and some types of radiation (such as ultraviolet rays in sunlight and X-rays) increase the frequency of base pairing errors during replication, or even induce changes in DNA composition between replications. Most of these changes in DNA sequence are fixed by repair enzymes in the cell. However, some inevitably remain.

Mutations Range from Changes in Single Nucleotide Pairs to Movements of Large Pieces of Chromosomes

During replication, a pair of bases is occasionally mismatched. Usually, repair enzymes recognize the mismatch, cut out the incorrect nucleotide, and replace it with a nucleotide that bears a complementary base. Sometimes, however, the enzymes replace the original nucleotide instead of the mismatched one. The resulting base pair is complementary, but incorrect. These **nucleotide substitutions** are also called **point mutations,** because individual nucleotides in the DNA sequence are changed (Fig. 11-8a). An **insertion mutation** occurs when one or more nucleotide pairs are inserted into the DNA double helix (Fig. 11-8b). A **deletion mutation** occurs when one or more nucleotide pairs are removed from the double helix (Fig. 11-8c).

Pieces of chromosomes ranging in size from a single nucleotide pair to massive pieces of DNA are occasionally rearranged. An **inversion** occurs when a piece of DNA is cut out of a chromosome, turned around, and reinserted into the gap (Fig. 11-8d). Finally, a **translocation** results when a chunk of DNA, often very large, is removed from one chromosome and attached to another one (Fig. 11-8e).

Mutations May Have Varying Effects on Function

Mutations are often harmful, much as randomly changing words in the middle of Shakespeare's *Hamlet* would probably interrupt the flow of the play. If they are really damaging, a cell or an organism inheriting such a mutation may quickly die. Some mutations, however, have no effect or, in very rare instances, are even beneficial, as you will learn in Chapter 12. Mutations that are beneficial, at least in certain environments, may be favored by natural selection, and are the basis for the evolution of life on Earth (see Unit 3).

▲ FIGURE 11-8 **Mutations (a)** Nucleotide substitution. **(b)** Insertion mutation. **(c)** Deletion mutation. **(d)** Inversion mutation. **(e)** Translocation of pieces of DNA between two different chromosomes. In parts (a) through (d), the original DNA bases are in pale colors with black letters; mutations are in deep colors with white letters.

Have you ever wondered

How Much Genes Influence Athletic Prowess?

Face it—you'll never swim like Michael Phelps. But how much of his fantastic ability is genetic? In some cases, genes clearly make a huge difference. Myostatin mutations, for example, can boost speed and strength, as we explain in the Case Study Revisited section. The effects of most individual genes, however, are small. Over 240 genes contribute to athletic performance. Do super-athletes have all the best "athletic alleles"? How many athletic alleles do Phelps, and you, have? Right now, no one can tell.

Muscles, Mutations, and Myostatin

Belgian Blue cattle have a deletion mutation in their myostatin gene. The result is that their cells stop synthesizing the myostatin protein about halfway through. (In Chapter 12, we'll explain why some mutations cause short, or truncated, proteins to be synthesized.) Several other breeds of "double muscled" cattle have the same mutation, but some have totally different mutations. Other animals, including some breeds of dogs (**Fig. 11-9**), also have myostatin mutations. They are generally different than the

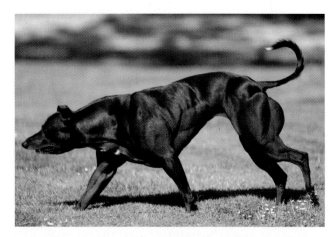

▲ **FIGURE 11-9 Myostatin mutation in a dog** Like Belgian Blue cattle, "bully" whippets have defective myostatin, resulting in enormous muscles.

mutations in any of the breeds of cattle, but produce similar phenotypic effects.

What they all have in common is that their myostatin proteins are nonfunctional. This is an important feature of the language of DNA: The nucleotide words must be spelled just right, or at least really close, for the resulting proteins to function. In contrast, any one of an enormous number of mistakes will render the proteins useless.

Humans have myostatin, too; not surprisingly, mutations can occur in the human myostatin gene. As you probably know, a child inherits two copies of most genes, one from each parent. A few years ago, a child was born in Germany who inherited a point mutation in his myostatin gene from both parents. This particular point mutation results in short, inactive, myostatin proteins. At 7 months, the boy already had well-developed calf, thigh, and buttock muscles. At 4 years, he could hold a 7-pound (3.2-kilogram) dumbbell in each hand, with his arms fully extended horizontally out to his sides (try it—it's not that easy for many adults).

Consider This

Mutations may be neutral, harmful, or beneficial. Into which category do myostatin mutations fall? Belgian Blue cattle are born so muscular and, consequently, so large, that they usually must be delivered by cesarean section. Myostatin-deficient mice have small, brittle tendons, so their oversize muscles are weakly attached to their bones. On the other hand, heterozygous whippets, with one normal and one defective myostatin allele, can run faster than ordinary whippets. The German boy's mother and some other relatives, presumably heterozygous for the myostatin mutation, were top-level athletes or unusually strong, or both. Is it possible that myostatin mutations are harmful in homozygotes but beneficial in heterozygotes? How do you think that natural selection might operate in this situation?

CHAPTER REVIEW

Summary of Key Concepts

11.1 How Did Scientists Discover That Genes Are Made of DNA?

By the turn of the century, scientists knew that genes must be made of either protein or DNA. Studies by Griffith showed that genes can be transferred from one bacterial strain into another. This transfer could transform the bacterial strain from harmless to deadly. Avery, MacLeod, and McCarty showed that DNA was the molecule that could transform bacteria. Hershey and Chase found that DNA is also the hereditary material of bacteriophage viruses. Thus, genes must be made of DNA.

11.2 What Is the Structure of DNA?

DNA consists of nucleotides that are linked into long strands. Each nucleotide consists of a phosphate group, the five-carbon sugar deoxyribose, and a nitrogen-containing base. Four types of bases occur in DNA: adenine, guanine, thymine, and cytosine. The sugar of one nucleotide is linked to the phosphate of the next nucleotide, forming a sugar-phosphate backbone for each strand. The bases stick out from this backbone. Two nucleotide strands wind together to form a DNA double helix, which resembles a twisted ladder. The sugar-phosphate backbones form the sides of the ladder. The bases of each strand pair up in the middle of the helix, held together by hydrogen bonds, forming the rungs of the ladder. Only complementary base pairs can bond together in the helix: Adenine bonds with thymine, and guanine bonds with cytosine.

11.3 How Does DNA Encode Information?

Genetic information is encoded as the sequence of bases in a DNA molecule. Just as a language can form thousands of words and complex sentences from a small number of letters by varying the sequence and number of letters in each word and sentence, so too can DNA encode large amounts of information with varying sequences and numbers of bases in different genes. Because DNA molecules are usually millions to billions of nucleotides long, DNA can encode huge amounts of information in its base sequence.

11.4 How Does DNA Replication Ensure Genetic Constancy During Cell Division?

When cells reproduce, they must replicate their DNA so that each daughter cell receives all the original genetic information. During DNA replication, enzymes unwind the two parental DNA strands. Then DNA polymerase enzymes bind to each parental DNA strand. Free nucleotides form hydrogen bonds with complementary bases on the parental strands, and DNA polymerase links the free nucleotides to form new DNA strands. Therefore, the sequence of nucleotides in each newly formed strand is complementary to the sequence of a parental strand. Replication is semiconservative because, when DNA replication is complete, both new DNA double helices consist of one parental DNA strand and one newly synthesized, complementary daughter strand. The two new DNA double helices are, therefore, duplicates of the parental DNA double helix.

BioFlix ™ DNA Replication

11.5 How Do Mutations Occur?

Mutations are changes in the base sequence in DNA. DNA polymerase and other repair enzymes "proofread" the DNA, minimizing the number of mistakes during replication, but mistakes do occur. Other base changes occur as a result of radiation and damage from certain chemicals. Mutations include substitutions, insertions, deletions, inversions, and translocations. Most mutations are harmful or neutral, but a few are beneficial and may be favored by natural selection.

Key Terms

adenine (A) 203	guanine (G) 203
bacteriophage 204	insertion mutation 213
base 203	inversion 213
complementary base pair 206	mutation 213
cytosine (C) 203	nucleotide substitution 213
deletion mutation 213	nucleotide 203
deoxyribonucleic acid (DNA) 200	point mutation 213
DNA helicase 209	semiconservative replication 213
DNA ligase 211	strand 206
DNA polymerase 209	sugar-phosphate backbone 206
DNA replication 209	thymine (T) 203
double helix 206	translocation 213
free nucleotide 209	

Thinking Through the Concepts

Fill-in-the-Blank

1. DNA consists of subunits called _____. Each subunit consists of three parts: _____, _____, and _____.

2. The subunits of DNA are assembled by linking the _____ of one nucleotide to the _____ of the next. As it is found in chromosomes, two DNA polymers are wound together into a structure called a(n) _____.

3. The "base-pairing rule" in DNA is that adenine pairs with _____, and guanine pairs with _____. Bases that can form pairs in DNA are called _____.

4. When DNA is replicated, two new DNA double helices are formed, each consisting of one parental strand and one new, daughter strand. For this reason, DNA replication is called _____.

5. The DNA double helix is unwound by an enzyme called _____. Daughter DNA strands are synthesized by the enzyme _____. In eukaryotic cells, the daughter DNA strands are synthesized in pieces; these pieces are joined by the enzyme _____.

6. Sometimes, mistakes are made during DNA replication. If uncorrected, these mistakes are called _____. When a single nucleotide is changed, this is called a(n) _____, or _____.

Review Questions

1. Draw the general structure of a nucleotide. Which parts are identical in all nucleotides, and which can vary?

2. Name the four types of nitrogen-containing bases found in DNA.

3. Which bases are complementary to one another? How are they held together in the double helix of DNA?

4. Describe the structure of DNA. Where are the bases, sugars, and phosphates in the structure?

5. Describe the process of DNA replication.

6. How do mutations occur? Describe the principal types of mutations.

Applying the Concepts

1. As you learned in "Scientific Inquiry: The Discovery of the Double Helix," scientists in different laboratories often compete with one another to make new discoveries. Do you think this competition helps promote scientific discoveries? Sometimes researchers in different laboratories collaborate with one another. What advantages does collaboration offer over competition? What factors might provide barriers to collaboration and lead to competition?

2. Genetic information is encoded in the sequence of nucleotides in DNA. Let's suppose that the nucleotide sequence on one strand of a double helix encodes the information needed to synthesize a hemoglobin molecule. Do you think that the sequence of nucleotides on the other strand of the double helix also encodes useful information? Why? (An analogy might help. Suppose that English were a "complementary language," with letters at opposite ends of the alphabet complementary to one another; that is, A is complementary to Z, B to Y, C to X, and so on. Would a sentence composed of letters complementary to "To be or not to be?" make sense?) Finally, why do you think DNA is double-stranded?

3. **BioEthics** Today, scientific advances are being made at an astounding rate, and nowhere is this more evident than in our understanding of the biology of heredity. Using DNA as a starting point, do you believe that there are limits to the knowledge that people should acquire? Defend your answer.

MB Go to www.masteringbiology.com for practice quizzes, activities, eText, videos, current events, and more.

Gene Expression and Regulation

Case Study

Cystic Fibrosis

IF ALL YOU knew was her music, you'd think Alice Martineau had it made—a young, pretty singer-songwriter signed to a recording contract with Sony Music Entertainment. But genetics dealt Alice Martineau a double whammy—two copies of a defective recessive allele that encodes a crucially important protein called CFTR. Martineau—like about 30,000 Americans, 3,000 Canadians, and 20,000 Europeans—had cystic fibrosis. Before modern medical care, most people with cystic fibrosis died by age 4 or 5; even now, the average life span is only 35 to 40 years.

CFTR is a channel protein that is permeable to chloride and is found in many parts of the body, including the sweat glands, lungs, and intestines. Let's look at its role in perspiration. When sweat is first secreted by glands deep in the skin, it contains a lot of salt (sodium chloride), about as much as in blood. Most of the salt, however, is reclaimed as the sweat moves through tubes leading from the secreting cells to the surface of the skin. Although researchers do not fully understand the precise mechanism, CFTR is required for reabsorption of both chloride and sodium. Mutations in the *CFTR* gene, however, produce defective CFTR proteins that prevent reabsorption of chloride and sodium, so salt stays in the sweat.

Salty sweat usually isn't very harmful. Unfortunately, the cells lining the airways in the lungs have the same CFTR proteins. Normally, the airways are covered with a thin film of watery mucus, which traps bacteria and debris. "Natural antibiotic" proteins in the fluid kill many bacteria. The bacteria are then swept out of the lungs by cilia on the cells lining the airways. CFTR is essential for fluid secretion in the airway. Defective CFTR proteins cause the mucus to be "dehydrated" and so thick that the cilia can't move it out of the lungs. Therefore, the airways are partially clogged and bacteria multiply, causing chronic lung infections. People with cystic fibrosis cough frequently, trying to clear their airways. Alice Martineau credited coughing with strengthening her vocal cords and helping to produce her deep, strong voice.

In this chapter, we will examine the processes by which the instructions in genes are translated into proteins. When a gene mutates, how does that affect the structure and function of the encoded protein, such as CFTR? Why might different mutations in the same gene have different consequences?

▲ Although she was diagnosed early in life with cystic fibrosis, Alice Martineau hoped that ". . . people will realise when they hear the music, I am a singer-songwriter who just happens to be ill."

12.1 HOW IS THE INFORMATION IN DNA USED IN A CELL?

Information, by itself, doesn't do anything. For example, a blueprint may describe the structure of a house in great detail, but unless that information is translated into action by construction workers, no house will be built. Likewise, although the base sequence of DNA, the "molecular blueprint" of every cell, contains an incredible amount of information, DNA cannot carry out any action on its own. So, how does DNA determine whether you have black, blond, or red hair, or have normal lung function or cystic fibrosis?

Most Genes Contain the Information for the Synthesis of a Single Protein

Long before they found out that genes are made of DNA, biologists tried to determine how genes affect the phenotype of individual cells and entire organisms. Starting with studies of the inheritance of human metabolic disorders in the early 1900s and culminating in a brilliant series of experiments with common bread molds in the 1940s, biologists discovered that most genes contain the information needed to direct the synthesis of a single protein (see "Scientific Inquiry: One Gene, One Protein" on pp. 220–221). Proteins, in turn, are the "molecular workers" of the cell, forming many of its cellular structures and

the enzymes that catalyze its chemical reactions. Therefore, there must be a flow of information from DNA to protein.

DNA Provides Instructions for Protein Synthesis via RNA Intermediaries

The DNA of a eukaryotic cell is housed in the nucleus, but protein synthesis occurs on ribosomes in the cytoplasm (see see pp. 66–67). Therefore, DNA cannot directly guide protein synthesis. There must be an intermediary, a molecule that carries information from DNA in the nucleus to the ribosomes in the cytoplasm. This molecule is **ribonucleic acid,** or **RNA.**

RNA is similar to DNA but differs structurally in three respects: (1) RNA is usually single-stranded; (2) RNA has the sugar ribose instead of deoxyribose in its backbone; and (3) RNA has the base uracil instead of the base thymine (**Table 12-1**).

DNA codes for the synthesis of many types of RNA, three of which play specific roles in protein synthesis: **messenger RNA (mRNA), ribosomal RNA (rRNA),** and **transfer RNA (tRNA)** (**Fig. 12-1**). There are several other types of RNA, including RNA used as the genetic material in some viruses, such as HIV; enzymatic RNA, called ribozymes, that catalyze various reactions, including cutting apart other molecules of RNA; and two types of RNA that we will briefly discuss later in this chapter: Xist RNA, which

Table 12-1	A Comparison of DNA and RNA		
	DNA	**RNA**	
Strands	2	1	
Sugar	Deoxyribose	Ribose	
Types of bases	adenine (A), thymine (T) cytosine (C), guanine (G)	adenine (A), uracil (U) cytosine (C), guanine (G)	
Base pairs	DNA–DNA	RNA–DNA	RNA–RNA
	A–T	A–T	A–U
	T–A	U–A	U–A
	C–G	C–G	C–G
	G–C	G–C	G–C
Function	Contains genes; the sequence of bases in most genes determines the amino acid sequence of a protein	Messenger RNA (mRNA): carries the code for a protein-coding gene from DNA to ribosomes Ribosomal RNA (rRNA): combines with proteins to form ribosomes, the structures that link amino acids to form a protein Transfer RNA (tRNA): carries amino acids to the ribosomes	

prevents most of the genetic information in one of the X chromosomes of female mammals from being used (see section 12.5), and microRNA, which plays a role in regulating development and fighting disease (see "Scientific Inquiry: RNA—It's Not Just a Messenger Anymore" on p. 234). Here we will focus on the functions of mRNA, rRNA, and tRNA in protein synthesis.

Messenger RNA Carries the Code for Protein Synthesis from DNA to Ribosomes

Messenger RNA carries the code for the amino acid sequence of a protein from DNA to the ribosomes, which synthesize the protein specified by the mRNA base sequence (Fig. 12-1a). In eukaryotic cells, the DNA remains safely stored in the nucleus, like a valuable document in a library,

◄ FIGURE 12-1 **Cells synthesize three major types of RNA that are required for protein synthesis**

The base sequence of mRNA carries the information for the amino acid sequence of a protein; groups of these bases, called codons, specify the amino acids

(a) Messenger RNA (mRNA)

rRNA combines with proteins to form ribosomes; the small subunit binds mRNA; the large subunit binds tRNA and catalyzes peptide bond formation between amino acids during protein synthesis

(b) Ribosome: contains ribosomal RNA (rRNA)

Each tRNA carries a specific amino acid (in this example, tyrosine [tyr]) to a ribosome during protein synthesis; the anticodon of tRNA pairs with a codon of mRNA, ensuring that the correct amino acid is incorporated into the protein

(c) Transfer RNA (tRNA)

Scientific Inquiry

One Gene, One Protein

In Chapter 10, we saw that genes can determine, or at least influence, traits as varied as hair texture, flower color, and inherited diseases such as sickle-cell anemia. But how? Just as Gregor Mendel discovered the principles of inheritance using edible peas as an understandable "model system," later biologists sought to learn how genes work using model systems with easily measurable, unambiguous phenotypes. These model systems were the metabolic pathways by which cells synthesize complex molecules (see pp. 105–106).

Many metabolic pathways synthesize molecules in a series of linked steps, with each step catalyzed by a specific protein enzyme. Within a metabolic pathway, the product produced by one enzyme becomes the substrate of the next enzyme, like a molecular assembly line (see Fig. 6-12). How do genes encode the information needed to produce these pathways?

The first hint came from children who are born with defective metabolic pathways. For example, defects in the metabolism of two amino acids, phenylalanine and tyrosine, can cause albinism (no pigmentation in skin or hair; see Fig. 10-22) or several diseases with symptoms as varied as urine that turns brown when exposed to the air (alkaptonuria) or phenylalanine accumulation in the brain, leading to mental retardation (phenylketonuria). In the early 1900s, the English physician Archibald Garrod studied the inheritance of these inborn errors of metabolism. He hypothesized that (1) each inborn error of metabolism is caused by a defective version of a specific enzyme; (2) each defective enzyme is caused by a defective allele of a single gene; and (3) therefore, at least some genes must encode the information needed for the synthesis of enzymes.

Given the technology of his time and the limitations of human genetic studies, Garrod couldn't definitively test his hypotheses, and they were largely ignored. However, in the early 1940s, geneticists George Beadle and Edward Tatum used the metabolic pathways of a common bread mold, *Neurospora crassa*, to show that Garrod was correct.

Although we usually encounter *Neurospora* growing on stale bread, it can survive on a much simpler diet. All it needs is an energy source such as sugar, a few minerals,

and vitamin B_6. Therefore, *Neurospora* manufactures the enzymes needed to make virtually all of its own organic molecules, including amino acids. (In contrast, we humans cannot synthesize many vitamins or 9 of the 20 common amino acids; we must obtain these from our food.) Beadle and Tatum used *Neurospora* to test the hypothesis that many of an organism's genes encode the information needed to synthesize enzymes.

If this hypothesis was correct, a mutation in a specific gene might disrupt the synthesis of a specific enzyme, which would disable one of the mold's metabolic pathways. Thus, a mutant mold couldn't synthesize some of the organic molecules, such as amino acids, that it needs to survive. The mutant *Neurospora* could grow on a simple medium of sugar, minerals, and vitamin B_6 only if the missing organic molecules were provided.

Beadle and Tatum induced mutations by exposing *Neurospora* to X-rays, and then studied the inheritance of the metabolic pathway that synthesizes the amino acid arginine (**Fig. E12-1**). In normal molds, arginine is synthesized from citrulline, which in turn is synthesized from ornithine (**Fig. E12-1a**). Mutant A could grow only if supplemented with arginine, but not if supplemented with citrulline or ornithine (**Fig. E12-1b**). Therefore, this strain had a defect in the enzyme that converts citrulline to arginine. Mutant B could grow if supplemented with either arginine or citrulline, but not with ornithine (see Fig. E12-1b). This mutant had a defect in the enzyme that converts ornithine to citrulline. Because a mutation in a single gene affected only a single enzyme within a single metabolic pathway, Beadle and Tatum concluded that one gene encodes the information for one enzyme. The importance of this observation was recognized in 1958 with a Nobel Prize, which Beadle and Tatum shared with Joshua Lederberg, one of Tatum's students.

Almost all enzymes are proteins, but many proteins are not enzymes. For example, keratin is a structural protein in hair and nails, but it does not catalyze any chemical reactions. In addition, many enzymes are composed of more than one protein subunit. DNA polymerase, for instance, consists of more than a dozen proteins. Thus, the "one gene, one enzyme" relationship proposed by Beadle and Tatum was later clarified to "one gene, one protein."

while mRNA, like a molecular photocopy, carries the information to the cytoplasm to be used in protein synthesis. As we will see shortly, groups of three bases in mRNA, called codons, specify which amino acids will be incorporated into a protein.

Ribosomal RNA and Proteins Form Ribosomes

Ribosomes, the structures that carry out translation, are composed of rRNA and many different proteins. Each ribosome consists of two subunits—one small and one large. The small subunit has binding sites for mRNA, a "start"

(methionine) tRNA (see the next section for a description of tRNA), and several other proteins that collectively make up the "preinitiation complex," which is essential for assembling the ribosome and starting protein synthesis (see Fig. 12-7 ❶). The large subunit has binding sites for two tRNA molecules and a catalytic site for joining the amino acids attached to the tRNA molecules. Unless they are actively synthesizing proteins, the two subunits remain separate (**Fig. 12-1b**). During protein synthesis, the subunits come together and clasp an mRNA molecule between them (see Fig. 12-7 ❸).

(As you know from Chapter 3, a protein is a chain of amino acids joined by peptide bonds. Depending on their length, proteins may be called peptides [short chains] or polypeptides [long chains]. In this text, we usually call any chain of amino acids, regardless of length, a peptide or protein.) There are exceptions to the "one gene, one protein" rule, including several in which the final product of a gene isn't protein, but ribonucleic acid (RNA). Nevertheless, most genes do encode the amino acid sequence of a protein.

(a) **The metabolic pathway for synthesizing the amino acid arginine**

Genotype of *Neurospora*	Supplements Added to Medium				Conclusions
	none	ornithine	citrulline	arginine	
Normal *Neurospora*					Normal *Neurospora* can synthesize arginine, citrulline, and ornithine.
Mutants with single gene defect — A					Mutant A grows only if arginine is added. It cannot synthesize arginine because it has a defect in enzyme 2; gene *A* is needed for synthesis of arginine.
Mutants with single gene defect — B					Mutant B grows if either arginine or citrulline is added. It cannot synthesize arginine because it has a defect in enzyme 1. Gene *B* is needed for synthesis of citrulline.

(b) **Growth of normal and mutant *Neurospora* on a simple medium with different supplements**

▲ **FIGURE E12-1 Beadle and Tatum's experiments with *Neurospora* mutants (a)** Each step in the metabolic pathway for arginine synthesis is catalyzed by a different enzyme. **(b)** By analyzing which supplements allowed mutant molds to grow on simple nutrient medium, Beadle and Tatum concluded that a single gene codes for the synthesis of a single enzyme.

QUESTION What result would you expect for a mutant that lacks an enzyme needed to produce ornithine?

Transfer RNA Carries Amino Acids to the Ribosomes

Transfer RNA delivers the appropriate amino acids to the ribosome for incorporation into a protein. Every cell synthesizes at least one (and sometimes several) tRNAs for each amino acid. Twenty enzymes in the cytoplasm, one for each amino acid, recognize the tRNA molecules and use the energy of ATP to attach the correct amino acid to one end (**Fig. 12-1c**). These "loaded" tRNA molecules deliver their amino acids to a ribosome. A group of three bases, called an anticodon, protrudes from each tRNA. Complementary base pairing between codons of mRNA and anticodons of tRNA directs the correct amino acids to be used to synthesize a protein (see section 12.3).

Overview: Genetic Information Is Transcribed into RNA and Then Translated into Protein

Information in DNA is used to direct the synthesis of proteins in two steps, called transcription and translation (**Fig. 12-2** and **Table 12-2**):

1. In **transcription** (**Fig. 12-2a**), the information contained in the DNA of a specific gene is copied into messenger RNA (mRNA), transfer RNA (tRNA), or ribosomal RNA (rRNA). Thus, a gene is a segment of DNA that can be copied, or transcribed, into RNA. In eukaryotic cells, transcription occurs in the nucleus.

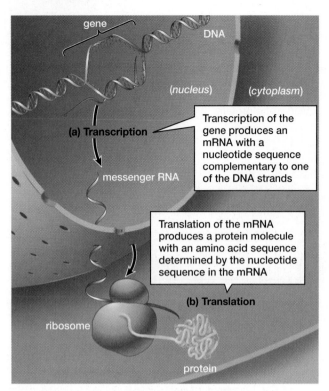

▲ FIGURE 12-2 **Genetic information flows from DNA to RNA to protein (a)** During transcription, the nucleotide sequence in a gene specifies the nucleotide sequence of a complementary RNA molecule. For protein-encoding genes, the product is an mRNA molecule that exits from the nucleus and enters the cytoplasm. **(b)** During translation, the sequence in an mRNA molecule specifies the amino acid sequence of a protein.

2. The base sequence of mRNA encodes the amino acid sequence of a protein. During protein synthesis, or **translation (Fig. 12-2b)**, this mRNA base sequence is decoded. Ribosomal RNA combines with dozens of proteins to form a ribosome. Transfer RNA molecules bring amino acids to the ribosome. Messenger RNA binds to the ribosome, where base pairing between mRNA and tRNA converts the base sequence of mRNA into the amino acid sequence of the protein. In eukaryotic cells, ribosomes are found in the cytoplasm and, thus, translation occurs there as well.

It's easy to confuse the terms transcription and translation. Comparing their common English meanings with their biological meanings may help you to remember the difference. In English, to *transcribe* means to make a written copy of

something, almost always in the same language. In an American courtroom, for example, verbal testimony is transcribed into a written copy, and both the testimony of the witnesses and the transcriptions are in English. In biology, transcription is the process of copying information from DNA to RNA using the common "language" of nucleotides. In contrast, the common English meaning of *translation* is to convert words from one language to a different language. In biology, translation means to convert information from the "nucleotide language" of RNA to the "amino acid language" of proteins.

The Genetic Code Uses Three Bases to Specify an Amino Acid

We will investigate both transcription and translation in more detail in sections 12.2 and 12.3. First, however, let's see how geneticists broke the language barrier: How does the language of nucleotide sequences in DNA and messenger RNA translate into the language of amino acid sequences in proteins? This translation relies on a "dictionary" called the genetic code.

The **genetic code** translates the sequence of bases in nucleic acids into the sequence of amino acids in proteins. Which combinations of bases code for which amino acids? Both DNA and RNA contain four different bases: A, T (or U in RNA), G, and C (see Table 12-1). However, proteins are made of 20 different amino acids, so one base cannot code for one amino acid: there are not enough different bases. If a sequence of two bases codes for an amino acid, there would be 16 possible combinations (each of four possible first bases paired with each of four possible second bases, or $4 \times 4 = 16$). This still isn't enough to code for 20 amino acids. A three-base sequence gives 64 possible combinations ($4 \times 4 \times 4 = 64$), which is more than enough. Based on this mathematical exercise, physicist George Gamow hypothesized that three bases specify a single amino acid. In 1961, Francis Crick and three coworkers demonstrated that this hypothesis is correct.

For any language to be understood, its users must know what the words mean, where words start and stop, and where sentences begin and end. To decipher the "words" of the genetic code, Marshall Nirenberg and Heinrich Matthaei ground up bacteria and isolated the components needed to synthesize proteins. To this mixture, they added artificial mRNA, allowing them to control which "words" were to be translated. They could then see which amino acids were incorporated into proteins. For example, an mRNA strand composed entirely of uracil (UUUUUUUU . . .) directed the mixture to synthesize a protein composed solely of the amino acid phenylalanine.

Table 12-2	**Transcription and Translation**			
Process	**Information for the Process**	**Product**	**Major Enzyme or Structure Involved in the Process**	**Type of Base Pairing Required**
Transcription (synthesis of RNA)	A segment of one DNA strand	One RNA molecule (e.g., mRNA, tRNA, or rRNA)	RNA polymerase	RNA with DNA: RNA bases pair with DNA bases as an RNA molecule is synthesized
Translation (synthesis of a protein)	mRNA	One protein molecule	Ribosome (also requires tRNA)	mRNA with tRNA: a codon in mRNA forms base pairs with an anticodon in tRNA

Therefore, the triplet UUU must specify phenylalanine. Because the genetic code was deciphered by using these artificial mRNAs, it is usually written in terms of the base triplets in mRNA (rather than in DNA) that code for each amino acid (**Table 12-3**). These mRNA triplets are called **codons.**

What about punctuation? How does a cell recognize where codons start and stop, and where the code for an entire protein starts and stops? Translation begins with the codon AUG, appropriately known as the **start codon.** Because AUG also codes for the amino acid methionine, all proteins originally begin with methionine (though it may be removed after the protein is synthesized). Three codons—UAG, UAA, and UGA—are **stop codons.** When the ribosome encounters a stop codon, it releases both the newly synthesized protein and the mRNA. Because all codons consist of three bases, and the beginning and end of a protein are specified, then punctuation ("spaces") between codons is unnecessary. Why? Consider what would happen if English used only three-letter words: a sentence such as THEDOGSAWTHECAT would be perfectly understandable, even without spaces between the words.

Because the genetic code has three stop codons, 61 nucleotide triplets remain to specify only 20 amino acids. Therefore, most amino acids are specified by several different codons. For example, six codons—UUA, UUG, CUU, CUC, CUA, and CUG—all specify leucine (see Table 12-3). However, each codon specifies one, and only one, amino acid; UUA always specifies leucine, never isoleucine, glycine, or any other amino acid.

How are codons used to direct protein synthesis? Decoding the codons of mRNA is the job of tRNA and ribosomes. Remember that tRNA transports amino acids to the ribosome, and that there are unique tRNA molecules that carry each different type of amino acid. Each of these unique tRNAs has three exposed bases, called an **anticodon,** which are complementary to the bases of a codon in mRNA. For example, the mRNA codon GUU forms base pairs with the anticodon CAA of a tRNA that has the amino acid valine attached to its end. As we will see in section 12.3, a ribosome can then incorporate valine into a growing protein chain.

12.2 HOW IS THE INFORMATION IN A GENE TRANSCRIBED INTO RNA?

Transcription (**Fig. 12-3**) consists of three steps: (1) initiation, (2) elongation, and (3) termination. These three steps correspond to the three major parts of most genes in both eukaryotes and prokaryotes: (1) a promoter region at the beginning of the gene, where transcription is started, or initiated; (2) the "body" of the gene where elongation of the RNA strand occurs; and (3) a termination signal at the end of the gene, where RNA synthesis ceases, or terminates.

Transcription Begins When RNA Polymerase Binds to the Promoter of a Gene

The enzyme **RNA polymerase** synthesizes RNA. To initiate transcription, RNA polymerase must first locate the beginning of a gene. Near the beginning of every gene is an untranscribed sequence of DNA called the **promoter.** In eukaryotic cells, a promoter consists of two main parts: (1) a short sequence of bases, often TATAAA, that binds RNA polymerase, and (2) one or more other sequences, often called transcription factor binding sites or response elements. When specific cellular proteins, called transcription factors, attach to one of these binding sites, they enhance or suppress binding of RNA polymerase to the promoter and, consequently, they enhance or suppress transcription of the gene. We will return to the important topic of gene regulation in section 12.5.

Table 12-3	**The Genetic Code (Codons of mRNA)**							
		Second Base						
		U	C	A	G			
U	UUU	Phenylalanine (Phe)	UCU	Serine (Ser)	UAU	Tyrosine (Tyr)	UGU	Cysteine (Cys)	U
	UUC	Phenylalanine	UCC	Serine	UAC	Tyrosine	UGC	Cysteine	C
	UUA	Leucine (Leu)	UCA	Serine	UAA	Stop	UGA	Stop	A
	UUG	Leucine	UCG	Serine	UAG	Stop	UGG	Tryptophan (Trp)	G
C	CUU	Leucine	CCU	Proline (Pro)	CAU	Histidine (His)	CGU	Arginine (Arg)	U
	CUC	Leucine	CCC	Proline	CAC	Histidine	CGC	Arginine	C
	CUA	Leucine	CCA	Proline	CAA	Glutamine (Gln)	CGA	Arginine	A
	CUG	Leucine	CCG	Proline	CAG	Glutamine	CGG	Arginine	G
A	AUU	Isoleucine (Ile)	ACU	Threonine (Thr)	AAU	Asparagine (Asp)	AGU	Serine (Ser)	U
	AUC	Isoleucine	ACC	Threonine	AAC	Asparagine	AGC	Serine	C
	AUA	Isoleucine	ACA	Threonine	AAA	Lysine (Lys)	AGA	Arginine (Arg)	A
	AUG	Methionine (Met) Start	ACG	Threonine	AAG	Lysine	AGG	Arginine	G
G	GUU	Valine (Val)	GCU	Alanine (Ala)	GAU	Aspartic acid (Asp)	GGU	Glycine (Gly)	U
	GUC	Valine	GCC	Alanine	GAC	Aspartic acid	GGC	Glycine	C
	GUA	Valine	GCA	Alanine	GAA	Glutamic acid (Glu)	GGA	Glycine	A
	GUG	Valine	GCG	Alanine	GAG	Glutamic acid	GGG	Glycine	G

First Base (left margin), Third Base (right margin)

▶ **FIGURE 12-3 Transcription is the synthesis of RNA from instructions in DNA** A gene is a segment of a chromosome's DNA. One of the DNA strands will serve as the template for the synthesis of an RNA molecule with bases complementary to the bases in the DNA strand.

QUESTION If the other DNA strand of this molecule were the template strand, in which direction would the RNA polymerase travel?

gene 1   gene 2   gene 3   DNA

RNA polymerase
DNA
promoter
beginning of gene (3′ end)
direction of transcription

❶ **Initiation:** RNA polymerase binds to the promoter region of DNA near the beginning of a gene, separating the double helix near the promoter.

RNA
DNA template strand

❷ **Elongation:** RNA polymerase travels along the DNA **template** strand (blue), unwinding the DNA double helix and synthesizing RNA by catalyzing the addition of ribose nucleotides into an RNA molecule (red). The nucleotides in the RNA are complementary to the template strand of the DNA.

termination signal

❸ **Termination:** At the end of the gene, RNA polymerase encounters a DNA sequence called a termination signal. RNA polymerase detaches from the DNA and releases the RNA molecule.

DNA
RNA

❹ **Conclusion of transcription:** After termination, the DNA completely rewinds into a double helix. The RNA molecule is free to move from the nucleus to the cytoplasm for translation, and RNA polymerase may move to another gene and begin transcription once again.

When RNA polymerase binds to the promoter region of a gene, the DNA double helix at the beginning of the gene unwinds and transcription begins (Fig. 12-3 ❶).

Elongation Generates a Growing Strand of RNA

RNA polymerase then travels down one of the DNA strands, called the **template strand,** synthesizing a single strand of RNA with bases complementary to those in the DNA (Fig. 12-3 ❷).

Like DNA polymerase (see p. 211), RNA polymerase always travels along the DNA template strand starting at the 3′ end of a gene and moving toward the 5′ end. Base pairing between RNA and DNA is the same as between two strands of DNA, except that uracil in RNA pairs with adenine in DNA (see Table 12-1).

After about 10 nucleotides have been added to the growing RNA chain, the first nucleotides in the RNA molecule separate from the DNA template strand. This separation allows the two DNA strands to rewind into a double helix (**Fig. 12-3 ❸**). As transcription continues to elongate the RNA molecule, one end of the RNA drifts away from the DNA, while RNA polymerase keeps the other end attached to the template strand of the DNA (**Fig. 12-3 ❸**, and **Fig. 12-4**).

Transcription Stops When RNA Polymerase Reaches the Termination Signal

RNA polymerase continues along the template strand of the gene until it reaches a sequence of DNA bases known as the termination signal. At this point, RNA polymerase releases the completed RNA molecule and detaches from the DNA (**Fig. 12-3 ❸** and **❹**). The RNA polymerase is then free to bind to the promoter region of another gene and to synthesize another RNA molecule.

12.3 HOW IS THE BASE SEQUENCE OF MESSENGER RNA TRANSLATED INTO PROTEIN?

Messenger RNA Synthesis Differs Between Prokaryotes and Eukaryotes

The first step in synthesizing a protein is to produce a messenger RNA molecule with the base sequence specified by the gene that encodes the amino acid sequence of the protein. Prokaryotic and eukaryotic cells differ considerably in how they produce a functional mRNA molecule from the instructions in their DNA.

Messenger RNA Synthesis in Prokaryotes

Prokaryotic genes are typically compact: All the nucleotides of a gene code for the amino acids in a protein. What's more, most or all of the genes for a complete metabolic pathway sit end to end on the chromosome (**Fig. 12-5a**). Therefore, prokaryotic cells commonly transcribe a single, very long mRNA from a series of adjacent genes. Because prokaryotic cells do not have a nuclear membrane separating their DNA from the cytoplasm (see Fig. 4-19), transcription and translation are usually not separated, either in space or in time. In most cases, as an mRNA molecule begins to separate from the DNA during transcription, ribosomes immediately begin translating the mRNA into protein (**Fig. 12-5b**).

(a) Gene organization on a prokaryotic chromosome

(b) Simultaneous transcription and translation in prokaryotes

▲ **FIGURE 12-5 Messenger RNA synthesis in prokaryotic cells (a)** In prokaryotes, many or all of the genes for a complete metabolic pathway lie side by side on the chromosome. **(b)** Transcription and translation are simultaneous in prokaryotes. In the electron micrograph, RNA polymerase (not visible at this magnification) travels from left to right on a strand of DNA. As it synthesizes a messenger RNA molecule, ribosomes bind to the mRNA and immediately begin synthesizing a protein (not visible). The diagram below the micrograph shows all of the key molecules involved.

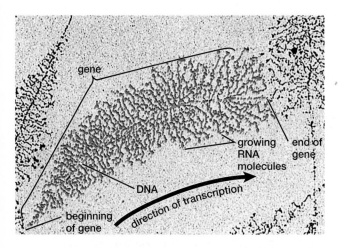

▲ **FIGURE 12-4 RNA transcription in action** This colorized electron micrograph shows the progress of RNA transcription in the egg of an African clawed toad. In each treelike structure, the central "trunk" is DNA and the "branches" are RNA molecules. A series of RNA polymerase molecules (too small to be seen in this micrograph) are traveling down the DNA, synthesizing RNA as they go. The beginning of the gene is on the left. The short RNA molecules on the left have just begun to be synthesized; the long RNA molecules on the right are almost finished.

QUESTION Why do you think so many mRNA molecules are being synthesized from the same gene?

Messenger RNA Synthesis in Eukaryotes

In contrast, the DNA of eukaryotic cells is contained in the nucleus, whereas the ribosomes reside in the cytoplasm. Further, the genes that encode the proteins needed for a metabolic pathway in eukaryotes are not clustered together as they are in prokaryotes, but may be dispersed among several chromosomes. Finally, each eukaryotic gene typically consists of two or more segments of DNA with nucleotide sequences that encode for a protein, interrupted by other nucleotide sequences that are not translated into protein. The coding segments are called **exons,** because they are *ex*pressed in protein, and the noncoding segments are called **introns,** because they are "*intr*agenic," meaning "within a gene" (Fig. 12-6a). Most eukaryotic genes have introns; the dystrophin gene (see pp. 194–195) contains almost 80!

Transcription of a eukaryotic gene produces a very long RNA strand, often called a precursor mRNA or pre-mRNA, which starts before the first exon and ends after the last exon (Fig. 12-6b ❶). More nucleotides are added at the beginning and end of this pre-mRNA molecule, forming a "cap" and "tail" (Fig. 12-6b ❷). These nucleotides will help to move the finished mRNA through the nuclear envelope to the cytoplasm, to bind the mRNA to a ribosome, and to prevent cellular enzymes from breaking down the mRNA molecule. To convert this pre-mRNA molecule into the finished mRNA, enzymes in the nucleus cut the pre-mRNA apart at the junctions between introns and exons, splice together the protein-coding exons, and discard the introns (Fig. 12-6b ❸). The finished mRNA molecules then leave the nucleus and enter the cytoplasm through pores in the nuclear envelope (Fig. 12-6b ❹). In the cytoplasm, the mRNA binds to ribosomes, which synthesize a protein specified by the mRNA base sequence.

Possible Functions of Intron-Exon Gene Structure

Why do eukaryotic genes contain introns and exons? This gene structure appears to serve at least two functions. The first function is to allow a cell to produce multiple proteins from a single gene by splicing exons together in different ways. For example, a gene called *CT/CGRP* is transcribed in both the thyroid and the brain. In the thyroid, one splicing arrangement results in the synthesis of the hormone calcitonin, which helps regulate calcium concentrations in the blood. In the brain, a different splicing arrangement results in the synthesis of a protein used as a messenger for communication between nerve cells. Alternative splicing may occur in the RNA transcribed from more than half of all eukaryotic genes. Therefore, in eukaryotes, the "one gene, one protein" rule must be reworded as "one gene, one *or more* proteins."

The second function of interrupted genes is more speculative, but is supported by some good experimental evidence: Fragmented genes may provide a quick and efficient way for eukaryotes to evolve new proteins with new functions. Chromosomes sometimes break apart, and their parts may reattach to different chromosomes. If the breaks occur within the noncoding introns of genes, exons may be moved intact from one chromosome to another. Most such errors would be harmful. But sometimes, the accidental exchange of exons among genes produces new eukaryotic genes that will enhance the survival and reproduction of the organism that carries them.

▶ **FIGURE 12-6 Messenger RNA synthesis in eukaryotic cells (a)** Eukaryotic genes consist of exons (medium blue), which code for the amino acid sequence of a protein, and introns (dark blue), which do not. **(b)** Messenger RNA synthesis in eukaryotes involves several steps: ❶ transcribing the gene into a long pre-mRNA molecule; ❷ adding additional RNA nucleotides to form the cap and tail; ❸ cutting out the introns and splicing the exons together into the finished mRNA; and ❹ moving the finished mRNA out of the nucleus into the cytoplasm for translation.

(a) Eukaryotic gene structure

exons

DNA

promoter   introns

DNA

❶ Transcription

pre-mRNA

❷ An RNA cap and tail are added

cap   tail

❸ RNA splicing

finished mRNA

introns are cut out and broken down

❹ Finished mRNA is moved to the cytoplasm for translation

(b) RNA synthesis and processing in eukaryotes

Health Watch

Genetics, Evolution, and Medicine

All life on Earth is related through evolution, sometimes closely (dogs and foxes), sometimes distantly (bacteria and people). Although often still similar, the genes of distantly related organisms may differ by many bases. Medicine takes advantage of these differences to develop antibiotics to treat bacterial infections.

Streptomycin and neomycin, commonly prescribed antibiotics, bind to a specific sequence of RNA in the small subunits of the ribosomes of certain bacteria, thereby inhibiting protein synthesis. Without adequate protein synthesis, the bacteria die. Patients infected by these bacteria don't die, however, because the small subunits of human eukaryotic ribosomes have a different base sequence than the bacteria's prokaryotic ribosomes do.

You have probably heard of antibiotic resistance, in which bacteria that are frequently exposed to antibiotics evolve defenses against those antibiotics. Bacteria evolve resistance against neomycin and related antibiotics rather rapidly. How? Well, if eukaryotic ribosomes are insensitive to neomycin, then eukaryotic ribosomes must function perfectly well with a different RNA sequence than prokaryotic ribosomes have. Bacteria that are resistant to neomycin and its relatives have a mutation that changes just a single base in their ribosomal RNA from adenine to guanine, which is precisely the base found at the comparable position in eukaryotic ribosomal RNA.

As this example illustrates, genetics, mutations, the mechanisms of protein synthesis, and evolution are important not only to biologists, but to physicians, too. In fact, a whole discipline called evolutionary medicine has arisen that uses the evolutionary relationships between people and microbes to help fight disease.

During Translation, mRNA, tRNA, and Ribosomes Cooperate to Synthesize Proteins

We will describe translation only in eukaryotic cells (Fig. 12-7), but the differences between eukaryotes and prokaryotes are crucial to the action of many antibiotics commonly used to treat bacterial infections (see "Health Watch: Genetics, Evolution, and Medicine").

Like transcription, translation has three steps: (1) initiation, (2) elongation of the protein chain, and (3) termination.

Initiation: Translation Begins When tRNA and mRNA Bind to a Ribosome

A preinitiation complex—composed of a small ribosomal subunit, a methionine (start) tRNA, and several other proteins (Fig. 12-7 ❶)—binds to the beginning of an mRNA molecule. The preinitiation complex scans the mRNA until it finds a start (AUG) codon, which forms base pairs with the UAC anticodon of the methionine tRNA (Fig. 12-7 ❷). A large ribosomal subunit then attaches to the small subunit, sandwiching the mRNA between the two subunits and holding the methionine tRNA in its first tRNA binding site (Fig. 12-7 ❸). The ribosome is now fully assembled and ready to begin translation.

Elongation: Amino Acids Are Added One at a Time to the Growing Protein Chain

A ribosome holds two mRNA codons in alignment with the two tRNA binding sites of the large subunit. A second tRNA, with an anticodon complementary to the second codon of the mRNA, moves into the second tRNA binding site on the large subunit (Fig. 12-7 ❹). The catalytic site of the large subunit breaks the bond holding the first amino acid (methionine) to its tRNA and forms a peptide bond between this amino acid and the amino acid attached to the second tRNA (Fig. 12-7 ❺). Interestingly, ribosomal RNA, and not one of the proteins of

the large subunit, catalyzes the formation of the peptide bond. Therefore, this enzymatic RNA is often called a "ribozyme."

After the peptide bond is formed, the first tRNA is "empty," and the second tRNA carries a two-amino-acid chain. The ribosome then releases the empty tRNA and shifts to the next codon on the mRNA molecule (Fig. 12-7 ❻). The tRNA holding the elongating chain of amino acids also shifts, moving from the second to the first binding site of the ribosome. A new tRNA, with an anticodon complementary to the third codon of the mRNA, binds to the empty second site (Fig. 12-7 ❼). The catalytic site on the large subunit now links the third amino acid onto the growing protein chain (Fig. 12-7 ❽). The empty tRNA leaves the ribosome, the ribosome shifts to the next codon on the mRNA, and the process repeats, one codon at a time.

Termination: A Stop Codon Signals the End of Translation

A stop codon in the mRNA molecule signals the ribosome to terminate protein synthesis. Stop codons do not bind to tRNA. Instead, proteins called "release factors" bind to the ribosome

---

Case Study continued

Cystic Fibrosis

Recall from Chapter 4 that proteins destined to be inserted into the plasma membrane are synthesized by ribosomes on rough endoplasmic reticulum (ER) and move into the ER for processing. The most common defective allele causing cystic fibrosis produces a misshapen CFTR protein that is broken down within the ER. Four other common mutant alleles code for a stop codon in the middle of the protein, so translation terminates partway through. These alleles cause a complete lack of the CFTR protein and, consequently, very severe cystic fibrosis.

Initiation:

1 A tRNA with an attached methionine amino acid binds to a small ribosomal subunit, forming a preinitiation complex.

2 The preinitiation complex binds to an mRNA molecule. The methionine (met) tRNA anticodon (UAC) base-pairs with the start codon (AUG) of the mRNA.

3 The large ribosomal subunit binds to the small subunit. The methionine tRNA binds to the first tRNA site on the large subunit.

Elongation:

4 The second codon of mRNA (GUU) base-pairs with the anticodon (CAA) of a second tRNA carrying the amino acid valine (val). This tRNA binds to the second tRNA site on the large subunit.

5 The catalytic site on the large subunit catalyzes the formation of a peptide bond linking the amino acids methionine and valine. The two amino acids are now attached to the tRNA in the second binding site.

6 The "empty" tRNA is released and the ribosome moves down the mRNA, one codon to the right. The tRNA that is attached to the two amino acids is now in the first tRNA binding site and the second tRNA binding site is empty.

ribosome moves one codon to the right

Termination:

7 The third codon of mRNA (CAU) base-pairs with the anticodon (GUA) of a tRNA carrying the amino acid histidine (his). This tRNA enters the second tRNA binding site on the large subunit.

8 The catalytic site forms a peptide bond between valine and histidine, leaving the peptide attached to the tRNA in the second binding site. The tRNA in the first site leaves, and the ribosome moves one codon over on the mRNA.

9 This process repeats until a stop codon is reached; the mRNA and the completed peptide are released from the ribosome, and the subunits separate.

▲ **FIGURE 12-7 Translation is the process of protein synthesis** Translation decodes the base sequence of an mRNA into the amino acid sequence of a protein.

QUESTION Examine step **9**. If mutations changed all of the guanine molecules visible in the mRNA sequence shown here to uracil, how would translated peptide differ from the one shown?

when it encounters a stop codon, forcing the ribosome to release the finished protein chain and the mRNA (Fig. 12-7 ❾). The ribosome disassembles into its large and small subunits, which can then be used to translate another mRNA.

BioFlix ™ Protein Synthesis

Summing Up Decoding the Sequence of Bases in DNA into the Sequence of Amino Acids in Protein Requires Transcription and Translation

Let's summarize how a eukaryotic cell decodes the genetic information stored in its DNA to synthesize a protein (**Fig. 12-8**):

a. With some exceptions, such as the genes for tRNA and rRNA, each gene codes for the amino acid sequence of a protein. The DNA of the gene consists of the template strand, which is transcribed into mRNA, and its complementary strand, which is not transcribed.

b. Transcription of a protein-coding gene produces an mRNA molecule that is complementary to the template strand of the DNA of a gene. Starting from the first AUG, each codon within the mRNA is a sequence of three bases that specifies an amino acid or a "stop."

c. Enzymes in the cytoplasm attach the appropriate amino acid to each tRNA based on the tRNA's anticodon.

d. The mRNA moves out of the nucleus to a ribosome in the cytoplasm. Transfer RNAs carry their attached amino acids to the ribosome. There, the bases in tRNA anticodons bind to the complementary bases in mRNA codons, so the amino acids attached to the tRNAs line up in the sequence specified by the codons. The ribosome joins the amino acids with peptide bonds to form a protein. When a stop codon is reached, the finished protein is released from the ribosome.

This decoding chain, from DNA bases to mRNA codons to tRNA anticodons to amino acids, results in the synthesis of a protein with an amino acid sequence determined by the base sequence of a gene.

12.4 HOW DO MUTATIONS AFFECT PROTEIN FUNCTION?

As we saw in Chapter 11, mistakes during DNA replication, ultraviolet rays in sunlight, chemicals in cigarette smoke, and a host of other environmental factors may change the sequence of bases in DNA. These changes are called **mutations.** The consequences for an organism's structure and function depend on how the mutation affects the functioning of the protein encoded by the mutated gene.

Mutations May Have a Variety of Effects on Protein Structure and Function

Most mutations may be categorized as substitutions, deletions, insertions, inversions, or translocations (see pp. 213–214).

▲ **FIGURE 12-8 Complementary base pairing is critical to the process of decoding genetic information (a)** The DNA of a gene contains two strands; only the template strand is used by RNA polymerase to synthesize an RNA molecule. **(b)** Bases in the template strand of DNA are transcribed into a complementary mRNA. Codons are sequences of three bases that specify an amino acid or a stop during protein synthesis. **(c)** Unless it is a stop codon, each mRNA codon forms base pairs with the anticodon of a tRNA molecule that carries a specific amino acid. **(d)** The amino acids borne by the tRNAs are joined to form a protein.

Inversions and Translocations

Inversions and **translocations** occur when pieces of DNA—sometimes most or even all of a chromosome—are broken apart and reattached, sometimes within a single chromosome, sometimes to a different chromosome. These mutations may be relatively benign if entire genes, including their promoters, are merely moved from one place to another. However, if a gene is split in two, it will no longer code for a complete, functional protein. For example, almost half the cases of severe hemophilia are caused by an inversion in the gene that encodes a protein required for blood clotting.

Deletions and Insertions

The effects of **deletion mutations** and **insertion mutations** usually depend on how many nucleotides are removed or added, respectively. Why? Think back to the genetic code: Three nucleotides encode a single amino acid. Therefore, adding or deleting three nucleotides will add or delete a single amino acid to the encoded protein. In many cases, this doesn't alter the function of the protein very much. In contrast, deletions and insertions of one or two nucleotides, or any deletion or insertion that isn't a multiple of three nucleotides, can have particularly catastrophic effects, because all of the codons that follow the deletion or insertion will be altered.

Recall our English sentence with all three-letter words: THEDOGSAWTHECAT. Deleting or inserting a letter (deleting the first E, for example) means that all of the following three-letter words will be nonsense, such as THD OGS AWT HEC AT. Similarly, most—and possibly all—of the amino acids of the protein synthesized from an mRNA containing such a mutation, called a frameshift mutation, will be the wrong ones. Sometimes, one of the new codons following an insertion or deletion will be a stop codon, cutting the protein short. Such proteins will almost always be nonfunctional. Remember the Belgian Blue cattle in the Chapter 11 Case Study? The defective myostatin gene of a Belgian Blue has an 11-nucleotide deletion, generating a premature stop codon that terminates translation before the myostatin protein is complete.

Substitutions

A **nucleotide substitution** (also called a **point mutation**) within a protein-coding gene can produce one of four possible outcomes. As an example, let's consider mutations that occur in the gene encoding beta-globin, one of the subunits of hemoglobin, the oxygen-carrying protein in red blood cells (**Table 12-4**). The other type of subunit in hemoglobin is called alpha-globin; a normal hemoglobin molecule consists of two alpha and two beta subunits. In all but the last example, we will consider the results of mutations that occur in the sixth codon of the beta-globin gene (CTC in DNA, GAG in mRNA), which specifies glutamic acid—a charged, hydrophilic, water-soluble amino acid.

- **The protein may be unchanged.** Recall that most amino acids can be encoded by several different codons. If a mutation changes the beta-globin DNA base sequence from CTC to CTT, this sequence still codes for glutamic acid. Therefore, the protein synthesized from the mutated gene remains the same.
- **The new protein may be functionally equivalent to the original one.** Many proteins have regions whose exact amino acid sequence is relatively unimportant. In beta-globin, the amino acids on the outside of the protein must be hydrophilic to keep the protein dissolved in the cytoplasm of red blood cells. Exactly *which* hydrophilic amino acids are on the outside doesn't matter much. For example, a family in the Japanese town of Machida was found to contain a mutation from CTC to GTC, replacing glutamic acid (hydrophilic) with glutamine (also hydrophilic). Hemoglobin containing this mutant beta-globin protein—known as Hemoglobin Machida—functions well. Mutations such as the ones in Hemoglobin Machida and in the previous example are called **neutral mutations** because they do not detectably change the function of the encoded protein.

- **Protein function may be changed by an altered amino acid sequence.** A mutation from CTC to CAC replaces glutamic acid (hydrophilic) with valine (hydrophobic). This substitution is the genetic defect that causes sickle-cell anemia (see see pp. 190–191). The valines on the outside of the hemoglobin molecules cause them to clump together, distorting the shape of the red blood cells. These changes can cause serious illness.

- **Protein function may be destroyed by a premature stop codon.** A particularly catastrophic mutation occasionally occurs in the 17th codon of the beta-globin gene (TTC in DNA, AAG in mRNA). This codon specifies the amino acid lysine. A mutation from TTC to ATC (UAG in mRNA) results in a stop codon, halting translation of beta-globin mRNA before the protein is completed. People who inherit this mutant gene from both their mother and their father do not synthesize any functional beta-globin protein; they manufacture hemoglobin consisting entirely of alpha-globin subunits. This "pure alpha" hemoglobin does not bind oxygen very well. This condition, called beta-thalassemia, can be fatal unless treated with regular blood transfusions throughout life.

Mutations Provide the Raw Material for Evolution

Mutations in gametes (sperm or eggs) can be passed on to future generations. In humans, mutation rates range from about 1 in every 100,000 gametes to 1 in 1,000,000 gametes. For reference, a man releases about 300 to 400 million sperm per ejaculation; each ejaculate contains about 600 sperm with new mutations. Although most mutations are neutral or potentially harmful, mutations are essential for evolution, because these random changes in DNA sequence are the ultimate source of

Table 12-4	Effects of Mutations in the Hemoglobin Gene					
	DNA (Template Strand)	mRNA	Amino Acid	Properties of Amino Acid	Functional Effect on Protein	Disease
Original codon 6	CTC	GAG	Glutamic acid	Hydrophilic	Normal protein function	None
Mutation 1	CTT	GAA	Glutamic acid	Hydrophilic	Neutral; normal protein function	None
Mutation 2	GTC	CAG	Glutamine	Hydrophilic	Neutral; normal protein function	None
Mutation 3	CAC	GUG	Valine	Hydrophobic	Loses water solubility; compromises protein function	Sickle-cell anemia
Original codon 17	TTC	AAG	Lysine	Hydrophilic	Normal protein function	None
Mutation 4	ATC	UAG	Stop codon	Ends translation after amino acid 16	Synthesizes only part of the protein; eliminates protein function	Beta-thalassemia

Case Study continued
Cystic Fibrosis

Why hasn't natural selection eliminated mutated *CFTR* alleles? Perhaps because the mutated alleles provide protection against cholera and typhoid. The normal CFTR protein is activated by cholera toxin, causing excessive chloride secretion from intestinal cells. Water follows by osmosis, and so cholera victims have debilitating, and often fatal, diarrhea. Defective CFTR proteins cannot be activated by cholera toxin. The CFTR protein is also the site by which typhoid bacteria enter cells, but typhoid bacteria cannot enter via mutated CFTR proteins. Such protection cannot make up for the devastating effects of cystic fibrosis. However, heterozygotes, with one normal and one mutated *CFTR* allele, have nearly normal CFTR function, but might be less severely affected by cholera and typhoid. This "heterozygote advantage" may explain the high frequency of mutated *CFTR* alleles (about 4% of people of European descent carry mutated *CFTR* alleles), as it does for the sickle-cell anemia allele (see p. 190).

all genetic variation. New base sequences undergo natural selection as organisms compete to survive and reproduce. Occasionally, a mutation proves beneficial in an organism's interactions with its environment. Through reproduction over time, the mutant base sequence may spread throughout the population, as organisms possessing it outcompete and outreproduce rivals bearing the original base sequence. This process is described in detail in Unit 3.

12.5 HOW ARE GENES REGULATED?

The complete human genome contains 20,000 to 25,000 genes. Each of these genes is present in most of your body cells, but any individual cell expresses (transcribes and, if the gene product is a protein, translates) only a small fraction of them. Some genes are expressed in all cells, because they encode proteins or RNA molecules that are essential for the life of any cell. For example, all cells need to synthesize proteins, so they all transcribe tRNA genes, rRNA genes, and genes for ribosomal proteins. Other genes are expressed exclusively in certain types of cells, at certain times in an organism's life, or under specific environmental conditions. For example, even though every cell in your body contains the gene for casein, the major protein in milk, that gene is expressed only in mature women, only in certain cells in the breast, and only when a woman is breast-feeding.

Regulation of gene expression may occur at the level of transcription (which genes are used to make mRNA in a given cell), translation (how much protein is made from a particular type of mRNA), or protein activity (how long the protein lasts in a cell and how rapidly protein enzymes catalyze spe-

cific reactions). Although these general principles apply to both prokaryotic and eukaryotic organisms, there are some differences as well, as we describe below.

Gene Regulation in Prokaryotes

Prokaryotic DNA is often organized in packages called **operons,** in which the genes for related functions lie close to one another (**Fig. 12-9a**). An operon consists of four parts: (1) a **regulatory gene,** which controls the timing

regulatory gene: codes for repressor protein

operator: repressor protein binds here

promoter: RNA polymerase binds here

structural genes that code for enzymes of lactose metabolism

(a) Structure of the lactose operon

RNA polymerase

transcription blocked

a repressor protein bound to the operator site overlaps the promoter

free repressor proteins

(b) Lactose absent

RNA polymerase binds to the promoter and transcribes the structural genes

lactose bound to repressor proteins

lactose-metabolizing enzymes are synthesized

(c) Lactose present

▲ **FIGURE 12-9 Regulation of the lactose operon (a)** The lactose operon consists of a regulatory gene, a promoter, an operator, and three structural genes that code for enzymes necessary for lactose metabolism. **(b)** In the absence of lactose, repressor proteins bind to the operator of the lactose operon. RNA polymerase can bind to the promoter but cannot move past the repressor protein to transcribe the structural genes. **(c)** When lactose is present, it binds to the repressor proteins, making the repressor proteins unable to bind to the operator. RNA polymerase binds to the promoter, moves past the unoccupied operator, and transcribes the structural genes.

or rate of transcription of other genes; (2) a promoter, which RNA polymerase recognizes as the place to start transcribing; (3) an **operator,** which governs access of RNA polymerase to the promoter or to the (4) **structural genes,** which actually encode the related enzymes or other proteins. Whole operons are regulated as units, so that functionally related proteins are synthesized simultaneously when the need arises.

Prokaryotic operons may be regulated in a variety of ways, depending on the functions that they control. Some operons encode enzymes that are needed by the cell just about all the time, such as the enzymes that synthesize many amino acids. These operons are usually transcribed continuously, unless the bacterium encounters a surplus of a particular amino acid. Other operons encode enzymes that are needed only occasionally, for instance, to digest a relatively rare food. They are transcribed only when the bacterium encounters the rare food.

Consider the common intestinal bacterium, *Escherichia coli (E. coli)*. This bacterium must live on whatever types of nutrients its host eats, and it can synthesize many different enzymes to metabolize a wide variety of foods. The genes that code for these enzymes are transcribed only when the enzymes are needed. The enzymes that metabolize lactose, the principal sugar in milk, are a case in point. The **lactose operon** contains three structural genes, each coding for an enzyme that aids in lactose metabolism (see Fig. 12-9a).

The lactose operon is shut off, or repressed, unless specifically activated by the presence of lactose. The regulatory gene of the lactose operon directs the synthesis of a protein, called a **repressor protein,** which can bind to the operator site. RNA polymerase, although still able to bind to the promoter, cannot get past the repressor protein to transcribe the structural genes. Consequently, lactose-metabolizing enzymes are not synthesized (**Fig. 12-9b**).

When *E. coli* colonize the intestines of a newborn mammal, however, they find themselves bathed in a sea of lactose whenever their host nurses from its mother. Lactose molecules enter the bacteria and bind to the repressor proteins, changing their shape (**Fig. 12-9c**). The lactose-repressor complex cannot attach to the operator site. Therefore, when RNA polymerase binds to the promoter of the lactose operon, it can transcribe the structural genes for lactose-metabolizing enzymes, allowing the bacteria to use lactose as an energy source. After the young mammal is weaned, it usually does not consume milk again. The intestinal bacteria no longer encounter lactose, the repressor proteins are free to bind to the operator, and the genes for lactose metabolism are shut down.

Gene Regulation in Eukaryotes

Eukaryotic gene regulation is similar to prokaryotic regulation in some respects. In both, not all genes are transcribed and translated all the time. Further, controlling the rate of transcription is an important mechanism of gene regulation in both. However, the compartmentalization of the DNA in a membrane-bound nucleus, the variety of cell types in multicellular eukaryotes, a very different organization of the genome, and complex processing of RNA transcripts all distinguish gene regulation in eukaryotes from regulation in prokaryotes.

Expression of genetic information by a eukaryotic cell is a multistep process, beginning with transcription of DNA and commonly ending with a protein that performs a particular function. Regulation of gene expression can occur at any of these steps, which are illustrated in **Figure 12-10**:

❶ **Cells can control the frequency at which an individual gene is transcribed.** The rate at which cells transcribe specific genes depends on the demand for the protein or RNA product that they encode. Gene transcription differs between organisms, between cell types in a given organism, and within a given cell at different stages in the organism's life or when it is stimulated by different environmental conditions (see the following section).

❷ **The same gene may be used to produce different mRNAs and protein products.** As we described in section 12.3, the same gene may be used to produce several different protein products, depending on how the pre-mRNA is spliced to form the finished mRNA that will be translated on the ribosomes.

❸ **Cells may control the stability and translation of messenger RNAs.** Some mRNAs are long lasting and are translated into protein many times. Others are translated only a few times before they are degraded. Recently, molecular biologists have discovered that small "regulatory RNA" molecules may block translation of some mRNAs, or may even target some mRNAs for destruction (see "Scientific Inquiry: RNA—It's Not Just a Messenger Anymore" on p. 234).

❹ **Proteins may require modification before they can carry out their functions.** Many proteins must be modified before they become active. For instance, the protein-digesting enzymes produced by cells in your stomach wall and pancreas are initially synthesized in an inactive form, which prevents the enzymes from digesting the cells that produce them. After these inactive forms are secreted into the digestive tract, portions of the enzymes are snipped out to unveil the enzyme's active site, allowing the enzymes to digest the proteins in food (their substrate) into smaller proteins or even into individual amino acids (the resulting products). Other modifications, such as adding or removing phosphate groups, can temporarily activate or inactivate a protein, allowing second-to-second control of the protein's activity. Similar regulation of protein structure and function occurs in prokaryotic cells.

❺ **Cells can control the rate at which proteins are degraded.** By preventing or promoting a protein's degradation, a cell can rapidly adjust the amount of a particular protein it contains. Protein degradation may also be regulated in prokaryotic cells.

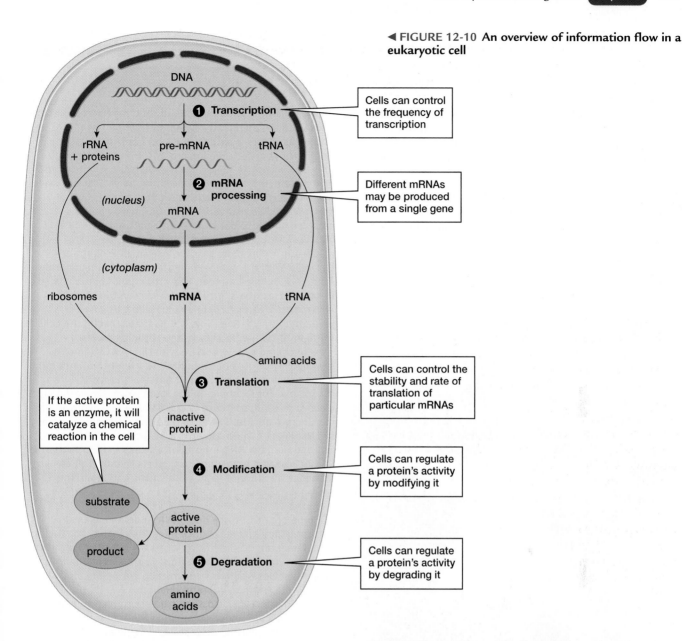

◄ FIGURE 12-10 **An overview of information flow in a eukaryotic cell**

Eukaryotic Cells May Regulate the Transcription of Individual Genes, Regions of Chromosomes, or Entire Chromosomes

In eukaryotic cells, transcriptional regulation can operate on at least three levels: the individual gene, regions of chromosomes, or entire chromosomes.

Regulatory Proteins That Bind to a Gene's Promoter Alter Its Rate of Transcription

The promoter regions of virtually all genes contain several different transcription factor binding sites, or response elements. Therefore, whether these genes are transcribed depends on which transcription factors are synthesized by the cell and whether those transcription factors are active. For example, when cells are exposed to free radicals (see pp. 24–25), a transcription factor binds to antioxidant

Have you ever wondered

Why Bruises Turn Colors?

Bruises typically progress from purple to green to yellow. This sequence is visual evidence of the control of gene expression. If you bang your shin on a chair, blood vessels break and release red blood cells, which burst and spill their hemoglobin. Hemoglobin and its iron-containing heme group are dark bluish-purple in the deoxygenated state, so fresh bruises are purple. Heme is toxic to the liver, kidneys, brain, and blood vessels. However, heme stimulates transcription of the heme oxygenase gene. Heme oxygenase converts heme to biliverdin, which is green. A second enzyme, which is always present because its gene is always expressed, converts biliverdin to bilirubin, which is yellow. Eventually, bilirubin moves to the liver, where it is excreted into the bile. You can follow the detoxification of heme by watching your bruise change color.

Scientific Inquiry

RNA—It's Not Just a Messenger Anymore

In recent years, molecular biologists have discovered an entirely new class of RNA molecules, called "regulatory RNA." Various types of regulatory RNA have many different functions. Here, we will focus on only one function, called RNA interference. RNA interference was discovered, accidentally, in petunias. Trying to make petunias with more vibrant flower colors, researchers inserted extra genes for flower pigment production into petunias. Much to their surprise, many of the petunias produced variegated flowers (Fig. E12-2). Why?

As you know, messenger RNA is transcribed from DNA and translated into protein, which then performs cellular functions such as catalyzing biochemical reactions. How much protein is synthesized depends both on how much

▲ FIGURE E12-2 **RNA interference in petunias** The white patches on this petunia flower consist of cells in which RNA interference blocked production of the enzymes that produce purple pigment. (The variegated petunias sold in your local greenhouse are made by a different process.)

mRNA is made and on how rapidly and for how long the mRNA is translated. Enter RNA interference. Organisms as diverse as plants, roundworms, and humans transcribe small RNA strands, called microRNA, from hundreds of different microRNA genes. MicroRNAs are not translated into protein. Instead, after processing by cellular enzymes, microRNAs give rise to very short RNA strands, usually about 20 to 25 nucleotides in length, which are complementary to parts of specific mRNAs and interfere with translation of the mRNA (hence, the name "RNA interference"). In some cases, these small RNA strands base-pair with the complementary mRNA, forming a little section of double-stranded RNA that cannot be translated. In other cases, the short RNA strands combine with enzymes to degrade complementary mRNA, also preventing translation. This is what happened in the cells forming the white patches of the petunia flowers.

Why should a cell interfere with the translation of its own mRNA? It turns out that RNA interference is important in the development of many, if not all, eukaryotic organisms. For example, in the roundworm *Caenorhabditis elegans*, RNA interference is crucial for a juvenile worm to mature into an adult. (Andrew Fire and Craig Mello shared the Nobel Prize in Physiology or Medicine in 2006 for figuring out how RNA interference works in roundworms.) Recent research in mammals suggests that microRNAs influence the development of the heart and brain, the secretion of insulin by the pancreas, and even learning and memory.

Some organisms use microRNA to defend against disease. Many plants produce microRNA that is complementary to the nucleic acids (usually RNA) of plant viruses. When the microRNA finds complementary viral RNA molecules, it directs enzymes to cut up the viral RNA, thereby preventing viral reproduction.

RNA interference also shows great promise in medicine. Clinical trials are under way testing the safety and efficacy of RNA interference in diseases as diverse as macular (retinal) degeneration, hepatitis B, and a respiratory virus that is the most common cause of pneumonia in infants. Basic research in animals suggests that RNA interference may also be used to treat prostate cancer and defects in cholesterol metabolism. Some experts expect RNA interference to reach patients by 2010.

---

response elements in the promoters of several genes. As a result, the cell produces enzymes that break down free radicals to harmless substances.

Many transcription factors require activation before they can affect gene transcription. One of the best-known examples is the role that the sex hormone, estrogen, plays in controlling egg production in birds. The gene for albumin, the major protein in egg white, is not transcribed in the winter when birds are not breeding and estrogen levels are low. During the breeding season, the ovaries in female

birds release estrogen, which enters cells in the oviduct and binds to a transcription factor (usually called an estrogen receptor). The estrogen–receptor complex then attaches to an estrogen response element in the promoter of the albumin gene, making it easier for RNA polymerase to bind to the promoter and initiate transcription of mRNA. The mRNA is then translated into large amounts of albumin. Similar activation of gene transcription by steroid hormones occurs in other animals, including humans. The importance of hormonal regulation of transcription during development is illustrated by genetic defects in which receptors for sex hormones are nonfunctional (see "Health Watch: Sex, Aging, and Mutations" on pp. 236–237).

Some Regions of Chromosomes Are Condensed and Not Normally Transcribed

Certain parts of eukaryotic chromosomes are in a highly condensed, compact state in which most of the DNA seems to be inaccessible to RNA polymerase. Some of these regions are structural parts of chromosomes that don't contain genes. Other tightly condensed regions contain functional genes that are not currently being transcribed. When the product of a gene is needed, the portion of the chromosome containing that gene becomes "decondensed"—loosened so that the DNA is accessible to RNA polymerase and transcription can occur.

Large Parts of Chromosomes May Be Inactivated, Preventing Transcription

In some cases, most of a chromosome may be condensed, making it inaccessible to RNA polymerase. An example occurs in the sex chromosomes of female mammals. Male mammals usually have an X and a Y chromosome (XY), and females usually have two X chromosomes (XX). As a consequence, females have the capacity to synthesize mRNA from genes on their two X chromosomes, whereas males, with only one X chromosome, may produce only half as much. In 1961, the geneticist Mary Lyon hypothesized that one of the two X chromosomes in females was inactivated in some way, so that its genes were not expressed. We now know that about 85% of the genes on an inactivated X chromosome are not transcribed. Early in development (about the 16th day in humans), one X chromosome in each of a female's cells begins to produce large amounts of a regulatory RNA molecule called Xist, which coats most of the chromosome, condenses it into a tight mass, and prevents transcription. The condensed X chromosome, called a **Barr body** after its discoverer, Murray Barr, appears as a discrete spot in the nuclei of the cells of female mammals (**Fig. 12-11**).

Usually, large clusters of cells (with each cluster descended from a single cell of the very early embryo) have the same X chromosome inactivated. As a result, the bodies of female mammals (including women) are composed of patches of cells in which one of the X chromosomes is fully active, and patches of cells in which the other X chromosome is active. The results of this phenomenon are easily observed in calico cats (**Fig. 12-12**). The X chromosome of a cat contains a gene encoding an enzyme that produces fur pigment. There are two common alleles of this gene: One produces orange fur and the other produces black fur. If one X chromosome in a female cat has the orange allele and the other X chromosome has the black allele, the cat will have patches of orange and black fur. These patches represent areas of skin that developed from cells in the early embryo in which different X chromosomes were inactivated. Calico

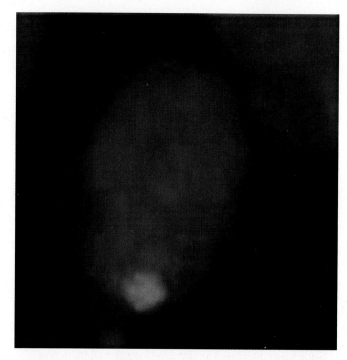

▲ FIGURE 12-11 **A Barr body** The red spot at the bottom of the nucleus is an inactivated X chromosome called a Barr body. In this fluorescence micrograph, the Barr body is stained with a dye that binds to the Xist RNA coating the inactivated X chromosome.

coloring is almost exclusively found in female cats. Because male cats normally have only one X chromosome, which is active in all of their cells, male cats usually have black fur or orange fur, but not both.

▲ FIGURE 12-12 **Inactivation of the X chromosome regulates gene expression** This female calico kitten carries a gene for orange fur on one X chromosome and a gene for black fur on her other X chromosome. Inactivation of different X chromosomes produces the black and orange patches. The white color is due to an entirely different gene that prevents pigment formation altogether.

Health Watch

Sex, Aging, and Mutations

Sometime in her early to mid-teens, a girl usually goes through puberty: Her breasts swell, her hips widen, and she begins to menstruate. In rare instances, however, a girl may develop all of the outward signs of womanhood, but does not menstruate. Eventually, she reports this symptom to her physician, who may take a blood sample to do a chromosome test. In some cases, the chromosome test gives what might seem to be an impossible result: the girl's sex chromosomes are XY, a combination that would usually give rise to a boy. The reason she has not begun to menstruate is that she lacks ovaries and a uterus, but instead has testes inside her abdominal cavity. She has about the same concentrations of androgens (male sex hormones, such as testosterone) circulating in her blood as would be found in a boy her age. In fact, androgens have been present since early in her development. However, her cells cannot respond to them—a condition called androgen insensitivity (**Fig. E12-3**).

The affected gene codes for a protein known as an androgen receptor. In normal males, androgens bind to the receptor molecules. The hormone–receptor combination stimulates the transcription of genes that help to produce many male features, including the formation of a penis and the descent of the testes into sacs outside the body cavity. There are more than 200 mutant alleles of the androgen receptor gene. The most serious are mutations that create a premature stop codon. As you know, these mutations are likely to have catastrophic effects on protein structure and function. Because the androgen receptor gene is on the X chromosome, a person who is genetically male (XY) inherits a single allele for the androgen receptor. If this allele is seriously defective, the person will not synthesize functional androgen receptor proteins. The person's cells will be unable to respond to testosterone, and male characteristics will not develop. Thus, a mutation that changes the nucleotide

sequence of a single gene, causing a single type of defective protein to be produced, can cause a person who is genetically male to look like and perceive herself to be a woman (see **Fig. E12-3**).

A second type of mutation provides clues to why people age. Why will your hair whiten, skin wrinkle,

▲ **FIGURE E12-3 Androgen insensitivity leads to female features** This individual has an X and a Y chromosome. She has testes that produce testosterone, but a mutation in her androgen receptor genes makes her cells unable to respond to testosterone, resulting in her female appearance.

Case Study revisited

Cystic Fibrosis

Researchers have identified more than 1,200 defective alleles of the *CFTR* gene, all of which are recessive to the functional *CFTR* allele. People who are heterozygous, with one normal *CFTR* allele and one copy of any of the defective alleles, produce enough functional *CFTR* protein for adequate chloride transport. Therefore, they are phenotypically normal—that is, they produce watery secretions in their lungs and do not develop cystic fibrosis. Someone with two defective alleles will have proteins that don't work properly and will develop the disease.

Genetic diseases such as cystic fibrosis can't be "cured" in the way that an infection can be cured by killing offending bacteria or viruses. Typically, genetic diseases are treated by replacing the lost function, such as giving insulin to diabetics, or by relieving the symptoms. In cystic fibrosis, the most common treatments relieve some of the symptoms. These include antibiotics, medicines that open the airways, and physical therapy to drain the lungs. In the next chapter, we

will see that biotechnology offers some hope of replacing the lost function by delivering functioning *CFTR* genes to the cells lining the airways.

What ultimately happens to a person with cystic fibrosis depends on how defective the mutant alleles are. Canadian triathlete Lisa Bentley, for example, has a relatively mild case of cystic fibrosis (**Fig. 12-13**). However, during a 9-hour triathlon, she produces copious amounts of very salty sweat. It is a constant challenge for Bentley to keep her body supplied with salt during the race. Nevertheless, Bentley has won 11 triathlons, including the Canadian Ironman Triathlon in 2007 and the Australian Ironman Triathlon five straight years, from 2002 through 2006. Bentley carefully controls her diet, especially her salt intake. Vigorous exercise helps to clear out her lungs. She also scrupulously avoids situations where she might be exposed to contagious diseases. Her cystic fibrosis hasn't kept her from becoming one of the finest athletes in the world. Alice Martineau, on the other hand, had extremely defective alleles. By the age of 30, Martineau needed a triple transplant—heart, lung, and liver. She died before a suitable donor could be found.

joints ache, and eyes cloud as you become elderly? A small number of people inherit Werner syndrome, which causes a type of premature aging (Fig. E12-4). Most people with Werner syndrome have inherited two defective recessive alleles for a gene that codes for a protein involved in DNA replication and repair. If cells cannot replicate DNA accurately and repair errors in DNA, mutations will accumulate rapidly throughout the body. This is what happens in people with Werner syndrome, who often die of aging-related conditions while still in their 40s or 50s.

The fact that an overall increase in mutations caused by defective replication and repair enzymes produces symptoms of old age provides support for one hypothesis to explain many of the symptoms of normal aging: During a reasonably long, 80-year life span, mutations gradually accumulate because of environmentally induced DNA damage and mistakes in DNA replication. Eventually, these mutations interfere with nearly every aspect of body functioning and contribute to death from "old age." In Werner syndrome, this process occurs much more rapidly. Disorders such as androgen insensitivity and Werner syndrome provide insights into the impact of mutations, the function of specific genes and their protein products, the ways hormones regulate gene transcription, and even the causes of aging.

◄ FIGURE E12-4 **Werner syndrome** This condition is the result of a mutation that interferes with proper DNA replication and repair, increasing the incidence of mutations throughout the body.

(a) Werner's syndrome patient at age 13   (b) At age 56

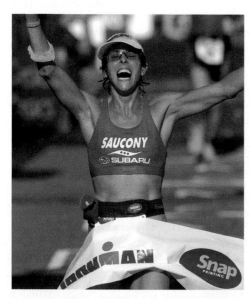

▲ FIGURE 12-13 **Lisa Bentley, sometimes called the Iron Queen, wins another triathlon**

BioEthics **Consider This**

The vast majority of biomedical research is funded by government agencies, such as the National Institutes of Health (NIH). The NIH funds research on genetic disorders such as cystic fibrosis and muscular dystrophy; infectious diseases such as AIDS and tuberculosis; and a host of other conditions, including heart disease and cancer. The NIH also funds research on diseases, such as malaria, that are uncommon in the United States but claim hundreds of thousands of lives each year in impoverished countries. How do you think that NIH funds should be spent—in proportion to disease severity and incidence in the United States, which might mean that almost all NIH funds should be spent on heart disease and cancer; or according to the prospective life span of the victims, so that diseases of the young, such as cystic fibrosis, receive much more? Does the United States have a responsibility to help people in other countries suffering from diseases that are rare in America?

CHAPTER REVIEW

Summary of Key Concepts

12.1 How Is the Information in DNA Used in a Cell?

Genes are segments of DNA that can be transcribed into RNA and, for most genes, translated into protein. Transcription produces the three types of RNA needed for translation: messenger RNA (mRNA), transfer RNA (tRNA), and ribosomal RNA (rRNA). Messenger RNA carries the genetic information of a gene from the nucleus to the cytoplasm, where ribosomes use the information to synthesize a protein. Ribosomes contain rRNA and proteins organized into large and small subunits. There are many different tRNAs. Each tRNA binds a specific amino acid and carries it to a ribosome for incorporation into a protein. The genetic code consists of codons, sequences of three bases in mRNA that specify either an amino acid in the protein chain or the end of protein synthesis (stop codons).

12.2 How Is the Information in a Gene Transcribed into RNA?

Within an individual cell, only certain genes are transcribed. When the cell requires the product of a gene, RNA polymerase binds to the promoter region of the gene and synthesizes a single strand of RNA. This RNA is complementary to the template strand in the gene's DNA double helix. Cellular proteins called transcription factors may bind to DNA near the promoter and enhance or suppress transcription of a given gene.

12.3 How Is the Base Sequence of Messenger RNA Translated into Protein?

In prokaryotic cells, all of the nucleotides of a protein-coding gene code for amino acids; therefore, the RNA transcribed from the gene is the mRNA that will be translated on a ribosome. In eukaryotic cells, protein-coding genes consist of two parts: exons, which code for amino acids in a protein, and introns, which do not. The entire gene, including both introns and exons, is transcribed into a pre-mRNA molecule. Therefore, the introns of the pre-mRNA must be cut out and the exons spliced together to produce a finished mRNA.

In eukaryotes, mRNA carries the genetic information from the nucleus to the cytoplasm, where ribosomes can use this information to synthesize a protein. Ribosomes contain rRNA and proteins organized into large and small subunits. These subunits come together at the first AUG (start) codon of the mRNA molecule to form the complete protein-synthesizing machine. Transfer RNAs deliver the appropriate amino acids to the ribosome for incorporation into the growing protein. Which tRNA binds and, consequently, which amino acid is delivered depend on base pairing between the anticodon of the tRNA and the codon of the mRNA. Two tRNAs, each carrying an amino acid, bind simultaneously to the ribosome; the large subunit catalyzes the formation of peptide bonds between the amino acids. As each new amino acid is attached, one tRNA detaches, and the ribosome moves over one codon, binding to another tRNA that carries the next amino acid specified by mRNA. Addition of amino acids to the growing protein continues until a stop codon is reached, causing the ribosome to disassemble and to release both the mRNA and the newly formed protein.

BioFlix™ Protein Synthesis

12.4 How Do Mutations Affect Protein Function?

A mutation is a change in the nucleotide sequence of a gene. Mutations can be caused by mistakes in base pairing during replication, by chemical agents, and by environmental factors such as radiation. Common types of mutations include inversions, translocations, deletions, insertions, and substitutions (point mutations). Mutations may be neutral or harmful, but in rare cases a mutation will promote better adaptation to the environment and thus will be favored by natural selection.

12.5 How Are Genes Regulated?

The expression of a gene requires that it be transcribed and translated, and the resulting protein must perform some action within the cell. Which genes are expressed in a cell at any given time is regulated by the function of the cell, the developmental stage of the organism, and the environment. Control of gene regulation can occur at many steps. The amount of mRNA synthesized from a particular gene can be regulated by increasing or decreasing the rate of its transcription, as well as by changing the stability of the mRNA itself. Rates of translation of mRNAs can also be regulated. Regulation of transcription and translation affects how many protein molecules are produced from a particular gene. Even after they are synthesized, many proteins must be modified before they can function. Proteins also vary in how rapidly they are degraded in a cell. In addition to regulation of individual genes, cells can regulate transcription of groups of genes. For example, entire chromosomes or parts of chromosomes may be condensed and inaccessible to RNA polymerase, whereas other portions may be expanded, allowing transcription to occur.

Key Terms

anticodon *223*	point mutation *230*
Barr body *235*	promoter *223*
codon *223*	regulatory gene *231*
deletion mutation *229*	repressor protein *232*
exon *226*	ribonucleic acid (RNA) *218*
genetic code *222*	ribosomal RNA (rRNA) *218*
insertion mutation *229*	ribosome *220*
intron *226*	RNA polymerase *223*
inversion *229*	start codon *223*
lactose operon *232*	stop codon *223*
messenger RNA	structural gene *232*
(mRNA) *218*	template strand *224*
mutation *229*	transcription *221*
neutral mutation *230*	transfer RNA (tRNA) *218*
nucleotide substitution *230*	translation *222*
operator *232*	translocation *229*
operon *231*	

Thinking Through the Concepts

Fill-in-the-Blank

1. Synthesis of RNA from the instructions in DNA is called _____. Synthesis of a protein from the instructions in messenger RNA is called _____. Which structure in the cell is the site of protein synthesis? _____

2. The three types of RNA that are essential for protein synthesis are_____, _____, and_____. Another type of RNA, which can interfere with translation, is called _____.

3. The genetic code uses _____ (how many?) bases to code for a single amino acid. This short sequence of bases in messenger RNA is called a(n) _____. The complementary sequence of bases in transfer RNA is called a(n) _____.

4. The enzyme _____ synthesizes RNA from the instructions in DNA. DNA has two strands, but for any given gene, usually only one strand, called the _____ strand, is transcribed. To begin transcribing a gene, this enzyme binds to a specific sequence of DNA bases located at the beginning of the gene. This DNA sequence is called the _____. Transcription ends when the enzyme encounters a DNA sequence at the end of the gene called the _____.

5. Protein synthesis begins when messenger RNA binds to a ribosome. Translation begins with the _____ codon of messenger RNA and continues until a(n) _____ codon is reached. Individual amino acids are brought to the ribosome by _____ RNA. These amino acids are linked into protein by _____ bonds.

6. There are several different types of mutations in DNA. If one nucleotide is substituted for another, this is called a(n) _____ mutation. _____ mutations occur if nucleotides are added in the middle of a gene. _____ mutations occur if nucleotides are removed from the middle of a gene.

Review Questions

1. How does RNA differ from DNA?

2. What are the three types of RNA that are essential to protein synthesis? What is the function of each?

3. Define the following terms: *genetic code, codon,* and *anticodon.* What is the relationship among the bases in DNA, the codons of mRNA, and the anticodons of tRNA?

4. How is mRNA formed from a eukaryotic gene?

5. Diagram and describe protein synthesis.

6. Explain how complementary base pairing is involved in both transcription and translation.

7. Describe some mechanisms of gene regulation.

8. Define *mutation.* Are most mutations likely to be beneficial or harmful? Explain your answer.

Applying the Concepts

1. **BioEthics** As you have learned in this chapter, many factors influence gene expression, including hormones. The use of anabolic steroids and growth hormones among athletes has created controversy in recent years. Hormones certainly affect gene expression, but, in the broadest sense, so do vitamins and foods. What do you think are appropriate guidelines for the use of hormones? Should athletes take steroids or growth hormones? Should children at risk of being unusually short be given growth hormones? Should parents be allowed to request growth hormones for a child of normal height in the hope of producing a future basketball player?

2. About 40 years ago, some researchers reported that they could transfer learning from one animal (a flatworm) to another by feeding trained animals to untrained animals. Further, they claimed that RNA was the active molecule of learning. Given your knowledge of the roles of RNA and protein in cells, do you think that a *specific* memory (for example, remembering the base sequences of codons of the genetic code) could be encoded by a *specific* molecule of RNA and that this RNA molecule could transfer that memory to another person? In other words, in the future, could you learn biology by popping an RNA pill? If so, how would this work? If not, can you propose a reasonable hypothesis for the results with flatworms? How would you test your hypothesis?

3. Androgen insensitivity is inherited as a simple recessive trait, because one copy of the normal androgen receptor allele produces sufficient amounts of androgen receptors. Given this information and your knowledge of the chromosomal basis of inheritance, can androgen insensitivity be inherited, or must it arise as a new mutation each time it occurs? If it can be inherited, would inheritance be through the mother or through the father? Why?

MB *Go to www.masteringbiology.com for practice quizzes, activities, eText, videos, current events, and more.*

Biotechnology

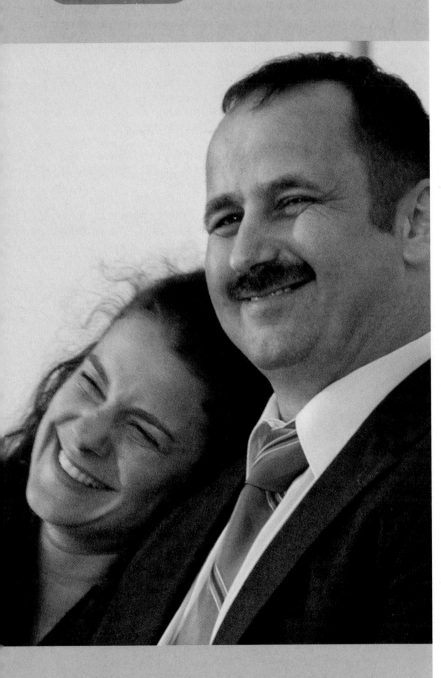

▲ DNA profiling proved that Dennis Maher, shown here with attorney Aliza Kaplan, was innocent of the crimes for which he spent 19 years in prison.

Case Study

Guilty or Innocent?

"IT'S OK TO CRY," Innocence Project attorney Aliza Kaplan told Dennis Maher, on his way to court for his release from prison in 2003. Maher seemed calm as District Attorney Martha Coakley asked the judge to dismiss all of the charges for which Maher had been imprisoned for 19 years, 2 months, and 29 days. The judge ordered Maher's immediate release. Although outwardly composed in court, Maher and his family hugged and wept in the hall outside. "We're a bunch of crybabies," said his father, Donat.

Nineteen years earlier, Maher had been convicted of two counts of rape and one of attempted rape. As it turned out, his only crimes were to live in the vicinity of the rapes, to wear a red sweatshirt, and to look like the real assailant. All three victims picked Maher out of lineups. How can three people all identify the wrong man? It was dark, the assaults were swift, and, obviously, the women were tremendously stressed. In fact, contrary to popular belief, eyewitness testimony is really very unreliable. Various studies have found error rates for eyewitness identification from about 35% to 80%, depending on the conditions used in the experiments.

You have probably already guessed what led to Maher's eventual exoneration—DNA evidence. In 1993, while watching the *Phil Donahue Show* in prison, Maher heard about the Innocence Project, founded in 1992 by Barry Scheck and Peter Neufeld of the Benjamin Cardozo School of Law at Yeshiva University. He wrote to Scheck asking for help. Scheck agreed, but the Innocence Project hit a brick wall—no biological evidence was available for any of the cases.

Finally, 7 years later, an Innocence Project law student found the semen-stained underwear of one of the rape victims, lost in a box in a courthouse storage room. A few months later, a semen specimen from the second rape turned up as well. DNA profiling proved that Maher was not the assailant in either case.

In this chapter, we'll investigate the techniques of biotechnology that now pervade much of modern life. How do crime scene investigators decide that two DNA samples match? How can biotechnology diagnose inherited disorders? Should biotechnology be used to change the genetic makeup of crops, livestock, and even people?

At a Glance

13.1 WHAT IS BIOTECHNOLOGY?

Biotechnology is the use, and especially the alteration, of organisms, cells, or biological molecules to produce food, drugs, or other goods. Therefore, some aspects of biotechnology are ancient. For example, people have used yeast cells to produce bread, beer, and wine for the past 10,000 years. Selective breeding of plants and animals has an equally long history: 8,000- to 10,000-year-old fragments of squash, found in a dry cave in Mexico, have larger seeds and thicker rinds than wild squash, suggesting selective breeding for higher nutritional content. Prehistoric art and animal remains indicate that dogs, sheep, goats, pigs, and cattle were domesticated and selectively bred at least 10,000 years ago. Selective breeding causes domestic plants and animals to differ genetically from their wild relatives; for instance, the short legs and floppy ears of beagles are genetically determined, and differ enormously from the comparable characteristics of wolves, the ancestors of all dogs.

Even today, selective breeding remains an important tool. Modern biotechnology, however, also frequently uses **genetic engineering,** a term that refers to more direct methods for modifying genetic material. Genetically engineered cells or organisms have had genes deleted, added, or changed. Genetic engineering can be used to learn more about how cells and genes work; to develop better treatments for diseases; to produce valuable biological molecules, including hormones and vaccines; and to improve plants and animals for agriculture.

A key tool in genetic engineering is **recombinant DNA,** which is DNA that has been altered to contain genes or portions of genes from different organisms. Large amounts of recombinant DNA can be produced in bacteria, viruses, or yeast, and then transferred into other species. Plants and animals that express DNA that has been modified or derived from other species are called **transgenic,** or **genetically modified organisms (GMOs).**

Modern biotechnology includes many methods of manipulating DNA, whether or not the DNA is subsequently put into a cell or an organism. For example, determining the nucleotide sequence of specific pieces of DNA is crucial to forensic science, to the diagnosis of inherited disorders, and to studies of evolutionary relationships among organisms.

In this chapter, we will provide an overview of modern biotechnology. Our emphasis will be on applications of biotechnology and their impacts on society, but we will also briefly describe some of the important methods used in those applications. We will organize our discussion around five major themes: (1) recombinant DNA mechanisms found in nature; (2) biotechnology in criminal forensics, principally DNA matching; (3) biotechnology in agriculture, specifically the production of transgenic plants and animals; (4) the Human Genome Project and its applications; and (5) biotechnology in medicine, focusing on the diagnosis and treatment of inherited disorders.

13.2 HOW DOES DNA RECOMBINE IN NATURE?

Most people think that a species' genetic makeup is constant, except for the occasional mutation, but genetic reality is far more fluid. Many natural processes can transfer DNA from one organism to another, sometimes even to organisms of different species.

Sexual Reproduction Recombines DNA

As we saw in Chapter 9, homologous chromosomes exchange DNA by crossing over during meiosis I. As a result, each chromosome in a gamete contains a mixture of alleles from the two parental chromosomes. Thus, every egg and sperm contain recombinant DNA, derived from the two parents. When a sperm fertilizes an egg, the resulting offspring also contains recombinant DNA.

Transformation May Combine DNA from Different Bacterial Species

Bacteria can undergo several types of recombination that allow gene transfer between species (**Fig. 13-1**). In **transformation,** bacteria pick up pieces of DNA from the environment (**Fig. 13-1b**). The DNA may be part of the chromosome from another bacterium, even from another species. Transformation

may also occur when bacteria pick up tiny circular DNA molecules called **plasmids** (**Fig. 13-1c**). Many types of bacteria contain plasmids, ranging in length from about 1,000 to 100,000 nucleotides. For comparison, the *E. coli* chromosome is around 4,600,000 nucleotides long. A single bacterium may contain dozens or even hundreds of copies of a plasmid. When the bacterium dies, it releases these plasmids into the environment, where they may be picked up by other bacteria of the same or different species. In addition, living bacteria can often pass plasmids directly to other living bacteria. Transfer of plasmids from bacteria to yeast may also occur, moving genes from a prokaryotic cell to a eukaryotic cell.

What use are plasmids? A bacterium's chromosome contains all the genes the cell normally needs for basic survival. However, genes carried by plasmids may permit the bacteria to thrive in novel environments. Some plasmids contain genes that allow bacteria to metabolize unusual energy sources, such as petroleum. Other plasmids may carry genes that enable bacteria to grow in the presence of antibiotics, such as penicillin. In environments where antibiotic use is high, particularly in

▶ **FIGURE 13-1 Transformation in bacteria (a)** In addition to their large circular chromosome, bacteria commonly possess small rings of DNA called plasmids, which often carry additional useful genes. Bacterial transformation occurs when living bacteria take up **(b)** fragments of chromosomes or **(c)** plasmids.

(a) Bacterium

1 micrometer

bacterial chromosome

plasmid

bacterial chromosome

DNA fragments

plasmid

The plasmid replicates in the cytoplasm

(c) Transformation with a plasmid

A DNA fragment is incorporated into the chromosome

(b) Transformation with a DNA fragment

hospitals, bacteria carrying antibiotic-resistance plasmids can quickly spread among patients and health care workers, making antibiotic-resistant infections a serious problem.

Viruses May Transfer DNA Between Species

Viruses, which are often little more than genetic material encased in a protein coat, can reproduce only inside cells. A virus attaches to specific molecules on the surface of a suitable host cell (**Fig. 13-2 ❶**). The rabies virus, for example, attaches to the receptors on muscle cells that the nervous system uses to stimulate contraction of the muscle. Both HIV (the AIDS virus) and cold viruses attach to molecules that are involved in the immune response to an infection. Usually the virus then enters the cytoplasm of the host cell (**Fig. 13-2 ❷**), where it releases its genetic material (**Fig. 13-2 ❸**). Unable to distinguish which genetic information is its own, and which is from the virus, the host cell replicates the viral genetic material (DNA or sometimes RNA) and synthesizes viral proteins (**Fig. 13-2 ❹**). The replicated genes and viral proteins assemble inside the cell (**Fig. 13-2 ❺**), forming new viruses that are released and may infect new cells (**Fig. 13-2 ❻**).

Some viruses can transfer genes from one organism to another. In these instances, the viral DNA is inserted into one of the host cell's chromosomes (see Fig. 13-2 ❸). The viral DNA may remain there for days, months, or even years. Every time the cell divides, it replicates the viral DNA along with its own DNA. When new viruses are finally produced, some of the host cell's genes may be attached to the viral DNA. If such recombinant viruses infect another cell and insert their DNA into the new host cell's chromosomes, pieces of the previous host cell's DNA will also be inserted.

Most viruses infect and replicate only in the cells of specific bacterial, animal, or plant species. Therefore, most of the time, viruses move host DNA between different individuals of a single, or fairly closely related, species. However, some viruses may infect species only distantly related to one another; for example, influenza infects birds, pigs, and humans. Gene transfer between viruses that infect multiple species can produce extremely lethal recombined viruses. This happened in

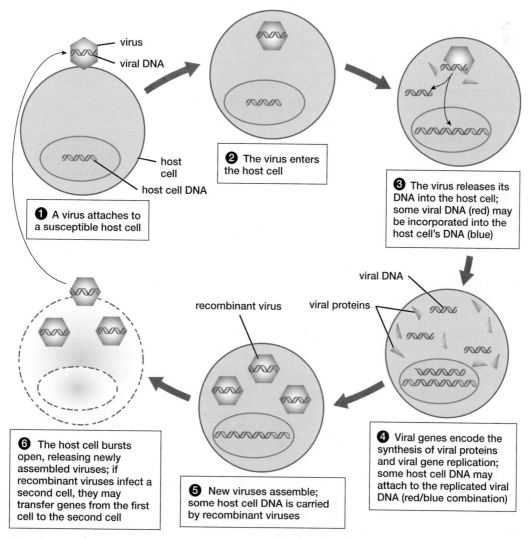

▲ FIGURE 13-2 The life cycle of a typical virus In some cases, viral infections may transfer DNA from one host cell to another.

1957 and again in 1968, when recombination between bird flu viruses and human flu viruses caused global epidemics that killed hundreds of thousands of people.

13.3 HOW IS BIOTECHNOLOGY USED IN FORENSIC SCIENCE?

Applications of DNA biotechnology vary, depending on the goals of those who use it. Forensic scientists need to identify victims and criminals; biotechnology firms need to identify specific genes and insert them into organisms such as bacteria, cattle, or crop plants; and biomedical firms and physicians need to detect defective alleles and, ideally, devise ways to fix them or to insert normally functioning alleles into patients. We will begin by describing a few common methods of manipulating DNA, using their application to forensic DNA analysis as a specific example. Later, we will investigate how biotechnology is used in agriculture and medicine.

The Polymerase Chain Reaction Amplifies DNA

Developed by Kary Mullis of the Cetus Corporation in 1986, the **polymerase chain reaction (PCR)** can be used to make billions, even trillions, of copies of selected pieces of DNA. Further, PCR can be used to amplify selected pieces of DNA. PCR is so crucial to molecular biology that it earned Mullis a share in the Nobel Prize for Chemistry in 1993. Let's see how PCR amplifies a specific piece of DNA.

When we described DNA replication in Chapter 11, we omitted some of its real-life complexity. One of the things we did not discuss is crucial to PCR: By itself, DNA polymerase doesn't know where to start copying a strand of DNA. When a DNA double helix is unwound, enzymes first put a little piece of complementary RNA, called a primer, on each strand. DNA polymerase recognizes this "primed" region of DNA as the place to start replicating the rest of the DNA strand.

PCR generally uses artificial primers made of DNA. To copy a specific segment of DNA, PCR needs two DNA primers, which are complementary to the two ends of the DNA segment. One primer is complementary to one strand of the double helix and the other primer is complementary to the other strand. Therefore, at least this much of the DNA sequence of interest must be known. DNA primers for PCR are manufactured in a DNA synthesizer, a machine that can be programmed to make short pieces of DNA with any desired sequence of nucleotides. DNA polymerase recognizes these DNA primers as the nucleotide sequences where DNA replication should begin.

In a small test tube, DNA is mixed with primers, free nucleotides, and a special DNA polymerase that works at the high temperatures used in PCR (this DNA polymerase was first isolated from microbes that live in hot springs; see "Scientific Inquiry: Hot Springs and Hot Science"). PCR involves the following steps (**Fig. 13-3**):

1. The test tube is heated to 194° to 203°F (90° to 95°C) (**Fig. 13-3a** ❶). High temperatures break the hydrogen bonds between complementary bases, separating the DNA into single strands.

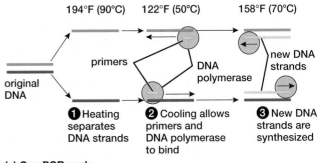

| | 194°F (90°C) | 122°F (50°C) | 158°F (70°C) |

❶ Heating separates DNA strands   ❷ Cooling allows primers and DNA polymerase to bind   ❸ New DNA strands are synthesized

(a) One PCR cycle

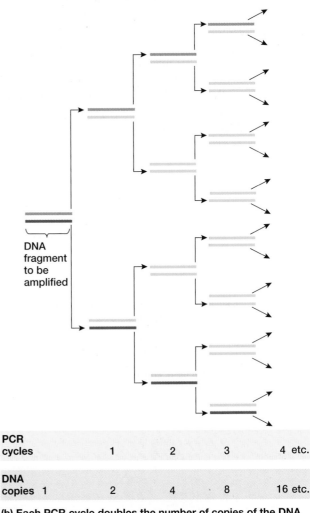

| PCR cycles | 1 | 2 | 3 | 4 etc. |
| DNA copies 1 | 2 | 4 | 8 | 16 etc. |

(b) Each PCR cycle doubles the number of copies of the DNA

▲ FIGURE 13-3 **PCR copies a specific DNA sequence** **(a)** The polymerase chain reaction consists of a cycle of heating, cooling, and warming that is repeated 30 to 40 times. **(b)** Each cycle doubles the amount of target DNA. After a little more than 30 cycles, a billion copies of the target DNA have been synthesized.

QUESTION Why do you think that the reaction is warmed up to about 158°F (70°C) for DNA synthesis [see part (a) of the figure]? *Hint:* Consider the normal living conditions of *Thermus aquaticus* (see "Scientific Inquiry: Hot Springs and Hot Science"); do you think that its DNA polymerase would work most rapidly at about 122°F (50°C) or 158°F (70°C)?

Scientific Inquiry

Hot Springs and Hot Science

At a hot spring, such as those found in Yellowstone National Park, water literally boils out of the ground, gradually cooling as it flows to the nearest stream (**Fig. E13-1**). You might think that such springs, scalding hot and often containing poisonous metals and sulfur compounds, must be lifeless. However, closer examination often reveals a diversity of microorganisms, each adapted to a different temperature zone in the spring. Back in 1966, in a Yellowstone hot spring, Thomas Brock of the University of Wisconsin discovered *Thermus aquaticus*, a bacterium that lives in water as hot as 176°F (80°C).

When Kary Mullis first developed the polymerase chain reaction, he encountered a major technical difficulty. The DNA solution must be heated almost to boiling to separate the double helix into single strands, then cooled so DNA polymerase can synthesize new DNA, and this process must be repeated again and again. "Ordinary" DNA polymerase, like most proteins, is ruined, or denatured, by high temperatures. Therefore, new DNA polymerase had to be added after every heat cycle, which was expensive and labor intensive. Enter *Thermus aquaticus*. Like other organisms, it replicates its DNA when it reproduces. But because it lives in hot springs, it has a particularly heat-resistant DNA polymerase. When DNA polymerase from *T. aquaticus* is used in PCR, it needs to be added to the DNA solution only once, at the start of the reaction.

▲ **FIGURE E13-1 Thomas Brock surveys Mushroom Spring** The colors in hot springs arise from minerals dissolved in the water and from various types of microbes that live at different temperatures.

2. The temperature is lowered to about 122°F (50°C) (**Fig. 13-3a ❷**), which allows the two primers to form complementary base pairs with the original DNA strands.
3. The temperature is raised to 158° to 162°F (70° to 72°C) (**Fig. 13-3a ❸**). DNA polymerase uses the free nucleotides to make copies of the DNA segment bounded by the primers.
4. This cycle is repeated, usually 30 to 40 times, until the reactants have been used up.

PCR synthesizes DNA in a geometric progression (1 → 2 → 4 → 8, etc.), so 20 PCR cycles make about a million copies, and a little over 30 cycles make a billion copies (**Fig. 13-3b**). Each cycle takes only a few minutes, so PCR can produce billions of copies of a DNA segment in a single afternoon, starting, if necessary, from a single molecule of DNA. The DNA is then available for forensics, cloning, making transgenic organisms, or many other purposes in biotechnology.

Differences in Short Tandem Repeats Can Identify Individuals by Their DNA

In many criminal investigations, PCR is used to amplify the DNA so that there is enough to compare the DNA left at a crime scene with a suspect's DNA. How is this comparison done? After years of painstaking work, forensics experts have found that small, repeating segments of DNA, called **short tandem repeats (STRs),** can be used to identify people with

astonishing accuracy. It may be helpful to think of STRs as very short, stuttering genes (**Fig. 13-4**). Each STR is *short* (consisting of 2 to 5 nucleotides), *repeat*ed (up to 50 times), and *tandem* (having all the repetitions right alongside one another). As with any gene, different people may have different alleles of the STRs. In the case of an STR, each allele simply has a different number of repeats of the same few nucleotides. In the United States, the Department of Justice established a standard set of 13 different STRs, each with repeats four nucleotides long, to identify individuals by DNA samples. Worldwide, different people may have as few as five to as many 38 repeats of a given STR. As we will see, STR analysis is fairly simple, making it ideal for forensic use.

Eight side-by-side (tandem) repeats of the same four-nucleotide sequence

▲ **FIGURE 13-4 Short tandem repeats are common in noncoding regions of DNA** This STR contains the sequence AGAT, repeated from 7 to 15 times in different individuals.

Case Study continued
Guilty or Innocent?

When a law student finally located semen samples in the Dennis Maher case, the Innocence Project team needed to find out if the samples collected from the rape victims came from Maher. Fortunately, DNA doesn't degrade very fast, so even old DNA samples, such as those in the Maher case, usually have STRs that are mostly intact. First, lab technicians amplified the DNA with PCR so that they had enough material to analyze. Then, they determined whether the DNA from the semen samples matched Maher's DNA.

Forensics labs use PCR primers that amplify only the STRs and the DNA immediately surrounding them. Because STR alleles vary in how many repeats they contain, they vary in size: An STR allele with more repeats is larger than one with fewer repeats. Therefore, a forensic lab needs to identify each STR in a DNA sample and then must determine its size to find out which alleles occur in the sample.

Modern forensics labs use sophisticated and expensive machines to determine how many repeats each STR in their samples contain. Most of these machines, however, are based on two methods that are used in molecular biology labs around the world: first, separating DNA segments by size, and second, labeling specific DNA segments of interest.

Gel Electrophoresis Separates DNA Segments

A mixture of DNA pieces is separated by a technique called **gel electrophoresis** (Fig. 13-5). First, a laboratory technician loads the DNA into shallow grooves, or wells, in a slab of agarose, a carbohydrate purified from certain types of seaweed (Fig. 13-5 ❶). Agarose forms a gel, which is simply a

❶ DNA samples are pipetted into wells (shallow slots) in the gel. Electrical current is sent through the gel (negative at the end with the wells and positive at the opposite end).

power supply

pipetter

gel

wells

❷ Electrical current moves the DNA segments through the gel. Smaller pieces of DNA move farther toward the positive electrode.

DNA "bands" (not yet visible)

❸ The gel is placed on special nylon "paper." Electrical current drives the DNA out of the gel onto the nylon.

gel

nylon paper

❹ The nylon paper with the DNA bound to it is bathed in a solution of labeled DNA probes (red) that are complementary to specific DNA segments in the original DNA sample.

solution of DNA probes (red)

nylon paper

❺ Complementary DNA segments are labeled by the probes (red bands).

▲ FIGURE 13-5 **Gel electrophoresis and labeling with DNA probes separates and identifies segments of DNA.**

meshwork of fibers with holes of various sizes between the fibers. The gel is put into a chamber with electrodes connected to each end. One electrode is made positive and the other negative; therefore, current will flow between the electrodes through the gel. How does this process separate pieces of DNA? Remember, the phosphate groups in the backbones of DNA are negatively charged. When electrical current flows through the gel, the negatively charged DNA fragments move toward the positively charged electrode. Because smaller fragments slip through the holes in the gel more easily than larger fragments do, they move more rapidly toward the positively charged electrode. Eventually the DNA fragments are separated by size, forming distinct bands on the gel (**Fig. 13-5 ❷**).

DNA Probes Are Used to Label Specific Nucleotide Sequences

Unfortunately, the DNA bands are invisible. There are several dyes that stain DNA, but these are often not very useful in either forensics or medicine. Why not? Because there may be many DNA fragments of approximately the same size; for example, five or six different STRs with the same numbers of repeats might be mixed together in the same band. How can a technician identify a *specific* STR? Well, how does *nature* identify sequences of DNA? Right—by base pairing!

When the gel is finished running, the technician treats it with chemicals that break apart the double helices into single DNA strands. These DNA strands are transferred out of the gel onto a piece of paper made of nylon (**Fig. 13-5 ❸**). Because the DNA samples are now single-stranded, pieces of synthetic DNA, called **DNA probes,** can base-pair with specific DNA fragments in the sample. DNA probes are short pieces of single-stranded DNA that are complementary to the nucleotide sequence of a given STR (or any other DNA of interest in the gel). The DNA probes are labeled, either by radioactivity or by attaching colored molecules to them. Therefore, a given DNA probe will label certain DNA sequences, but not others (**Fig. 13-6**).

To visualize a specific STR, the paper is bathed in a solution containing a DNA probe that will base-pair with, and therefore bind to, only that particular STR (**Fig. 13-5 ❹**). Any extra DNA probe is then washed off the paper. The result: The DNA probe shows where that specific STR ran in the gel (**Fig. 13-5 ❺**). (Labeling the DNA fragments with radioactive or colored DNA probes is standard procedure in most research applications. In modern forensic applications, however, the STRs are usually directly labeled with colored molecules during the PCR reaction. Therefore, the STRs are immediately visible in the gel and do not have to be stained with DNA probes.)

Unrelated People Almost Never Have Identical DNA Profiles

DNA samples run on STR gels produce a pattern, called a **DNA profile** (**Fig. 13-7**). The positions of the bands on the gel are determined by the numbers of repeats of each STR allele. If the same STRs are analyzed, then a particular DNA sample will produce the same profile every time.

STR #1: The probe base-pairs and binds to the DNA

STR #2: The probe cannot base-pair with the DNA, so it does not bind

▲ **FIGURE 13-6 DNA probes base-pair with complementary DNA sequences** A short, single-stranded piece of DNA is labeled with a colored molecule (red ball). This labeled DNA will base-pair with a target strand of DNA with a complementary base sequence (top), but not with a noncomplementary strand (bottom).

What does a DNA profile tell us? As with any gene, every person has two alleles of each STR, one on each homologous chromosome. The two alleles of a given STR might have the same number of repeats (the person would be homozygous for that STR gene) or a different number of repeats (the person would be heterozygous). For example, in the enlargement of the D16 STR on the right side of Figure 13-7, the first person's DNA has a single band at 12 repeats (this person is homozygous for the D16 STR), but the second person's DNA has two bands—at 13 and 12 repeats (this person is heterozygous for the D16 STR). If you look closely at all of the DNA samples in Figure 13-7, you will see that, although the DNA from some people had the same repeats for one of the STRs (e.g., the fourth and fifth samples for D16), no one's DNA had the same repeats for all four STRs.

Remember, in the United States, a standard set of 13 STRs is used for DNA identification, A perfect DNA profile match would mean that both alleles of all 13 STRs would be identical between the crime scene DNA and the suspect's DNA. How definitive is an STR match? A perfect match of both alleles for all 13 STRs means that there is far less than one chance in a trillion that the two DNA samples matched purely by random chance. For complicated statistical reasons, there are probably a few unrelated people in the world who have the same DNA profile, but the odds of anyone who could possibly be a likely suspect in a criminal case being misidentified is extremely small. Finally, a *mismatch* in DNA profiles is absolute proof that two samples did not come from the same source. In the Maher case, when DNA profiling showed that the STR alleles in the semen did not match Maher's, that ruled him out as the perpetrator.

▲ **FIGURE 13-7 DNA profiling** The lengths of short tandem repeats of DNA form characteristic patterns on a gel. This gel displays four different STRs (Penta D, CSF, etc.). The columns of evenly spaced yellow bands on the far left and far right sides of the gel show the number of repeats in the individual STRs. DNA samples from 13 different people were run between these standards, resulting in one or two yellow bands in each vertical lane. The position of each band corresponds to the number of repeats in that STR allele (more repeats means more nucleotides, which in turn means that the allele is larger). (Photo courtesy of Dr. Margaret Kline, National Institute of Standards and Technology.)

QUESTION For any single person, a given STR always has either one or two bands. Why? Further, single bands are always about twice as bright as each band of a pair. For example, in the D16 STR on the right, the single bands of the first and third DNA samples are twice as bright as the pairs of bands of the second, fourth, and fifth samples. Why?

In the United States, anyone convicted of certain crimes (assault, burglary, attempted murder, etc.) must give a blood sample. Using the standard array of STRs, technicians determine the criminal's DNA profile, and code the results as the number of repeats of each STR. The profile is stored in computer files at a state agency, at the FBI, or both. (On *CSI* and other TV crime shows, when the actors refer to "CODIS," that acronym stands for "Combined DNA Index System," a DNA profile database kept on FBI computers.) Because all forensic labs use the same 13 STRs, computers can easily determine if DNA left behind at another crime scene, even years before or years later (after the criminal may have been released from prison), matches one of the profiles stored in the CODIS database. If the STRs match, then the odds are overwhelming that the crime scene DNA was left by the person with the matching profile. If there aren't any matches, the crime scene DNA profile will remain on file. Sometimes, years later, a new DNA profile will match an archived crime-scene profile, and a "cold case" will be solved (see "Case Study Revisited" at the end of this chapter).

13.4 HOW IS BIOTECHNOLOGY USED IN AGRICULTURE?

The main goals of agriculture are to grow as much food as possible, as cheaply as possible, with minimal loss from pests such as insects and weeds. Many commercial farmers and seed suppliers have turned to biotechnology to achieve these goals. Many people, however, feel that the risks of genetically modified food to human health or the environment are not worth the benefits. We will explore this controversy later in section 13.7.

Many Crops Are Genetically Modified

Currently, almost all of the genetically modified organisms used in agriculture are plants. According to the U.S. Department of Agriculture (USDA), in 2008, about 80% of the corn, 86% of the cotton, and 92% of the soybeans grown in the United States were transgenic; that is, they contained genes from other species (**Table 13-1**). Globally, more than 280 million acres of land were planted with transgenic crops in 2007, a 40% increase in just 3 years.

Case Study continued

Guilty or Innocent?

If you are a regular viewer of *CSI*, you may have heard an investigator say that a parent and child have "seven alleles in common." However, each person has two alleles of each of the 13 STR loci used in the United States—one allele at each locus inherited from the mother, the other allele inherited from the father. Further, even unrelated people usually have a few of the same STRs (see Fig. 13-7). So how many alleles should a father share with his child? The answer, of course, is at least 13, not merely 7.

Table 13-1 Genetically Engineered Crops with USDA Approval

Genetically Engineered Trait	Potential Advantage	Examples of Bioengineered Crops with USDA Approval
Resistance to herbicide	Application of herbicide kills weeds but not crop plants, producing higher crop yields	Beet, canola, corn, cotton, flax, potato, rice, soybean, tomato
Resistance to pests	Crop plants suffer less damage from insects, producing higher crop yields	Corn, cotton, potato, rice, soybean
Resistance to disease	Plants are less prone to infection by viruses, bacteria, or fungi, producing higher crop yields	Papaya, potato, squash
Sterile	Transgenic plants cannot cross with wild varieties, making them safer for the environment and more economically productive for the seed companies that produce them	Chicory, corn
Altered oil content	Oils can be made healthier for human consumption or can be made similar to more expensive oils (such as palm or coconut)	Canola, soybean
Altered ripening	Fruits can be more easily shipped with less damage, producing higher returns for the farmer	Tomato

Crops are most commonly modified to improve their resistance to insects, herbicides, or both. Many herbicides kill plants by inhibiting an enzyme that is used by plants, fungi, and some bacteria—but not animals—to synthesize amino acids such as tyrosine, tryptophan, and phenylalanine. Without these amino acids, the plants cannot synthesize proteins, and they die. Many herbicide-resistant transgenic crops have been given a bacterial gene encoding an enzyme that functions even in the presence of these herbicides, so the plants continue to synthesize normal amounts of amino acids and proteins. Herbicide-resistant crops allow farmers to kill weeds without harming their crops. Less competition from weeds means more water, nutrients, and light for the crops, and hence, larger harvests.

The insect resistance of many crops has been enhanced by giving them a gene, called *Bt*, from the bacterium *Bacillus thuringiensis*. The protein encoded by the *Bt* gene damages the digestive tract of insects, but not mammals. Transgenic *Bt* crops often suffer far less damage from insects (**Fig. 13-8**) than do regular crops, so farmers can apply less pesticide to their fields.

How would a seed company make a transgenic plant? Let's examine the process, using insect-resistant *Bt* plants as an example.

▲ FIGURE 13-8 *Bt* plants resist insect attack Transgenic cotton plants expressing the *Bt* gene (right) resist attack by bollworms, which eat cotton seeds. The transgenic plants therefore produce far more cotton than nontransgenic plants (left).

Have you ever wondered

If the Food You Eat Has Been Genetically Modified?

In addition to obvious things—tortilla chips, soy sauce, cooking oil, and margarine—corn and soy products are found in an amazing variety of foods. For example, corn syrup is an ingredient in foods as diverse as soda, ketchup, and bran flakes; corn starch is found in many baked goods. According to the Grocery Manufacturers of America, about 70% of the foods in your local supermarket contain products made from genetically modified (GM) crops. Many countries, including the European Union, require labeling of GM foods, but the U.S. Food and Drug Administration does not, so you can't tell if a food contains GM ingredients just by looking at the label. Therefore, unless you have been extremely motivated and careful, you have probably eaten GM foods.

The Desired Gene Is Cloned

Cloning a gene usually involves two tasks: (1) obtaining the gene and (2) inserting it into a plasmid so that huge numbers of copies of the gene can be made.

Two common methods are used to obtain a gene. For a long time, the only practical method was to isolate the gene from the organism that makes it. Now, biotechnologists can often synthesize the gene—or a modified version of it—in the lab, using DNA synthesizers.

Once the gene has been obtained, why insert it into a plasmid? Plasmids are replicated when the bacteria multiply. Therefore, once the desired gene has been inserted into a plasmid, producing huge numbers of copies of the gene is as simple as raising lots of bacteria. Inserting the gene into a plasmid also allows it to be easily separated from the bacteria, achieving partial purification of the gene, free of the DNA of the bacterial chromosome. Finally, plasmids may be taken up by other bacteria (this is important when making transgenic *Bt* plants) or injected into animal eggs.

One common method for making transgenic plants employs the bacterium *Agrobacterium tumefaciens*, which infects many plant species. *A. tumefaciens* often contains a specialized plasmid called the Ti (tumor-inducing) plasmid. (As the name implies, Ti plasmids normally cause plant tumors. However, biotechnologists can disable Ti plasmids by taking out the tumor-causing genes, so the plasmids become harmless.) When *A. tumefaciens* infects a plant cell, the Ti plasmid inserts itself into one of the plant cell's chromosomes. Thereafter, any time that plant cell divides, it replicates the Ti plasmid DNA as well, and all of its daughter cells inherit the Ti DNA. Most other plasmids don't insert themselves into their host cell's chromosomes, so the plasmid's genes aren't always passed down faithfully to the daughter cells when the host cell divides.

To insert a cloned gene into a plant cell, biotechnologists first must insert the gene into a Ti plasmid, then transform *A. tumefaciens* bacteria with the new recombinant plasmid, infect plant cells with the transformed bacteria, and finally make entire plants from these individual recombinant plant cells, as we describe below.

Restriction Enzymes Cut DNA at Specific Nucleotide Sequences

Genes are inserted into plasmids through the action of **restriction enzymes** isolated from bacteria. Each restriction enzyme cuts DNA at a specific nucleotide sequence. Many restriction enzymes cut "straight across" a double helix of DNA. Others make a "staggered" cut, snipping the DNA in a different location on each of the two strands, so that single-stranded sections hang off the ends of the DNA. These single-stranded regions are commonly called "sticky ends," because they can base-pair with, and thus stick to, other single-stranded pieces of DNA with complementary bases (Fig. 13-9).

Cutting Two Pieces of DNA with the Same Restriction Enzyme Allows the Pieces to Be Joined Together

To insert the *Bt* gene into a Ti plasmid, the same restriction enzyme is used to cut the DNA on either side of the *Bt* gene and to split open the circle of Ti plasmid DNA (Fig. 13-10 ❶). As a result, the ends of the *Bt* gene and the opened-up Ti plasmid both have complementary nucleotides in their sticky ends, and can base-pair with each other. When the cut *Bt* genes and Ti plasmids are mixed together, some of the *Bt* genes will be temporarily inserted between the ends of the Ti plasmids, held together by their complementary sticky ends. Adding DNA ligase (see pp. 211–212) permanently bonds the *Bt* gene into the Ti plasmid, forming a recombinant Ti plasmid (Fig. 13-10 ❷).

Plasmid-Transformed Bacteria Insert the *Bt* Gene into a Plant

To make insect-resistant plants, *Bt* genes are inserted into disabled Ti plasmids. *A. tumefaciens* bacteria are then transformed with the recombinant Ti plasmids (Fig. 13-10 ❸). When the transformed bacteria enter a plant cell, the Ti plasmids insert their DNA, including the *Bt* gene, into the plant cell's chromosomes, so that the plant cells now permanently carry the *Bt* gene (Fig. 13-10 ❹). Hormones are used to stimulate the transgenic plant cells to divide and differentiate into entire plants. These plants are bred to one another, or to other plants, to create commercially valuable plants that resist insect attack.

Another way of making transgenic plants is to use a "gene gun." Tiny metallic particles are coated with the desired DNA, often as part of a recombinant plasmid, and shot into a lump of plant cells growing in a Petri dish. This process is literally "hit or miss." Many of the cells are destroyed, many others never receive the DNA pellets, and only some of those that do receive the DNA successfully insert the DNA into a chromosome. However, because gene gun technology is quite straightforward and even a single successful cell can be grown into a transgenic plant, gene guns are increasingly used to produce genetically modified plants.

Genetically Modified Plants May Be Used to Produce Medicines

Similar techniques can be used to insert medically useful genes into plants, producing medicines down on the "pharm." For example, a plant can be engineered to produce harmless proteins that are normally found in disease-causing bacteria or viruses. If these proteins resisted digestion in the stomach and small intestine, simply eating such plants could act as a vaccination against the disease organisms. Several years ago, such "edible vaccines" were touted as a great way to provide vaccinations—no need to produce purified vaccines, no refrigeration needed, and, of course, no needles. Recently, however, many biomedical researchers have warned that edible vaccine plants are not really a good idea, because there is no simple way to control the dose: Too little and the user doesn't develop decent immunity; too much, and the vaccine proteins might be harmful. Nevertheless, producing vaccine proteins in plants is still worthwhile; pharmaceutical companies just have to extract and purify the proteins before use. Plant-produced vaccines against hepatitis B, tooth decay, avian flu, and certain types of diarrhea are now in clinical trials.

Molecular biologists can also engineer plants to produce human antibodies to combat various diseases. When a microbe invades your body, it takes several days for your immune system to respond and produce enough antibodies to

▲ FIGURE 13-9 Restriction enzymes cut DNA at specific nucleotide sequences

① The DNA containing the *Bt* gene and the Ti plasmid are cut with the same restriction enzyme.

DNA including *Bt* gene (blue)　Ti plasmid

recombinant Ti plasmid with *Bt* gene

② *Bt* genes and Ti plasmids, both with the same complementary sticky ends, are mixed together; DNA ligase bonds the *Bt* genes into the plasmids.

bacterial chromosome

A. tumefaciens bacterium

recombinant Ti plasmids

③ Bacteria are transformed with the recombinant plasmids.

plant chromosome

plant cell

Bt gene

④ Transgenic bacteria enter the plant cells, and *Bt* genes are inserted into the chromosomes of the plant cells.

▲ **FIGURE 13-10 Using plasmids to insert a bacterial gene into a plant chromosome**

overcome the infection. Meanwhile, you feel terrible, and might even die if the disease is serious enough. A direct injection of large quantities of the right antibodies might be able to cure the disease very quickly. Although none have yet entered medical practice, plant-derived antibodies against bacteria that cause tooth decay and non-Hodgkin's lymphoma (a cancer of the lymphatic system) are in clinical trials. Ideally, such "plantibodies" can be produced very cheaply, making such therapies available to rich and poor alike.

Genetically Modified Animals May Be Useful in Agriculture and Medicine

Producing transgenic animals usually involves injecting the desired DNA, often incorporated into a disabled virus that cannot

produce disease, into a fertilized egg. The egg is allowed to divide a few times in culture before being implanted into a surrogate mother. If the offspring are healthy and express the foreign gene, they are then bred to one another produce homozygous transgenic organisms. So far, it has proven difficult to produce commercially valuable transgenic livestock, but several companies in countries around the world are working on it.

One example is Nexia Biotech, which has engineered a herd of goats to carry the genes for spider silk, and to secrete silk protein into their milk. The resulting BioSteel® is five times stronger than steel and twice as strong as Kevlar®, the fiber usually used in bulletproof vests. Nexia has encountered difficulties in spinning BioSteel® into commercially usable silk, but has successfully manufactured "nanofibers" for medical and microelectronic applications.

Biotechnologists are also developing animals that will produce medicines, such as human antibodies or other essential proteins. For example, there are sheep whose milk contains a protein, alpha-1-antitrypsin, that may prove valuable in treating cystic fibrosis. Other livestock have been engineered so that their milk contains erythropoietin (a hormone that stimulates red blood cell synthesis), clotting factors (for treatment of hemophilia), or clot-busting proteins (to treat heart attacks caused by blood clots in the coronary arteries).

13.5 HOW IS BIOTECHNOLOGY USED TO LEARN ABOUT THE HUMAN GENOME?

Genes influence virtually all the traits of human beings, including gender, size, hair color, intelligence, and susceptibility to disease organisms and toxic substances in the environment. To begin to understand how our genes influence our lives, the Human Genome Project was launched in 1990, with the goal of determining the nucleotide sequence of all the DNA in our entire set of genes, called the human genome.

By 2003, this joint project of molecular biologists in several countries sequenced the human genome with an accuracy of about 99.99%. The human genome contains between 20,000 and 25,000 genes, comprising approximately 2% of the DNA. Some of the other 98% consists of promoters and regions that regulate how often individual genes are transcribed, but it's not really known what most of our DNA does.

Why did scientists want to sequence the human genome? First, many genes were discovered whose functions are unknown. Using the genetic code to translate the DNA sequences of novel genes, biologists can predict the amino acid sequences of the proteins they encode. Comparing these proteins to familiar proteins whose functions are already known will enable us to find out what many of these genes do.

Second, knowing the nucleotide sequences of human genes will have an enormous impact on medical practice. In 1990, fewer than 100 genes known to be associated with human diseases had been discovered. By 2006, this number had jumped to more than 1,800.

Third, there is no single "human genome" (or else all of us would be genetically identical). Most of the DNA of everyone on the planet is the same, but we each also carry our own unique set of alleles. Some of those alleles can cause or predispose people to develop various medical conditions, including sickle-cell anemia, cystic fibrosis, breast cancer, alcoholism, schizophrenia, heart disease, Alzheimer's disease, and many others. Ongoing human genome research involves sequencing the DNA of many different people, looking for small differences in allele DNA sequences that might contribute to diseases, susceptibility to toxic pollutants or chemicals in tobacco smoke, or responses to drugs. Researchers hope to use this information to help diagnose genetic disorders or predispositions, and to devise treatments or even cures in the future. Knowing how different people respond to drug treatments— for example, different people's bodies break down drugs at tremendously different rates—will someday allow custom-tailored treatments for diseases.

Fourth, the Human Genome Project, along with companion projects that have sequenced the genomes of organisms as diverse as bacteria, mice, and chimpanzees, helps us to appreciate our place in the evolution of life on Earth. For example, the DNA of humans and chimps differs by only about 1%. Comparing the similarities and differences may help biologists to understand what genetic differences help to make us human, and why we are susceptible to certain diseases that chimps are not.

13.6 HOW IS BIOTECHNOLOGY USED FOR MEDICAL DIAGNOSIS AND TREATMENT?

For more than a decade, biotechnology has been routinely used to diagnose some inherited disorders, even in fetuses (see "Health Watch: Prenatal Genetic Screening" on pp. 258–259). More recently, medical researchers have begun using biotechnology in an attempt to cure, or at least treat, genetic diseases.

DNA Technology Can Be Used to Diagnose Inherited Disorders

A person inherits a genetic disease because he or she inherits one or more defective alleles, which differ from normal, functional alleles because they have different nucleotide sequences. Two methods are commonly used to find out if a person carries a normal allele or a malfunctioning allele.

Restriction Enzymes May Cut Different Alleles of a Gene at Different Locations

Recall that restriction enzymes cut DNA only at specific nucleotide sequences. Because chromosomes are so large, any given restriction enzyme usually cuts the DNA of a chromosome in many places. What if two homologous chromosomes have different alleles of several genes, and some alleles have nucleotide sequences that *can* be cut by a restriction enzyme, whereas others have nucleotide sequences that *cannot* be cut by the same enzyme? The result will be a mixture of DNA segments of various lengths. These are called **restriction fragment length polymorphisms (RFLPs;** pronounced "riff-lips"). This rather daunting phrase simply means that *restriction* enzymes have cut DNA into *fragments* that vary in *length*, and that homologous chromosomes (from the same person or from

different people) may differ (or be *polymorphic*) in the lengths of the fragments. Why is this useful? First, if different people have different RFLPs, this can be used to identify DNA samples. In fact, in the early 1990s, before STRs became the gold standard in DNA forensics, RFLPs were used to determine if DNA from a crime scene matched the DNA of a suspect. Second, medically important alleles can sometimes be identified by differences in the lengths of the restriction fragments produced by cutting with a specific restriction enzyme.

RFLP analysis has become a standard technique for diagnosing sickle-cell anemia, even in an embryo. Sickle-cell anemia is caused by a point mutation in which thymine replaces adenine near the beginning of the globin gene (see Table 12-4). A restriction enzyme called MstII cuts DNA just "ahead" of the globin gene locus (cut #1 in **Figs. 13-11a,b**). It also makes a cut in about the middle of both the normal and sickle-cell alleles (cut #3 in Figs. 13-11a,b). Crucially, MstII also makes a cut near the beginning of the normal globin allele (cut #2 in Fig. 13-11a), but, because of the point mutation, cannot make this cut in the sickle-cell allele (Fig. 13-11b). How can this difference be used to diagnose sickle-cell anemia?

A DNA probe is synthesized that is complementary to the part of the globin allele spanning the second cut site. When sickle-cell DNA is cut with MstII and run on a gel, this probe labels a single band near the top of the gel, consisting of very large pieces of DNA (**Fig. 13-11c**). When normal DNA is cut with MstII, the probe labels two bands, one with small pieces of DNA (near the bottom of the gel) and one with pieces that are not quite as large as the sickle-cell pieces. The genotypes of parents, children, and fetuses can be determined by this simple test. Someone who is homozygous for the normal globin allele will have two bands. Someone who is homozygous for the sickle-cell allele will have one band. A heterozygote will have three bands (see Fig. 13-11c).

Different Alleles Bind to Different DNA Probes

The Chapter 12 case study introduced you to cystic fibrosis, a disease caused by a defect in a protein, called CFTR, that normally helps to move chloride ions across the plasma membrane. There are more than 1,200 different *CFTR* alleles, all at the same locus, each encoding a different, defective CFTR protein. People with either one or two normal alleles synthesize enough functioning chloride transport proteins that they do not develop cystic fibrosis. People with two defective alleles (they may be the same or different alleles) do not synthesize fully functional transport proteins and develop cystic fibrosis.

How can anyone hope to diagnose a disorder with 1,200 different alleles? Fortunately, 32 alleles account for about 90% of the cases of cystic fibrosis—the rest of the alleles are extremely rare. Although 32 alleles is still a lot, each of these defective alleles has a different nucleotide sequence. As you know, a DNA strand will form perfect base pairs only with a perfectly complementary strand. Several companies now produce cystic fibrosis "arrays," which are pieces of specialized filter paper to which single-stranded DNA probes are bound (**Fig. 13-12**). Each probe is complementary to one strand of a different *CFTR* allele (**Fig. 13-12a**). A person's DNA is tested for cystic fibrosis by cutting

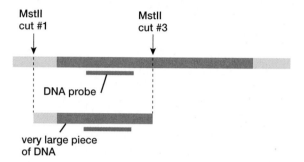

(a) **MstII cuts the normal globin allele into two pieces that can be labeled by a probe**

(b) **MstII cuts the sickle-cell allele into one very large piece that can be labeled by the same probe**

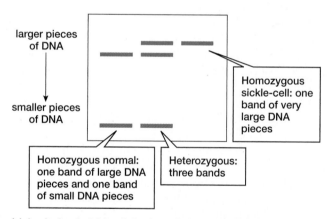

larger pieces of DNA

smaller pieces of DNA

Homozygous sickle-cell: one band of very large DNA pieces

Homozygous normal: one band of large DNA pieces and one band of small DNA pieces

Heterozygous: three bands

(c) **Analysis of globin alleles by gel electrophoresis**

▲ **FIGURE 13-11 Diagnosing sickle-cell anemia with restriction enzymes** The globin gene locus is shown in red; adjacent DNA on the chromosome is shown in yellow. **(a)** The restriction enzyme MstII cuts the normal globin allele somewhat "ahead" of the globin locus (cut site #1), near the beginning of the allele (cut site #2), and about in the middle of the allele (cut site #3). A DNA probe (blue) is synthesized that is complementary to the DNA on both sides of cut site #2. This probe can therefore label one large and one small piece of DNA from the normal allele. **(b)** MstII cuts the sickle-cell allele only at cut sites #1 and #3. The DNA probe will label only one, very large piece of DNA from the sickle-cell allele. **(c)** DNA is extracted from cells and cut with MstII. The cut DNA is separated on the gel and labeled with the DNA probe. The large single pieces of DNA from sickle-cell alleles run close to the beginning (top) of the gel, while the smaller pieces from normal alleles run farther into the gel (lower down). The pattern of DNA bands shows the genotype of the person from whom the DNA sample was obtained.

QUESTION Why do heterozygotes have three bands? Would these bands have the same intensity (brightness) as the bands from homozygotes?

(a) **Linear array of probes for cystic fibrosis**

(b) *CFTR* allele **labeled with a colored molecule**

#1

Homozygous for normal *CFTR* alleles— the person is phenotypically normal

#2

One normal and one defective *CFTR* allele— the person is phenotypically normal

#3

Two different defective *CFTR* alleles— the person develops cystic fibrosis

(c) **Linear arrays with labeled DNA samples from three different people**

▲ **FIGURE 13-12 A cystic fibrosis diagnostic array**
(a) A "linear array" for cystic fibrosis consists of special paper to which DNA probes complementary to the normal *CFTR* allele (far left spot) and several of the most common defective *CFTR* alleles (the other 10 spots) are attached. **(b)** DNA from a patient is cut into small pieces, separated into single strands, and the *CFTR* alleles are labeled with colored molecules. **(c)** The array is bathed in a solution of the patient's labeled DNA. Different spots on the array are labeled, depending on which *CFTR* alleles the patient possesses.

it into small pieces, separating the pieces into single strands, and labeling the strands with a colored molecule (**Fig. 13-12b**). The array is then bathed in the resulting solution of labeled DNA fragments. Only a perfect complementary strand of the person's DNA will bind to any given probe on the array, thereby showing which *CFTR* alleles the person possesses (**Fig. 13-12c**).

Although not yet practical for routine medical use, an expanded version of this type of DNA analysis may one day offer customized medical care. Different people have different alleles of hundreds of genes; these may cause them to be more or less susceptible to many diseases, or to respond more or less well to various treatments. Someday, physicians might be able to use an array containing hundreds, even thousands, of probes for disease-related alleles, to determine which susceptibility

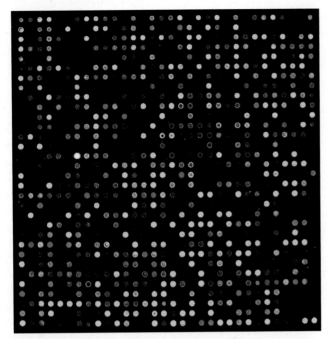

▲ **FIGURE 13-13 A human DNA microarray** Each spot contains a DNA probe for a specific human gene. In most research applications, messenger RNA is isolated from a subject (for example, from a human cancer), and labeled with a fluorescent dye. The mRNA is then poured onto the array, and each base-pairs with its complementary template DNA probe. Genes that are particularly active in the cancer will "light up" the corresponding DNA.

alleles each patient carries, and tailor medical care accordingly. Sound like science fiction? Well, arrays containing probes for thousands of human genes are already being manufactured (Fig. 13-13).

Several companies produce small arrays tailored to investigate gene activity in specific diseases, such as breast cancer. Some hospitals use them to provide patients with treatments that are most likely to succeed with their specific cancer.

Finally, as of 2008, at least three companies—deCODE, 23andMe, and Navigenics—offered individualized DNA screening to the public, at prices ranging from about $1,000 to $2,500. These screening tests look for alleles that might predispose an individual to develop heart disease, breast cancer, arthritis, or other diseases. The companies even offer health ad-vice, presumably based on the individual DNA analysis, although most of the advice—to exercise, keep blood pressure and cholesterol levels down, keep weight under control, and refrain from smoking—would be a good idea for anyone, regardless of whatever disease susceptibility alleles they carry.

DNA Technology Can Help to Treat Disease

DNA technology can be used to treat disease as well as diagnose it. Thanks to recombinant DNA technology, several medically important proteins are now routinely made in bacteria. The first human protein made by recombinant DNA technology was insulin. Prior to 1982, when recombinant human insulin was first licensed for use, the insulin needed by diabetics was extracted from the pancreases of cattle or pigs slaughtered for meat. Although the insulin from these animals is very similar to human insulin, the slight differences caused an allergic reaction in about 5% of diabetics. Recombinant human insulin does not cause allergic reactions.

Other human proteins, such as growth hormone and clotting factors, can also be produced in transgenic bacteria. Before recombinant DNA technology, some of these proteins were obtained from either human blood or human cadavers; these sources are expensive and sometimes dangerous. As you know, blood can be contaminated by HIV, the virus that causes AIDS. Cadavers may also contain several hard-to-diagnose infectious diseases, such as Creutzfeldt-Jakob syndrome, in which an abnormal protein can be passed from the tissues of an infected cadaver to a patient and cause irreversible, fatal brain degeneration (see the Chapter 3 Case Study). Engineered proteins grown in bacteria or other cultured cells circumvent these dangers. Some of the categories of human proteins produced by recombinant DNA technology are listed in **Table 13-2**.

Biotechnology offers the potential to treat diseases such as cystic fibrosis and possibly cure diseases such as diabetes, although progress has been painfully slow thus far. Let's look at two specific examples of how these advances may treat, or even cure, life-threatening illnesses.

Using Biotechnology to Treat Cystic Fibrosis

Cystic fibrosis causes devastating effects in the lungs, where the lack of chloride transport causes the usually thin, watery

---

Table 13-2 **Examples of Medical Products Produced by Recombinant DNA Methods**

Type of Product	Purpose	Product	Genetic Engineering
Human hormones	Used in the treatment of diabetes and growth deficiency	Humulin™ (human insulin)	Human gene inserted into bacteria
Human cytokines (regulate immune system function)	Used in bone marrow transplants and to treat cancers and viral infections, including hepatitis and genital warts	Leukine™ (granulocyte-macrophage colony stimulating factor)	Human gene inserted into yeast
Antibodies (immune system proteins)	Used to fight infections, cancers, diabetes, organ rejection, and multiple sclerosis	Herceptin™ (antibodies to a protein expressed in some breast cancer cells)	Recombinant antibody genes inserted into cultured hamster cells
Viral proteins	Used to generate vaccines against viral diseases and for diagnosing viral infections	Energiz-B™ (hepatitis B vaccine)	Viral gene inserted into yeast
Enzymes	Used in the treatment of heart attacks, cystic fibrosis, and other diseases, and in the production of cheeses and detergents	Activase™ (tissue plasminogen activator)	Human gene inserted into cultured hamster cells

mucus lining the airways to become thick, clogging the airways (see the Case Study in Chapter 12). Several research groups are developing methods to deliver the normal *CFTR* allele to the cells of the lungs, get them to synthesize functioning CFTR chloride transport proteins, and insert the CFTR proteins into their plasma membranes.

To treat cystic fibrosis, the researchers first disable a suitable virus, so that the treatment itself doesn't cause disease. Cold viruses are often used, because they normally infect cells of the respiratory tract. The DNA of the functional *CFTR* allele is inserted into the DNA of the virus. The recombinant viruses are suspended in a solution and sprayed into the patient's nose or dripped directly into the lungs through a nasal tube. The viruses enter cells of the lungs and release the normal *CFTR* allele into the cells. The cells then manufacture functional CFTR proteins, insert them into their plasma membranes, and transport chloride into the fluid lining the airways.

Clinical trials of these treatments have been reasonably successful, but for only a few weeks. The patients' immune systems probably attack the viruses and eliminate them—and the helpful genes they carry. Because lung cells are continually replaced over time, a single dose "wears off" as the modified cells die. Researchers are trying both to increase the expression of the normal *CFTR* alleles in the viruses and to extend the effective lifetime of a single treatment.

Using Biotechnology to Cure Severe Combined Immune Deficiency

Like the cells of the lung, the vast majority of cells in the human body eventually die and are replaced by new cells. In many cases, the new cells come from special populations of cells called stem cells; when they divide, stem cells give rise to daughter cells that can differentiate into several different types of mature cells (see p. 146). In the brain, for example, stem cells give rise to several types of nerve cells and multiple types of non-nervous, support cells as well. It's possible that some stem cells, under the right conditions in the laboratory, might be able to give rise to *any* cell type of the entire body! For now, we will look at a more limited function of stem cells: producing or replacing just one or two types of cells.

All the cells of the immune system (mostly white blood cells) originate in the bone marrow. Some go on to produce antibodies, some kill cells that have been infected by viruses, and some regulate the actions of the other cells. As mature cells die, they are replaced by new cells that arise from division of stem cells in the bone marrow.

Severe combined immune deficiency (SCID) is a rare disorder in which a child fails to develop an immune system. About 1 in 80,000 children is born with some form of SCID. Infections that would be trivial in a normal child become life threatening. In some cases, if the child has an unaffected relative with a similar genetic makeup, a bone marrow transplant from the healthy relative can give the child functioning stem cells, so that he or she can develop a working immune system. Most SCID victims, however, die before their first birthday.

Most forms of SCID are single-gene, recessive defects. In some cases, children are homozygous recessive for a defec-

tive allele that normally codes for an enzyme called adenosine deaminase. In 1990, the first test of human gene therapy was performed on such a SCID patient, 4-year-old Ashanti DeSilva. Some of her white blood cells were removed, genetically altered with a virus containing a functional version of her defective allele, and then returned to her bloodstream. Now, Ashanti is a healthy adult, with a reasonably functional immune system. However, as the altered white blood cells die, they must be replaced with new ones; therefore, Ashanti needs repeated treatments. She is also given regular injections of a form of adenosine deaminase, which makes it difficult to assess the exact benefits of her gene therapy. Nevertheless, Ashanti receives a much smaller dose of adenosine deaminase than is typically given to an adult, so the gene therapy, although not perfect, is certainly making a major difference.

In 2005, Italian researchers appeared to have completely cured Ashanti's type of SCID in six children. Instead of inserting a normal copy of the adenosine deaminase gene into mature white blood cells, the Italian team inserted the gene into stem cells. Because the "cured" stem cells should continue to multiply and churn out new white blood cells, these children will probably have functioning immune systems for the rest of their lives. (In 1990, when Ashanti received her pioneering treatments, stem cell research was in its infancy. At that time, it would not have been possible to isolate her stem cells and correct their adenosine deaminase genes.)

13.7 WHAT ARE THE MAJOR ETHICAL ISSUES OF MODERN BIOTECHNOLOGY?

Modern biotechnology offers the promise—some would say the threat—of greatly changing our lives, and the lives of many other organisms on Earth. As Spider-Man noted, "With great power comes great responsibility." Is humanity capable of handling the responsibility of biotechnology? Here we will explore two important debates about biotechnology: the use of genetically modified organisms in agriculture and prospects for genetically modifying human beings.

Should Genetically Modified Organisms Be Permitted in Agriculture?

The aims of "traditional" and "modern" agricultural biotechnology are the same: to modify the genetic makeup of living organisms to make them more useful. However, there are three principal differences. First, traditional biotechnology is usually slow; many generations of selective breeding are necessary before significantly useful new traits appear in plants or animals. Genetic engineering, in contrast, can potentially introduce massive genetic changes in a single generation. Second, traditional biotechnology almost always recombines genetic material from the same, or at least very closely related, species, whereas genetic engineering can recombine DNA from very different species in one organism. Finally, traditional biotechnologists had no way to manipulate the DNA sequence of genes themselves. Genetic engineering, however, can produce new genes never before seen on Earth.

The best transgenic crops have clear advantages for farmers. Herbicide-resistant crops allow farmers to rid their fields of weeds, which reduce harvests by 10% or more, through the use of powerful, nonselective herbicides at virtually any stage of crop growth. Insect-resistant crops decrease the need to apply synthetic pesticides, saving the cost of the pesticides themselves, as well as tractor fuel and labor. Therefore, transgenic crops may produce larger harvests at less cost. These savings may be passed along to the consumer. Transgenic crops also have the potential to be more nutritious than "standard" crops (see "Health Watch: Golden Rice").

However, many people strenuously object to transgenic crops or livestock. For example, in November 2005, citizens in Switzerland voted to ban the cultivation of transgenic crops (although food made from transgenic crops, grown elsewhere, can be imported and sold). The principal concerns are that GMOs may be harmful to human health or dangerous to the environment.

Are Foods from GMOs Dangerous to Eat?

In most cases, there is no reason to think that GMOs are dangerous to eat. For example, tests have shown that the protein encoded by the *Bt* gene is not toxic to mammals, and should not prove a danger to human health. If growth-enhanced livestock are ever marketed, they will simply have more meat, composed of exactly the same proteins that exist in nontransgenic animals, so they shouldn't be dangerous either.

On the other hand, some people might be allergic to genetically modified plants. In the 1990s, a gene from Brazil nuts was inserted into soybeans in an attempt to improve the balance of amino acids in soybean protein. It was soon discovered that people allergic to Brazil nuts would probably also be allergic to the transgenic soybeans. These transgenic soybean plants never made it to the farm. The U.S. Food and Drug Administration now monitors all new transgenic crop plants for allergenic potential.

In 2003, the U.S. Society of Toxicology studied the risks of genetically modified plants and concluded that the current transgenic plants pose no significant dangers to human health. The society also recognized that past safety does not guarantee future safety, and recommended continued testing and evaluation of all new genetically modified plants. Similar conclusions were drawn by the U.S. National Academy of Sciences in 2004, which found that "the process of genetic engineering has not been shown to be inherently dangerous but . . . any technique, including genetic engineering, carries the potential to result in unintended changes in the composition of the food."

Are GMOs Hazardous to the Environment?

The environmental effects of GMOs are much more debatable. One clear positive effect of *Bt* crops is that farmers apply less pesticide to their fields. This should translate into less pollution of the environment, and less harm to the farmers as well. For example, in 2002 and 2003, Chinese farmers planting *Bt* rice reduced pesticide use by 80% compared to farmers planting conventional rice. Further, they suffered no instances of pesticide poisoning, compared to about 5% of farmers planting conventional rice. A 10-year study in Arizona showed that *Bt* cotton allowed farmers to use less pesticide while obtaining the same yields of cotton.

On the other hand, *Bt* or herbicide-resistance genes might spread outside a farmer's fields. Because these genes are incorporated into the genome of the transgenic crop, the genes will be in its pollen, too. A farmer cannot control where pollen from a transgenic crop will go. In 2006, researchers at the U.S. Environmental Protection Agency identified "escaped" herbicide-resistant grasses more than 2 miles away from a test plot in Oregon. Based on genetic analyses, some of the herbicide-resistance genes escaped in pollen (most grasses are wind-pollinated) and some escaped in seeds (most grasses have very lightweight seeds).

Does this matter? Many crops, including corn, sunflowers, and, in Eastern Europe and the Middle East, wheat, barley and oats, have wild relatives living nearby. Suppose these wild plants interbred with transgenic crops and became resistant to herbicides or pests. Would they become significant weed problems? Would they displace other plants in the wild, because they would be less likely to be eaten by insects? Even if transgenic crops have no close relatives in the wild, bacteria and viruses can carry genes from one plant to another, even between unrelated species. Could viruses spread unwanted genes into wild plant populations? No one really knows the answers to these questions.

In 2002, a committee of the U.S. National Academy of Sciences studied the potential impact of transgenic crops on the environment. The committee pointed out that crops modified by both traditional breeding methods and recombinant DNA technologies have the potential to cause major changes in the environment. In addition, the committee found that the United States does not have an adequate system for monitoring changes in ecosystems that might be caused by transgenic crops. It recommended more thorough screening of transgenic plants before they are used commercially, and sustained ecological monitoring of both the agricultural and natural environments after commercialization.

What about transgenic animals? Unlike pollen, most domesticated animals, such as cattle or sheep, are relatively immobile. Further, most have few wild relatives with which they might exchange genes, so the dangers to natural ecosystems appear minimal. However, some transgenic animals, especially fish, have the potential to pose more significant threats, because they can disperse rapidly and are nearly impossible to recapture. If they were more aggressive, grew faster, or matured faster than wild fish, they might rapidly replace native populations. One possible way out of this dilemma, pioneered by a company called Aqua Bounty, is to raise only sterile transgenic fish, so that any escapees would die without reproducing and thus have minimal impact on natural ecosystems.

Should the Genome of Humans Be Changed by Biotechnology?

Many of the ethical implications of human applications of biotechnology are fundamentally the same as those connected with other medical procedures. For example, long before biotechnology enabled prenatal testing for cystic fibrosis or sickle-cell anemia, trisomy 21 (Down syndrome) could be diagnosed in embryos by simply counting the chromosomes in cells taken from amniotic fluid (see "Health Watch: Prenatal Genetic Screening" on pp. 258–259). Whether parents should use such

Health Watch

Golden Rice

Rice is the principal food for about two-thirds of the people on Earth (**Fig. E13-2**). Rice provides carbohydrates and some protein, but is a poor source of many vitamins, including vitamin A. Unless people eat enough fruits and vegetables, they often lack sufficient vitamin A, and may suffer from poor vision, immune system defects, and damage to the respiratory, digestive, and urinary tracts. According to the World Health Organization, more than 100 million children suffer from vitamin A deficiency; as a result, each year 250,000 to 500,000 children become blind, principally in Asia, Africa, and Latin America. Vitamin A deficiency typically strikes the poor, because rice may be all they can afford to eat. In 1999, biotechnology provided a possible remedy: rice genetically engineered to contain beta-carotene, a pigment that makes daffodils bright yellow and that the human body easily converts into vitamin A.

Creating a rice strain with high levels of beta-carotene wasn't simple. However, funding from the Rockefeller Institute, the European Community Biotech Program, and the Swiss Federal Office for Education and Science enabled molecular biologists Ingo Potrykus and Peter Beyer to tackle the task. They inserted three genes into the rice genome, two from daffodils and one from a bacterium. As a result, "Golden Rice" grains synthesize beta-carotene (**Fig. E13-3**, upper right).

The trouble was, the original Golden Rice didn't make very much beta-carotene, so people would have had to eat enormous amounts to get enough vitamin A. The Golden Rice community didn't give up. It turns out that daffodils aren't the best source for genes that direct beta-carotene synthesis. Golden Rice 2, with genes from corn, produces more than 20 times more beta-carotene than the original Golden Rice (compare the rice in the upper right and the

▲ **FIGURE E13-3 Golden Rice** Conventional milled rice is white or very pale tan (lower right). The original Golden Rice (upper right) was pale golden-yellow because of its increased beta-carotene content. Second-generation Golden Rice 2 (left) is much deeper yellow, because it contains about 20 times more beta-carotene than did the original Golden Rice.

left-hand sections of Fig. E13-3). About 3 cups of cooked Golden Rice 2 should provide enough beta-carotene to equal the full recommended daily amount of vitamin A. Golden Rice 2 was given, free, to the Humanitarian Rice Board for experiments and planting in Southeast Asia.

However, Golden Rice faces other hurdles. First, many people strongly resist large-scale planting of Golden Rice (or many other transgenic crops). Second, the strain of rice used to make Golden Rice is not a strain that is acceptable to people in southeast Asia. Getting these genes into the popular Asian strains required years of traditional genetic crosses. By 2007, the International Rice Research Institute succeeded in incorporating the carotene-synthesizing genes of Golden Rice into Asian rice strains, and the first field trials of these Golden Rice varieties began in the Philippines in April 2008.

Is Golden Rice the best way, or the only way, to solve the problems of malnutrition in poor people? Perhaps not. For one thing, many poor people's diets are deficient in many nutrients, not just vitamin A. To help solve that problem, the Bill and Melinda Gates Foundation is funding research to increase the levels of vitamin E, iron, and zinc in rice. Further, not all poor people eat mostly rice. In parts of Africa, sweet potatoes are the main source of starches. Eating orange, instead of white, sweet potatoes, has dramatically increased vitamin A intake for many of these people. Finally, in many parts of the world, governments and humanitarian organizations have started vitamin A supplementation programs. In some parts of Africa and Asia, as many as 80% of the children receive large doses of vitamin A a few times when they are very young. Some day, the combination of these efforts may result in a world in which no children suffer blindness from the lack of a simple nutrient in their diets.

▲ **FIGURE E13-2 A field of dreams?** For hundreds of millions of people, rice provides the major source of calories, but not enough vitamins and minerals. Can biotechnology improve the quality of rice and, hence, the quality of life for these people?

Health Watch

Prenatal Genetic Screening

Prenatal diagnosis of a variety of genetic disorders, including cystic fibrosis, sickle-cell anemia, and Down syndrome, requires samples of fetal cells or chemicals produced by the fetus. Presently, three techniques are commonly used to obtain samples for prenatal diagnosis: amniocentesis, chorionic villus sampling, and maternal blood collection.

Amniocentesis

The human fetus, like all animal embryos, develops in a watery environment. A waterproof membrane called the amnion surrounds the fetus and holds the fluid. As the fetus develops, it releases various chemicals (often in its urine) and sheds some of its cells into the amniotic fluid. When a fetus is 15 weeks or older, amniotic fluid can be collected safely by a procedure called **amniocentesis.**

First, the physician determines the position of the fetus by ultrasound scanning. You probably already know how bats find moths at night: They shriek extremely high-frequency sound (far above the limits of human hearing) and listen for echoes bouncing off the moth's body. To locate a fetus with ultrasound, high-frequency sound is broadcast into a pregnant woman's abdomen, and sophisticated instruments convert the resulting echoes into a real-time image of the fetus (**Fig. E13-4**). Using the ultrasound image as a guide, the physician carefully inserts a sterilized needle through the abdominal wall, the uterus, and the amnion (being sure to avoid the fetus and placenta), and withdraws 10 to 20 milliliters of amniotic fluid (**Fig. E13-5**). Amniocentesis carries a slight risk of miscarriage, about 0.5% or less.

Chorionic Villus Sampling

The chorion is a membrane that is produced by the fetus and becomes part of the placenta. The chorion produces many small projections, called villi. In **chorionic villus sampling (CVS),** a physician inserts a small tube into the uterus through the mother's vagina and suctions off a few villi for analysis (see Fig. E13-5). The loss of a few villi does

not harm the fetus. CVS has two major advantages over amniocentesis. First, it can be done much earlier in pregnancy—as early as the 8th week, but usually between the 10th and 12th weeks. This is especially important if the woman is contemplating a therapeutic abortion if her fetus has a major defect. Second, the sample contains far more fetal cells than can be obtained by amniocentesis. However, CVS appears to have a slightly greater risk of causing miscarriages than amniocentesis does. Also, because the chorion is outside of the amniotic sac, CVS does not obtain a sample of the amniotic fluid. Finally, in some cases chorionic cells have chromosomal abnormalities that are in fact not present in the fetus, which complicates karyotyping. For these reasons, CVS is less commonly performed than amniocentesis.

Maternal Blood Collection

A tiny number of fetal cells cross the placenta and enter the mother's bloodstream as early as the 6th week of pregnancy. Separating fetal cells (perhaps as few as one per milliliter of blood) from the huge numbers of maternal cells is challenging, but it can be done. Surprisingly, there is also fetal DNA floating free in the mother's blood. In addition, a variety of proteins and other chemicals produced by the fetus may enter the mother's bloodstream.

Analyzing the Samples

Both amniotic fluid and maternal blood are briefly centrifuged to separate the cells from the fluids (amniotic fluid or plasma, respectively). Biochemical analysis may be performed to measure the concentrations of various proteins, hormones, or enzymes in the fluids. For example, if the amniotic fluid contains high concentrations of an embryonic protein called alpha-fetoprotein, this indicates that the fetus may have certain nervous system disorders, such as spina bifida, in which the spinal cord is incomplete, or anencephaly, in which major portions of the brain fail to develop. Specific combinations of alpha-fetoprotein, estrogen, and other chemicals in maternal serum (called a triple screen, quad screen, or penta screen, depending on whether three, four, or five chemicals are analyzed) indicate the likelihood of Down syndrome, spina bifida, or certain other disorders. However, these biochemical assays do not provide definitive diagnoses, so other tests, such as karyotyping or DNA analysis of fetal cells, or highly detailed ultrasound examination of the fetus, are employed to ascertain whether or not the fetus actually has one of these defects.

Fetal cells, or at least fetal DNA, are required for karyotyping or DNA analysis. Prenatal diagnosis using fetal cells or fetal DNA in maternal blood was mostly an experimental procedure as of 2008, although several companies now offer paternity testing based on fetal cells and DNA in maternal blood. Amniotic fluid contains small numbers of fetal cells, so to obtain enough cells for karyotyping or DNA analysis, the usual procedure is to grow the cells in culture for a week or two. The large number of fetal cells obtained by CVS means that karyotyping and DNA analyses can usually be performed

amniotic fluid

head

neck

torso

▲ FIGURE E13-4 **A human fetus imaged with ultrasound**

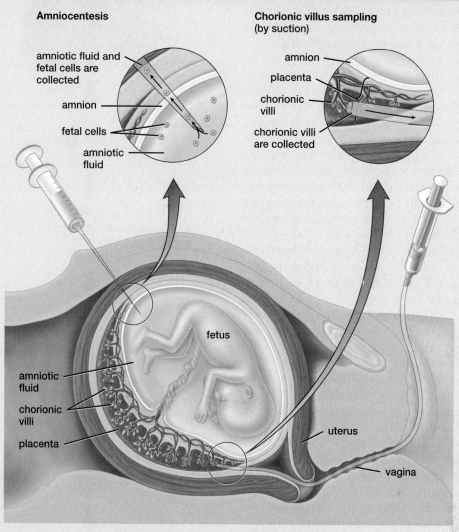

Amniocentesis

amniotic fluid and
fetal cells are
collected

amnion

fetal cells

amniotic
fluid

Chorionic villus sampling
(by suction)

amnion

placenta

chorionic
villi

chorionic villi
are collected

fetus

amniotic
fluid

chorionic
villi

placenta

uterus

vagina

▲ FIGURE E13-5 **Prenatal sampling techniques** The two most common ways of obtaining samples for prenatal diagnosis are amniocentesis and chorionic villus sampling. (In reality, CVS is usually performed when the fetus is much younger than the one depicted in this illustration.)

without culturing the cells first (although some labs do culture the cells for a few days). Karyotyping the fetal cells can show if there are too many or too few copies of the chromosomes, and if any chromosomes show structural abnormalities. Down syndrome, for example, results from the presence of three copies of chromosome 21 (see pp. 195–196).

Various biotechnology techniques can be used to analyze fetal DNA for many defective alleles; for example, RFLP analysis for sickle-cell anemia (see Fig. 13-11) or DNA array analysis for cystic fibrosis (see Fig. 13-12). Although not yet commonly available, some labs use PCR to amplify fetal DNA before testing for Down syndrome or a few other genetic disorders. If widely adopted, PCR amplification would eliminate the need to culture fetal cells obtained by amniocentesis, sometimes for as long as 2 weeks, to obtain a large enough supply of cells and DNA.

You may think that prenatal diagnosis is useful mainly when the parents are contemplating an abortion if the fetus has a serious genetic disorder. However, prenatal diagnosis can also be used to provide better care for an affected infant. For example, if the fetus is homozygous for the sickle-cell allele, some therapeutic measures can be taken beginning at birth. In particular, regular doses of penicillin greatly reduce bacterial infections that otherwise kill about 15% of homozygous children. Further, knowing that a child has the disorder ensures correct diagnosis and rapid treatment during a "sickling crisis," when malformed red blood cells clump and block blood flow. Fetuses with spina bifida are often delivered by planned cesarean section, both to reduce damage to the spinal cord during birth and so that a neurosurgical team can be standing by in case immediate surgery on the infant is necessary. Comparable medical or behavioral interventions can be planned for several other disorders as well.

information as a basis for abortion or to prepare to care for the affected child generates enormous controversy. Other ethical concerns, however, have arisen purely as a result of advances in biotechnology. For instance, should people be allowed to select, or even change, the genomes of their offspring?

On July 4, 1994, a girl in Colorado was born with Fanconi anemia, a genetic disorder that is fatal without a bone marrow transplant. Her parents wanted another child—a very special child. They wanted one without Fanconi anemia, of course, but they also wanted a child who could serve as a donor for their daughter. They went to Yury Verlinsky of the Reproductive Genetics Institute for help. Verlinsky used the parents' sperm and eggs to create dozens of embryos in culture. The embryos were tested both for the genetic defect and for tissue compatibility with the couple's daughter. Verlinsky chose an embryo with the desired genotype and implanted it into the mother's uterus. Nine months later, a son was born. Blood from his umbilical cord provided cells to transplant into his sister's bone marrow. Today, the girl's bone marrow failure has been cured, although she will always have anemia and many accompanying symptoms. Were these appropriate uses of genetic screening? Should dozens of embryos be created, knowing that the vast majority will be discarded? Is this ethical if it is the only way to save the life of another child?

Today's technology allows physicians only to select among existing embryos, not to change their genomes. But technologies do exist to alter the genomes of, for example, bone marrow stem cells to cure SCID. What if biotechnology could change the genes of fertilized eggs (**Fig. 13-14**)? This is not possible yet, but with enough research, the time will come. Suppose it were possible to insert functional *CFTR* alleles into human eggs, thereby preventing cystic fibrosis. Would this be an ethical change to the human genome? What about making bigger and stronger football players? If and when the technology is developed to cure diseases, it will be difficult to prevent it from being used for nonmedical purposes. Who will determine which uses are appropriate and which are trivial vanity?

parents with a genetic disease

fertilized egg with a defective gene

embryo with a genetic defect

cell removed and cultured

treated culture

therapeutic gene

viral vector

genetically corrected cell from culture

egg cell without a nucleus

genetically corrected egg cell

genetically corrected clone of the original embryo

healthy baby

▶ FIGURE 13-14 **Using biotechnology to correct genetic defects in human embryos** In this hypothetical example, human embryos would be derived from eggs fertilized in culture dishes using sperm and eggs from a man and woman, one or both of whom have a genetic disorder. When an embryo containing a defective gene grows into a small cluster of cells, a single cell would be removed from the embryo and the defective gene replaced using an appropriate vector, usually a disabled virus. The repaired nucleus could then be implanted into another egg (taken from the same woman) whose nucleus had been removed. The repaired egg cell would then be implanted in the woman's uterus for normal development.

Case Study revisited
Guilty or Innocent?

DNA profiling is often considered the gold standard of evidence, because of its extremely low error rate. Thanks to the power of DNA profiling, Dennis Maher is now a free man.

Many people exonerated after years in prison have a hard time adjusting to life "outside." Maher, however, is a real success story. Soon after his release, he got a job servicing trucks for Waste Management, a trash pickup and recycling company. He met his wife, Melissa, through an online dating service, using the name DNADennis. They have two children, one named Aliza after his Innocence Project attorney. He's even a movie star of sorts, having been featured in *After Innocence*, an award-winning film following the lives of eight exonerated men. Does Maher harbor any resentment against the system that cost him 19 years of his life? Sure. As he puts it, "I lost what I can never get back." But he also says, "I don't have time to be angry. If I'm an angry person, I won't have the things I have in my life."

If you've ever watched the *CSI* or *Cold Case* TV shows, you know that DNA profiling also helps police all over the country to solve cases. Most police departments in large cities now have a "cold case unit" that takes a fresh look at stale evidence, sometimes leading to convictions many years after a perpetrator seemed to have gotten away with a crime. In Pasadena, California, for example, a 72-year-old woman was murdered in her home in 1987, before DNA profiling had been invented. Although police thought they knew the assailant, they didn't have enough evidence to prove it, so the man was freed. In 2007, however, Pasadena set up an Unsolved Homicide Case Unit. Their first success was to use DNA profiling to identify, arrest, and convict the murderer, now serving 15 years to life in prison.

Consider This

Who are the "heroes" in these stories? There are the obvious ones, of course—Barry Scheck and Peter Neufeld, the founders of the Innocence Project (**Fig. 13-15**), attorney Aliza Kaplan, the law students who spent many hours slogging through poorly labeled boxes searching for evidence, the members of the Pasadena Police Department, and, of course, Dennis Maher himself. But what about Thomas Brock, who discovered *Thermus aquaticus* and its unusual lifestyle in Yellowstone hot springs? Or molecular biologist Kary Mullis, who discovered PCR? Or the hundreds of biologists, chemists, and mathematicians who developed procedures for gel electrophoresis, DNA labeling, and statistical analysis of sample matching?

Scientists often say that science is worthwhile for its own sake, and that it is difficult or impossible to predict which discoveries will lead to the greatest benefits for humanity. Nonscientists, when asked to pay the costs of scientific projects, are sometimes skeptical of such claims. How do you think that public support of science should be allocated? Forty-five years ago, would you have voted to give Thomas Brock public funds to see what types of organisms lived in hot springs?

▲ FIGURE 13-15 **Peter Neufeld and Barry Scheck, cofounders of the Innocence Project**

CHAPTER REVIEW

Summary of Key Concepts

13.1 What Is Biotechnology?

Biotechnology is the use, and especially the alteration, of organisms, cells, or biological molecules to produce food, drugs, or other goods. Modern biotechnology generates altered genetic material by genetic engineering. Genetic engineering frequently involves the production of recombinant DNA by combining DNA from different organisms. When DNA is transferred from one organism to another, the recipients are called transgenic or genetically modified organisms (GMOs). Major applications of modern biotechnology include increasing our understanding of gene function, treating disease, improving agriculture, and solving crimes.

13.2 How Does DNA Recombine in Nature?

DNA recombination occurs naturally through processes such as sexual reproduction; bacterial transformation, in which bacteria acquire DNA from plasmids or other bacteria; and viral infection, in which viruses incorporate fragments of DNA from their hosts and transfer the fragments to members of the same or other species.

13.3 How Is Biotechnology Used in Forensic Science?

Specific regions of very small quantities of DNA, such as might be obtained at a crime scene, can be amplified by the polymerase chain reaction (PCR). The most common regions used in forensics are short tandem repeats (STRs). The STRs are separated by gel electrophoresis and made visible with DNA probes. The pattern of STRs, called a DNA profile, can be used to match DNA found at a crime scene with DNA from suspects with extremely high accuracy.

13.4 How Is Biotechnology Used in Agriculture?

Many crop plants have been modified by the addition of genes that promote herbicide resistance or pest resistance. The most common procedure uses restriction enzymes to insert the gene into a Ti plasmid from the bacterium *Agrobacterium tumefaciens*. The genetically modified Ti plasmid is then used to transform the bacteria, which are allowed to infect plant cells. The Ti plasmid inserts the new gene into one of the plant chromosomes. Using cell cultures, entire plants are produced from the transgenic cells and eventually grown commercially. Plants may also be modified to produce human proteins, vaccines, or antibodies. Transgenic animals may be produced as well, with properties such as faster growth, increased production of valuable products such as milk, or the ability to produce human proteins, vaccines, or antibodies.

13.5 How Is Biotechnology Used to Learn About the Human Genome?

Techniques of biotechnology were used to discover the complete nucleotide sequence of the human genome. This knowledge will be used to learn the identities and functions of new genes, to discover medically important genes, to explore genetic variability among individuals, and to better understand the evolutionary relationships between humans and other organisms.

13.6 How Is Biotechnology Used for Medical Diagnosis and Treatment?

Biotechnology may be used to diagnose genetic disorders such as sickle-cell anemia or cystic fibrosis. For example, in the diagnosis of sickle-cell anemia, restriction enzymes cut normal and defective globin alleles in different locations. The resulting DNA fragments of different lengths may then be separated and identified by gel electrophoresis. In the diagnosis of cystic fibrosis, DNA probes complementary to various cystic fibrosis alleles are placed on a DNA array. Base-pairing of a patient's DNA to specific probes on the array identifies which alleles are present in the patient.

Inherited diseases are caused by defective alleles of crucial genes. Genetic engineering may be used to insert functional alleles of these genes into normal cells, stem cells, or even into eggs to correct the genetic disorder.

13.7 What Are the Major Ethical Issues of Modern Biotechnology?

The use of genetically modified organisms in agriculture is controversial for two major reasons: consumer safety concerns and the potentially harmful effects on the environment. In general, GMOs contain proteins that are harmless to mammals, are readily digested, or are already found in other foods. The transfer of potentially allergenic proteins to normally nonallergenic foods can be avoided by thorough testing. Environmental effects of GMOs are more difficult to predict. It is possible that foreign genes, such as those for pest resistance or herbicide resistance, might be transferred to wild plants, with resulting damage to agriculture and/or disruption of ecosystems. If they escape, highly mobile transgenic animals might displace their wild relatives.

Genetically selecting or modifying human embryos is highly controversial. As technologies improve, society may be faced with decisions about the extent to which parents should be allowed to correct or enhance the genomes of their children.

Key Terms

amniocentesis 258
biotechnology 241
chorionic villus sampling (CVS) 258
DNA probe 247
DNA profile 247
gel electrophoresis 246
genetic engineering 241
genetically modified organism (GMO) 241
plasmid 242
polymerase chain reaction (PCR) 244
recombinant DNA 241
restriction enzyme 250
restriction fragment length polymorphism (RFLP) 252
short tandem repeat (STR) 245
transformation 242
transgenic 241

Thinking Through the Concepts

Fill-in-the-Blank

1. _____ are organisms that contain DNA that has been modified, usually using recombinant DNA technology, or that was derived from other species.

2. _____ is the process whereby bacteria pick up DNA, from the same or other species, from their environment. This DNA may be part of a chromosome, or it may be tiny circles of DNA called _____.

3. The _____ is a technique for multiplying DNA in the laboratory.

4. Matching DNA samples in forensics uses a specific set of small "genes" called _____. The alleles of these genes in different people vary in the _____ of the allele. The pattern of these alleles that a given person possesses is called his or her _____.

5. Pieces of DNA can be separated according to size by a process known as _____. The identity of a specific sample of DNA is usually determined by binding a synthetic piece of DNA called a(n) _____, which binds to the sample DNA by _____.

Review Questions

1. Describe three natural forms of genetic recombination, and discuss the similarities and differences between recombinant DNA technology and these natural forms of genetic recombination.

2. What is a plasmid? How are plasmids involved in bacterial transformation?

3. What is a restriction enzyme? How can restriction enzymes be used to splice a piece of human DNA into a plasmid?

4. Describe the polymerase chain reaction.

5. What is a short tandem repeat? How are short tandem repeats used in forensics?

6. How does gel electrophoresis separate pieces of DNA?

7. How are DNA probes used to identify specific nucleotide sequences of DNA? How are they used in the diagnosis of genetic disorders?

8. Describe several uses of genetic engineering in agriculture.

9. Describe several uses of genetic engineering in human medicine.

10. Describe amniocentesis and chorionic villus sampling, including the advantages and disadvantages of each. What are their medical uses?

Applying the Concepts

1. **BioEthics** In a 2004 Web survey conducted by the Canadian Museum of Nature, 84% of the people polled said they would eat a genetically modified banana that contained a vaccine against an infectious disease, whereas only 47% said they would eat a GM banana with extra vitamin C produced by the action of a rat gene. Do you think that this difference in acceptance of GMOs is scientifically valid? Why or why not?

2. **BioEthics** As you may know, many insects have evolved resistance to common pesticides. Do you think that insects might evolve resistance to *Bt* crops? If this is a risk, do you think that *Bt* crops should be planted anyway? Why or why not?

3. **BioEthics** Discuss the ethical issues that surround the release of genetically modified organisms (plants, animals, or bacteria) into the environment. What could go wrong? What precautions might prevent the problems you listed from occurring? What benefits do you think would justify the risks?

4. **BioEthics** If you were contemplating having a child, would you want both yourself and your spouse tested for the cystic fibrosis gene? If both of you were carriers, how would you deal with this decision?

(MB) *Go to www.masteringbiology.com for practice quizzes, activities, eText, videos, current events, and more.*

Evolution and Diversity of Life

All of Earth's species, including this
strikingly colored chameleon, are linked
by descent from a common ancestor.

Principles of Evolution

Case Study

What Good Are Wisdom Teeth?

HAVE YOU HAD YOUR WISDOM TEETH REMOVED YET? If not, it's probably only a matter of time. Almost all of us will visit an oral surgeon to have our wisdom teeth extracted. There's just not enough room in our jaws for these rearmost molars, and removing them is the best way to prevent the pain, infections, and gum disease that can accompany the emergence of wisdom teeth. Removal is harmless because we don't really need wisdom teeth—they're pretty much useless.

If you've already suffered through a wisdom tooth extraction, you may have found yourself wondering why we even *have* these extra molars. Biologists hypothesize that we have them because our apelike ancestors had them and we inherited them, even though we don't need them. The presence in a living species of structures that have no current essential function, but that *are* useful in other living species, demonstrates shared ancestry among these species.

Some excellent evidence of the connection between useless traits and evolutionary ancestry is provided by flightless birds. Consider the ostrich, a bird that can grow to 8 feet tall and weigh 300 pounds (see the photo at left). These massive creatures cannot fly. Nonetheless, they have wings, just as sparrows and ducks do. Why do ostriches have wings? Because the common ancestor of sparrows, ducks, and ostriches had wings, as do all of its descendants, even those that cannot fly. The bodies of today's organisms may contain now-useless hand-me-downs from their ancestors.

At a Glance

14.1 HOW DID EVOLUTIONARY THOUGHT DEVELOP?

When you began studying biology, you may not have seen a connection between your wisdom teeth and an ostrich's wings. But the connection is there, provided by the concept that unites all of biology: **evolution,** or change over time in the characteristics of populations.

Modern biology is based on our understanding that life has evolved, but early scientists did not recognize this fundamental principle. The main ideas of evolutionary biology became widely accepted only after the publication of Charles Darwin's work in the late nineteenth century. Nonetheless, the intellectual foundation on which these ideas rest developed gradually over the centuries before Darwin's time. (You may wish to refer to the timeline in **Fig. 14-1** as you read the following historical account.)

Early Biological Thought Did Not Include the Concept of Evolution

Pre-Darwinian science, heavily influenced by theology, held that all organisms were created simultaneously by God and that each distinct life-form remained fixed and unchanging from the moment of its creation. This explanation of how life's diversity arose was elegantly expressed by the ancient Greek philosophers, especially Plato and Aristotle. Plato (427–347 B.C.) proposed that each object on Earth was merely a temporary reflection of its divinely inspired "ideal form." Plato's student Aristotle (384–322 B.C.) categorized all organisms into a linear hierarchy that he called the "Ladder of Nature" (**Fig. 14-2**).

These ideas formed the basis of the view that the form of each type of organism is permanently fixed. This view reigned unchallenged for nearly 2,000 years. By the eighteenth century,

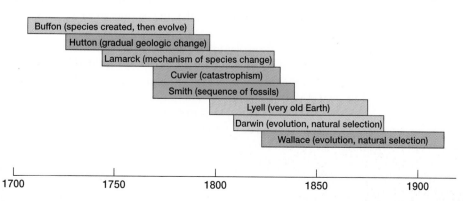

◄ **FIGURE 14-1 A timeline of the roots of evolutionary thought** Each bar represents the life span of a scientist who played a key role in the development of modern evolutionary biology.

Buffon (species created, then evolve)
Hutton (gradual geologic change)
Lamarck (mechanism of species change)
Cuvier (catastrophism)
Smith (sequence of fossils)
Lyell (very old Earth)
Darwin (evolution, natural selection)
Wallace (evolution, natural selection)

1700   1750   1800   1850   1900

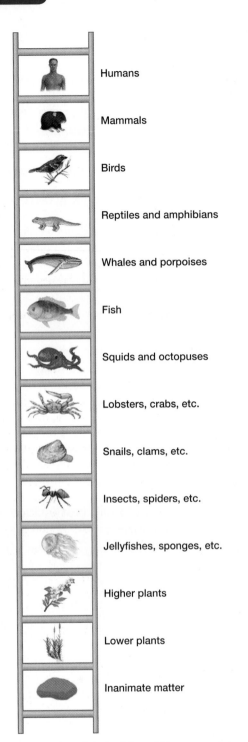

	Humans
	Mammals
	Birds
	Reptiles and amphibians
	Whales and porpoises
	Fish
	Squids and octopuses
	Lobsters, crabs, etc.
	Snails, clams, etc.
	Insects, spiders, etc.
	Jellyfishes, sponges, etc.
	Higher plants
	Lower plants
	Inanimate matter

▲ FIGURE 14-2 **Aristotle's Ladder of Nature** In Aristotle's view, fixed, unchanging species can be arranged in order of increasing closeness to perfection, with inferior types at the bottom and superior types above.

however, several lines of newly emerging evidence began to erode the dominance of this static view of creation.

Exploration of New Lands Revealed a Staggering Diversity of Life

The Europeans who explored and colonized Africa, Asia, and the Americas were often accompanied by naturalists who observed and collected the plants and animals of these previously unknown (to Europeans) lands. By the 1700s, the accumulated observations and collections of the naturalists had begun to reveal the true scope of life's variety. The number of species, or different types of organisms, was much greater than anyone had suspected.

Stimulated by the new evidence of life's incredible diversity, some eighteenth-century naturalists began to take note of some fascinating patterns. They noticed, for example, that each area had its own distinctive set of species. In addition, the naturalists saw that some of the species in a given location closely resembled one another, yet differed in some characteristics. To some scientists of the day, the differences between the species of different geographical areas and the existence of clusters of similar species within areas seemed inconsistent with the idea that species were fixed and unchanging.

A Few Scientists Speculated That Life Had Evolved

A few eighteenth-century scientists went so far as to speculate that species had, in fact, changed over time. For example, the French naturalist Georges Louis LeClerc (1707–1788), known by the title Comte de Buffon, suggested that perhaps the original creation provided a relatively small number of founding species and that some modern species had been "conceived by Nature and produced by Time"—that is, they had changed over time through natural processes.

Fossil Discoveries Showed That Life Has Changed over Time

As Buffon and his contemporaries pondered the implications of new biological discoveries, developments in geology cast further doubt on the idea of permanently fixed species. Especially important was the discovery, during excavations for roads, mines, and canals, of rock fragments that resembled parts of living organisms. People had known of such objects since the fifteenth century, but most thought they were ordinary rocks that wind, water, or people had worked into lifelike forms. As more and more organism-shaped rocks were discovered, however, it became obvious that they were **fossils,** the preserved remains or traces of organisms that had died long ago (**Fig. 14-3**). Many fossils are bones, wood, shells, or their impressions in mud that have been petrified, or converted to stone. Fossils also include other kinds of preserved traces, such as tracks, burrows, pollen grains, eggs, and feces.

By the beginning of the nineteenth century, some pioneering investigators realized that the manner in which fossils were distributed in rock was also significant. Many rocks occur in layers, with newer layers positioned over older layers. The British surveyor William Smith (1769–1839), who studied rock layers and the fossils embedded in them, recognized that certain fossils were always found in the same layers of rock. Further, the organization of fossils and rock layers was consistent: Fossil type A could always be found in a rock layer resting beneath a younger layer containing fossil type B, which in turn rested beneath a still-younger layer containing fossil type C, and so on.

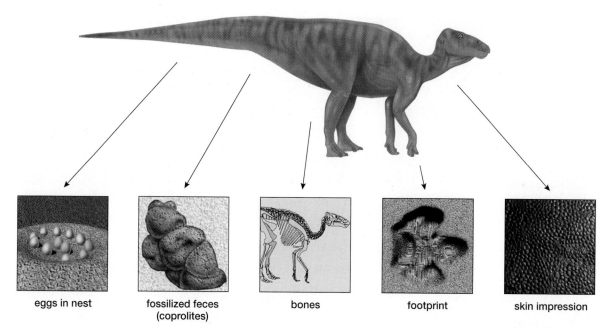

| eggs in nest | fossilized feces (coprolites) | bones | footprint | skin impression |

▲ FIGURE 14-3 **Types of fossils** Any preserved part or trace of an organism is a fossil.

Scientists of the period also discovered that fossil remains showed a remarkable progression. Most fossils found in the oldest layers were very different from modern organisms, and the resemblance to modern organisms gradually increased in progressively younger rocks. Many of the fossils were from plant or animal species that had gone *extinct*; that is, no members of the species still lived on Earth (**Fig. 14-4**).

Putting all of these facts together, some scientists came to an inescapable conclusion: Different types of organisms had lived at different times in the past.

Some Scientists Devised Nonevolutionary Explanations for Fossils

Despite the growing fossil evidence, many scientists of the period did not accept the proposition that species changed and new ones had arisen over time. To account for extinct species while preserving the notion of a single creation by God, Georges Cuvier (1769–1832) advanced the idea of *catastrophism*. Cuvier, a French paleontologist, hypothesized that a vast supply of species was created initially. Successive catastrophes (such as the Great Flood described in the Bible) produced layers of rock and destroyed many species, fossilizing some of their remains in the process. The organisms of the modern world, he speculated, are the species that survived the catastrophes.

Geology Provided Evidence That Earth Is Exceedingly Old

Cuvier's hypothesis of a world shaped by successive catastrophes was challenged by the work of the geologist Charles Lyell (1797–1875). Lyell, building on the earlier thinking of James Hutton (1726–1797), considered the forces of wind, water, and volcanoes and concluded that there was no need to invoke catastrophes to explain the findings of geology. Don't flooding rivers lay down layers of sediment? Don't lava flows produce layers of

basalt? Shouldn't we conclude, then, that layers of rock are evidence of ordinary natural processes, occurring repeatedly over long periods of time? This concept, that Earth's present landscape was produced by past action of the same gradual geological processes that we observe today, is called *uniformitarianism*. Acceptance of uniformitarianism by scientists of the time had a profound impact, because the idea implies that Earth is very old.

Before the 1830 publication of Lyell's evidence in support of uniformitarianism, few scientists suspected that Earth could be more than a few thousand years old. Counting generations in the Old Testament, for example, yields a maximum age of 4,000 to 6,000 years. An Earth this young poses problems for the idea that life has evolved. For example, ancient writers such as Aristotle described wolves, deer, lions, and other organisms that were identical to those present in Europe more than 2,000 years later. If organisms had changed so little over that time, how could whole new species possibly have arisen if Earth was created only a couple of thousand years before Aristotle's time?

But if, as Lyell suggested, rock layers thousands of feet thick were produced by slow, natural processes, then Earth must be old indeed, many millions of years old. Lyell, in fact, concluded that Earth was eternal. Modern geologists estimate that Earth is about 4.5 billion years old (see "Scientific Inquiry: How Do We Know How Old a Fossil Is?" on p. 324).

Lyell (and his intellectual predecessor Hutton) showed that there was enough time for evolution to occur. But what was the mechanism? What process could cause evolution?

Some Pre-Darwin Biologists Proposed Mechanisms for Evolution

One of the first scientists to propose a mechanism for evolution was the French biologist Jean Baptiste Lamarck (1744–1829). Lamarck was impressed by the sequences of organisms in the rock layers. He observed that older fossils tend

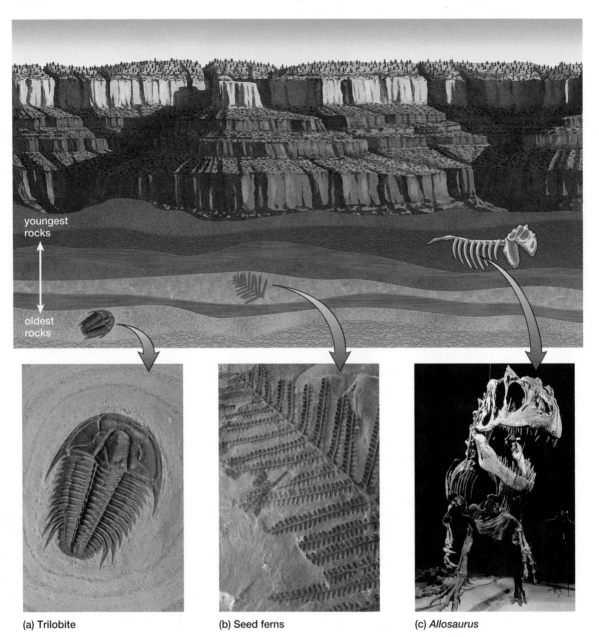

youngest
rocks

oldest
rocks

(a) Trilobite   (b) Seed ferns   (c) *Allosaurus*

▲ FIGURE 14-4 **Fossils of extinct organisms** Fossils provide strong support for the idea that today's organisms were not created all at once but arose over time by the process of evolution. If all species had been created simultaneously, we would not expect **(a)** the earliest trilobites to be found in older rock layers than **(b)** the earliest seed ferns, which in turn would not be expected in older layers than **(c)** dinosaurs, such as *Allosaurus*. Trilobites first appeared about 520 million years ago, seed ferns about 380 million years ago, and dinosaurs about 230 million years ago.

to be simple, whereas younger fossils tend to be more complex and more like existing organisms. In 1801, Lamarck hypothesized that organisms evolved through the inheritance of acquired characteristics, a process in which the bodies of living organisms are modified through the use or disuse of parts, and these modifications are inherited by offspring. Why would bodies be modified? Lamarck proposed that all organisms possess an innate drive for perfection. For example, if ancestral giraffes tried to improve their lot by stretching upward to feed on leaves that grow high up in trees, their necks became slightly longer as a result. Their offspring would inherit these longer necks and then stretch even farther to reach still higher leaves.

Eventually, this process would produce modern giraffes with very long necks indeed.

Today, we understand how inheritance works and can see that Lamarck's proposed evolutionary process could not work as he described it. Acquired characteristics are not inherited. The fact that a prospective father pumps iron doesn't mean that his child will look like a champion body-builder. Remember, though, that in Lamarck's time the principles of inheritance had not yet been discovered. (Gregor Mendel was born a few years before Lamarck's death, and his work with inheritance in pea plants was not universally recognized until 1900—see pp. 181–182.) In any case, Lamarck's insight that inheritance plays an important role in evolution had an important influence on the later biologists who discovered the key mechanism of evolution.

Darwin and Wallace Proposed a Mechanism of Evolution

By the mid-1800s, a growing number of biologists had concluded that present-day species had evolved from earlier ones. But how? In 1858, Charles Darwin (1809–1882) and Alfred Russel Wallace (1823–1913), working separately, provided convincing evidence that evolution was driven by a simple yet powerful process.

Although their social and educational backgrounds were very different, Darwin and Wallace were quite similar in some respects. Both had traveled extensively in the tropics and had studied the plants and animals living there. Both found that some species differed in only a few features (**Fig. 14-5**). Both were familiar with the fossils that had been discovered, which showed a trend toward increasing complexity through time. Finally, both were aware of the studies of Hutton and Lyell, who had proposed that Earth is extremely ancient. These facts suggested to both Darwin and Wallace that species change over time. Both men sought a mechanism that might cause such evolutionary change.

Of the two, Darwin was the first to propose a mechanism for evolution, which he described in a paper he wrote in 1842. But he did not submit the paper for publication, perhaps because he was fearful of the controversy that publication would cause. Some historians wonder if Darwin would ever have pub-

licized his ideas had he not received, 16 years later, a draft of a paper by Wallace that outlined ideas remarkably similar to Darwin's own. Darwin realized that he could delay no longer.

In separate but similar papers that were presented to the Linnaean Society in London in 1858, Darwin and Wallace each described the same mechanism for evolution. Initially, their papers had little impact. The secretary of the society, in fact, wrote in his annual report that nothing very interesting happened that year. Fortunately, the next year, Darwin published his monumental book, *On the Origin of Species by Means of Natural Selection*, which attracted a great deal of attention to the new ideas about how species evolve. (To learn more about Darwin's life, see "Scientific Inquiry: Charles Darwin—Nature Was His Laboratory" on p. 272.)

14.2 HOW DOES NATURAL SELECTION WORK?

Darwin and Wallace proposed that life's huge variety of excellent designs arose by a process of descent with modification, in which individuals in each generation differ slightly from the members of the preceding generation. Over long stretches of time, these small differences accumulate to produce major transformations.

Darwin and Wallace's Theory Rests on Four Postulates

The chain of logic that led Darwin and Wallace to their proposed process of evolution turns out to be surprisingly simple and

◄ FIGURE 14-5 **Darwin's finches, residents of the Galápagos Islands** Darwin studied a group of closely related species of finches on the Galápagos Islands. Each species specializes in eating a different type of food and has a beak of characteristic size and shape, because natural selection has favored the individuals best suited to exploit each local food source efficiently.

(a) Large ground finch, beak suited to large seeds

(b) Small ground finch, beak suited to small seeds

(c) Warbler finch, beak suited to insects

(d) Vegetarian tree finch, beak suited to leaves

Scientific Inquiry

Charles Darwin—Nature Was His Laboratory

In 1831, when Charles Darwin was 22 years old (**Fig. E14-1**), he secured a position as "gentleman companion" to Captain Robert Fitzroy of the HMS *Beagle*. The Beagle soon embarked on a 5-year surveying expedition along the coastline of South America and then around the world.

Darwin's voyage on the *Beagle* sowed the seeds for his theory of evolution. In addition to his duties as companion to the captain, Darwin served as the expedition's official naturalist, whose task was to observe and collect geological and biological specimens. The *Beagle* sailed to South America and made many stops along its coast. There Darwin observed the plants and animals of the tropics and was stunned by the greater diversity of species compared with that of Europe.

Although he had boarded the *Beagle* convinced of the permanence of species, Darwin's experiences soon led him to doubt it. He discovered a snake with rudimentary hind limbs, calling it "the passage by which Nature joins the lizards to the snakes" (**Fig. E14-2**). Darwin also noticed that penguins used their wings to paddle through the water rather than fly through the air, and he observed a snake that had no rattles but vibrated its tail like a rattlesnake. If a creator had individually created each animal in its present form, to suit its present environment, what could be the purpose behind these makeshift arrangements?

Perhaps the most significant stopover of the voyage was the month spent on the Galápagos Islands off the northwestern coast of South America. There, Darwin found

▲ **FIGURE E14-2 The vestigial remnants of hind legs in a snake** Some snakes have small "spurs" where their distant ancestors had rear legs. In some species, these vestigial structures even retain claws.

huge tortoises. Different islands were home to distinctively different types of tortoises. Darwin also found several types of finches and, as with the tortoises, different islands had slightly different finches. Could the differences in these organisms have arisen after they became isolated from one another on separate islands? The diversity of tortoises and finches haunted him for years afterward.

In 1836, Darwin returned to England and became established as one of the foremost naturalists of his time. But the problem of how isolated populations come to differ from each other gnawed constantly at his mind.

From his experience as a naturalist, Darwin realized that members of a species typically compete with one another for survival. He also recognized that the competition's winners and losers were determined not by chance, but by the characteristics and abilities of the individual competitors. As his colleague Alfred Wallace put it, "Those which, year by year, survived this terrible destruction must be, on the whole, those which have some little superiority enabling them to escape each special form of death to which the great majority succumbed." Darwin understood that if these "little superiorities" were inherited by their possessors' offspring, species would evolve by natural selection. He wrote that "under these circumstances favorable variations would tend to be preserved, and unfavorable ones to be destroyed" and that "the result . . . would be the formation of new species. Here, then, I had at last got a theory by which to work."

When Darwin finally published *On the Origin of Species* in 1859, his evidence had become truly overwhelming. Although its full implications would not be realized for decades, Darwin's theory of evolution by natural selection has become a unifying concept for virtually all of biology.

▲ FIGURE E14-1 **A painting of Charles Darwin as a young man**

straightforward. It is based on four postulates about **populations,** or all the individuals of one species in a particular area.

Postulate 1 Individual members of a population differ from one another in many respects.

Postulate 2 At least some of the differences among members of a population are due to characteristics that may be passed from parent to offspring.

Postulate 3 In each generation, some individuals in a population survive and reproduce successfully but others do not.

Postulate 4 The fate of individuals is not determined entirely by chance or luck. Instead, an individual's likelihood of survival and reproduction depends on its characteristics. Individuals with advantageous traits survive longest and leave the most offspring, a process known as **natural selection.**

Darwin and Wallace understood that if all four postulates were true, populations would inevitably change over time. If members of a population have different traits, and if the individuals that are best suited to their environment leave more offspring, and if those individuals pass their favorable traits to the next generation, then the favorable traits will be more common in subsequent generations. The characteristics of the population will change slightly with each generation. This process is evolution by natural selection.

Are the four postulates true? Darwin thought so, and devoted much of *On the Origin of Species* to describing supporting evidence. Let's briefly examine each postulate, in some cases with the advantage of knowledge that was not available to Darwin and Wallace.

Postulate 1: Individuals in a Population Vary

The accuracy of postulate 1 is apparent to anyone who has glanced around a crowded room. People differ in size, eye color, skin color, and many other physical features. Similar variability is present in populations of other organisms, although it may be less obvious to the casual observer (**Fig. 14-6**). We now know that the variations in natural populations arise purely by chance, as a result of random mutations in DNA (see pp. 213–214, 229–231). Thus, the differences among individuals extend to the molecular level. The reason that DNA tests can match blood from a crime scene to a suspect is that each person's exact DNA sequence is unique.

Postulate 2: Traits Are Passed from Parent to Offspring

The principles of genetics had not yet been discovered when Darwin published *On the Origin of Species*. Therefore, although observation of people, pets, and farm animals seemed to show that offspring generally resemble their parents, Darwin and Wallace did not have scientific evidence in support of postulate 2. Mendel's later work, however, demonstrated conclusively that particular traits can be passed to offspring. Since Mendel's time, genetics researchers have produced a detailed picture of how inheritance works.

▲ FIGURE 14-6 **Variation in a population of snails** Although these snails are all members of the same population, no two are exactly alike.

QUESTION Is sexual reproduction required to generate the variability in structures and behaviors that is necessary for natural selection?

Postulate 3: Some Individuals Fail to Survive and Reproduce

Darwin's formulation of postulate 3 was heavily influenced by Thomas Malthus's *Essay on the Principle of Population* (1798), which described the perils of unchecked growth of human populations. Darwin was keenly aware that organisms can produce far more offspring than are required merely to replace the parents. He calculated, for example, that a single pair of elephants would multiply to a population of 19 million in 750 years if each descendant had six offspring.

But we aren't overrun with elephants. The number of elephants, like the number of individuals in most natural populations, tends to remain relatively constant. Therefore, more organisms must be born than survive long enough to reproduce. In each generation, many individuals must die young. Even among those that survive, many must fail to reproduce, produce few offspring, or produce less-vigorous offspring that, in turn, fail to survive and reproduce. As you might expect, whenever biologists have measured reproduction in a population, they have found that some individuals have more offspring than others.

Postulate 4: Survival and Reproduction Are Not Determined by Chance

If unequal reproduction is the norm in populations, what determines which individuals leave the most offspring? A large amount of scientific evidence has shown that reproductive success depends on an individual's characteristics. For example, scientists found that larger male elephant seals in a California population had more offspring than smaller males (because females preferred to mate with large males). In a Colorado population, snapdragon plants with white flowers had more offspring than plants with yellow flowers (because pollinators found white flowers more attractive). In a hospital patient's body, antibiotic-resistant tuberculosis bacteria reproduced more rapidly than antibiotic-sensitive ones (because the patient was being treated with antibiotics). These results, and hundreds of other similar ones, show that in the competition to survive and reproduce, winners are determined not by chance but by the traits they possess.

Natural Selection Modifies Populations over Time

Observation and experiment suggest that the four postulates of Darwin and Wallace are sound. Logic suggests that the resulting consequence ought to be change over time in the characteristics of populations. In *On the Origin of Species*, Darwin proposed the following example: "Let us take the case of a wolf, which preys on various animals, securing [them] by . . . fleetness. . . . The swiftest and slimmest wolves would have the best chance of surviving, and so be preserved or selected. . . . Now if any slight innate change of habit or structure benefited an individual wolf, it would have the best chance of surviving and of leaving offspring. Some of its young would probably inherit the same habits or structure, and by the repetition of this process, a new variety might be formed." The same logic applies to the wolf's prey; the fastest or most alert would be most likely to avoid predation and would pass these traits to its offspring.

Notice that natural selection acts on individuals within a population. Selection's influence on the fates of individuals eventually has consequences for the population as a whole. Over generations, the population changes as the percentage of individuals inheriting favorable traits increases. An individual cannot evolve, but a population can.

Although it is easier to understand how natural selection would cause changes within a species, under the right circumstances, the process might produce entirely *new* species. We will discuss the circumstances that might give rise to new species in Chapter 16.

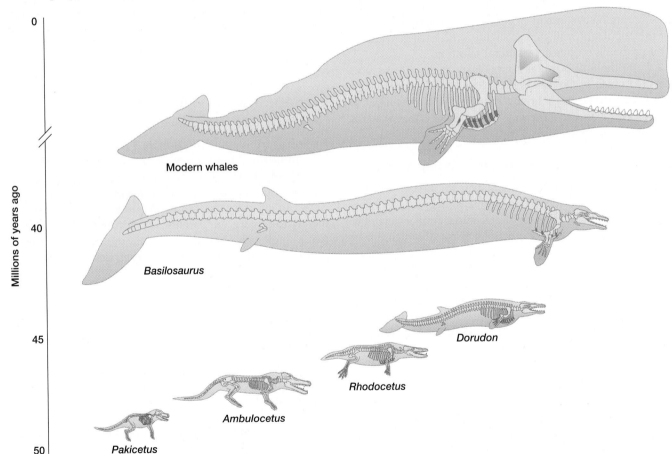

▲ **FIGURE 14-7 The evolution of the whale** During the past 50 million years, whales have evolved from four-legged land dwellers, to semi-aquatic paddlers, to fully aquatic swimmers with shrunken hind legs, to today's sleek ocean dwellers.

QUESTION The fossil history of some kinds of modern organisms, such as sharks and crocodiles, shows that their structure and appearance have changed very little over hundreds of millions of years. Is this lack of change evidence that such organisms have not evolved over that time?

14.3 HOW DO WE KNOW THAT EVOLUTION HAS OCCURRED?

Today, evolution is an accepted scientific theory. You may recall from Chapter 1 that a scientific theory is a general explanation of important natural phenomena, developed through extensive, reproducible observations. An overwhelming body of evidence supports the conclusion that evolution has occurred. The key lines of evidence come from fossils, comparative anatomy (the study of how body structures differ among species), embryology, biochemistry, and genetics.

Fossils Provide Evidence of Evolutionary Change over Time

If it is true that many fossils are the remains of species ancestral to modern species, we might expect to find progressive series of fossils that start with an ancient organism, progress through several intermediate stages, and culminate in a modern species. Such series have indeed been found. For example, fossils of the ancestors of modern whales illustrate stages in the evolution of an aquatic species from land-dwelling ancestors (Fig. 14-7). Series of fossil giraffes, elephants, horses, and mollusks also show the evolution of body structures over time. These fossil series suggest that new species evolved from, and replaced, previous species.

Comparative Anatomy Gives Evidence of Descent with Modification

Fossils provide snapshots of the past that allow biologists to trace evolutionary changes, but careful examination of today's organisms can also uncover evidence of evolution. Comparing the bodies of organisms of different species can reveal similarities that can be explained only by shared ancestry and differences that could result only from evolutionary change during descent from a common ancestor. In this way, the study of comparative anatomy has supplied strong evidence that different species are linked by a common evolutionary heritage.

Homologous Structures Provide Evidence of Common Ancestry

A body structure may be modified by evolution to serve different functions in different species. The forelimbs of birds and mammals, for example, are variously used for flying, swimming, running over several types of terrain, and grasping objects, such as branches and tools. Despite this enormous diversity of function, the internal anatomy of all bird and mammal forelimbs is remarkably similar (Fig. 14-8). It seems inconceivable that the same bone arrangements would be used to serve such diverse functions if each animal had been created separately. Such similarity is exactly what we would

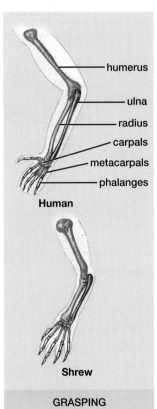

Pterodactyl · Bird · Bat — FLYING

Dolphin · Seal — SWIMMING

Dog · Sheep — RUNNING

Human · Shrew — GRASPING

humerus, ulna, radius, carpals, metacarpals, phalanges

▲ FIGURE 14-8 **Homologous structures** Despite wide differences in function, the forelimbs of all of these animals contain the same set of bones, inherited from a common ancestor. The different colors of the bones highlight the correspondences among the various species.

QUESTION Compile a list of human vestigial structures. For each structure, name the corresponding homologous structure in a nonhuman species.

expect, however, if bird and mammal forelimbs were derived from a common ancestor. Through natural selection, the ancestral forelimb has undergone different modifications in different kinds of animals. The resulting internally similar structures are called **homologous structures,** meaning that they have the same evolutionary origin despite any differences in current function or appearance.

Functionless Structures Are Inherited from Ancestors

Evolution by natural selection also helps explain the curious circumstance of **vestigial structures** that serve no apparent purpose. Examples include such things as molar teeth in vampire bats (which live on a diet of blood and, therefore, don't chew their food) and pelvic bones in whales and certain snakes (**Fig. 14-9**). Both of these vestigial structures are clearly homologous to structures that are found in—and used by—other vertebrates (animals with a backbone). Their continued existence in animals that have no use for them is best explained as a sort of "evolutionary baggage." For example, the ancestral mammals from which whales evolved had four legs and a well-developed set of pelvic bones (see Fig. 14-7). Whales do not have hind legs, yet they have small pelvic and leg bones embedded in their sides. During whale evolution, losing the hind legs provided an advantage, better streamlining the body for movement through water. The result is the modern whale with small, useless pelvic bones.

Have You Ever Wondered

Why Backaches Are So Common?

Between 70% and 85% of people will experience lower back pain at some point in life and, for many people, the condition is chronic. This state of affairs is an unfortunately painful consequence of the evolutionary process. We walk upright on two legs, but our distant ancestors walked on all fours. Thus, natural selection formed our vertically oriented spine by remodeling one whose normal orientation was parallel to the ground. Our spinal anatomy evolved some modifications in response to its new posture but, as is often the case with evolution, the changes involved some trade-offs. The arrangements of bone and muscle that permit our smooth, bipedal gait also generate vertical compression of the spine, and the resulting pressure can, and frequently does, cause painful damage to muscle and nerve tissues.

Some Anatomical Similarities Result from Evolution in Similar Environments

The study of comparative anatomy has demonstrated the shared ancestry of life by identifying a host of homologous structures that different species have inherited from common ancestors, but comparative anatomists have also identified many anatomical similarities that do not stem from common ancestry. Instead, these similarities stem from

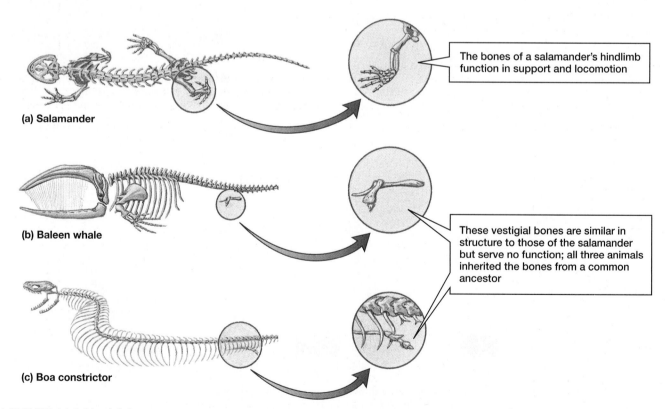

(a) Salamander

The bones of a salamander's hindlimb function in support and locomotion

(b) Baleen whale

(c) Boa constrictor

These vestigial bones are similar in structure to those of the salamander but serve no function; all three animals inherited the bones from a common ancestor

▲ **FIGURE 14-9 Vestigial structures** Many organisms have vestigial structures that serve no apparent function. The **(a)** salamander, **(b)** baleen whale, and **(c)** boa constrictor all inherited hind limb bones from a common ancestor. These bones remain functional in the salamander but are vestigial in the whale and snake.

convergent evolution, in which natural selection causes non-homologous structures that serve similar functions to resemble one another. For example, both birds and insects have wings, but this similarity did not arise from evolutionary modification of a structure that both birds and insects inherited from a common ancestor. Instead, the similarity arose from modification of two different, non-homologous structures that eventually gave rise to superficially similar structures. Because natural selection favored flight in both birds and insects, the two groups evolved superficially similar structures—wings—that are useful for flight. Such outwardly similar but non-homologous structures are called **analogous structures** (Fig. 14-10). Analogous structures are typically very different in internal anatomy, because the parts are not derived from common ancestral structures.

Embryological Similarity Suggests Common Ancestry

In the early 1800s, German embryologist Karl von Baer noted that all vertebrate embryos (developing organisms in the period from fertilization to birth or hatching) look quite similar to one another early in their development (Fig. 14-11). In their early embryonic stages, fish, turtles, chickens, mice, and humans all develop tails and gill slits (also called gill grooves). But among this group of animals, only fish retain gills as adults, and only fish, turtles, and mice retain substantial tails.

Why do vertebrates that are so different have similar developmental stages? The only plausible explanation is that ancestral vertebrates possessed genes that directed the development of gills and tails. All of their descendants still have those genes. In fish, these genes are active throughout development, resulting in adults with fully developed tails and gills. In humans and chickens, these genes are active only during early developmental stages, and the structures are lost or inconspicuous in adults.

(a) Damselfly

(b) Swallow

▲ FIGURE 14-10 **Analogous structures** Convergent evolution can produce outwardly similar structures that differ anatomically, such as the wings of **(a)** insects and **(b)** birds.

QUESTION Are a peacock's tail and a dog's tail homologous structures or analogous structures?

(a) Lemur

(b) Pig

(c) Human

▲ FIGURE 14-11 **Embryological stages reveal evolutionary relationships** Early embryonic stages of a **(a)** lemur, **(b)** pig, and **(c)** human, showing strikingly similar anatomical features.

Modern Biochemical and Genetic Analyses Reveal Relatedness Among Diverse Organisms

Biologists have been aware of anatomical and embryological similarities among organisms for centuries, but it took the emergence of modern technology to reveal similarity at the molecular level. Biochemical similarities among organisms provide perhaps the most striking evidence of their evolutionary relatedness. Just as relatedness is revealed by homologous anatomical structures, it is also revealed by homologous molecules.

Today's scientists have access to a powerful tool for revealing molecular homologies: DNA sequencing. It is now possible to quickly determine the sequence of nucleotides in a DNA molecule and to compare the DNA of different organisms. For example, consider the gene that encodes the protein cytochrome *c* (see Chapters 11 and 12 for information on DNA and how it encodes proteins). Cytochrome *c* is present in all plants and animals (and many single-celled organisms) and performs the same function in all of them. The sequence of nucleotides in the gene for cytochrome *c* is similar in these diverse species (**Fig. 14-12**). The widespread presence of the same complex protein, encoded by the same gene and performing the same function, is evidence that the common ancestor of plants and animals had cytochrome *c* in its cells. At the same time, though, the sequence of the cytochrome *c* gene differs slightly in different species, showing that variations arose during the independent evolution of Earth's multitude of plant and animal species.

Some biochemical similarities are so fundamental that they extend to all living cells. For example:

- All cells have DNA as the carrier of genetic information.
- All cells use RNA, ribosomes, and approximately the same genetic code to translate that genetic information into proteins.

Case Study continued

What Good Are Wisdom Teeth?

Just as anatomical homology can lead to vestigial structures such as human wisdom teeth and the wings of flightless birds, genetic homology can lead to vestigial DNA sequences. For example, many mammal species produce an enzyme, L-gulonolactone oxidase, that catalyzes the last step in the production of vitamin C. The species that produce the enzyme are able to do so because they all inherited the gene that encodes it from a common ancestor. Humans, however, do not produce L-gulonolactone oxidase, so we can't produce vitamin C ourselves and must consume it in our diets. But even though we don't produce the enzyme, our cells do contain a stretch of DNA with a sequence very similar to that of the enzyme-producing gene present in rats and most other mammals. The human version, though, does not encode the enzyme (or any protein). We inherited this stretch of DNA from an ancestor that we share with other mammal species, but in us, the sequence has undergone a change that rendered it nonfunctional. It remains as a vestigial trait, evidence of our shared ancestry.

- All cells use roughly the same set of 20 amino acids to build proteins.
- All cells use ATP as a cellular energy carrier.

The most plausible explanation for such widespread sharing of complex and specific biochemical traits is that the traits are homologies. That is, they arose only once, in the common ancestor of all living things, from which all of today's organisms inherited them.

▶ **FIGURE 14-12 Molecular similarity shows evolutionary relationships** The DNA sequences of the genes that code for cytochrome *c* in a human and a mouse. Of the 315 nucleotides in the gene, only 30 (shaded blue) differ between the two species.

```
human ATGGGTGATGTTGAGAAAGGCAAGAAGATTTTTATTATGAAG
mouse ATGGGTGATGTTGAAAAAGGCAAGAAGATTTTTGTTCAGAAG

human TGTTCCCAGTGCCACACCGTTGAAAAGGGAGGCAAGCACAAG
mouse TGTGCCCAGTGCCACACTGTGGAAAAGGGAGGCAAGCATAAG

human ACTGGGCCAAATCTCCATGGTCTCTTTGGGCGGAAGACAGGT
mouse ACTGGACCAAATCTCCACGGTCTGTTCGGGCGGAAGACAGGC

human CAGGCCCCTGGATACTCTTACACAGCCGCCAATAAGAACAAA
mouse CAGGCTGCTGGATTCTCTTACACAGATGCCAACAAGAACAAA

human GGCATCATCTGGGGAGAGGATACACTGATGGAGTATTTGGAG
mouse GGCATCACCTGGGGAGAGGATACCCTGATGGAGTATTTGGAG

human AATCCCAAGAAGTACATCCCTGGAACAAAAATGATCTTTGTC
mouse AATCCCAAAAAGTACATCCCTGGAACAAAAATGATCTTCGCT

human GGCATTAAGAAGAAGGAAGAAAGGGCAGACTTAATAGCTTAT
mouse GGAATTAAGAAGAAGGGAGAAAGGGCAGACCTAATAGCTTAT

human CTCAAAAAAGTACTAATGAG
mouse CTTAAAAAGGTACTAATGAG
```

14.4 WHAT IS THE EVIDENCE THAT POPULATIONS EVOLVE BY NATURAL SELECTION?

We have seen that evidence of evolution comes from many sources. But what is the evidence that evolution occurs by the process of natural selection?

Controlled Breeding Modifies Organisms

One line of evidence supporting evolution by natural selection is **artificial selection,** the breeding of domestic plants and animals to produce specific desirable features. The various dog breeds provide a striking example of artificial selection (Fig. 14-13). Dogs descended from wolves, and even today, the two will readily crossbreed. With few exceptions, however, modern dogs do not resemble wolves. Some breeds are so different from one another that they would be considered separate species if they were found in the wild. Humans produced these radically different dogs in a few thousand years by doing nothing more than repeatedly selecting individuals with desirable traits for breeding. Therefore, it is quite plausible that natural selection could, by an analogous process acting over hundreds of millions of years, produce the spectrum of living organisms. Darwin was so impressed by the connection between artificial selection and natural selection that he devoted a chapter of *Origin of Species* to the topic.

Evolution by Natural Selection Occurs Today

The logic of natural selection gives us no reason to believe that evolutionary change is limited to the past. After all, inherited variation and competition for access to resources are certainly not limited to the past. If Darwin and Wallace were correct that those conditions lead inevitably to evolution by natural selection, then scientific observers and experimenters ought to be able to detect evolutionary change as it occurs. And they have. Next, we will consider some examples that give us a glimpse of natural selection at work.

Brighter Coloration Can Evolve When Fewer Predators Are Present

On the island of Trinidad, guppies live in streams that are also inhabited by several species of larger, predatory fish that frequently dine on guppies (Fig. 14-14). In upstream portions of these streams, however, the water is too shallow for the predators, and guppies are free of danger from predators. When scientists compared male guppies in an upstream area with ones in a downstream area, they found that the upstream guppies were much more brightly colored than the downstream

(a) Gray wolf

(b) Diverse dogs

▲ FIGURE 14-13 Dog diversity illustrates artificial selection A comparison of **(a)** the ancestral dog (the gray wolf, *Canis lupus*) and **(b)** various breeds of dog. Artificial selection by humans has caused great divergence in the size and shape of dogs in only a few thousand years.

▲ FIGURE 14-14 Guppies evolve to become more colorful in predator-free environments Male guppies (top) are more brightly colored than females (bottom). Some male guppies are more colorful than others. In some environments, brighter males are selected; in other environments, duller males are selected.

guppies. The scientists knew that the source of the upstream population was guppies that had found their way up into the shallower waters many generations earlier.

The explanation for the difference in coloration between the two populations stems from the sexual preferences of female guppies. The females prefer to mate with the most brightly colored males, so the brightest males have a large advantage when it comes to reproduction. In predator-free areas, male guppies with the bright colors that females prefer have more offspring than duller males. Bright color, however, makes guppies more conspicuous to predators and, therefore, more likely to be eaten. Thus, where predators are common, they act as agents of natural selection by eliminating the bright-colored males before they can reproduce. In these areas, the duller males have the advantage and produce more offspring. The color difference between the upstream and downstream guppy populations is a direct result of natural selection.

Natural Selection Can Lead to Pesticide Resistance

Natural selection is also evident in numerous instances of insect pests evolving resistance to the pesticides with which we try to control them. For example, a few decades ago, Florida homeowners were dismayed to realize that roaches were ignoring a formerly effective poison bait called Combat®. Researchers discovered that the bait had acted as an agent of natural selection. Roaches that liked it were consistently killed; those that survived inherited a rare mutation that caused them to dislike glucose, a type of sugar found in the corn syrup used as bait in Combat®. By the time researchers identified the problem, the formerly rare mutation had become common in Florida's urban roach population. (For additional examples of how humans influence evolution, see "Earth Watch: People Promote High-Speed Evolution.")

Unfortunately, the evolution of pesticide resistance in insects is a common example of natural selection in action. Such resistance has been documented in more than 500 species of crop-damaging insects, and virtually every pesticide has fostered the evolution of resistance in at least one insect species. We pay a heavy price for this evolutionary phenomenon. The additional pesticides that farmers apply in their attempts to control resistant insects cost almost $2 billion each year in the United States alone and add millions of tons of poisons to Earth's soil and water.

Experiments Can Demonstrate Natural Selection

In addition to observing natural selection in the wild, scientists have also devised numerous experiments that confirm the action of natural selection. For example, one group of evolutionary biologists released small groups of *Anolis sagrei* lizards onto 14 small Bahamian islands that were previously uninhabited by lizards (**Fig. 14-15**). The original lizards came from a population on Staniel Cay, an island with tall vegetation, including plenty of trees. In contrast, the islands to which the small colonial groups were introduced had few or no trees and were covered mainly with small shrubs and other low-growing plants.

The biologists returned to those islands 14 years after releasing the colonists and found that the original small

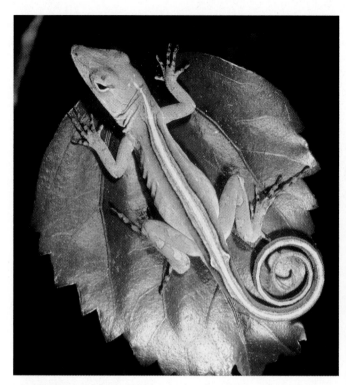

▲ **FIGURE 14-15 Anole leg size evolves in response to a changed environment**

groups of lizards had given rise to thriving populations of hundreds of individuals. On all 14 of the experimental islands, lizards had legs that were shorter and thinner than lizards from the original source population on Staniel Cay. In just over a decade, it appeared, the lizard populations had changed in response to new environments.

Why had the new lizard populations evolved shorter, thinner legs? Long legs allow greater speed, but shorter legs allow for more agility and maneuverability on narrow surfaces. So, natural selection favors legs that are as long and thick as possible while still allowing sufficient maneuverability. When the lizards were moved from an environment with thick-branched trees to an environment with only thin-branched bushes, the individuals with formerly favorable long legs were at a disadvantage. In the new environment, more agile, shorter-legged individuals were better able to escape predators and survive to produce a greater number of offspring. Thus, members of subsequent generations had shorter legs on average.

Selection Acts on Random Variation to Favor the Phenotypes That Work Best in Particular Environments

Two important points underlie the evolutionary changes just described:

- **The variations on which natural selection works are produced by chance mutations.** The bright coloration in Trinidadian guppies, distaste for glucose in Florida cockroaches, and shorter legs in Bahamian lizards were not *produced* by the female mating preferences, poisoned corn syrup, or thinner branches. The mutations that produced each of these beneficial traits arose spontaneously.

Earth Watch

People Promote High-Speed Evolution

You probably don't think of yourself as a major engine of evolution. Nonetheless, as you go about the routines of your daily life, you are contributing to what is perhaps today's most significant cause of rapid evolutionary change. Human activity has changed Earth's environments tremendously, and when environments change, populations adapt or perish. The biological logic of natural selection, spelled out so clearly by Darwin, tells us that environmental change leads inevitably to evolutionary change. Thus, by changing the environment, humans have become a major agent of natural selection.

Unfortunately, many of the evolutionary changes we have caused have turned out to be bad news for us. Our liberal use of pesticides has selected for resistant pests that frustrate efforts to protect our food supply. By overmedicating ourselves with antibiotics and other drugs, we have selected for resistant "supergerms" and diseases that are ever more difficult to treat. Heavy fishing in the world's oceans has favored smaller fish that can slip through nets more easily, thereby selecting for slow-growing individuals that remain small even as mature adults. As a result, fish of many commercially important species are now so small that our ability to extract food from the sea is compromised.

Our use of pesticides, antibiotics, and fishing technology has caused evolutionary changes that threaten our health and welfare, but the scope of these changes may be dwarfed by those that will arise from human-caused modification of Earth's climate. Human activities, especially activities that use energy derived from fossil fuels, modify the climate by contributing to global warming. In coming years, species' evolution will be influenced by environmental changes associated with a warming climate, such as reduced ice and snow, longer growing seasons, and shifts in the life cycles of other species that provide food or shelter.

There is growing evidence that global warming is already causing evolutionary change. Warming-related evolution has been found in a number of plant and animal populations. For example, researchers have discovered that, in northern populations of a mosquito species, the insects' genetically programmed response to changing day length has shifted during the past four decades. (Mosquitoes use day length as a cue to tell them what time of year it is.) As a result, shorter days are now required to stimulate mosquito larvae to enter their overwintering pupal stage, and the transition takes place much later in the autumn. The delay allows the larvae to take advantage of the longer feeding and growing season produced by global warming.

In Canada, red squirrels in a colony closely monitored by scientists now produce litters 18 days earlier, on average, than they did 10 years ago (**Fig. E14-3**). The change is tied to a warming climate, because spring now arrives earlier and spruce trees produce earlier crops of seeds, the squirrels' only food. Squirrels that breed earlier gain a competitive edge by better exploiting the warmer weather and more abundant food. And, because the time at which a squirrel gives birth is influenced by the animal's genetic makeup, early-breeding squirrels pass to their offspring the genes that confer this advantage. As a result, the genetic makeup of the squirrel population is changing, and early-breeding squirrels are becoming more common than later-breeding ones.

The available evidence suggests that global climate change will have an enormous evolutionary impact, potentially affecting the evolution of almost every species. How will these evolutionary changes affect us and the ecosystems on which we depend? This question is not readily answerable, because the path of evolution is not predictable. We can hope, however, that careful monitoring of evolving species and increased understanding of evolutionary processes will help us take appropriate steps to safeguard our health and well-being as Earth warms.

▲ FIGURE E14-3 **Red squirrels have evolved in response to global warming**

• **Natural selection favors organisms that are best adapted to a particular environment.** Natural selection is not a process for producing ever-greater degrees of perfection. Natural selection does not select for the "best" in any absolute sense, but only for what is best in the context of a particular environment, which varies from place to place and which may change over time. A trait that is advantageous under one set of conditions may become disadvantageous if conditions change. For example, in the presence of poisoned corn syrup, a distaste for glucose yields an advantage to a cockroach, but under natural conditions avoiding glucose would cause the insect to bypass good sources of food.

Case Study revisited

What Good Are Wisdom Teeth?

Wisdom teeth are but one of many human anatomical structures that appear to no longer serve an important function (**Fig. 14-16**). Darwin himself noted many of these "useless, or nearly useless" traits in the very first chapter of *Origin* and declared them to be prime evidence that humans had evolved from earlier species.

Body hair is another vestigial human trait. It seems to be an evolutionary relic of the fur that kept our distant ancestors warm (and that still warms our closest evolutionary relatives, the great apes). Not only do we retain useless body hair, we also still have arrector pili, the muscle fibers that allow other mammals to puff up their fur for better insulation. In humans, these vestigial structures just give us goose bumps.

Though humans don't have and don't need a tail, we nonetheless have a tailbone. The tailbone consists of a few tiny vertebrae fused into a small structure at the base of the backbone, where a tail would be if we had one. People born without a tailbone or who have theirs surgically removed suffer no ill effects.

Consider This

Advocates of creationism argue that there are no vestigial organs because if a structure can do *anything*, it cannot be

▲ **FIGURE 14-16 Wisdom teeth** Squeezed into a jaw that is too short to contain them, wisdom teeth often become impacted—unable to erupt through the surface of the gum. The leftmost upper and lower teeth in this X-ray image are impacted wisdom teeth.

considered functionless, even if its removal has no effect. Thus, according to this view, wisdom teeth are not evidence of evolution, because they *can* be used to chew if not removed. Do you find this argument persuasive?

CHAPTER REVIEW

Summary of Key Concepts

14.1 How Did Evolutionary Thought Develop?

Historically, the most common explanation for the origin of species was the divine creation of each species in its present form, and species were believed to remain unchanged after their creation. This view was challenged by evidence from fossils, geology, and biological exploration of the tropics. Since the middle of the nineteenth century, scientists have realized that species originate and evolve by the operation of natural processes that change the genetic makeup of populations.

14.2 How Does Natural Selection Work?

Charles Darwin and Alfred Russel Wallace independently proposed the theory of evolution by natural selection. Their theory expresses the logical consequences of four postulates about populations. If (1) populations are variable, (2) the variable traits can be inherited, (3) there is differential (unequal) reproduction, and (4) differences in reproductive success depend on the traits of individuals, then the characteristics of successful individuals will be "naturally selected" and become more common over time.

14.3 How Do We Know That Evolution Has Occurred?

Many lines of evidence indicate that evolution has occurred, including the following:

- Fossils of ancient species tend to be simpler in form than modern species. Sequences of fossils have been discovered that show a graded series of changes in form. Both of these observations would be expected if modern species evolved from older species.
- Species thought to be related through evolution from a common ancestor possess many similar anatomical structures. An example is the forelimbs of amphibians, reptiles, birds, and mammals.
- Stages in early embryological development are quite similar among very different types of vertebrates.
- Similarities in such biochemical traits as the use of DNA as the carrier of genetic information support the notion of descent of related species through evolution from common ancestors.

14.4 What Is the Evidence That Populations Evolve by Natural Selection?

Similarly, many lines of evidence indicate that natural selection is the chief mechanism driving changes in the characteristics of species over time, including the following:

- Inheritable traits have been changed rapidly in populations of domestic animals and plants by selectively breeding organisms with desired features (artificial selection).

The immense variations in species produced in a few thousand years of artificial selection by humans makes it almost inevitable that much larger changes would be wrought by hundreds of millions of years of natural selection.

• Evolution can be observed today. Both natural and human activities drastically change the environment over short periods of time. Inherited characteristics of species have been observed to change significantly in response to such environmental changes.

Key Terms

analogous structure *277*	homologous structure *276*
artificial selection *279*	natural selection *273*
convergent evolution *277*	population *273*
evolution *267*	vestigial structure *276*
fossil *268*	

Thinking Through the Concepts

Fill-in-the-Blank

1. The flipper of a seal is homologous with the _____ of a bird, and both of these are homologous with the _____ of a human. The wing of a bird and the wing of a butterfly are described as _____ structures that arose as a result of _____ evolution. Remnants of structures in animals that have no use for them, such as the small hind leg bones of whales, are described as _____ structures.

2. The finding that all organisms share the same genetic code provides evidence that all descended from a(n) _____. Further evidence is provided by the fact that all cells use roughly the same set of _____ to build proteins, and all cells use the molecule _____ as an energy carrier.

3. Georges Cuvier espoused a concept called _____ to explain layers of rock with embedded fossils. Charles Lyell, building on the work of James Hutton, proposed an alternative explanation called _____, which states that layers of rock and many other geological features can be explained by gradual processes that occurred in the past just as they do in the present. This concept provided important support for evolution because it required that Earth be extremely _____.

4. The process by which inherited characteristics of populations change over time is called _____. Variability among individuals is the result of chance changes called _____ that occur in the hereditary molecule _____.

5. The process by which individuals with traits that provide an advantage in their natural habitats are more successful at reproducing is called _____. People who breed animals or plants can produce large changes in their characteristics in a relatively short time, a process called _____.

6. Darwin's postulate 2 states: _____. The work of _____ provided the first experimental evidence for this postulate.

Review Questions

1. Selection acts on individuals, but only populations evolve. Explain why this statement is true.

2. Distinguish between catastrophism and uniformitarianism. How did these hypotheses contribute to the development of evolutionary theory?

3. Describe Lamarck's theory of inheritance of acquired characteristics. Why is it invalid?

4. What is natural selection? Describe how natural selection might have caused differential reproduction among the ancestors of a fast-swimming predatory fish, such as the barracuda.

5. Describe how evolution occurs through the interactions among the reproductive potential of a species, the normally constant size of natural populations, variation among individuals of a species, natural selection, and inheritance.

6. What is convergent evolution? Give an example.

7. How do biochemistry and molecular genetics contribute to the evidence that evolution occurred?

Applying the Concepts

1. In discussions of untapped human potential, it is commonly said that the average person uses only 10% of his or her brain. Is this conclusion likely to be correct? Explain your answer in terms of natural selection.

2. Both the theory of evolution by natural selection and the theory of special creation (which states that all species were simultaneously created by God) have had an impact on evolutionary thought. Discuss why one is considered to be a scientific theory and the other is not.

3. Does evolution through natural selection produce "better" organisms in an absolute sense? Are we climbing the "Ladder of Nature"? Defend your answer.

4. In what sense are humans currently acting as agents of selection on other species? Name some organisms that are *favored* by the environmental changes humans cause.

5. Darwin and Wallace's discovery of natural selection is one of the great revolutions in scientific thought. Some scientific revolutions spill over and affect the development of philosophy and religion. Is this true of evolution? Does (or should) the idea of evolution by natural selection affect the way humans view their place in the world?

(MB) *Go to www.masteringbiology.com for practice quizzes, activities, eText, videos, current events, and more.*

How Populations Evolve

Evolution of a Menace

ON A FEBRUARY DAY IN 2008, a 20-year-old student arrived at the health center at Western Washington University. He had been bothered by a lingering cough for a couple of weeks and, when his symptoms worsened to include a fever and vomiting, he sought medical attention. The health center staff quickly determined that the student had pneumonia, and began treatment. His condition, however, deteriorated, and he was transferred to the local hospital. A few days later, he died.

Why couldn't doctors save a previously healthy young man from a normally curable disease? Because the victim's pneumonia was caused by methicillin-resistant *Staphylococcus aureus* (MRSA) bacteria. *Staphylococcus aureus*, sometimes referred to as "staph," is a common bacterium that can infect the skin, blood, or respiratory system. Many staph infections can be successfully treated with antibiotics, but MRSA bacteria are antibiotic resistant and cannot be killed by many of the most commonly used antibiotics. Until about 10 years ago, MRSA infections occurred almost exclusively in hospitals. Today, however, resistant staph is widespread, and more than 10% of MRSA infections occur in non-hospital settings.

In the United States, MRSA infections kill about 19,000 people each year. And, unfortunately, *Staphylococcus* is by no means the only disease-causing bacterium that is becoming less susceptible to antibiotic drugs. For example, antibiotic resistance has also appeared in the bacteria that cause tuberculosis, a disease that kills almost 2 million people each year. In an increasing number of tuberculosis cases, the disease does not respond to any of the drugs commonly used to treat it. Drug resistance is also common in the bacteria that cause food poisoning, blood poisoning, dysentery, pneumonia, gonorrhea, meningitis, and urinary tract infections. We are experiencing a global onslaught of resistant "supergerms," and are facing the specter of diseases that cannot be cured.

Many physicians and scientists believe that the most effective way to combat the rise of resistant diseases is to reduce the use of antibiotics. Why might such a strategy be effective? Because the upsurge of antibiotic resistance is a consequence of evolutionary change in populations of bacteria, and the agent of this change is natural selection applied by antibiotic drugs. To understand how this crisis arose and to devise a strategy to resolve it, we must have a clear understanding of the mechanisms by which populations evolve.

▲ *Staphylococcus aureus*, a common source of human infections, is among the many bacterial species that have evolved resistance to antibiotics.

At a Glance

15.1 HOW ARE POPULATIONS, GENES, AND EVOLUTION RELATED?

If you live in an area with a seasonal climate and you own a dog or cat, you have probably noticed that your pet's fur gets thicker and heavier as winter approaches. Has the animal evolved? No. The changes that we see in an individual organism over the course of its lifetime are not evolutionary changes. Instead, evolutionary changes occur from generation to generation, causing descendants to be different from their ancestors.

Furthermore, we can't detect evolutionary change across generations by looking at a single set of parents and offspring. For example, if you observed that a 6-foot-tall man had an adult son who stood 5 feet tall, could you conclude that humans were evolving to become shorter? Obviously not. Rather, if you wanted to learn about evolutionary change in human height, you would begin by measuring many humans of many generations to see if the average height is changing over time. Evolution is a property not of individuals but of populations. (A **population** is a group that includes all the members of a species living in a given area.)

The recognition that evolution is a population-level phenomenon was one of Darwin's key insights. But populations are composed of individuals, and the actions and fates of individuals determine which characteristics will be passed to descendant populations. In this fashion, inheritance provides the link between the lives of individual organisms and the evolution of populations. We will therefore begin our discussion of the processes of evolution by reviewing some principles of genetics as they apply to individuals. We will then extend those principles to the genetics of populations.

Genes and the Environment Interact to Determine Traits

Each cell of every organism contains genetic information encoded in the DNA of its chromosomes. Recall from Chapter 9 that a *gene* is a segment of DNA located at a particular place on a chromosome. The sequence of nucleotides in a gene encodes the sequence of amino acids in a protein, usually an enzyme that catalyzes a particular reaction in the cell. At a given gene's location, different members of a species may have slightly different nucleotide sequences, called *alleles*. Different alleles generate different forms of the same enzyme. In this way, various alleles of the gene that influences eye color in humans, for example, help produce eyes that are brown, or blue, or green, and so on.

In any population of organisms, there are usually two or more alleles of each gene. An individual of a diploid species whose alleles of a particular gene are both the same is *homozygous* for that gene, and an individual with different alleles for that gene is *heterozygous*. The specific alleles borne on an organism's chromosomes (its *genotype*) interact with the environment to influence the development of its physical and behavioral traits (its *phenotype*).

Let's illustrate these principles with an example. A black hamster's coat is colored black because a chemical reaction in its hair follicles produces a black pigment. When we say that a hamster has the allele for a black coat, we mean that a particular stretch of DNA on one of its chromosomes contains a sequence of nucleotides that codes for the enzyme that catalyzes the pigment-producing reaction. A hamster with the allele for a brown coat has a different sequence of nucleotides at the corresponding chromosomal position. That different sequence codes for an enzyme that cannot produce black pigment. If a hamster is homozygous for the black allele or is heterozygous (one black allele and one brown allele), its fur contains the pigment and is black. But if a hamster is homozygous for the brown allele, its hair follicles produce no black pigment and its coat is brown (**Fig. 15-1**). Because the hamster's coat is black even when only one copy of the black allele is present, the black allele is considered *dominant* and the brown allele *recessive*.

▶ **FIGURE 15-1 Alleles, genotype, and phenotype in individuals** An individual's particular combination of alleles is its genotype. The word "genotype" can refer to the alleles of a single gene (as shown here), to a set of genes, or to all of an organism's genes. An individual's phenotype is determined by its genotype and environment. Phenotype can refer to a single trait, a set of traits, or all of an organism's traits.

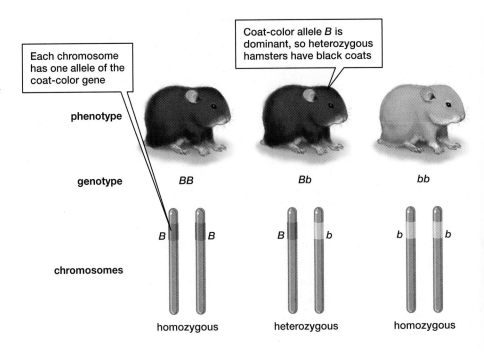

Coat-color allele *B* is dominant, so heterozygous hamsters have black coats

Each chromosome has one allele of the coat-color gene

phenotype

genotype
BB   *Bb*   *bb*

chromosomes
B *B*   *B* *b*   *b* *b*

homozygous   heterozygous   homozygous

The Gene Pool Is the Sum of the Genes in a Population

In studying evolution, looking at the process from the point of view of a gene has proven to be an enormously effective tool. In particular, evolutionary biologists have made excellent use of the tools of a branch of genetics called population genetics, which deals with the frequency, distribution, and inheritance of alleles in populations. To take advantage of this powerful aid to understanding evolution, you will need to learn a few of the basic concepts of population genetics.

Population genetics defines the **gene pool** as the sum of all the genes in a population. In other words, the gene pool consists of all the alleles of all the genes in all the individuals of a population. Each particular gene can also be considered to have its own gene pool, which consists of all the alleles of that specific gene in a population (**Fig. 15-2**). If we added up all the copies of each allele of that gene in all the individuals in a population, we could determine the relative proportion of each allele, a number called the **allele frequency.** For example, the population of 25 hamsters portrayed in Figure 15-2 contains 50 alleles of the gene that controls coat color (because hamsters are diploid and each hamster thus has two copies of each gene). Twenty of those 50 alleles are of the type that codes for black coats, so the frequency of that allele in the population is 0.40 (or 40%), because 20/50 = 0.40.

Evolution Is the Change of Allele Frequencies Within a Population

A casual observer might define evolution on the basis of changes in the outward appearance or behaviors of the members of a population. A population geneticist, however, looks at a population and sees a gene pool that just happens to be divided into the packages that we call individual organisms. So many of the outward changes that we observe in the

individuals that make up the population can also be viewed as the visible expression of underlying changes to the gene pool. A population geneticist, therefore, defines evolution as the changes in allele frequencies that occur in a gene pool over time. Evolution is change in the genetic makeup of populations over generations.

The Equilibrium Population Is a Hypothetical Population in Which Evolution Does Not Occur

It is easier to understand what causes populations to evolve if the characteristics of a population that would *not* evolve are considered first. In 1908, English mathematician Godfrey H. Hardy and German physician Wilhelm Weinberg independently developed a simple mathematical model now known as the **Hardy–Weinberg principle** (for more information about the model, see "A Closer Look at the Hardy–Weinberg Principle" on p. 288). This model showed that, under certain conditions, allele frequencies and genotype frequencies in a population will remain constant no matter how many generations pass. In other words, this population will not evolve. Population geneticists use the term **equilibrium population** for this hypothetical nonevolving population in which allele frequencies do not change, as long as the following conditions are met:

- There must be no mutation.
- There must be no **gene flow.** That is, there must be no movement of alleles into or out of the population (as would be caused, for example, by the movement of organisms into or out of the population).
- The population must be very large.
- All mating must be random, with no tendency for certain genotypes to mate with specific other genotypes.
- There must be no natural selection. That is, all genotypes must reproduce with equal success.

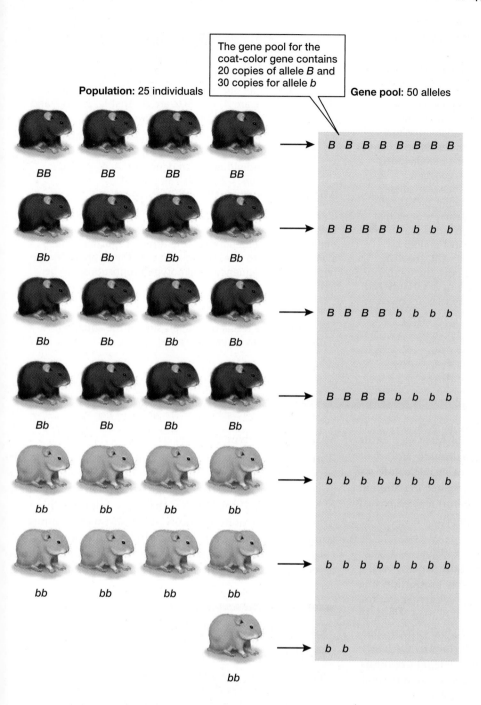

The gene pool for the coat-color gene contains 20 copies of allele *B* and 30 copies for allele *b*

Population: 25 individuals

Gene pool: 50 alleles

◀ FIGURE 15-2 **A gene pool** In diploid organisms, each individual in a population contributes two alleles of each gene to the gene pool.

Under these conditions, allele frequencies in a population will remain the same indefinitely. If one or more of these conditions is violated, then allele frequencies may change: The population will evolve.

As you might expect, few if any natural populations are truly in equilibrium. What, then, is the importance of the Hardy–Weinberg principle? The Hardy–Weinberg conditions are useful starting points for studying the mechanisms of evolution. In the following sections, we will examine some of the conditions, show that natural populations often fail to meet them, and illustrate the consequences of such failures. In this way, we can better understand both the inevitability of evolution and the processes that drive evolutionary change.

15.2 WHAT CAUSES EVOLUTION?

Population genetics theory predicts that the Hardy–Weinberg equilibrium can be disturbed by deviations from any of its five conditions. Therefore, we might predict five major causes of evolutionary change: mutation, gene flow, small population size, nonrandom mating, and natural selection.

Mutations Are the Original Source of Genetic Variability

A population remains in evolutionary equilibrium only if there are no **mutations** (changes in DNA sequence). Most mutations occur during cell division, when a cell must make a copy of its DNA. Sometimes, errors occur during the copying process and

A Closer Look At *The Hardy–Weinberg Principle*

The Hardy–Weinberg principle states that allele frequencies will remain constant over time in the gene pool of a large population in which there is random mating but no mutation, no gene flow, and no natural selection. In addition, Hardy and Weinberg showed that if allele frequencies do not change in an equilibrium population, the proportion of individuals with a particular genotype will also remain constant.

To better understand the relationship between allele frequencies and the occurrence of genotypes, picture an equilibrium population whose members carry a gene that has two alleles, A_1 and A_2. Note that each individual in this population must carry one of three possible diploid genotypes (combinations of alleles): A_1A_1, A_1A_2, or A_2A_2.

Suppose that in our population's gene pool, the frequency of allele A_1 is p and the frequency of allele A_2 is q. Hardy and Weinberg demonstrated that if allele frequencies are given as p and q, then the proportions of the different genotypes in the population can be calculated as:

Proportion of individuals with genotype $A_1A_1 = p^2$
Proportion of individuals with genotype $A_1A_2 = 2pq$
Proportion of individuals with genotype $A_2A_2 = q^2$

For example, if, in our population's gene pool, 70% of the alleles of a gene are A_1 and 30% are A_2 (that is, $p = 0.7$ and $q = 0.3$), then genotype proportions would be:

Proportion of individuals with genotype $A_1A_1 = 49\%$
    (because $p^2 = 0.7 \times 0.7 = 0.49$)
Proportion of individuals with genotype $A_1A_2 = 42\%$
    (because $2pq = 2 \times 0.7 \times 0.3 = 0.42$)
Proportion of individuals with genotype $A_2A_2 = 9\%$
    (because $q^2 = 0.3 \times 0.3 = 0.09$)

Because every member of the population must possess one of the three genotypes, the three proportions must always add up to one. For this reason, the expression that relates allele frequency to genotype proportions can be written as:

$$p^2 + 2pq + q^2 = 1$$

where the three terms on the left side of the equation represent the three genotypes.

---

the copied DNA does not match the original. Most such errors are quickly corrected by cellular systems that identify and repair DNA copying mistakes, but some changes in nucleotide sequence slip past the repair systems. An unrepaired mutation in a cell that gives rise to gametes (eggs or sperm) may be passed to offspring and enter the gene pool of a population.

Inherited Mutations Are Rare But Important

How significant is mutation in changing the gene pool of a population? For any given gene, only a tiny proportion of a population inherits a mutation from the previous generation. For example, a mutant version of a typical human gene will appear in only about one out of every 100,000 gametes produced and, because new individuals are formed by the fusion of two gametes, in only about one of every 50,000 newborns. Therefore, mutation by itself generally causes only very small changes in the frequency of any particular allele.

Despite the rarity of inherited mutations of any particular gene, the cumulative effect of mutations is essential to evolution. Most organisms have a large number of different genes, so even if the rate of mutation is low for any one gene, the sheer number of possibilities means that each new generation of a population is likely to include some mutations. For example, geneticists estimate that humans have between 20,000 and 25,000 different genes, so each person carries between 40,000 and 50,000 alleles. Thus, even if each allele has, on average, only a one in 100,000 chance of mutation, most newborn individuals will probably carry one or two mutations overall. These mutations are new alleles—new variations on which other evolutionary processes can work. As such, they are the foundation of evolutionary change. Without mutations there would be no evolution.

Mutations Are Not Goal Directed

A mutation does not arise as a result of, or in anticipation of, environmental necessities. A mutation simply happens and may in turn produce a change in a structure or function of an organism. Whether that change is helpful or harmful or neutral, now or in the future, depends on environmental conditions over which the organism has little or no control (**Fig. 15-3**). The mutation provides a potential for evolutionary change. Other processes, especially natural selection,

---

Case Study c o n t i n u e d

Evolution of a Menace

If mutations are rare and random, why do mutant alleles that confer antibiotic resistance arise so commonly in bacterial populations? The seemingly inevitable emergence of resistance results in large measure from the huge size of bacteria populations and from their very short generation times. A single drop of human saliva contains about 150 million bacteria, and an entire human body contains hundreds of trillions. With so many bacteria present, even an extremely rare resistance mutation that occurs in only a tiny percentage of the population will be present in some individuals. Also, because many mutations occur during cell division (when DNA replicates and copying errors can occur), rapid reproduction creates many opportunities for mutations to arise. Bacteria reproduce very rapidly, as often as every 15 minutes in some species. This rapid reproduction, taking place in huge populations, results in a high likelihood that mutations leading to antibiotic resistance will be present in bacterial populations.

1 Start with bacterial colonies that have never been exposed to antibiotics

2 Use velvet to transfer colonies to identical positions in three dishes containing the antibiotic streptomycin

3 Incubate the dishes

4 Only streptomycin-resistant colonies grow; the few colonies are in the exact same positions in each dish

▲ **FIGURE 15-3 Mutations occur spontaneously** This experiment demonstrates that mutations occur spontaneously and not in response to environmental conditions. When bacterial colonies that have never been exposed to antibiotics are exposed to the antibiotic streptomycin, only a few colonies grow. The observation that these surviving colonies grow in the exact same positions in all dishes shows that the mutations for resistance to streptomycin were present in the original dish before exposure to streptomycin.

QUESTION If it were true that mutations *do* occur in response to the presence of antibiotic, how would the result of this experiment have differed from the actual result?

may act to spread the mutation through the population or to eliminate it from the population.

Gene Flow Between Populations Changes Allele Frequencies

The movement of alleles between populations, known as gene flow, changes how alleles are distributed among populations. When individuals move from one population to another and interbreed at the new location, alleles are transferred from one gene pool to another. In baboons, for example, individuals routinely move to new populations. Baboons live in social groupings called troops. Within each troop, all the females mate with a handful of dominant males. Juvenile males usually leave the troop. If they are lucky, they join and perhaps even become dominant in another troop. Thus, the male offspring of one troop carry alleles to the gene pools of other troops.

Although movement of individuals is a common cause of gene flow, alleles can move between populations even if organisms do not. Flowering plants, for example, cannot move, but their seeds and pollen can (**Fig. 15-4**). Pollen, which contains sperm cells, may be carried long distances by wind or by animal pollinators. If the pollen ultimately reaches the flowers of a different population of its species, it may fertilize eggs and add its collection of alleles to the local gene pool. Similarly, seeds may be borne by wind or water or animals to distant locations where they can germinate to become part of a population far from their place of origin.

The main evolutionary effect of gene flow is to increase the genetic similarity of different populations of a species. To see why, picture two glasses, one containing fresh water and the other salty seawater. If a few spoonfuls are transferred from the seawater glass to the freshwater glass, the liquid in the freshwater glass becomes saltier. In the same way, movement of alleles from one population to another tends to

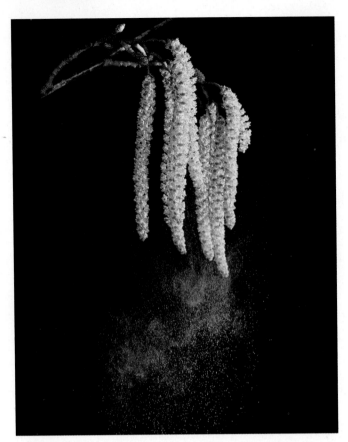

▲ **FIGURE 15-4 Pollen can be an agent of gene flow** Pollen, drifting on the wind, can carry alleles from one population to another.

change the gene pool of the destination population so that it is more similar to the source population.

If alleles move continually back and forth between different populations, the gene pools of the different populations will, in effect, mix. This mixing prevents the development of large differences in the genetic compositions of the populations. But if gene flow between populations of a species is blocked, the resulting genetic differences may grow so large that one of the populations becomes a new species, a process we will discuss in Chapter 16.

Allele Frequencies May Drift in Small Populations

Allele frequencies in populations can be changed by chance events other than mutations. For example, if bad luck prevents some members of a population from reproducing, their alleles will ultimately be removed from the gene pool, altering its makeup. What kinds of bad-luck events can randomly prevent some individuals from reproducing? Seeds can fall into a pond and never sprout; flowers can be destroyed by a hailstorm; organisms can be killed by a fire or by a volcanic eruption. Any event that arbitrarily cuts lives short or otherwise allows only a random subset of a population to reproduce can cause random changes in allele frequencies. The process by which chance events change allele frequencies is called **genetic drift.**

To see how genetic drift works, imagine a population of 20 hamsters in which the frequency of the black coat-color allele *B* is 0.50 and the frequency of the brown coat-color allele *b* is 0.50 (**Fig. 15-5,** top). If all of the hamsters in the population were to interbreed to yield another population of 20 animals, the frequencies of the two alleles would not change in the next generation. But if we instead allow only two, randomly chosen hamsters (the ones circled in Fig. 15-5, top) to breed and become the parents of the next generation of 20 animals, allele frequencies might be quite different in generation 2 (**Fig. 15-5,** center; the frequency of *B* has decreased and the frequency of *b* has increased). And if breeding in the second generation were again restricted to two randomly chosen hamsters (circled in Fig. 15-5, center), allele frequencies might change again in the third generation (**Fig. 15-5,** bottom). Allele frequencies will continue to change in random fashion for as long as reproduction is restricted to a random subset of the population. Note that the changes caused by genetic drift can include the disappearance of an allele from the population, as illustrated by the disappearance of the *B* allele in generation 3 of the example shown in Figure 15-5.

Population Size Matters

Genetic drift occurs to some extent in all populations, but it occurs more rapidly and has a bigger effect in small populations than in large ones. If a population is sufficiently large, chance events are unlikely to significantly alter its genetic composition, because random removal of a few individuals' alleles won't have a big impact on allele frequencies in the population as a whole. In a small population, however, a particular allele may be carried by only a few organisms. Chance events could eliminate most or all examples of such an allele from the population.

To see how population size affects genetic drift, let's return to generation 1 of our imaginary hamster population (see Fig. 15-5, top). Three-quarters of the hamsters are black and one-quarter are brown; the frequencies of alleles *B* and *b* are each 50%. Now imagine two additional populations with same coat color and allele frequencies. However, imagine that one population has only eight individuals in it, whereas the other has 20,000.

Now let's picture reproduction in our two populations. Let's select, at random, a quarter of the individuals in each population and allow them to reproduce, such that each pair of hamsters produces eight offspring and then dies. In the large population, 5,000 hamsters reproduce, yielding a new generation of 20,000. What are the chances that all 20,000 members of the new generation will be brown? Just about nil; that would happen only if all 5,000 randomly chosen breeders were brown (*bb*) hamsters. In fact, it would be extremely unlikely for even 15,000 offspring hamsters to be brown, or for 12,000 to be brown. The most likely outcome is that about a quarter of the breeders will be brown and three-quarters black, which would yield a new generation that is also 25% brown and 75% black (with allele frequencies of *B* = 50% and *b* = 50%), just as in the original population. In the large population, then, we would not expect a major change in allele frequencies from generation to generation.

▶ FIGURE 15-8 **A human example of the founder effect** **(a)** An Amish woman with her child, who suffers from a set of genetic defects known as Ellis–van Creveld syndrome. Symptoms of the syndrome include short arms and legs, **(b)** extra fingers, and, in some cases, heart defects. The founder effect accounts for the prevalence of Ellis–van Creveld syndrome among the Amish residents of Lancaster County, Pennsylvania.

(b) A six-fingered hand

(a) A child with Ellis–van Creveld syndrome

(**Fig. 15-8**). In such a small founder population, this single occurrence meant that the allele was carried by a comparatively high proportion of the Amish founder population (1 or 2 carriers out of 200, versus perhaps 1 in 1,000 in the general population). This high initial allele frequency, combined with subsequent genetic drift, has led to extraordinarily high levels of Ellis–van Creveld syndrome among this Amish group.

Mating Within a Population Is Almost Never Random

Nonrandom mating by itself will not alter allele frequencies in a population. Nonetheless, it can have large effects on the distribution of different genotypes, and thus on the distribution of phenotypes, in the population. Certain genotypes may become more common, which can affect the outcome of natural selection.

The effects of nonrandom mating can play a significant role in evolution, because organisms seldom mate strictly randomly. For example, many organisms have limited mobility and tend to remain near their place of birth, hatching, or germination. In such species, most of the offspring of a given parent live in the same area and thus, when they reproduce, there is a good chance that they will be related to their reproductive partners. Sexual reproduction among relatives is called *inbreeding*.

Because relatives are genetically similar, inbreeding tends to increase the number of individuals that inherit the same alleles from both parents and are therefore homozygous for many genes. This increase in homozygotes can have harmful effects, such as increased occurrence of genetic diseases or defects. Many gene pools include harmful recessive alleles that persist in the population because their negative effects are masked in heterozygous carriers (which have only a single copy of the harmful allele). Inbreeding, however, increases the odds of producing homozygous offspring with two copies of the harmful allele.

In animals, nonrandom mating can also arise if individuals have preferences or biases that influence their choice of mates. The snow goose is a case in point. Individuals of this species come in two "color phases"; some snow geese are white, while others are blue-gray (**Fig. 15-9**). Although both white and blue-gray geese belong to the same species, mate choice is not random with respect to color. The birds exhibit a strong tendency to mate with a partner of the same color. This preference for mates that are similar is known as *assortative mating*.

All Genotypes Are Not Equally Beneficial

In a hypothetical equilibrium population, individuals of all genotypes survive and reproduce equally well; no genotype has any advantage over the others. This condition, however, is probably met only rarely, if ever, in real populations. Even though some alleles are neutral, in the sense that organisms possessing any of several alleles are equally likely to survive and reproduce, not all alleles are neutral in all environments. Any time an allele

▲ FIGURE 15-9 **Nonrandom mating among snow geese** Snow geese, which have either white plumage or blue-gray plumage, are most likely to mate with other birds of the same color.

Case Study continued
Evolution of a Menace

Antibiotic resistance evolves by natural selection. To see how, imagine a hospital patient with an infected wound. A doctor decides to treat the infection with an intravenous drip of penicillin. As the antibiotic courses through the patient's blood vessels, millions of bacteria die before they can reproduce. A few bacteria, however, carry a rare allele that codes for a variant enzyme that destroys any penicillin that comes into contact with the bacterial cell. The bacteria carrying this rare allele are able to survive and reproduce, and their offspring inherit the penicillin-destroying allele. After a few generations, the frequency of the penicillin-destroying allele has soared to nearly 100%, and the frequency of the normal allele has declined to near zero. As a result of natural selection imposed by the antibiotic's killing power, the population of bacteria within the patient's body has evolved. The gene pool of the population has changed, and natural selection, in the form of bacterial destruction by penicillin, has caused the change.

provides, in Alfred Russel Wallace's words, "some little superiority," natural selection favors the individuals who possess it. That is, those individuals have higher reproductive success.

Antibiotic Resistance Illustrates Key Points about Evolution

The example of antibiotic resistance highlights some important features of natural selection and evolution.

Natural selection does not cause genetic changes in individuals. Alleles for antibiotic resistance arise spontaneously in some bacteria, long before the bacteria encounter an antibiotic. Antibiotics do not cause resistance to appear; their presence merely favors the survival of bacteria with antibiotic-destroying alleles over that of bacteria without such alleles.

Natural selection acts on individuals, but it is populations that are changed by evolution. The agent of natural selection, antibiotics, acts on individual bacteria. As a result, some individuals reproduce and some do not. However, it is the population as a whole that evolves as its allele frequencies change.

Evolution is change in the allele frequencies of a population, owing to unequal success at reproduction among organisms bearing different alleles. In evolutionary terminology, the **fitness** of an organism is measured by its reproductive success. In our example, the antibiotic-resistant bacteria had greater fitness than the nonresistant bacteria did, because the resistant bacteria produced greater numbers of viable (able to survive) offspring.

Evolution is not progressive; it does not make organisms "better." The traits favored by natural selection change as the environment changes. Resistant bacteria are favored only when antibiotics are present. At a later time, when the environment no longer contains antibiotics, resistant bacteria may be at a disadvantage relative to other bacteria. Similarly, the long necks and legs of male giraffes are helpful when the animals battle to establish dominance, but are a hindrance to drinking (**Fig. 15-10**). The length of male

(a) A contest for dominance

(b) Drinking at a water hole

▲ **FIGURE 15-10 A compromise between opposing environmental pressures (a)** A male giraffe with a long neck and long legs is at a definite advantage in combat to establish dominance. **(b)** But a giraffe's long appendages force it to assume an extremely awkward and vulnerable position when drinking. Thus, drinking and male–male contests generate opposing evolutionary pressures.

Table 15-1 Causes of Evolution

Process	Consequence
Mutation	Creates new alleles; increases variability
Gene flow	Increases similarity of different populations
Genetic drift	Causes random change of allele frequencies; can eliminate alleles
Nonrandom mating	Changes genotype frequencies but not allele frequencies
Natural and sexual selection	Increases frequency of favored alleles; produces adaptations

Have you ever wondered ?

Why Antibiotics Can't Cure a Cold?

Antibiotics kill or inhibit the reproduction of bacteria, usually by blocking a metabolic pathway that the bacteria use to replicate DNA, synthesize proteins, or build a cell wall. Colds and flu, however, are caused by viruses. Viruses do not have metabolism (as you will learn in Chapter 19) and are not affected by antibiotics. So, taking antibiotics when you have a cold or the flu won't help you get better.

giraffe necks and legs represents an evolutionary compromise between the advantage of being able to win contests with other males and the disadvantage of vulnerability while drinking water.

Table 15-1 summarizes the different causes of evolution.

15.3 HOW DOES NATURAL SELECTION WORK?

Natural selection is not the only evolutionary force. As we have seen, mutation provides variability in heritable traits, and the chance effects of genetic drift may change allele frequencies. Further, evolutionary biologists are now beginning to appreciate the power of random catastrophes in shaping the history of life on Earth; massively destructive events may exterminate thriving and failing species alike. Nevertheless, it is natural selection that shapes the evolution of populations as they adapt to their changing environment. For this reason, we will examine natural selection in more detail.

Natural Selection Stems from Unequal Reproduction

The British economist Herbert Spencer, writing in 1864, coined the phrase "survival of the fittest" to summarize the process that Darwin had named **natural selection.** Natural selection, however, favors traits that increase their possessors' survival only to the extent that improved survival leads to improved reproduction. A trait that improves survival may, for example, increase

the likelihood that an individual survives long enough to reproduce, or might increase an organism's life span and, therefore, its number of opportunities to reproduce. But ultimately, it is reproductive success that determines the future of an individual's alleles, and the prevalence in the next generation of the traits associated with those alleles. Thus, the main driver of natural selection is differences in reproduction: Individuals bearing certain alleles leave more offspring (who inherit those alleles) than do other individuals with different alleles.

Natural Selection Acts on Phenotypes

Although we have defined evolution as changes in the genetic composition of a population, it is important to recognize that natural selection does not act directly on the genotypes of individual organisms. Rather, natural selection acts on phenotypes, the structures and behaviors displayed by the members of a population. This selection of phenotypes, however, inevitably affects the genotypes present in a population, because phenotypes and genotypes are closely tied. For example, we know that a pea plant's height is strongly influenced by the plant's alleles of certain genes. If a population of pea plants were to encounter environmental conditions that favored taller plants, then taller plants would leave more offspring. These offspring would carry the alleles that contributed to their parents' height. Thus, if natural selection favors a particular phenotype, it will necessarily also favor the underlying genotype.

BioFlix ™ Mechanisms of Evolution

Some Phenotypes Reproduce More Successfully Than Others

As we have seen, natural selection simply means that some phenotypes reproduce more successfully than others do. This simple process is such a powerful agent of change because only the fittest phenotypes pass traits to subsequent generations. But what makes a phenotype fit? Successful phenotypes are those that have the best adaptations to their particular environment. **Adaptations** are characteristics that help an individual survive and reproduce.

An Environment Has Nonliving and Living Components

Individual organisms must cope with an environment that includes not only physical factors but also the other organisms with which the individual interacts. The nonliving (*abiotic*) component of the environment includes such factors as climate, availability of water, and minerals in the soil. The abiotic environment plays a large role in determining the traits that help an organism to survive and reproduce. However, adaptations also arise because of interactions with other organisms—the living (*biotic*) component of the environment. As Darwin wrote, "The structure of every organic being is related . . . to that of all other organic beings, with which it comes into competition for food or residence, or from which it has to escape, or on which it preys." A simple example illustrates this concept.

Consider a buffalo grass plant growing in a small patch of soil in the eastern Wyoming plains. Its roots must be able to take up enough water and minerals for growth and reproduction, and to that extent, it must be adapted to its abiotic environment. But even in the dry prairies of Wyoming, this requirement is relatively trivial, provided that the plant is alone and protected in its square yard of soil. In reality, however, many other plants—other buffalo grass plants as well as other grasses, sagebrush bushes, and annual wildflowers— also sprout in that same patch of soil. If our buffalo grass is to survive, it must compete with the other plants for resources. Its long, deep roots and efficient methods of mineral uptake have evolved not so much because the plains are dry as because the buffalo grass must share the dry prairies with other plants. Further, buffalo grass must also coexist with animals that wish to eat it, such as the cattle that graze the prairie (and the bison that grazed it in the past). As a result, buffalo grass is extremely tough. Silica compounds reinforce its leaves, an adaptation that discourages grazing. Over time, tougher, hard-to-eat plants survived better and reproduced more than did less-tough plants—another adaptation to the biotic environment.

Competition Acts As an Agent of Selection

As the buffalo grass example shows, one of the major agents of natural selection in the biotic environment is **competition** with other organisms for scarce resources. Competition for resources is most intense among members of the same species. As Darwin wrote in *On the Origin of Species*, "The struggle almost invariably will be most severe between the individuals of the same species, for they frequent the same districts, require the same food, and are exposed to the same dangers." In other words, no competing organism has such similar requirements for survival as does another member of the same species. Different species may also compete for the same resources, although generally to a lesser extent than do individuals within a species.

Both Predator and Prey Act As Agents of Selection

When two species interact extensively, each exerts strong selection on the other. When one evolves a new feature or modifies an old one, the other typically evolves new adaptations in response. This constant, mutual feedback between two species is called **coevolution.** Perhaps the most familiar form of coevolution is found in predator–prey relationships.

Predation includes any situation in which one organism eats another. In some instances, coevolution between predators (those who do the eating) and prey (those who are eaten) is a sort of "biological arms race," with each side evolving new adaptations in response to "escalations" by the other. Darwin used the example of wolves and deer: Wolf predation selects against slow or careless deer, thus leaving faster, more-alert deer to reproduce and pass on these traits. The resulting alert, swift deer select in turn against slow, clumsy wolves, because such predators cannot acquire enough food.

Sexual Selection Favors Traits That Help an Organism Mate

In many animal species, males have conspicuous features such as bright colors, long feathers or fins, or elaborate antlers. Males may also exhibit complex courtship behaviors or sing loud, complex songs. Although these extravagant features typically play a role in mating, they also seem to be at odds with efficient survival and reproduction. Exaggerated ornaments and displays may help males gain access to females, but they also make the males more conspicuous and thus vulnerable to predators. Darwin was intrigued by this apparent contradiction. He coined the term **sexual selection** to describe the special kind of selection that acts on traits that help an animal acquire a mate.

Darwin recognized that sexual selection could be driven either by sexual contests among males or by female preference for particular male phenotypes. Male–male competition for access to females can favor the evolution of features that provide an advantage in fights or ritual displays of aggression (**Fig. 15-11**). Female mate choice provides a second source of sexual selection. In animal species in which females actively choose their mates from among males, females often seem to prefer males with the most elaborate ornaments or most extravagant displays (**Fig. 15-12**). Why?

One hypothesis is that male structures, colors, and displays that do not enhance survival might instead provide a female with an outward sign of a male's condition. Only a vigorous, energetic male can survive when burdened with conspicuous coloration or a large tail that might make him more vulnerable to predators. Conversely, males that are sick or under parasitic attack are dull and frumpy compared with healthy males. A female that chooses the brightest, most ornamented male is also choosing the healthiest, most vigorous male. By doing so, she gains fitness if, for example, the most vigorous male

▲ **FIGURE 15-11 Competition between males favors the evolution, through sexual selection, of structures for ritual combat** Two male bighorn sheep spar during the fall mating season. In many species, the losers of such contests are unlikely to mate, while winners enjoy tremendous reproductive success. QUESTION If we studied a population of bighorn sheep and were able to identify the father and mother of each lamb born, would you predict that the difference in number of offspring between the most reproductively successful adult and the least successful adult would be greater for males or for females?

provides superior parental care to offspring or if he carries alleles for disease resistance that will be inherited by offspring and help ensure their survival. Females thus gain a reproductive advantage by choosing the most highly ornamented males, and the traits (including the exaggerated ornament) of these flashy males will be passed to subsequent generations.

Selection Can Influence Populations in Three Ways

Natural selection and sexual selection can lead to various patterns of evolutionary change. Evolutionary biologists group these patterns into three categories (**Fig. 15-13**):

- **Directional selection** favors individuals with an extreme value of a trait and selects against both average individuals and individuals at the opposite extreme. For example, directional selection might favor small size and select against both average and large individuals in a population.

▲ FIGURE 15-12 **The peacock's showy tail has evolved through sexual selection** The ancestors of today's peahens were apparently picky when deciding on a male with which to mate, favoring males with longer and more colorful tails.

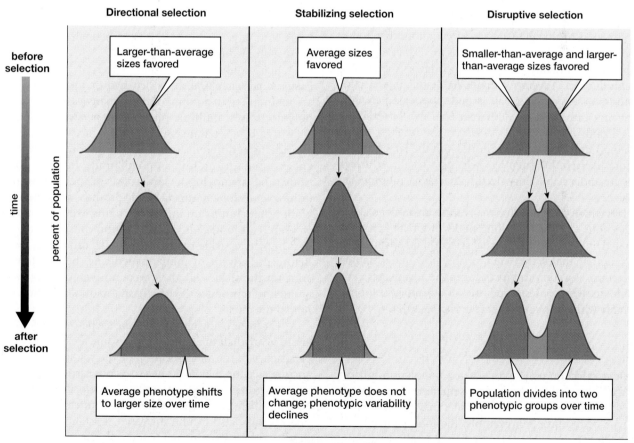

▲ FIGURE 15-13 **Three ways that selection affects a population over time** A graphical illustration of three ways natural and/or sexual selection, acting on a normal distribution of phenotypes, can affect a population over time. In all graphs, the blue areas represent individuals that are selected against—that is, the individuals that do not reproduce as successfully as do the individuals in the purple range.

QUESTION When selection is directional, is there any limit to how extreme the trait under selection will become? Why or why not?

- **Stabilizing selection** favors individuals with the average value of a trait (for example, intermediate body size) and selects against individuals with extreme values.
- **Disruptive selection** favors individuals at both extremes of a trait (for example, both large and small body sizes) and selects against individuals with intermediate values.

Directional Selection Shifts Character Traits in a Specific Direction

If environmental conditions change in a consistent way, a species may respond by evolving in a consistent direction. For example, if the climate becomes colder, mammal species may evolve thicker fur. The evolution of antibiotic resistance in bacteria is an example of directional selection: When antibiotics are present in a bacterial species' environment, individuals with greater resistance reproduce more prolifically than do individuals with less resistance.

Stabilizing Selection Acts Against Individuals Who Deviate Too Far from the Average

Directional selection can't go on forever. What happens once a species is well adapted to a particular environment? If the environment is unchanging, most new variations that appear will be harmful. Under these conditions, we expect species to be subject to stabilizing selection, which favors the survival and reproduction of average individuals. Stabilizing selection commonly occurs when a trait is under opposing environmental pressures from two different sources. For example, among lizards of the genus *Aristelliger*, the smallest lizards have a hard time defending territories, but the largest lizards are more likely to be eaten by owls. As a result, *Aristelliger* lizards are under stabilizing selection that favors intermediate body size.

It is widely assumed that many traits are under stabilizing selection. Although the long necks of giraffes probably originated under directional sexual selection for advantage in combat among males, they are probably now under stabilizing selection, as a compromise between the advantages of being able to win contests and the disadvantage of being vulnerable while drinking water (see Fig. 15-10).

Disruptive Selection Adapts Individuals Within a Population to Different Habitats

Disruptive selection may occur when a population inhabits an area with more than one type of useful resource. In this situation, the most adaptive characteristics may be different for each type of resource. For example, the food source of the black-bellied seedcracker (**Fig. 15-14**), a small, seed-eating bird found in the forests of Africa, includes both hard seeds and soft seeds. Cracking hard seeds requires a large, stout beak, but a smaller, pointier beak is a more efficient tool for processing soft seeds. Consequently, black-bellied seedcrackers have beaks in one of two sizes. A bird may have a large

▲ FIGURE 15-14 **Black-bellied seedcrackers** As a result of disruptive selection, each black-bellied seedcracker has either a large (left) or small (right) beak.

beak or small beak, but very few birds have a medium-sized beak; individuals with intermediate-sized beaks have a lower survival rate than individuals with either large or small beaks. Disruptive selection in black-bellied seedcrackers thus favors birds with large beaks and birds with small beaks, but not those with medium-sized beaks.

Black-bellied seedcrackers represent an example of *balanced polymorphism*, in which two or more phenotypes are maintained in a population. In many cases of balanced polymorphism, multiple phenotypes persist because each is favored by a separate environmental factor. For example, consider two different forms of hemoglobin that are present in some African human populations. In these populations, the hemoglobin molecules of people who are homozygous for a particular allele produce defective hemoglobin that clumps up into long chains, which distort and weaken red blood cells. This distortion causes a serious illness known as sickle-cell anemia, which can kill its victims. Before the advent of modern medicine, people homozygous for the sickle-cell allele were unlikely to survive long enough to reproduce. So why hasn't natural selection eliminated the allele?

Far from being eliminated, the sickle-cell allele is present in nearly half the population in some areas of Africa. The persistence of the allele seems to be the result of counterbalancing selection that favors heterozygous carriers of the allele. Heterozygotes, who have one allele for defective hemoglobin and one allele for normal hemoglobin, suffer from mild anemia but they also exhibit increased resistance to malaria, a deadly disease affecting red blood cells that is widespread in equatorial Africa. In areas of Africa with high risk of malaria infection, heterozygotes must have survived and reproduced more successfully than either type of homozygote. As a result, both the normal hemoglobin allele and the sickle-cell allele have been preserved.

Evolution of a Menace

The evolution of antibiotic resistance in populations of bacteria—such as the MRSA bacteria that cause so many deadly infections—is a direct consequence of natural selection by antibiotic drugs. When a population of disease-causing bacteria begins to grow in a human body, physicians try to halt population growth by introducing an antibiotic drug to the bacteria's environment. Although many bacteria are killed, some surviving bacteria have genomes with a mutant allele that confers resistance. Bacteria carrying the "resistance allele" produce a disproportionately large share of offspring, which inherit the allele. Soon, resistant bacteria predominate within the population.

By introducing massive quantities of antibiotics into the bacteria's environment, humans have accelerated the pace of the evolution of antibiotic resistance. Each year, U.S. physicians write more than 100 million prescriptions for antibiotics; the Centers for Disease Control and Prevention estimates that about half of these prescriptions are unnecessary.

Although medical use and misuse of antibiotics is the most important source of natural selection for antibiotic resistance, antibiotics also pervade the environment outside our bodies. Our food supply, especially meat, contains a portion of the 20 million pounds of antibiotics that are fed to farm animals each year. In addition, Earth's soils and water are laced with antibiotics that enter the environment through human and animal wastes, and from the antibacterial soaps and cleansers that are now routinely used in many households and workplaces. As a result of this massive alteration of the environment, resistant bacteria are now found not only in hospitals and the bodies of sick people but also in our food, water, and soil. Susceptible bacteria are under constant attack, and resistant strains have little competition. In our fight against disease, we have rashly overlooked some basic principles of evolutionary biology and are now paying a heavy price.

Consider This

Because natural selection acts only on existing variation among phenotypes, antibiotic resistance could not evolve if bacteria in natural populations did not already carry alleles that help them resist attack by antibiotic chemicals. Why are such alleles present (albeit at low levels) in bacterial populations? Conversely, if resistance alleles are beneficial, why are they rare in natural populations of bacteria?

CHAPTER REVIEW

Summary of Key Concepts

15.1 How Are Populations, Genes, and Evolution Related?
Evolution is change in the frequencies of alleles in a population's gene pool. Allele frequencies in a population will remain constant over generations only if the following conditions are met: (1) There is no mutation, (2) there is no gene flow, (3) the population is very large, (4) all mating is random, and (5) all genotypes reproduce equally well (that is, there is no natural selection). These conditions are rarely, if ever, met in nature. Understanding what happens when they are not met helps reveal the mechanisms of evolution.

15.2 What Causes Evolution?
Evolutionary change is caused by mutation, gene flow, small population size, nonrandom mating, and natural selection.

- Mutations are random, undirected changes in DNA composition. Although most mutations are neutral or harmful to the organism, some prove advantageous in certain environments. Mutations are rare and do not change allele frequencies very much, but they provide the raw material for evolution.
- Gene flow is the movement of alleles between different populations of a species. Gene flow tends to reduce differences in the genetic composition of different populations.

- In any population, chance events kill or prevent reproduction by some of the individuals. If the population is small, chance events may affect the survival and reproduction of a disproportionate number of individuals who bear a particular allele, thereby greatly changing the allele frequency in the population; this is genetic drift.
- Nonrandom mating, such as assortative mating and inbreeding, can change the distribution of genotypes in a population, in particular by increasing the proportion of homozygotes.
- The survival and reproduction of organisms are influenced by their phenotypes. Because phenotype depends at least partly on genotype, natural selection tends to favor the reproduction of certain alleles at the expense of others.

15.3 How Does Natural Selection Work?
Natural selection is driven by differences in reproductive success among different genotypes. Natural selection proceeds from the interactions of organisms with both the biotic and abiotic parts of their environments. When two or more species exert mutual environmental pressures on each other for long periods of time, both of them evolve in response. Such coevolution can result from any type of relationship between organisms, including competition and predation. Phenotypes that help organisms mate can evolve by sexual selection.

BioFlix™ Mechanisms of Evolution

Key Terms

adaptation 297	competition 298
allele frequency 286	directional selection 299
coevolution 298	disruptive selection 300

Thinking Through the Concepts

Fill-in-the-Blank

1. The _____ provides a simple mathematical model for a nonevolving population, also called a(n) _____ population, in which _____ frequencies do not change over time. Are such populations likely to be found in nature? _____

2. Different versions of the same gene are called _____. These versions arise as a result of changes in the sequence of _____ that form the gene. These changes are caused by _____. An individual with two identical copies of a given gene is described as being _____ for that gene, while an individual with two different versions of that gene is described as _____.

3. An organism's _____ refers to the specific alleles found within its chromosomes, while the traits that these alleles produce are called its _____. Which of these does natural selection act on? _____

4. A random form of evolution is called _____. This form of evolution will only occur in populations that are _____. Two important causes of this form of evolution are the _____ and _____. Which of these would apply to a population started by a breeding pair that was stranded on an island? _____

5. Competition is most intense between members of _____. Predators and their prey act as agents of _____ on one another, resulting in a form of evolution called _____. This results in the evolution of characteristics called _____ that help both predators and their prey survive and reproduce.

6. The evolutionary fitness of an organism is measured by its success at _____. The fitness of an organism can change if its _____ changes.

Review Questions

1. What is a gene pool? How would you determine the allele frequencies in a gene pool?

2. Define *equilibrium population*. Outline the conditions that must be met for a population to stay in genetic equilibrium.

3. How does population size affect the likelihood of changes in allele frequencies by chance alone? Can significant changes in allele frequencies (that is, evolution) occur as a result of genetic drift?

4. If you measured the allele frequencies of a gene and found large differences from those predicted by the Hardy–Weinberg principle, would that prove that natural selection is occurring in the population you are studying? Review the conditions that lead to an equilibrium population, and explain your answer.

5. People like to say that "you can't prove a negative." Study the experiment in Figure 15-3 again, and comment on what it demonstrates.

6. Describe the three ways in which natural selection can affect a population over time. Which way(s) is (are) most likely to occur in stable environments, and which way(s) might occur in rapidly changing environments?

7. What is sexual selection? How is sexual selection similar to and different from other forms of natural selection?

Applying the Concepts

1. In North America, the average height of adult humans has been increasing steadily for decades. Is directional selection occurring? What data would justify your answer?

2. Malaria is rare in North America. In populations of African Americans, what would you predict is happening to the frequency of the hemoglobin allele that leads to sickling in red blood cells? How would you go about determining whether your prediction is true?

3. By the 1940s, the whooping crane population had been reduced to fewer than 50 individuals. Thanks to conservation measures, its numbers are now increasing. What special evolutionary problems do whooping cranes face now that they have passed through a population bottleneck?

4. In many countries, conservationists are trying to design national park systems so that "islands" of natural area (the big parks) are connected by thin "corridors" of undisturbed habitat. The idea is that this arrangement will allow animals and plants to migrate between refuges. Why would such migration be important?

5. A preview question for Chapter 16: A *species* is all the populations of organisms that potentially interbreed with one another but that are reproductively isolated from (cannot interbreed with) other populations. Using the five conditions of the Hardy–Weinberg principle as a starting point, what factors do you think would be important in the splitting of a single ancestral species into two modern species?

(MB) *Go to www.masteringbiology.com for practice quizzes, activities, eText, videos, current events, and more.*

The Origin of Species

Case Study

Lost World

THE STEEP, rain-drenched slopes of Vietnam's Annamite Mountains are remote and forbidding, cloaked in tropical mists that lend an air of mystery and concealment to the forested peaks. As it turns out, this remote refuge conceals a most astonishing biological surprise: the saola, a hoofed, horned mammal that was unknown to science until the early 1990s. The discovery of a new species of large mammal at this late date was a complete shock. After centuries of human exploration and exploitation of every corner of the world's forests, deserts, and savannas, scientists were certain that no large mammal species could have escaped detection. As long ago as 1812, French naturalist Georges Cuvier wrote that "there is little hope of discovering new species of large quadrupeds." And yet, the saola—3 feet high at the shoulder, weighing up to 200 pounds and sporting 20-inch black horns—remained hidden in Annamite Mountain forests, outside the realm of scientific knowledge.

It is surprising that the saola stayed hidden from scientists for so long because people tend to notice large animals. But as the discovery of the saola showed, even relatively conspicuous organisms may remain unknown if they live in a sufficiently remote area. The Annamite Mountains, isolated by inhospitable terrain and the wars fought in Vietnam during the last century, concealed the saola and other undiscovered plant, mammal, and reptile species. Similarly, the remote Foja Mountains of New Guinea hid a new bird species and dozens of new species of butterflies, frogs, and flowering plants, which were not discovered until a 2006 scientific expedition to the region. A recent survey of unexplored underwater habitats in Indonesia revealed more than 50 new species of fish, coral, and shrimp. A curious biologist might wonder why these distinctive species are concentrated in particular geographic areas. But before we can fully consider that question, we will need to explore the evolutionary process by which new species arise.

▲ The saola, unknown to science until 1992, is one of a number of previously undiscovered species recently found in the mountains of Vietnam.

16.1 WHAT IS A SPECIES?

Although Darwin brilliantly explained how evolution shapes complex, amazingly well-designed organisms, his ideas did not fully explain life's diversity. In particular, the process of natural selection cannot by itself explain how living things came to be divided into groups, with each group distinctly different from all other groups. When we look at big cats, we don't see a continuous array of different tiger phenotypes that gradually grades into a lion phenotype. We see lions and tigers as separate, distinct types with no overlap. Each distinct type is known as a species. (Would you like to name a species? See "Links to Everyday Life: Biological Vanity Plates.")

Biologists Need a Clear Definition of Species

Before we can study the origin of species, we must first clarify our definition of the term. Throughout most of human history, "species" was a poorly defined concept. In pre-Darwinian Europe, the word "species" simply referred to one of the "kinds" produced by the biblical creation. In this view, humans could not possibly know the criteria of the creator, but could only attempt to distinguish among species on the basis of visible differences in structure. In fact, "species" is Latin for "appearance."

On a coarse scale, it is easy to use quick visual comparisons to distinguish species. For example, warblers are clearly different from eagles, which are obviously different from ducks. But it is far more difficult to distinguish among different species of warblers, eagles, or ducks. How do scientists make these finer distinctions?

Each Species Evolves Independently

Today, biologists define a **species** as a group of populations that evolves independently. Each species follows a separate evolutionary path because alleles do not move between the gene pools of different species. This definition, however, does not clearly state the standard by which such evolutionary independence is judged. The most widely used standard defines species as "groups of actually or potentially interbreeding natural populations, which are reproductively isolated from other such groups." This definition, known as the *biological species concept*, is based on the observation that **reproductive isolation** (inability to successfully breed outside the group) ensures evolutionary independence.

The biological species concept has at least two major limitations. First, because the definition is based on patterns of sexual reproduction, it does not help us determine species boundaries among asexually reproducing organisms. Second, it is not always practical or even possible to directly observe whether members of two different groups interbreed. Thus, a biologist who wishes to determine if a group of organisms is a separate species must often make the determination without knowing for sure if group members breed with organisms outside the group.

Despite the limitations of the biological species concept, most biologists accept it for identifying species of sexually reproducing organisms. Nonetheless, scientists who study bacteria and other organisms that mainly reproduce asexually must use alternative definitions. Even some biologists who study sexually reproducing organisms prefer species definitions that do not depend on a property (reproductive isolation) that can be difficult to measure. Several such alternatives to the biological species concept have been proposed; one that has gained many adherents is described in Chapter 18 (p. 351).

Appearance Can Be Misleading

Biologists have found that some organisms with very similar appearances belong to different species. For example, the cordilleran flycatcher and the Pacific-slope flycatcher are so similar that even experienced birdwatchers cannot tell them apart (**Fig. 16-1**). Until recently, these birds were considered to be a single species. However, research revealed that the two kinds of birds do not interbreed and are in fact two different species.

Links to *Everyday Life*

Biological Vanity Plates

Looking for a special gift for a friend or loved one? Why not name a species after him or her? Or, for that matter, name one after yourself! Thanks to the BIOPAT project (www.biopat.de), anyone with $3,500 can be immortalized in the Latin name of a newly discovered plant or animal.

Typically, the scientist who discovers and describes a new species is entitled to choose its Latin name. Scientists usually choose a name that describes a trait of the species or perhaps the location where it was found. Sometimes, however, more whimsical choices are made. For example, a recently discovered beetle was named *Agra schwarzeneggeri*, in honor of the California governor and former film star, a frog was named *Hyla stingi* after the British rock star, and a spider was named *Aptostichus stephencolberti* to recognize the satiric news commentator. *Agathidium bushi* and *Agathidium cheneyi* are beetles named for the former U.S. president and vice president.

If you donate money to the BIOPAT project, the name of a new species will be entirely up to you. In return for a contribution that supports efforts to discover and conserve endangered species, the people at BIOPAT will offer you a selection of newly discovered but unnamed species. You can choose your species and pick a name, which is then given an appropriate Latin ending and published in a scientific journal. Your chosen name becomes the official, recognized scientific name of the new species.

In perhaps the most extraordinary example of purchased species naming rights, a newly discovered monkey was named after an online casino (**Fig. E16-1**). In return for a contribution of $650,000, the new species was named *Callicebus aureipalatii*; the species name is Latin for golden palace. The payment will be used for management of the Madidi National Park in Bolivia, where the new species was discovered.

▲ FIGURE E16-1 **The Golden Palace monkey is named after a casino**

Superficial similarity can sometimes hide multiple species. Researchers recently discovered that the species known until now as the two-barred flasher butterfly is actually a group of at least 10 different species. The caterpillars of the different species do differ in appearance, but the adult butterflies are all so similar that their species identities went undetected for more than two centuries after the butterfly was first described and named.

Conversely, differences in appearance do not always mean that two populations belong to different species. For example, bird field guides published in the 1970s list the myrtle warbler and Audubon's warbler as distinct species (**Fig. 16-2**).

(a) Cordilleran flycatcher   (b) Pacific-slope flycatcher

▲ FIGURE 16-1 **Members of different species may be similar in appearance** **(a)** The cordilleran flycatcher and **(b)** Pacific-slope flycatcher are different species.

(a) Myrtle warbler   (b) Audubon's warbler

▲ FIGURE 16-2 **Members of a species may differ in appearance** **(a)** The myrtle warbler and **(b)** Audubon's warbler are members of the same species.

These birds differ in geographic range and in the color of their throat feathers. More recently, scientists determined that these birds are local varieties of the same species. The reason: Where their ranges overlap, these warblers interbreed freely.

16.2 HOW IS REPRODUCTIVE ISOLATION BETWEEN SPECIES MAINTAINED?

What prevents different species from interbreeding? The traits that prevent interbreeding and maintain reproductive isolation are called **isolating mechanisms.** Isolating mechanisms give a clear benefit to individuals. An individual that mates with a member of another species will probably produce no offspring (or unfit or sterile offspring), thereby wasting its reproductive effort and failing to contribute to future generations. Thus, natural selection favors traits that prevent mating across species boundaries. Mechanisms that prevent mating between species are called **premating isolating mechanisms.**

When premating isolating mechanisms fail or have not yet evolved, members of different species may mate. If, however, all resulting hybrid offspring die during development, then the two species are still reproductively isolated from one another. Even if hybrid offspring are able to survive, if these hybrids are less fit than their parents or are themselves infertile, the two species may still remain separate, with little or no gene flow between them. Mechanisms that prevent the formation of vigorous, fertile hybrids between species are called **postmating isolating mechanisms.**

Premating Isolating Mechanisms Prevent Mating Between Species

Reproductive isolation can be maintained by a variety of mechanisms, but those that prevent mating attempts are especially effective. We next describe the most important types of such premating isolating mechanisms.

Members of Different Species May Be Prevented from Meeting

Members of different species cannot mate if they never get near one another. *Geographic isolation* prevents interbreeding between populations that do not come into contact because they live in different, physically separated places (**Fig. 16-3**). However, we cannot determine if geographically

▶ FIGURE 16-3 **Geographic isolation** To determine if these two squirrels are members of different species, we must know if they are "actually or potentially interbreeding." Unfortunately, it is hard to tell, because **(a)** the Kaibab squirrel lives only on the north rim of the Grand Canyon and **(b)** the Abert squirrel lives only on the south rim. The two populations are geographically isolated but still quite similar. Have they diverged enough since their separation to become reproductively isolated? Because they remain geographically isolated, we cannot say for sure.

(a) Kaibab squirrel   (b) Abert squirrel

separated populations are actually distinct species. Should the physical barrier separating the two populations disappear (a new channel might connect two previously isolated lakes, for example), the reunited populations might interbreed freely and not be separate species after all. If they cannot interbreed, then other mechanisms, such as those considered below, must have developed during their isolation. Geographic isolation, therefore, is usually considered to be a mechanism that allows new species to form rather than a mechanism that maintains reproductive isolation between species.

Different Species May Occupy Different Habitats

Two populations that use different resources may spend time in different habitats within the same general area and thus exhibit *ecological isolation*. White-crowned sparrows and white-throated sparrows, for example, have extensively overlapping geographic ranges. The white-throated sparrow, however, frequents dense thickets, whereas the white-crowned sparrow inhabits fields and meadows, seldom penetrating far into dense growth. The two species may coexist within a few hundred yards of one another and yet seldom meet during the breeding season. A more dramatic example is provided by the more than 300 species of fig wasp (**Fig. 16-4**). In most cases, fig wasps of a given species breed in (and pollinate) the fruits of one particular species of fig, and each fig species hosts only one or two species of pollinating wasp. Thus, fig wasps of different species only rarely encounter one another during breeding, and pollen from one fig species is not ordinarily carried to flowers of a different species.

Although ecological isolation may slow down interbreeding, it seems unlikely that it could prevent gene flow entirely. Other mechanisms normally also contribute to reproductive isolation.

▲ **FIGURE 16-4 Ecological isolation** This female fig wasp is carrying fertilized eggs from a mating that took place within a fig. She will find another fig of the same species, enter it through a pore, lay eggs, and die. Her offspring will hatch, develop, and mate within the fig. Because each species of fig wasp reproduces only in its own particular fig species, each wasp species is reproductively isolated.

Different Species May Breed at Different Times

Even if two species occupy similar habitats, they cannot mate if they have different breeding seasons, a phenomenon called *temporal (time-related) isolation*. For example, the spring field cricket and the fall field cricket both occur in many areas of North America but, as their names suggest, the former species breeds in spring and the latter in autumn. As a result, the two species do not interbreed.

In plants, the reproductive structures of different species may mature at different times. For example, Bishop pines and Monterey pines grow together near Monterey on the California coast (**Fig. 16-5**), but the two species release

(a) Bishop pine

(b) Monterey pine

▲ **FIGURE 16-5 Temporal isolation (a)** Bishop pines and **(b)** Monterey pines coexist in nature. In the laboratory they produce fertile hybrids. In the wild, however, they do not interbreed, because they release pollen at different times of the year.

their sperm-containing pollen (and have eggs ready to receive the pollen) at different times: The Monterey pine releases pollen in early spring, the Bishop pine in summer. For this reason, the two species never interbreed under natural conditions.

Different Species May Have Different Courtship Signals

Among animals, elaborate courtship colors and behaviors not only serve as recognition and evaluation signals between male and female, but also prevent mating with members of other species. Signals and behaviors that differ from species to species create *behavioral isolation*. The distinctive plumage and vocalizations of a male bird, for example, may attract females of his own species, whereas females of other species treat these displays with indifference. For example, the extravagant plumes and arresting pose of a courting male greater bird of paradise are conspicuous indicators of his species and there is little chance that females of another species will be mistakenly attracted (**Fig. 16-6**). Among frogs, males are often impressively indiscriminate, jumping on every female in sight, regardless of the species, when the spirit moves them. Females, however, approach only male frogs that utter the call appropriate to their species. If they do find themselves in an unwanted embrace, they utter the "release call," which causes the male to let go. As a result, few hybrids are produced.

Differing Sexual Organs May Foil Mating Attempts

In rare instances, a male and a female of different species attempt to mate. Their attempt is likely to fail. Among animal species with internal fertilization (in which the sperm is deposited inside the female's reproductive tract), the male's and female's sexual organs simply may not fit together. Incompatible body shapes may also make copulation between species impossible. For example, snails of species whose shells have left-handed spirals may be unable to successfully copulate with snails whose shells have right-handed spirals (**Fig. 16-7**). Among plants, differences in flower size or structure may prevent pollen transfer between species because the differing flowers may attract different pollinators. Isolating mechanisms of this type are called *mechanical incompatibilities*.

Postmating Isolating Mechanisms Limit Hybrid Offspring

Premating isolation sometimes fails. When it does, members of different species may mate, and the sperm of one species may reach the egg of another species. Such matings, however, often fail to produce vigorous, fertile hybrid offspring, owing to postmating isolating mechanisms.

One Species' Sperm May Fail to Fertilize Another Species' Eggs

Even if a male inseminates a female of a different species, his sperm may not be able to fertilize her eggs, an isolating mechanism called *gametic incompatibility*. For example, in animals with internal fertilization, fluids in the female reproductive tract may weaken or kill sperm of other species.

Gametic incompatibility may be an especially important isolating mechanism in species, such as marine invertebrate animals and wind-pollinated plants, that reproduce by scattering gametes in the water or in the air. For example, sea

(a) Shells of three snail species

(b) Matching coils   **(c) Non-matching coils**

▲ FIGURE 16-7 **Mechanical incompatibility (a)** The shells of different snail species may coil in different directions. Among the three closely related species shown, two have shells that coil left and one has a shell that coils right. **(b)** Two snails with matching coils can mate, but **(c)** snails of different species with mismatched coiling cannot mate because the mismatch keeps their genitals (arrows) apart.

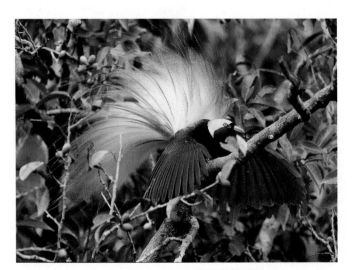

▲ FIGURE 16-6 **Behavioral isolation** The mate-attraction display of a male greater bird of paradise includes distinctive posture, movements, plumage, and vocalizations that do not resemble those of other bird-of-paradise species.

urchin sperm cells contain a protein that allows them to bind to eggs. The structure of the protein differs among species so that sperm of one sea urchin species cannot bind to the eggs of another species. In abalones (a type of mollusk), eggs are surrounded by a membrane that can be penetrated only by sperm containing a particular enzyme. Each abalone species has a distinctive version of the enzyme, so hybrids are rare, even though several species of abalones coexist in the same waters and spawn during the same period. Among plants, similar chemical incompatibility may prevent the germination of pollen from one species that lands on the stigma (pollen-catching structure) of the flower of another species.

Hybrid Offspring May Fail to Survive or Reproduce

If cross-species fertilization does occur, the resulting hybrid may be unable to survive, a situation called *hybrid inviability*. The genetic instructions directing development of the two species may be so different that hybrids abort early in development. For example, captive leopard frogs can be induced to mate with wood frogs, and the matings generally yield fertilized eggs. The resulting embryos, however, inevitably fail to survive more than a few days.

In other animal species, a hybrid might survive but display behaviors that are mixtures of the two parental types. In attempting to do some things the way species A does them and other things the way species B does them, the hybrid may be hopelessly uncoordinated and therefore unable to reproduce. Hybrids between certain species of lovebirds, for example, have great difficulty learning to carry nest materials during flight and probably could not reproduce in the wild.

Hybrid Offspring May Be Infertile

Most animal hybrids, such as the mule (a cross between a horse and a donkey) and the liger (a zoo-based cross between a male lion and a female tiger), are sterile (**Fig. 16-8**). *Hybrid infertility* prevents hybrids from passing on their genetic material to offspring, which blocks gene flow between the two parent populations. A common reason for hybrid infertility is the failure of chromosomes to pair properly during meiosis, so that eggs and sperm fail to develop. (To learn how hybrid inviability and infertility can threaten endangered species, see "Earth Watch: Hybridization and Extinction" on p. 310.)

▲ **FIGURE 16-8 Hybrid infertility** This liger, the hybrid offspring of a lion and a tiger, is sterile. The gene pools of its parent species remain separate.

Table 16-1 summarizes the different types of isolating mechanisms.

16.3 HOW DO NEW SPECIES FORM?

Despite his exhaustive exploration of the process of natural selection, Charles Darwin did not propose a complete mechanism of **speciation,** the process by which new species form. One scientist who did play a large role in describing the process of speciation was Ernst Mayr of Harvard University, an ornithologist (expert on birds) and a pivotal figure in the history of evolutionary biology. Mayr developed the biological species concept discussed above. He was also among the first to recognize that speciation depends on two factors acting on a pair of populations: isolation and genetic divergence.

- **Isolation of populations:** If individuals move freely between two populations, interbreeding and the resulting gene flow will cause changes in one population to soon become widespread in the other as well. Thus, two populations cannot grow increasingly different unless something happens to block interbreeding between them. Speciation depends on isolation.

Table 16-1	**Mechanisms of Reproductive Isolation**

Premating isolating mechanisms: factors that prevent organisms of two species from mating
- **Geographic isolation:** The species cannot interbreed because a physical barrier separates them.
- **Ecological isolation:** The species do not interbreed even if they are within the same area because they occupy different habitats.
- **Temporal isolation:** The species cannot interbreed because they breed at different times.
- **Behavioral isolation:** The species do not interbreed because they have different courtship and mating rituals.
- **Mechanical incompatibility:** The species cannot interbreed because their reproductive structures are incompatible.

Postmating isolating mechanisms: factors that prevent organisms of two species from producing vigorous, fertile offspring after mating
- **Gametic incompatibility:** Sperm from one species cannot fertilize eggs of another species.
- **Hybrid inviability:** Hybrid offspring fail to survive to maturity.
- **Hybrid infertility:** Hybrid offspring are sterile or have low fertility.

Earth Watch

Hybridization and Extinction

The main cause of extinction is environmental change, especially habitat destruction. Some species with small populations, however, are also threatened by a less obvious danger: hybridization. Although premating isolating mechanisms ensure that, for the most part, members of one species cannot interbreed with members of a different species, matings between members of different species are nonetheless possible. Between-species matings and the resulting hybrid offspring are especially common in birds and plants.

How can hybrid mating be dangerous to endangered species? Recall that postmating isolating mechanisms ensure that, in most cases, hybrid offspring will survive poorly and may even be sterile. Now, picture what happens when contact between two species produces hybrids, and one of the species has a much smaller population than the other. If the hybrid offspring fail to survive and reproduce, the numbers of each species will decline, but the decline will have a proportionally larger impact on the small population. When the more abundant species moves into the range of the rare species, the impact on the rare species can be severe. Even if the hybrid offspring survive well, high numbers of hybrids can overwhelm the rare species, essentially absorbing the rare species into the abundant species.

Damage from hybridization is most likely to occur when formerly isolated small populations come into contact with larger populations of a closely related species. For example, the plant *Clarkia lingulata* is extremely rare, known to exist only in two sites in the Sierra Nevada mountains of California. Unfortunately, it readily hybridizes with its abundant relative *Clarkia biloba* to produce sterile hybrid offspring. Because several populations of *C. biloba* grow near the *C. lingulata* populations, extinction by hybridization is a real possibility for this rare species.

▲ **FIGURE E16-2 Ethiopian wolves** Fewer than 500 Ethiopian wolves remain. Among the threats to their continued existence is hybridization with wild dogs.

Human activities often cause contact between an endangered species and a more abundant species with which it can hybridize. For example, the rare Hawaiian duck, found only on the Hawaiian Islands, hybridizes freely with mallard ducks, a non-native species introduced to Hawaii to provide hunters with a new game species. Similarly, the endangered Ethiopian wolf (**Fig. E16-2**) is threatened by interbreeding with feral domestic dogs, and the endangered European wildcat is at risk from hybridization with domestic cats. In these cases and others, a species first declined in number due to habitat destruction and then became vulnerable to further damage by hybridization with a more numerous species that was present as a result of human activities.

- **Genetic divergence of populations:** It is not sufficient for two populations simply to be isolated. They will become separate species only if, during the period of isolation, they evolve sufficiently large genetic differences. The differences must be large enough that, if the isolated populations are reunited, they can no longer interbreed and produce vigorous, fertile offspring. That is, speciation is complete only if divergence results in evolution of an isolating mechanism. Such differences can arise by chance (genetic drift), especially if at least one of the isolated populations is small (see pp. 290–292). Large genetic differences can also arise through natural selection, if the isolated populations experience different environmental conditions.

Speciation always requires isolation followed by divergence, but these steps can take place in several different ways. Evolutionary biologists group the different pathways to speciation into two broad categories: **allopatric speciation,** in which two populations are geographically separated from one an-other, and **sympatric speciation,** in which two populations share the same geographic area.

Geographic Separation of a Population Can Lead to Allopatric Speciation

New species can arise by allopatric speciation when an impassible barrier physically separates different parts of a population.

Organisms May Colonize Isolated Habitats

A small population can become isolated if it moves to a new location (**Fig. 16-9**). For example, some members of a population of land-dwelling organisms might colonize an oceanic island. The colonists might be birds, flying insects, fungal spores, or wind-borne seeds blown by a storm. More earth-bound organisms could reach the island on a drifting "raft" of vegetation torn from the mainland coast. Whatever the means, such colonization must occur regularly, given the presence of living things on even the remotest islands.

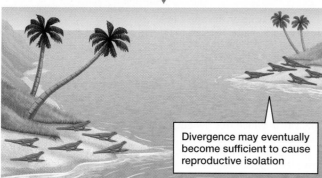

▲ FIGURE 16-9 **Allopatric isolation and divergence** In allopatric speciation, some event causes a population to be divided by an impassable geographic barrier. One way the division can occur is by colonization of an isolated island. The two now-separated populations may diverge genetically. If the genetic differences between the two populations become large enough to prevent interbreeding, then the two populations constitute separate species.

EXERCISE Make a list of events or processes that could cause geographic subdivision of a population. Are the items on your list sufficient to account for formation of the millions of species that have inhabited Earth?

Isolation by colonization need not be limited to islands. For example, different coral reefs may be separated by miles of open ocean, so any reef-dwelling sponges, fishes, or algae that were carried by ocean currents to a distant reef would be effectively isolated from their original populations. Any bounded habitat, such as a lake, a mountaintop, or a parasite's host can isolate arriving colonists.

Geological and Climate Changes May Divide Populations

Isolation can also result from landscape changes that divide a population. For example, rising sea levels might transform a coastal hilltop into an island, isolating the residents. New rock from a volcanic eruption can divide a previously continuous sea or lake, splitting populations. A river that changes course can also divide populations, as can a newly formed mountain range. Climate shifts, such as those that happened in past ice ages, can change the distribution of vegetation and strand portions of populations in isolated patches of suitable habitat. You can probably imagine many other scenarios that could lead to the geographic subdivision of a population.

Over the history of Earth, many populations have been divided by continental drift. Earth's continents float on molten rock and slowly move about the surface of the planet. On a number of occasions during Earth's long history, continental landmasses have broken into pieces that subsequently moved apart (see Fig. 17-12). Each of these breakups must have split a multitude of populations.

Natural Selection and Genetic Drift May Cause Isolated Populations to Diverge

If two populations become geographically isolated for any reason, there will be no gene flow between them. If the environments of the locations differ, then natural selection may favor different traits in the different locations, and the populations may accumulate genetic differences. Alternatively, genetic differences may arise if one or more of the separated populations is small enough that substantial genetic drift occurs, which may be especially likely in the aftermath of a founder event (in which a few individuals become isolated from the main body of the species). In either case, genetic differences between the separated populations may eventually become large enough to make interbreeding impossible. At that point, the two populations will have become separate species. Most evolutionary biologists believe that geographic isolation followed by allopatric speciation has been the most common source of new species, especially among animals.

Genetic Isolation Without Geographic Separation Can Lead to Sympatric Speciation

Genetic isolation—limited gene flow—is required for speciation, but populations can become genetically isolated without geographic separation. Thus, new species can arise by sympatric speciation.

Ecological Isolation Can Reduce Gene Flow

If a geographic area contains two distinct types of habitats (each with distinct food sources, places to raise young, and so on), different members of a single species may begin to specialize in one habitat or the other. If conditions are right, natural selection in the two different habitats may lead to the evolution of different traits in the two groups. Eventually, these differences may become large enough to prevent members of the

Case Study continued
Lost World

It is not unexpected that the forests of New Guinea's Foja Mountains would be home to a variety of distinctive species. New Guinea is, after all, an island. It is likely that, in the past, populations colonized the island and became genetically isolated from mainland populations, thereby initiating the process of speciation. Similarly, the distinctive species recently discovered on Indonesian coral reefs arose because reefs form in shallow seas, and are typically surrounded by deep, open-ocean waters that many reef-dwelling organisms cannot easily cross. But what about the saola and the other unique species of the Ammanite Mountains? How might populations inhabiting mainland forests in Vietnam have become isolated from other populations? Try to think of a possible answer to this question. We will return to this topic in the "Case Study Revisited" section at the end of this chapter.

Part of a fly population that lives only on hawthorne trees moves to an apple tree

The flies living on the apple tree do not encounter the flies living on the hawthorne tree, so the populations diverge

▲ **FIGURE 16-10 Sympatric isolation and divergence** In sympatric speciation, some event blocks gene flow between two parts of a population that remains in a single geographic area. One way in which this genetic isolation can occur is if a portion of a population begins to use a previously unexploited resource, as when some members of an insect population shift to a new host plant species (as has occurred in the fruit fly species *Rhagoletis pomonella*). The two now-isolated populations may diverge genetically. If the genetic differences between the two populations become large enough to prevent interbreeding, then the two populations constitute separate species.

QUESTION How might future scientists test whether the current *R. pomonella* has become two species?

two groups from interbreeding, and the formerly single species will have split into two species. Such a split seems to be taking place right before biologists' eyes, so to speak, in the case of the fruit fly *Rhagoletis pomonella*.

Rhagoletis is a parasite of the American hawthorn tree. This fly lays its eggs in the hawthorn's fruit; when the maggots hatch, they eat the fruit. About 150 years ago, entomologists (scientists who study insects) noticed that *Rhagoletis* had begun to infest apple trees, which were introduced into North America from Europe. Today, it appears that *Rhagoletis* is splitting into two species—one that breeds on apples, and one that breeds on hawthorns (**Fig. 16-10**). The two groups have evolved substantial genetic differences, some of which—such as those that affect the timing of emergence of the adult flies—are important for survival on a particular host plant.

The two kinds of flies will become two species only if they maintain reproductive separation. Apple trees and hawthorns typically grow in the same areas, and flies, after all, can fly. So why don't apple flies and hawthorn flies interbreed and cancel out any genetic differences between them? First, female flies usually lay their eggs in the same type of fruit in which they developed. Males also tend to prefer the same type of fruit in which they developed. Therefore, apple-liking males will encounter and mate with apple-liking females. Second, apples mature 2 or 3 weeks later than do hawthorn fruits, and the two types of flies emerge with timing appropriate for their chosen host fruit. Thus, the two varieties of flies have very little chance of meeting. Although some interbreeding between the two types of flies occurs, it seems they are well on their way to speciation. Will they make it? Entomologist Guy Bush suggests, "Check back with me in a few thousand years."

Mutations Can Lead to Genetic Isolation

In some instances, new species can arise nearly instantaneously as a result of mutations that change the number of chromosomes in an organism's cells. The acquisition of multiple copies of each chromosome is known as **polyploidy** and has been a frequent cause of sympatric speciation. In general, polyploid individuals cannot mate successfully with normal diploid individuals. Thus, a polyploid mutant is genetically isolated from its parent species. If, however, it could somehow reproduce and leave offspring, its descendents could form a new, reproductively isolated species.

Polyploid plants are more likely than polyploid animals to be able to reproduce; speciation by polyploidy is therefore more common in plants than in animals. Many plants can either self-fertilize or reproduce asexually, or both. Most animals, however, cannot self-fertilize or reproduce asexually. Therefore, a polyploid plant is much more likely than a polyploid animal to become the founding member of a new, polyploid species.

Under Some Conditions, Many New Species May Arise

In the same way that the history of your family can be represented by a family tree, the history of life can be represented by an *evolutionary tree*. The trunk at the base of the evolutionary tree of life represents Earth's earliest organisms, and each of the topmost branches represents one of today's living species. Each fork in the branches represents a speciation event, when one species split into two. Hypotheses and discoveries about the evolutionary relationships among species are often communicated by depictions of a portion of life's evolutionary tree (**Fig. 16-11a**).

  In some cases, many new species have arisen in a relatively short time (**Fig. 16-11b**). This process, called **adaptive radiation,** can occur when populations of one species invade a variety of new habitats and evolve in response to the differing environmental pressures in those habitats.

  Adaptive radiation has occurred many times and in many groups of organisms, typically when species encounter a wide variety of unoccupied habitats. For example, episodes of adaptive radiation took place when some wayward finches colonized the Galápagos Islands, when a population of cichlid fish reached isolated Lake Malawi in Africa, and when an ancestral silversword plant species arrived at the Hawaiian Islands (**Fig. 16-12**). These events gave rise to adaptive radiations of 13 species of Darwin's finches in the Galápagos, more than 300 species of cichlids in Lake Malawi, and 30 species of silversword plants in Hawaii. In these examples, the invading species faced no competitors except other members of their own species, and all the available habitats and food sources were rapidly exploited by new species that evolved from the original invaders.

Have you ever wondered

How Many Species Inhabit the Planet?

One way to determine the number of species on Earth might be to simply count them. You could comb the scientific literature to find all the species that scientists have discovered and named, and then tally up the total number. If you did that, you'd end up with a count of roughly 1.5 million species. But you still wouldn't know how many species are on Earth.

  Why doesn't counting work? Because most of the planet's species remain undiscovered. Relatively few scientists are engaged in the search for new species, and many undiscovered species are small and inconspicuous, or live in poorly explored habitats such as the floor of the ocean or the topmost branches of tropical rain forests. So, no one knows the actual number of species on Earth. But biologists agree that the number must be much higher than the number of named species. Estimates range from 2 million to 100 million or more.

16.4 WHAT CAUSES EXTINCTION?

Every living organism must eventually die, and the same is true of species. Just like individuals, species are "born" (through the process of speciation), persist for some period of time, and then perish. The ultimate fate of any species is **extinction,** the death of the last of its members. In fact, at least 99.9% of all the species that have ever existed are now extinct. The natural course of evolution, as revealed by fossils, is continual turnover of species as new ones arise and old ones become extinct.

  The immediate cause of extinction is probably always environmental change, in either the nonliving or the living parts of the environment. Environmental changes that can lead to extinction include habitat destruction and increased competition among species. In the face of such changes,

(a) Evolutionary tree

(b) Evolutionary tree representing adaptive radiation

▲ **FIGURE 16-11 Interpreting evolutionary trees** Evolutionary history is often represented by **(a)** an evolutionary tree, a graph in which the vertical axis plots time. In **(b)**, an evolutionary tree representing an adaptive radiation, many lines may branch from a single point. This pattern reflects biologists' uncertainty about the order in which the multiple speciation events of the radiation took place. With more research, it may be possible to replace the "starburst" pattern with a more informative tree.

(a) Ahinahina

(b) Waialeale dubautia

(c) Kupaoa

(d) Na'ena'e 'ula

▲ **FIGURE 16-12 Adaptive radiation** About 30 species of silversword plants inhabit the Hawaiian Islands. These species are found nowhere else, and all of them descended from a single ancestral population within a few million years. This adaptive radiation has led to a collection of closely related species of diverse form and appearance, with an array of adaptations for exploiting the many different habitats in Hawaii, from warm, moist rain forests to cool, barren volcanic mountaintops.

species with small geographic ranges or highly specialized adaptations are especially susceptible to extinction.

Localized Distribution Makes Species Vulnerable

Species vary widely in their range of distribution and, hence, in their vulnerability to extinction. Some species, such as herring gulls, white-tailed deer, and humans, inhabit entire continents or even the whole Earth; others, such as the Devil's Hole pupfish (**Fig. 16-13**), have extremely limited ranges. Obviously, if

▲ **FIGURE 16-13 Very localized distribution can endanger a species** The Devil's Hole pupfish is found in only one spring-fed water hole in the Nevada desert. This and other isolated small populations are at high risk of extinction.

a species inhabits only a very small area, any disturbance of that area could easily result in extinction. If Devil's Hole dries up due to a drought or well drilling nearby, its pupfish will immediately vanish. Conversely, wide-ranging species will not succumb to local environmental catastrophes.

Overspecialization Increases the Risk of Extinction

Another factor that may make a species vulnerable to extinction is overspecialization. Each species evolves adaptations that help it survive and reproduce in its environment. In some cases, these adaptations include specializations that favor survival in a particular and limited set of environmental conditions. The Karner blue butterfly, for example, feeds only on the blue lupine plant (**Fig. 16-14**). The butterfly is therefore found only where the plant thrives. But the blue lupine has become quite rare because its habitat of sandy, open woods and clearings in northeast North America has been largely replaced by farms and development. If the lupine disappears, the Karner blue butterfly will surely become extinct along with it.

Interactions with Other Species May Drive a Species to Extinction

As described in Chapter 15, interactions such as competition and predation serve as agents of natural selection (see p. **298**).

▲ **FIGURE 16-14 Extreme specialization places species at risk** The Karner blue butterfly feeds exclusively on the blue lupine, found in dry forests and clearings in the northeastern United States. Such behavioral specialization renders the butterfly extremely vulnerable to any environmental change that may exterminate its single host plant species.

QUESTION If specialization puts a species at risk for extinction, how could this hazardous trait have evolved?

In some cases, these same interactions can lead to extinction rather than to adaptation.

Organisms compete for limited resources in all environments. If a species' competitors evolve superior adaptations and the species doesn't evolve fast enough to keep up, it may become extinct. A particularly striking example of extinction through competition occurred in South America, beginning about 2.5 million years ago. At that time, the isthmus of Panama rose above sea level and formed a land bridge between North America and South America. After the previously separated continents were connected, the mammal species that had evolved in isolation on each continent were able to mix. Many species did indeed expand their ranges, as North American mammals moved southward and South American mammals moved northward. As they moved, each species encountered resident species that occupied the same kinds of habitats and exploited the same kinds of resources. The ultimate result of the ensuing competition was that the North American species diversified and underwent an adaptive radiation that displaced the vast majority of the South American species, many of which went extinct. Clearly, evolution had bestowed on the North American species some (as yet unknown) set of adaptations that enabled their descendants to exploit resources more efficiently and effectively than their South American counterparts could.

Habitat Change and Destruction Are the Leading Causes of Extinction

Habitat change, both contemporary and prehistoric, is the single greatest cause of extinctions. Present-day habitat destruction due to human activities is proceeding at a rapid pace. Many biologists believe that we are presently in the midst of the fastest-paced and most widespread episode of species extinction in the history of life. Loss of tropical forests is especially devastating to species diversity. As many as half the species presently on Earth may be lost during the next 50 years as the tropical forests that contain them are cut for timber or to clear land for cattle and crops. In Chapter 17, we will discuss extinctions due to prehistoric habitat change.

Case Study revisited
Lost World

One possible explanation for the distinctive collection of species found in the Annamite Mountains of Vietnam lies in the geological history of the region. During the ice ages that have occurred repeatedly during the past million years or so, the area covered by tropical forests must have shrunk dramatically. Organisms that depended on the forests for survival would have been restricted to any remaining "islands" of forest, isolated from their fellows in other, distant patches of forest. What is now the Annamite Mountain region may well have been an isolated forest during periods of glacial advance. As we learned in this chapter, this kind of isolation can set the stage for allopatric speciation and may have created the conditions that gave rise to the saola and other unique denizens of Vietnamese forests.

Ironically, we have discovered the lost world of Vietnamese animals at a moment when that world is in danger of disappearing. Economic development in Vietnam has brought logging and mining to ever more remote regions of the country, and Annamite Mountain forests are being cleared at an unprecedented rate. The increasing local human population means that animals are hunted heavily; most of our knowledge of the saola comes from carcasses found in local markets. All of the newly discovered mammals of Vietnam are quite rare, seen only infrequently even by local hunters. Fortunately, the Vietnamese government has established a number of national parks and nature preserves in key areas. Only time will tell if these measures are sufficient to ensure the survival of the mysterious mammals of the Annamites.

Consider This

The All Species Foundation is a nonprofit organization that promotes the goal of finding and naming all of Earth's undiscovered species within the next 25 years. According to the foundation, this task "deserves to be one of the great scientific goals of the new century." The foundation estimates the cost of the job at between $700 and $2,000 per species, with perhaps millions of undiscovered species remaining to be found. Do you think the search for undiscovered species should continue? What value or benefit to humans does the search for new species provide?

CHAPTER REVIEW

Summary of Key Concepts

16.1 What Is a Species?

According to the biological species concept, a species consists of all the populations of organisms that are potentially capable of interbreeding under natural conditions and that are reproductively isolated from other populations.

16.2 How Is Reproductive Isolation Between Species Maintained?

Reproductive isolation between species may be maintained by one or more of several mechanisms, collectively known as premating isolating mechanisms and postmating isolating mechanisms. Premating isolating mechanisms include geographic isolation, ecological isolation, temporal isolation, behavioral isolation, and mechanical incompatibility. Postmating isolating mechanisms include gametic incompatibility, hybrid inviability, and hybrid infertility.

16.3 How Do New Species Form?

Speciation, the formation of new species, takes place when gene flow between two populations is reduced or eliminated and the populations diverge genetically. Most commonly, speciation is allopatric—gene flow is restricted by geographic isolation. However, speciation can also be sympatric—gene flow is restricted by ecological isolation or by mutations that cause polyploidy. Whether genetic isolation initially arises allopatrically or sympatrically, speciation is completed by subsequent genetic divergence of the separated populations through genetic drift or natural selection.

16.4 What Causes Extinction?

Factors that cause extinctions include competition among species and habitat destruction. Localized distribution and over-specialization increase a species' vulnerability to extinction.

Key Terms

adaptive radiation 313	premating isolating
allopatric speciation 310	mechanism 306
extinction 313	reproductive isolation 304
isolating mechanism 306	speciation 309
polyploidy 312	species 304
postmating isolating	sympatric speciation 310
mechanism 306	

Thinking Through the Concepts

Fill-in-the-Blank

1. A species is a group of _____ that evolves _____. The biological species concept identifies species on the basis of their _____. The biological species concept cannot be applied to species that reproduce _____.

2. Fill in the following with the appropriate isolating mechanism: Occurs when members of two populations have different courtship behaviors: _____; occurs when hybrid offspring fail to survive to reproduce: _____; occurs when members of two populations have different breeding seasons: _____; occurs when sperm from one species fails to fertilize the eggs of another species: _____; occurs when the sexual organs of two species are incompatible: _____.

3. Formation of a new species occurs when two populations of an existing species first become _____ and then _____. The process in which geographic separation of parts of a population leads to the formation of new species is called _____. Isolated populations may diverge through the action of _____ or _____.

4. The process by which many new species arise in a relatively short period of time is known as _____. This process often occurs when a species arrives in a previously unoccupied _____.

5. A species may be at higher risk of extinction if its geographic range includes a(n) _____ area, or if its food or habitat requirements are _____. The leading direct cause of extinction is _____.

Review Questions

1. Define the following terms: *species*, *speciation*, *allopatric speciation*, and *sympatric speciation*. Explain how allopatric and sympatric speciation might work, and give a hypothetical example of each.

2. Many of the oak tree species in central and eastern North America hybridize (interbreed). Are they "true species"?

3. Review the material on the possibility of sympatric speciation in *Rhagoletis* flies. What types of genotypic, phenotypic, or behavioral data would convince you that the two forms have become separate species?

4. A drug called colchicine prevents cell division after the chromosomes have doubled at the start of meiosis. Describe how you would use colchicine to produce a new polyploid plant species.

5. What are the two major types of reproductive isolating mechanisms? Give examples of each type, and describe how they work.

Applying the Concepts

1. Why do you suppose there are so many *endemic* species—that is, species found nowhere else—on islands? Why have the overwhelming majority of recent extinctions occurred on islands?

2. A biologist you've met claims that the fact that humans are pushing other species into small, isolated populations is good for biodiversity because these are the conditions that lead to new speciation events. Comment.

3. Southern Wisconsin is home to several populations of gray squirrels (*Sciurus carolinensis*) with black fur. Design a study to determine if they are actually a separate species.

4. It is difficult to gather data on speciation events in the past or to perform interesting experiments about the process of speciation. Does this difficulty make the study of speciation "unscientific"? Should we abandon the study of speciation?

(MB) *Go to www.masteringbiology.com for practice quizzes, activities, eText, videos, current events, and more.*

Case Study

Little People, Big Story

MUCH OF OUR KNOWLEDGE of the evolutionary history of life comes from the work of paleontologists, the scientists who study fossils. Not long ago, a small group of paleontologists, digging beneath the floor of a cave on the Indonesian island of Flores, discovered what they at first believed to be the fossil skeleton of a human child. Closer examination of the skeleton, however, revealed that it instead belonged to a fully grown adult, but one that was no more than 3 feet tall. The researchers gave this extraordinary creature the nickname "Hobbit."

Unlike today's small humans, such as pygmies or pituitary dwarves, Hobbit had a very small brain, smaller even than the brain of a typical chimpanzee. Furthermore, the shapes and arrangements of the bones in Hobbit's wrist, shoulder, and other parts of its skeleton were unlike those of anatomically modern humans. On the basis of these findings, many researchers have concluded that Hobbit was not simply a small *Homo sapiens*, but was instead a different, related species. The new species was dubbed *Homo floresiensis* by its discoverers.

Some paleontologists are skeptical of the conclusion that the specimen represents a new human species. The skeptics contend that Hobbit might simply be a small-bodied *H. sapiens* who was victimized by a skeleton-deforming disease. Hobbit proponents, however, maintain that the available evidence supports the claim that *H. floresiensis* is a distinct species. The scientific disagreement about Hobbit's status may not be fully resolved until additional specimens are found.

If Hobbit is indeed *H. floresiensis*, we shared Earth with close relatives until much more recently than was previously thought. Hobbit's bones are about 18,000 years old. Until they were unearthed, scientists believed that, by well before 18,000 years ago, we were the only surviving member of the human family tree. Hobbit's discovery, however, raises the possibility that, not too long ago, in the forests of Flores, representatives of our species encountered members of another, tiny human species.

Although the tale of *H. floresiensis* is especially significant in our human-centered view of the world, it is but one thread among the millions that together make up the story of life's evolution. We therefore turn our attention from our hobbit-like cousin to a brief tour of some of the highlights of life's history.

▲ The skull of *Homo floresiensis*, a recently discovered diminutive human relative, is dwarfed by the skull of a modern *Homo sapiens*.

At a Glance

17.1 HOW DID LIFE BEGIN?

Pre-Darwinian thought held that all species were simultaneously created by God a few thousand years ago. Further, until the nineteenth century most people thought that new members of species sprang up all the time, through **spontaneous generation** from both nonliving matter and other, unrelated forms of life. In 1609, a French botanist wrote, "There is a tree . . . frequently observed in Scotland. From this tree leaves are falling; upon one side they strike the water and slowly turn into fishes, upon the other they strike the land and turn into birds." Medieval writings abound with similar observations. Microorganisms were thought to arise spontaneously from broth, maggots from meat, and mice from mixtures of sweaty shirts and wheat.

Experiments Refuted Spontaneous Generation

In 1668, the Italian physician Francesco Redi disproved the maggots-from-meat hypothesis simply by keeping flies (whose eggs hatch into maggots) away from uncontaminated meat (see "Scientific Inquiry: Controlled Experiments, Then and Now," on pp. 6–7). In the mid-1800s, Louis Pasteur in France and John Tyndall in England disproved the broth-to-microorganism idea by showing that microorganisms did not appear in sterile broth unless the broth was first exposed to existing microorganisms in the surrounding environment (**Fig. 17-1**). Although Pasteur and Tyndall's work effectively demolished the notion of spontaneous generation, it did not address the question of how life on Earth originated in the first place. Or, as the biochemist Stanley Miller put it, "Pasteur never proved it didn't happen once, he only showed that it doesn't happen all the time."

The First Living Things Arose from Nonliving Ones

Modern scientific ideas about the origin of life began to emerge in the 1920s, when Alexander Oparin in Russia and John B. S. Haldane in England noted that today's oxygen-rich atmosphere would not have permitted the spontaneous formation of the complex organic molecules necessary for life. Oxygen reacts readily with other molecules, disrupting chemical bonds. Thus, an oxygen-rich environment tends to keep molecules simple.

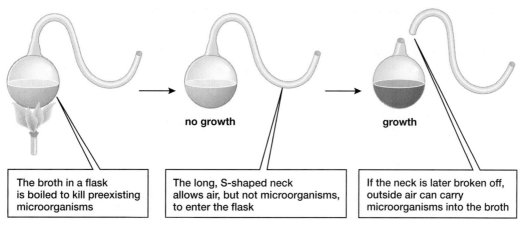

no growth

growth

| The broth in a flask is boiled to kill preexisting microorganisms | The long, S-shaped neck allows air, but not microorganisms, to enter the flask | If the neck is later broken off, outside air can carry microorganisms into the broth |

▲ FIGURE 17-1 **Spontaneous generation refuted** Louis Pasteur's experiment disproving the spontaneous generation of microorganisms in broth.

Oparin and Haldane speculated that the atmosphere of the young Earth must have contained very little oxygen and that, under such atmospheric conditions, complex organic molecules could have arisen through ordinary chemical reactions. Some kinds of molecules could persist in the lifeless environment of early Earth better than others and would therefore become more common over time. This chemical version of the "survival of the fittest" is called *prebiotic* (meaning "before life") evolution. In the scenario envisioned by Oparin and Haldane, prebiotic chemical evolution gave rise to progressively more complex molecules and eventually to living organisms.

Organic Molecules Can Form Spontaneously Under Prebiotic Conditions

Inspired by the ideas of Oparin and Haldane, Stanley Miller and Harold Urey set out in 1953 to simulate prebiotic evolution in the laboratory. They knew that, on the basis of the chemical composition of the rocks that formed early in Earth's history, geochemists had concluded that the early atmosphere probably contained virtually no oxygen gas, but did contain other substances, including methane (CH_4), ammonia (NH_3), hydrogen (H_2), and water vapor (H_2O). Miller and Urey simulated the oxygen-free atmosphere of early Earth by mixing these components in a flask. An electrical discharge mimicked the intense energy of early Earth's lightning storms. In this experimental microcosm, the researchers found that simple organic molecules appeared after just a few days (**Fig. 17-2**). The experiment showed that small molecules likely present in the early atmosphere can combine to form larger organic molecules if electrical energy is present (recall from Chapter 6 that reactions that synthesize biological molecules from smaller ones are endergonic—they consume energy). Similar experiments by Miller and others have produced amino acids, short proteins, nucleotides, adenosine triphosphate (ATP), and other molecules characteristic of living things.

In recent years, new evidence has convinced most geochemists that the actual composition of Earth's early atmosphere probably differed from the mixture of gases used in the pioneering Miller-Urey experiment. This improved understanding of the early atmosphere, however, has not undermined the basic finding of the Miller-Urey experiment. Additional experiments with more realistic (but still oxygen-free) simulated atmospheres have also yielded organic molecules. In addition, these experiments have shown that electricity is not the only suitable energy source. Other energy sources that were available on early Earth, such as heat or ultraviolet (UV) light, have also been shown to drive the formation of organic molecules in experimental simulations of prebiotic conditions. Thus, even though we may never know exactly what the earliest atmosphere was like, we can be confident that organic molecules formed on early Earth.

Additional organic molecules probably arrived from space when meteorites and comets crashed into Earth's surface. Analysis of present-day meteorites recovered from impact craters on Earth has revealed that some meteorites contain relatively high concentrations of amino acids and other simple organic molecules. Laboratory experiments suggest that these molecules could have formed in interstellar space before plummeting to Earth. When small molecules known to be present in space were placed under space-like conditions of very low temperature and pressure and bombarded with UV light, larger organic molecules were produced.

Organic Molecules Can Accumulate Under Prebiotic Conditions

Prebiotic synthesis was neither very efficient nor very fast. Nonetheless, in a few hundred million years, large quantities of organic molecules accumulated in the early Earth's oceans. Today, most organic molecules have a short life because they are either digested by living organisms or they react with atmospheric oxygen. Early Earth, however, lacked both life and free oxygen, so molecules would not have been exposed to these threats.

Still, the prebiotic molecules must have been threatened by the sun's high-energy UV radiation, because early Earth lacked an ozone layer. The ozone layer is a region high in today's atmosphere that is enriched with ozone molecules, which form when incoming solar energy splits some

▶ FIGURE 17-2 **The experimental apparatus of Stanley Miller and Harold Urey** Life's very earliest stages left no fossils, so evolutionary historians have pursued a strategy of re-creating in the laboratory the conditions that may have prevailed on early Earth. The mixture of gases in the spark chamber simulates Earth's early atmosphere.

QUESTION How would the experiment's result change if oxygen (O_2) were included in the spark chamber?

An electric spark simulates a lightning storm

electric spark chamber

Energy from the spark powers reactions among molecules thought to be present in Earth's early atmosphere

CH_4 NH_3 H_2 H_2O

Boiling water adds water vapor to the artificial atmosphere

condenser

cool water flow

When the hot gases in the spark chamber are cooled, water vapor condenses and any soluble molecules present are dissolved

boiling chamber

water

Organic molecules appear after a few days

O_2 molecules in the outer atmosphere into individual oxygen atoms (O) that then react with O_2 to form O_3 (ozone). The resulting high-altitude layer of ozone molecules absorbs some of the sun's UV light before it reaches Earth's surface. Early Earth, however, had no ozone layer, because there was little or no oxygen gas in the atmosphere and therefore no ozone formation.

Before the ozone layer formed, UV bombardment must have been fierce. UV radiation, as we have seen, can provide energy for the formation of organic molecules but it can also break them apart. Some places, however, such as those beneath rock ledges or at the bottoms of even fairly shallow seas, would have been protected from UV radiation. In these locations, organic molecules may have accumulated.

Clay May Have Catalyzed the Formation of Larger Organic Molecules

In the next stage of prebiotic evolution, simple molecules combined to form larger molecules. The chemical reactions that formed the larger molecules required that the reacting molecules be packed closely together. Scientists have proposed several processes by which the required high concentrations might have been achieved on early Earth. One possibility is that small molecules accumulated on the surfaces of clay particles, which may have a small electrical charge that attracts dissolved molecules with the opposite charge. Clustered on a clay particle, small molecules would have been sufficiently close together to allow chemical reactions between them. Researchers have demonstrated the plausibility of this scenario with experiments in which adding clay to solutions of dissolved small organic molecules catalyzed the formation of larger, more complex molecules. Such molecules might have formed on clay at the bottom of early Earth's oceans or lakes and gone on to become the building blocks of the first living organisms.

RNA May Have Been the First Self-Reproducing Molecule

Although all modern organisms use DNA to encode and store genetic information, it is unlikely that DNA was the earliest informational molecule. DNA can reproduce itself only with the help of large, complex protein enzymes, but the instructions for building these enzymes are encoded in DNA itself. For this reason, the origin of DNA's role as life's information storage molecule poses a "chicken and egg" puzzle: DNA requires proteins, but those proteins require DNA. It is thus difficult to construct a plausible scenario for the origin of self-replicating DNA from prebiotic molecules. It is therefore likely that the current DNA-based system of information storage evolved from an earlier system.

RNA Can Act as a Catalyst

A prime candidate for the first self-replicating informational molecule is RNA. In the 1980s, Thomas Cech and Sidney Altman, working with the single-celled organism *Tetrahymena*, discovered a cellular reaction that was catalyzed not by a protein, but by a small RNA molecule. Because this special RNA molecule performed a function previously thought to be performed only by protein enzymes, Cech and Altman decided to give their catalytic RNA molecule the name **ribozyme** (Fig. 17-3).

In the years since their discovery, researchers have found dozens of naturally occurring ribozymes that catalyze a variety of different reactions, including cutting other RNA molecules and splicing together different RNA fragments. Ribozymes have also been found in the protein-manufacturing machinery of cells, where they help catalyze the attachment of amino acid molecules to growing proteins. In addition, researchers have been able to synthesize various ribozymes in the laboratory, including some that can catalyze the replication of small RNA molecules.

Earth May Once Have Been an RNA World

The discovery that RNA molecules can act as catalysts for diverse reactions, including RNA replication, provides support for the hypothesis that life arose in an "RNA world." According to this view, the current era of DNA-based life was preceded by one in which RNA served as both the information-carrying genetic molecule and the catalyst for its own replication. This RNA world may have emerged after hundreds of millions of years of prebiotic chemical synthesis, during which RNA nucleotides would have been among the molecules synthesized. After reaching a sufficiently high concentration, perhaps on clay particles, the nucleotides probably bonded together to form short RNA chains.

Let's suppose that, purely by chance, one of these RNA chains was a ribozyme that could catalyze the production of copies of itself. This first self-reproducing ribozyme probably wasn't very good at its job and produced copies with lots of errors. These mistakes were the first mutations. Like modern mutations, most undoubtedly ruined the catalytic abilities of the "daughter molecules," but a few may have been improvements. Such improvements set the stage for the evolution of RNA molecules, as variant ribozymes with increased speed and accuracy of replication reproduced, copying themselves and displacing less efficient molecules. Molecular evolution in the RNA world proceeded until, by some still unknown chain of events, RNA gradually receded into its present role as an intermediary between DNA and protein enzymes.

Membrane-Like Vesicles May Have Enclosed Ribozymes

Self-replicating molecules alone do not constitute life; these molecules must be contained within some kind of enclosing membrane. The precursors of the earliest biological membranes may have been simple structures that formed spontaneously from purely physical, mechanical processes. For example, chemists have shown that if water containing proteins and lipids is agitated to simulate waves beating against ancient shores, the proteins and lipids combine to form hollow structures called *vesicles*. These hollow balls resemble living cells in several respects. They have a well-defined outer boundary that separates their internal contents from the external solution. If the composition of the vesicle is right, a "membrane" forms that is remarkably similar in appearance to a real cell membrane. Under certain conditions, vesicles can absorb material from the external solution, grow, and even divide.

If a vesicle happened to surround the right ribozymes, it would form something resembling a living cell. We could call it a **protocell,** structurally similar to a cell but not a living thing. In the protocell, ribozymes and any other enclosed molecules would have been protected from free-roaming ribozymes in the primordial soup. Nucleotides and other small molecules might have diffused across the membrane and been used to synthesize new ribozymes and other complex molecules. After sufficient growth, the vesicle may have divided, with a few copies of the ribozymes becoming incorporated into each daughter vesicle. If this process occurred, the evolution of the first cells would be nearly complete.

Was there a particular moment when a nonliving protocell gave rise to something alive? Probably not. Like most evolutionary transitions, the change from protocell to living cell was a continuous process, with no sharp boundary between one state and the next.

But Did All This Happen?

The above scenario, although plausible and consistent with many research findings, is by no means certain. One of the

▲ **FIGURE 17-3 A ribozyme** This RNA molecule, isolated from the single-celled organism *Tetrahymena*, acts like an enzyme, catalyzing metabolic reactions.

most striking aspects of origin-of-life research is a great diversity of assumptions, experiments, and contradictory hypotheses. Researchers disagree as to whether life arose in quiet pools, in the sea, in moist films on the surfaces of crystals, or in hot deep-sea vents. A few researchers even argue that life arrived on Earth from space. Can we draw any firm conclusions from the research conducted so far? No, but we can make a few observations.

First, the experiments of Miller and others show that amino acids, nucleotides, and other organic molecules, along with simple membrane-like structures, are likely to have formed in abundance on early Earth. Second, chemical evolution had long periods of time and huge areas of the Earth available to it. Given sufficient time and a sufficiently large pool of reactant molecules, even extremely rare events can occur many times. Given the vast expanses of time and space available, each small step on the path from primordial soup to living cell had ample opportunity to take place.

Most biologists accept that the origin of life was probably an inevitable consequence of the working of natural laws. We should emphasize, however, that this proposition cannot be definitively tested. The origin of life left no record, and researchers exploring this mystery can proceed only by developing a hypothetical scenario and then conducting laboratory investigations to determine if the scenario's steps are chemically and biologically possible and plausible.

17.2 WHAT WERE THE EARLIEST ORGANISMS LIKE?

When Earth first formed about 4.5 billion years ago, it was quite hot (**Fig. 17-4**). A multitude of meteorites smashed into the forming planet, and the kinetic energy of these extraterrestrial rocks was converted into heat on impact. Still more heat was released by the decay of radioactive atoms. The rock composing Earth melted, and heavier elements such as iron and nickel sank to the center of the planet, where they remain molten even today. It must have taken hundreds of millions of years for Earth to cool enough to allow water to exist as a liquid. Nonetheless, it appears that life arose in fairly short order once liquid water was available.

The oldest fossil organisms found so far are in rocks that are about 3.5 billion years old. (Their age was determined using radiometric dating techniques; see "Scientific Inquiry: How Do We Know How Old a Fossil Is?" on p. 324.) Chemical traces in older rocks have led some paleontologists to believe that life is even older, perhaps as old as 3.9 billion years.

The period in which life began is known as the Precambrian era. This interval was designated by geologists and paleontologists, who have devised a hierarchical naming system of eras, periods, and epochs to delineate the immense span of geological time (**Table 17-1**).

The First Organisms Were Anaerobic Prokaryotes

The first cells to arise in Earth's oceans were **prokaryotes,** cells whose genetic material was not contained within a nucleus. These cells probably obtained nutrients and energy by absorbing organic molecules from their environment. There was no oxygen gas in the atmosphere, so the cells must have metabolized the organic molecules anaerobically. You may recall from Chapter 8 that anaerobic metabolism yields only small amounts of energy.

Thus, the earliest cells were primitive anaerobic bacteria. As these bacteria multiplied, they must have eventually used up the organic molecules produced by prebiotic chemical reactions. Simpler molecules, such as carbon dioxide and

▲ FIGURE 17-4 **Early Earth** Life began on a planet characterized by abundant volcanic activity, frequent electrical storms, repeated meteorite strikes, and an atmosphere that lacked oxygen gas.

Table 17-1   The History of Life on Earth

Era	Period	Epoch	Millions of years ago	Major events
Cenozoic	Quaternary	Recent	0.01–present	Evolution of genus *Homo*
		Pleistocene	1.8–0.01	
	Tertiary	Pliocene	5–1.8	Widespread flourishing of birds, mammals, insects, and flowering plants
		Miocene	23–5	
		Oligocene	38–23	
		Eocene	54–38	
		Paleocene	65–54	
Mesozoic	Cretaceous		146–65	Flowering plants appear and become dominant Mass extinction of marine and terrestrial life, including dinosaurs
	Jurassic		208–146	Dominance of dinosaurs and conifers First birds
	Triassic		245–208	First mammals and dinosaurs Forests of gymnosperms and tree ferns
Paleozoic	Permian		286–245	Massive marine extinctions, including trilobites Flourishing of reptiles and the decline of amphibians
	Carboniferous		360–286	Forests of tree ferns and club mosses Dominance of amphibians and insects First reptiles and conifers
	Devonian		410–360	Fishes and trilobites flourish First amphibians, insects, seeds, and pollen
	Silurian		440–410	Many fishes, trilobites, and mollusks First vascular plants
	Ordovician		505–440	Dominance of arthropods and mollusks in the ocean Invasion of land by plants and arthropods First fungi
	Cambrian		544–505	Marine algae flourish Origin of most marine invertebrate phyla First fishes
Precambrian			About 1,000	First animals (soft-bodied marine invertebrates)
			1,200	First multicellular organisms
			2,000	First eukaryotes
			2,200	Accumulation of free oxygen in the atmosphere
			3,500	Origin of photosynthesis (in cyanobacteria)
			3,900–3,500	First living cells (prokaryotes)
			4,000–3,900	Appearance of the first rocks on Earth
			4,600	Origin of the solar system and Earth

Scientific Inquiry

How Do We Know How Old a Fossil Is?

Early geologists could date rock layers and their accompanying fossils only in a *relative* way: Fossils found in deeper layers of rock were generally older than those found in shallower layers. With the discovery of radioactivity, it became possible to determine *absolute* dates, within certain limits of uncertainty. The nuclei of radioactive elements spontaneously break down, or decay, into other elements. For example, carbon-14 (usually written ^{14}C) decays by emitting an electron to become nitrogen-14 (^{14}N). Each radioactive element decays at a rate that is independent of temperature, pressure, or the chemical compound of which the element is a part. The time it takes for half of a radioactive element's nuclei to decay at this characteristic rate is called its *half-life*. The half-life of ^{14}C, for example, is 5,730 years.

How are radioactive elements used in determining the age of rocks? If we know the rate of decay and measure the proportion of decayed nuclei to undecayed nuclei, we can estimate how much time has passed since these radioactive elements became trapped in the rock. This process is called *radiometric dating*.

A particularly straightforward radiometric dating technique measures the decay of potassium-40 (^{40}K), which has a half-life of about 1.25 billion years, into argon-40 (^{40}Ar). Potassium-40 is commonly found in volcanic rocks such as granite and basalt, and the argon-40 it decays into is a gas. Suppose that a volcano erupts with a massive lava flow, covering the countryside. All the ^{40}Ar, being a gas, will bubble out of the molten lava, so when the lava first cools and solidifies into rock, it will not contain any ^{40}Ar (Fig. E17-1). Over time, however, any ^{40}K present in the hardened lava will decay into ^{40}Ar, with half of the ^{40}K decaying every 1.25 billion years. This ^{40}Ar gas will be trapped in the rock. A geologist could take a sample of the

▲ FIGURE E17-1 The relationship between time and the decay of radioactive ^{40}K to ^{40}Ar

QUESTION Uranium-235, with a half-life of 713 million years, decays to lead-207. If you analyze a rock and find that it contains uranium-235 and lead-207 in a ratio of 1:1, how old is the rock?

rock and measure the ratio of ^{40}K to ^{40}Ar to determine the rock's age. For example, if the analysis finds equal amounts of the two elements, the geologist will conclude that the lava hardened 1.25 billion years ago (see Fig. E17-1). With appropriate care, such age estimates are quite reliable. If a fossil is found beneath a lava flow dated at, say, 500 million years, then we know that the fossil is at least that old.

water, would still have been very abundant, as was energy in the form of sunlight. What was lacking, then, was not materials or energy itself, but energetic molecules—molecules in which energy is stored in chemical bonds.

Some Organisms Evolved the Ability to Capture the Sun's Energy

Eventually, some cells evolved the ability to use the energy of sunlight to drive the synthesis of complex, high-energy molecules from simpler molecules; in other words, photosynthesis appeared. Photosynthesis requires a source of hydrogen, and the very earliest photosynthetic bacteria probably used hydrogen sulfide gas dissolved in water for this purpose (much as today's purple photosynthetic bacteria do). Eventually, however, Earth's supply of hydrogen sulfide (which is produced mainly by volcanoes) must have run low. The shortage of hydrogen sulfide set the stage for the evolution of photosynthetic bacteria that were able to use the planet's most abundant source of hydrogen—water (H_2O).

Photosynthesis Increased the Amount of Oxygen in the Atmosphere

Water-based photosynthesis converts water and carbon dioxide to energetic molecules of sugar, releasing oxygen as a by-product. The emergence of this new method for capturing energy introduced significant amounts of free oxygen to the atmosphere for the first time. At first, the newly liberated oxygen was quickly consumed by reactions with other molecules in the atmosphere and in Earth's crust (surface layer). One especially common reactive atom in the crust was iron, and much of the new oxygen combined with iron atoms to form huge deposits of iron oxide (also known as rust). As a result, iron oxide is abundant in rocks formed during this period.

After all the accessible iron had turned to rust, the concentration of oxygen gas in the atmosphere began to increase. Chemical analysis of rocks suggests that significant amounts of oxygen first appeared in the atmosphere about 2.3 billion years ago, produced by bacteria that were probably very similar to modern cyanobacteria. (Because Earth's supply of oxygen molecules is continually recycled, you will undoubtedly breathe in some oxygen molecules today that were expelled 2 billion years ago by one of these early cyanobacteria.)

Aerobic Metabolism Arose in Response to the Oxygen Crisis

Oxygen is potentially very dangerous to living things, because it can react with organic molecules, breaking them down. Many of today's anaerobic bacteria perish when exposed to what is for them a deadly poison—oxygen. The accumulation of oxygen in the atmosphere of early Earth probably exterminated many organisms and fostered the evolution of cellular mechanisms for detoxifying oxygen. This crisis for evolving life also provided the environmental pressure for the next great advance in the Age of Microbes: the ability to use oxygen in metabolism. This ability not only provides a defense against the chemical action of oxygen, but actually channels oxygen's destructive power through aerobic respiration to generate useful energy for the cell (see Chapter 8 for more information on aerobic respiration). Because the amount of energy available to a cell is vastly increased when oxygen is used to metabolize food molecules, aerobic cells had a significant selective advantage.

Some Organisms Acquired Membrane-Enclosed Organelles

Hordes of bacteria would offer a rich food supply to any organism that could eat them. Paleobiologists speculate that, once this potential prey population appeared, predation would have evolved quickly. These early predators were probably prokaryotes that had evolved to become larger than typical bacteria. In addition, they must have lost the rigid cell wall that surrounds most bacterial cells, so that their flexible plasma membrane was in contact with the surrounding environment. Thus, the predatory cells were able to envelop smaller bacteria in an infolded pouch of membrane and in this fashion engulf whole bacteria as prey.

These early predators were probably capable of neither photosynthesis nor aerobic metabolism. Although they could capture large food particles, namely bacteria, they metabolized them inefficiently. By about 1.7 billion years ago, however, one predator probably gave rise to the first eukaryotic cell. Eukaryotic cells differ from prokaryotic cells in that they have an elaborate system of internal membranes, many of which enclose organelles such as a nucleus that contains the cell's genetic material. Organisms composed of one or more eukaryotic cells are known as **eukaryotes.**

The Internal Membranes of Eukaryotes May Have Arisen Through Infolding of the Plasma Membrane

The internal membranes of eukaryotic cells may have originally arisen through inward folding of the cell membrane of a single-celled predator. If, as in most of today's bacteria, the DNA of the eukaryotes' ancestor was attached to the inside of its cell membrane, an infolding of the membrane near the point of DNA attachment may have pinched off and become the precursor of the cell nucleus.

In addition to the nucleus, other key eukaryotic structures include the organelles used for energy metabolism: mitochondria and (in plants and algae) chloroplasts. How did these organelles evolve?

Mitochondria and Chloroplasts May Have Arisen from Engulfed Bacteria

The **endosymbiont hypothesis** proposes that early eukaryotic cells acquired the precursors of mitochondria and chloroplasts by engulfing certain types of bacteria. These cells and the bacteria trapped inside them (*endo* means "within") gradually entered into a *symbiotic* relationship, a close association between different types of organisms over an extended time. How might this have happened?

Let's suppose that an anaerobic predatory cell captured an aerobic bacterium for food, as it often did, but for some reason failed to digest this particular prey (**Fig. 17-5 ❶**). The

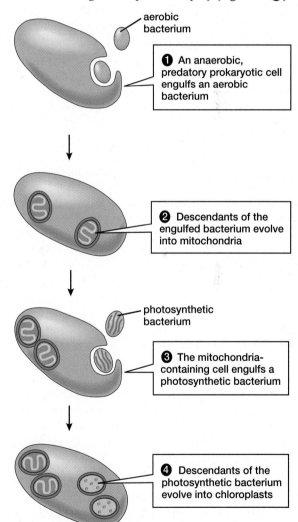

aerobic bacterium

❶ An anaerobic, predatory prokaryotic cell engulfs an aerobic bacterium

❷ Descendants of the engulfed bacterium evolve into mitochondria

photosynthetic bacterium

❸ The mitochondria-containing cell engulfs a photosynthetic bacterium

❹ Descendants of the photosynthetic bacterium evolve into chloroplasts

▲ **FIGURE 17-5 The probable origin of mitochondria and chloroplasts in eukaryotic cells**

QUESTION Scientists have identified a living bacterium believed to be descended from the endosymbiont that gave rise to mitochondria. Would you expect the DNA sequence of this modern bacterium to be most similar to the sequence of DNA from a plant chloroplast, an animal cell nucleus, or a plant mitochondrion?

aerobic bacterium remained alive and well. In fact, it was better off than ever, because the cytoplasm of its predator-host was chock-full of half-digested food molecules, the remnants of anaerobic metabolism. The aerobe absorbed these molecules and used oxygen to metabolize them, thereby gaining enormous amounts of energy and reproducing prolifically. So abundant were the aerobes' food resources, and so bountiful their energy production, that the aerobes must have leaked energy, probably as ATP or similar molecules, back into their host's cytoplasm. The anaerobic predatory cell with its symbiotic bacteria could now metabolize food aerobically, gaining a great advantage over other anaerobic cells and leaving a greater number of offspring. Eventually, the endosymbiotic bacterium lost its ability to live independently of its host, and the mitochondrion was born (**Fig. 17-5 ❷**).

One of these successful new cellular partnerships managed a second feat: It captured a photosynthetic bacterium and similarly failed to digest its prey (**Fig. 17-5 ❸**). The bacterium flourished in its new host and gradually evolved into the first chloroplast (**Fig. 17-5 ❹**). Other eukaryotic organelles may have also originated through endosymbiosis. Many biologists believe that cilia, flagella, centrioles, and microtubules may all have evolved from a symbiosis between a spirilla-like bacterium (a form of bacterium with an elongated corkscrew shape) and an early eukaryotic cell.

Evidence for the Endosymbiont Hypothesis Is Strong

Several types of evidence support the endosymbiont hypothesis. A particularly compelling line of evidence is the many distinctive biochemical features shared by eukaryotic organelles and living bacteria. In addition, mitochondria, chloroplasts, and centrioles each contain their own minute supply of DNA, which many researchers interpret as remnants of the DNA originally contained within the engulfed bacteria.

Another kind of support comes from *living intermediates*, organisms alive today that are similar to hypothetical ancestors and thus help show that a proposed evolutionary pathway is plausible. For example, the amoeba *Pelomyxa palustris* lacks mitochondria but hosts a permanent population of aerobic bacteria that carry out much the same role. Similarly, a variety of corals, some clams, a few snails, and at least one species of *Paramecium* harbor a collection of photosynthetic algae in their cells (**Fig. 17-6**). These examples of modern cells that host bacterial endosymbionts suggest that similar symbiotic associations could have occurred almost 2 billion years ago and led to the first eukaryotic cells.

17.3 WHAT WERE THE EARLIEST MULTICELLULAR ORGANISMS LIKE?

Once predation had evolved, increased size became an advantage. In the marine environments to which life was restricted, a larger cell could easily engulf a smaller cell and would also be difficult for other predatory cells to ingest. Larger organisms can also generally move faster than smaller ones, making successful predation and escape more likely. But enormous single cells have problems. Oxygen and nutri-

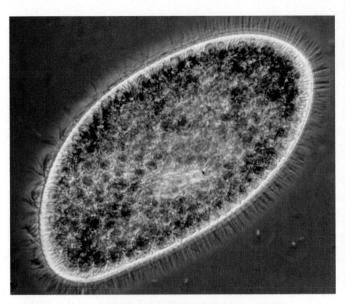

▲ **FIGURE 17-6 Symbiosis within a modern cell** The ancestors of the chloroplasts in today's plant cells may have resembled *Chlorella*, the green, photosynthetic, single-celled algae living symbiotically within the cytoplasm of the *Paramecium* pictured here.

ents going into the cell and waste products going out must diffuse through the plasma membrane. The larger a cell becomes, the less surface membrane is available per unit volume of cytoplasm (see Fig. 5-16).

There are only two ways that an organism larger than a millimeter or so in diameter can survive. First, it can have a low metabolic rate so that it doesn't need much oxygen or produce much carbon dioxide. This strategy seems to work for certain very large single-celled algae. Alternatively, an organism can be multicellular; that is, it can consist of many small cells packaged into a larger, unified body.

Some Algae Became Multicellular

The oldest fossils of multicellular organisms are about 1.2 billion years old and include impressions of the first multicellular algae, which arose from single-celled eukaryotic organisms containing chloroplasts. Multicellularity would have provided at least two advantages for these seaweeds. First, large, many-celled algae would have been difficult for single-celled predators to engulf. Second, specialization of cells would have provided the potential for staying in one place in the brightly lit waters of the shoreline, as rootlike structures burrowed in sand or clutched onto rocks, while leaflike structures floated above in the sunlight. The green, brown, and red algae lining our shores today—some, such as the brown kelp, more than 200 feet long—are the descendants of these early multicellular algae.

Animal Diversity Arose in the Precambrian Era

In addition to fossil algae, billion-year-old rocks have yielded fossil traces of animal tracks and burrows. This evidence of early animal life notwithstanding, fossils of animal bodies first appear in Precambrian rocks laid down between 610 million and 544 million years ago. Some of these ancient invertebrate animals (animals lacking a backbone) are quite different in appearance from any animals that appear in later fossil layers and may represent types of animals that left no descendants. Other fossils in these rock layers, however, appear to be ancestors of today's animals. Ancestral sponges and jellyfish appear in the oldest layers, followed later by ancestors of worms, mollusks, and arthropods.

The full range of modern invertebrate animals, however, does not appear in the fossil record until the Cambrian period, marking the beginning of the Paleozoic era, about 544 million years ago. (The phrase "fossil record" is a shorthand reference to the entire collection of all fossil evidence that has been found to date.) These Cambrian fossils reveal an adaptive radiation (see p. 313) that had already yielded a diverse array of complex body plans. Almost all of the major groups of animals on Earth today were already present in the early Cambrian. The apparently sudden appearance of so many different kinds of animals suggests that these groups actually arose earlier, but their early evolutionary history is not preserved in the fossil record.

Predation Favored the Evolution of Improved Mobility and Senses

The early diversification of animals was probably driven in part by the emergence of predatory lifestyles. For example, coevolution of predator and prey favored animals that were more mobile than their evolutionary predecessors. Mobile predators gained an advantage from an ability to travel over wide areas in search of suitable prey; mobile prey benefited if they were able to make a speedy escape. The evolution of efficient movement was often associated with the evolution of greater sensory capabilities and more complex nervous systems. Senses for detecting touch, chemicals, and light became highly developed, along with nervous systems capable of handling the sensory information and directing appropriate behaviors.

By the Silurian period (440 million to 410 million years ago), life in Earth's seas included an array of anatomically complex animals, including mud-skimming, armored trilobites, ammonites, and the chambered nautilus (**Fig. 17-7**). The nautilus survives today in almost unchanged form in deep Pacific waters.

(a) Silurian scene

(b) Trilobite

(c) Ammonite

(d) _Nautilus_

▲ FIGURE 17-7 **Diversity of ocean life during the Silurian period (a)** Life characteristic of the oceans during the Silurian period, 440 million to 410 million years ago. Among the most common fossils from that time are **(b)** the trilobites and their predators, the nautiloids, and **(c)** the ammonites. **(d)** This living _Nautilus_ is very similar in structure to the Silurian nautiloids, showing that a successful body plan may exist virtually unchanged for hundreds of millions of years.

Skeletons Improved Mobility and Protection

In many Paleozoic animal species, mobility was enhanced in part by the origin of hard external body coverings known as **exoskeletons.** Exoskeletons improved mobility by providing hard surfaces to which muscles attached; these attachments made it possible for animals to use their muscles to move appendages used to swim about or move over the sea floor. Exoskeletons also provided support for animals' bodies and protection from predators.

About 530 million years ago, one group of animals— the fishes—developed a new form of body support and muscle attachment: an internal skeleton. These early fishes were inconspicuous members of the ocean community, but by 400 million years ago, fishes were a diverse and prominent group. By and large, the fishes proved to be faster than the invertebrates, with more acute senses and larger brains. Eventually, they became the dominant predators of the open seas.

17.4 HOW DID LIFE INVADE THE LAND?

A compelling subplot in the long tale of life's history is the story of life's invasion of land after more than 3 billion years of a strictly watery existence. In moving to solid ground, organisms had many obstacles to overcome. Life in the sea provides buoyant support against gravity, but on land an organism must bear its weight against the crushing force of gravity. The sea provides ready access to life-sustaining water, but a terrestrial organism must find adequate water. Sea-dwelling plants and animals can reproduce by means of mobile sperm or eggs, or both, which swim or drift to each other through the water. The gametes of land-dwellers, however, must be protected from drying out.

Despite the obstacles to life on land, the vast empty spaces of the Paleozoic landmass represented a tremendous evolutionary opportunity. The potential rewards of terrestrial life were especially great for plants. Water strongly absorbs light, so even in the clearest water, photosynthesis is limited to the upper few hundred meters of depth, and usually much less. Out of the water, the dazzling brightness of the sun permits rapid photosynthesis. Furthermore, terrestrial soils are rich storehouses of nutrients, whereas seawater tends to be low in some nutrients, particularly nitrogen and phosphorus. Finally, the Paleozoic sea swarmed with plant-eating animals, but the land was devoid of animal life. The plants that first colonized the land would have had ample sunlight, untouched nutrient sources, and no predators.

Some Plants Became Adapted to Life on Dry Land

In moist soils at the water's edge, a few small green algae began to grow, taking advantage of the sunlight and nutrients. They didn't have large bodies to support against the force of gravity, and, living right in the film of water on the soil, they could easily obtain water. About 475 million years ago, some of these algae gave rise to the first multicellular land plants. Initially simple, low-growing forms, land plants rapidly evolved solutions to two of the main difficulties of plant life on land: obtaining and conserving water and staying upright despite gravity and winds. Water-resistant coatings on aboveground parts reduced water loss by evaporation, and rootlike structures delved into the soil, mining water and minerals. Specialized cells formed tubes called vascular tissues to conduct water from roots to leaves. Extra-thick walls surrounding certain cells enabled stems to stand erect.

Primitive Land Plants Retained Swimming Sperm and Required Water to Reproduce

Reproduction out of water presented challenges. As do animals, plants produce sperm and eggs, which must be able to meet to produce the next generation. The first land plants had swimming sperm, presumably much like those of today's mosses and ferns. Consequently, the earliest plants were restricted to swamps and marshes, where the sperm and eggs could be released into the water or to areas with abundant rainfall, where the ground would occasionally be covered with water. Later, plants with swimming sperm prospered during periods in which the climate was warm and moist. For example, the Carboniferous period (360 million to 286 million years ago) was characterized by vast forests of giant tree ferns and club mosses (**Fig. 17-8**). The coal we mine today is derived from the fossil remains of those forests.

Seed Plants Encased Sperm in Pollen Grains

Meanwhile, some plants inhabiting drier regions had evolved a means of reproduction that no longer depended on water. The eggs of these plants were retained on the parent plant, and the sperm were encased in drought-resistant pollen grains that traveled on the wind from plant to plant. When the pollen grains landed near an egg, they released sperm cells directly into living tissue, eliminating the need for a surface film of water. The fertilized egg remained on the parent plant, where it developed inside a seed, which provided protection and nutrients for the developing embryo within.

The earliest seed-bearing plants appeared in the late Devonian period (375 million years ago) and produced their seeds along branches, without any specialized structures to hold them. By the middle of the Carboniferous period, however, a new kind of seed-bearing plant had arisen. These plants, called **conifers,** protected their developing seeds inside cones. Conifers, which as wind-pollinated plants did not depend on water for reproduction, flourished and spread during the Permian period (286 to 245 million years ago), when mountains rose, swamps drained, and the climate became much drier. The conifers' good fortune, however, was not shared by the tree ferns and giant club mosses, which, with their swimming sperm, largely went extinct.

Flowering Plants Enticed Animals to Carry Pollen

About 140 million years ago, during the Cretaceous period, the flowering plants appeared, having evolved from a group of conifer-like plants. Many flowering plants are pollinated by insects and other animals, and this mode of pollination seems to have conferred an evolutionary advantage. Flower pollination by animals can be far more efficient than pollination

◀ FIGURE 17-8 **The swamp forest of the Carboniferous period** The treelike plants in this artist's reconstruction are tree ferns and giant club mosses, most species of which are now extinct.

QUESTION Why are today's ferns and club mosses so small in comparison to their giant ancestors?

by wind. Wind-pollinated plants must produce an enormous amount of pollen because the vast majority of pollen grains fail to reach their target. Today, flowering plants dominate the land, except in cold northern regions, where conifers still prevail.

Some Animals Became Adapted to Life on Dry Land

Soon after land plants evolved, providing potential food sources for other organisms, animals emerged from the sea. The first animals to move onto land were **arthropods** (the group that today includes insects, spiders, scorpions, centipedes, and crabs). Why arthropods? The answer seems to be that they already possessed certain structures that, purely by chance, were suited to life on land. Foremost among these structures was an exoskeleton, such as the shell of a lobster or crab. Exoskeletons are both waterproof and strong enough to support a small animal against the force of gravity.

For millions of years, arthropods had the land and its plants to themselves, and for tens of millions of years more, they were the dominant land animals. Dragonflies with a wingspan of 28 inches (70 centimeters) flew among the Carboniferous tree ferns, while millipedes 6.5 feet (2 meters) long munched their way across the swampy forest floor. Eventually, however, the arthropods' splendid isolation came to an end.

Amphibians Evolved from Lobefin Fishes

About 400 million years ago, a group of Silurian fishes called the lobefins appeared, probably in fresh water. **Lobefins** had two important features that would later enable their descendants to colonize land: (1) stout, fleshy fins with which they crawled about on the bottoms of shallow, quiet waters, and (2) an outpouching of the digestive tract that could be filled with air, like a primitive lung. One group of lobefins inhab-

ited very shallow ponds and streams, which shrank during droughts and often became oxygen poor. By taking air into their lungs, these lobefins could obtain oxygen anyway. Some began to use their fins to crawl from pond to pond in search of prey or water, as some modern fish do today (**Fig. 17-9**).

The benefits of feeding on land and moving from pool to pool favored the evolution of a group of animals that could stay out of water for longer periods and that could move about more effectively on land. With improvements in lungs and legs, **amphibians** evolved from lobefins, first appearing in the fossil record about 350 million years ago. To an amphibian, the Carboniferous swamp forests were a kind of paradise: no predators to speak of, abundant prey, and a warm, moist climate. As had the insects and millipedes, some amphibians

▲ FIGURE 17-9 **A fish that walks on land** Some modern fishes, such as this mudskipper, walk on land. As did the ancient lobefin fishes that gave rise to amphibians, mudskippers use their strong pectoral fins to move across dry areas in their swampy habitats.

QUESTION Does the mudskipper's ability to walk on land constitute evidence that lobefin fishes were the ancestors of amphibians?

evolved gigantic size, including salamanders more than 10 feet (3 meters) long.

Despite their success, the early amphibians were not fully adapted to life on land. Their lungs were simple sacs without very much surface area, so they had to obtain some of their oxygen through their skin. Therefore, their skin had to be kept moist, a requirement that restricted them to swampy habitats where they wouldn't dry out. Further, amphibian sperm and eggs could not survive in dry surroundings and had to be deposited in watery environments. So, although amphibians could move about on land, they could not stray too far from the water's edge. Along with the tree ferns and club mosses, amphibians declined when the climate turned dry at the beginning of the Permian period about 286 million years ago.

Reptiles Evolved from Amphibians

As the conifers were evolving on the fringes of the swamp forests, a group of amphibians was also evolving adaptations to drier conditions. These amphibians ultimately gave rise to the **reptiles,** which had three major adaptations to life on land. First, reptiles evolved shelled, waterproof eggs that enclosed a supply of water for the developing embryo. Thus, eggs could be laid on land without the reptiles' having to venture back to the dangerous swamps full of fish and amphibian predators. Second, ancestral reptiles evolved scaly, water-resistant skin that helped prevent the loss of body water to the dry air. Finally, reptiles evolved improved lungs that were able to provide the entire oxygen supply of an active animal. As the climate dried during the Permian period, reptiles became the dominant land vertebrates, relegating amphibians to the swampy backwaters where most remain today.

A few tens of millions of years later, the climate returned to more moist and stable conditions. This period saw the evolution of some very large reptiles, in particular, the dinosaurs (**Fig. 17-10**). The variety of dinosaur forms was enormous—large and small, fleet-footed and ponderous, predators and plant eaters. Dinosaurs were among the most successful animals ever, if we consider persistence as a measure of success. They flourished for more than 100 million years, until about 65 million years ago, when the last dinosaurs went extinct. No one is certain why they died out, but the aftereffects of a gigantic meteorite's impact with Earth seem to have been the final blow (as discussed in section 17.5).

Even during the age of dinosaurs, many reptiles remained quite small. One major difficulty faced by small reptiles is maintaining a high body temperature. A warm body is advantageous for an active animal, because warmer nerves and muscles work more efficiently. But a warm body loses heat to the environment unless the air is also warm. Heat loss is a big problem for small animals, which have a larger surface area per unit of volume than do larger animals. Many species of small reptiles have evolved slow metabolisms and cope with the heat-loss problem by confining activity to times when the air is sufficiently warm. One group of reptiles, however, followed a different evolutionary pathway. Members of this group, the birds, evolved insulation, in the form of feathers. (Birds were formerly placed in their own class, separate from reptiles. For more information on why birds are now understood to be a type of reptile, see "A Closer Look at Phylogenetic Trees" on pp. 348–349.)

In ancestral birds, feathers, which arose through evolutionary modification of scales, helped retain body heat. Consequently, these animals could be active in cool habitats and during the night, when their scaly relatives became sluggish. Later, some ancestral birds evolved longer, stronger feathers on their forelimbs, perhaps under selection for better ability

▶ FIGURE 17-10 **A reconstruction of a Cretaceous forest** By the Cretaceous period, flowering plants dominated terrestrial vegetation. Dinosaurs, such as the predatory pack of 6-foot-long *Velociraptors* shown here, were the preeminent land animals. Although small by dinosaur standards, *Velociraptors* were formidable predators with great running speed, sharp teeth, and deadly, sickle-like claws on their hind feet.

to glide from trees or to jump after insect prey. Ultimately, feathers evolved into structures capable of supporting powered flight. Fully developed, flight-capable feathers are present in 150-million-year-old fossils, so the earlier insulating structures that eventually developed into flight feathers must have been present well before that time.

Reptiles Gave Rise to Mammals

Unlike the egg-laying reptiles, **mammals** evolved live birth and the ability to feed their young with secretions of the mammary (milk-producing) glands. Ancestral mammals also developed hair, which provided insulation. Because the uterus, mammary glands, and hair do not fossilize, we may never know when these structures first appeared, or what their intermediate forms looked like. Recently, however, a team of paleontologists found bits of hair preserved in coprolites, which are fossilized animal feces. These coprolites, found in the Gobi Desert of China, were deposited by an anonymous predator 55 million years ago, so mammals have presumably had hair for at least that many years.

The earliest fossil mammal unearthed thus far is almost 200 million years old. Early mammals, which can be distinguished by distinctive skeletal features, thus coexisted with the dinosaurs. They were mostly small creatures. The largest known mammal from the dinosaur era was about the size of a modern raccoon, but most early mammal species were far smaller than that. When the dinosaurs went extinct, however, mammals colonized the habitats left empty by the extinctions. Mammal species prospered, diversifying into the array of modern forms that we see today.

17.5 WHAT ROLE HAS EXTINCTION PLAYED IN THE HISTORY OF LIFE?

If there is a lesson in the great tale of life's history, it is that nothing lasts forever. The story of life can be read as a long series of evolutionary dynasties, with each new dominant group rising, ruling the land or the seas for a time and, inevitably, falling into decline and extinction. Dinosaurs are the most famous of these fallen dynasties, but the list of extinct groups known only from fossils is impressively long. Despite the inevitability of extinction, however, the overall trend has been for species to arise at a faster rate than they disappear, so the number of species on Earth has tended to increase over time.

Evolutionary History Has Been Marked by Periodic Mass Extinctions

Over much of life's history, the origin and disappearance of species has proceeded in a steady, relentless manner. This slow and steady turnover of species, however, has been interrupted by episodes of **mass extinction** (Fig. 17-11). These mass extinctions are characterized by the relatively sudden disappearance of a wide variety of species over a large part of Earth. The worst episode of all, which occurred 245 million years ago at the end of the Permian period, wiped out more than 90% of the world's species, and life came perilously close to disappearing altogether.

Climate Change Contributed to Mass Extinctions

Mass extinctions have had a profound impact on the course of life's history, repeatedly redrawing the picture of life's diversity. What could have caused such dramatic changes in the fortunes of so many species? Many evolutionary biologists believe that changes in climate must have played an important role. When the climate changes, as it has done many times over the course of Earth's history, organisms that are adapted for survival in one climate may be unable to survive in a drastically different climate. In particular, at times when warm climates gave way to drier, colder climates with more variable temperatures, species may have gone extinct after failing to adapt to the harsh new conditions.

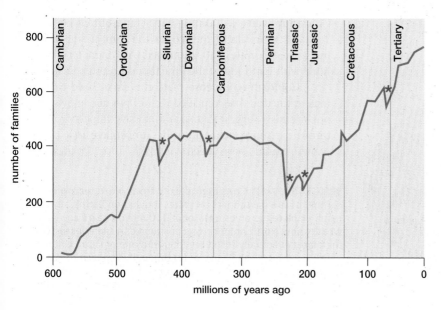

◀ FIGURE 17-11 **Mass extinctions** This graph plots the number of marine-animal groups against time, as reconstructed from the fossil record. Notice the general trend toward an increasing number of groups, punctuated by periods of sometimes rapid extinction. Five of these declines, marked by asterisks, are so steep that they qualify as catastrophic mass extinctions.

QUESTION If extinction is the ultimate fate of all species, how can the total number of species have increased over time?

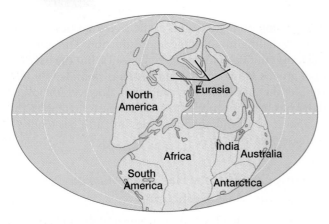

(a) 340 million years ago

(b) 225 million years ago

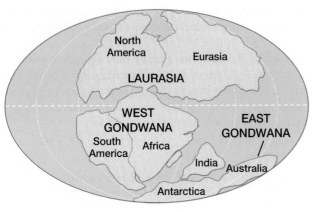

(c) 135 million years ago

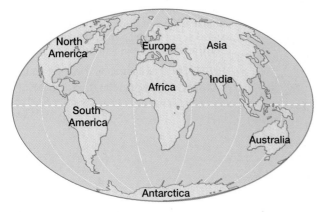

(d) Present

One cause of climate change is the shifting positions of continents. These movements are sometimes called *continental drift.* Continental drift is caused by **plate tectonics,** in which the Earth's surface, including the continents and the seafloor, is divided into plates that rest atop a viscous but fluid layer and move slowly about. As the plates wander, their positions may change in latitude (**Fig. 17-12**). For example, 340 million years ago, much of North America was located at or near the equator, an area characterized by consistently warm and wet tropical weather. But as time has passed, plate tectonics has carried the continent up into temperate and arctic regions. As a result, the once tropical climate was replaced by a regime of seasonal changes, cooler temperatures, and less rainfall. Plate tectonics continues today; the Atlantic Ocean, for example, widens by a few centimeters each year.

Catastrophic Events May Have Caused the Worst Mass Extinctions

Geological data indicate that most mass extinction events coincided with periods of climatic change. To many scientists, however, the rapidity of mass extinctions suggests that the slow process of climate change could not, by itself, be responsible for such large-scale disappearances of species. Perhaps more sudden events also play a role. For example, catastrophic geological events, such as massive volcanic eruptions, could have had devastating effects. Geologists have found evidence of past volcanic eruptions so huge that they make the 1980 Mount St. Helens explosion look like a firecracker by comparison. Even such gigantic eruptions, however, would directly affect only a relatively small portion of Earth's surface.

The search for the causes of mass extinctions took a fascinating turn in the early 1980s when Luis and Walter Alvarez proposed that the extinction event of 65 million years ago, which wiped out the dinosaurs and many other species, was caused by the impact of a huge meteorite. The Alvarezes' idea was met with great skepticism when it was first introduced, but geological research since that time has generated a great deal of evidence that a massive impact did indeed occur 65 million years ago. In fact, researchers have identified the Chicxulub crater, a 100-mile-wide crater buried beneath the Yucatan Peninsula of Mexico, as the impact site of a giant meteorite—6 miles (10 kilometers) in diameter—that collided with Earth just at the time that dinosaurs disappeared.

Could this immense meteorite strike have caused the mass extinction that coincided with it? No one knows for sure, but scientists suggest that such a massive impact would have thrown so much debris into the atmosphere that the entire planet would have been plunged into darkness for a

◄ **FIGURE 17-12 Continental drift from plate tectonics** The continents are passengers on plates moving on Earth's surface as a result of plate tectonics. **(a)** About 340 million years ago, much of what is now North America was positioned at the equator. **(b)** All the plates eventually fused together into one gigantic landmass, which geologists call Pangaea. **(c)** Gradually Pangaea broke up into Laurasia and Gondwanaland, which itself eventually broke up into West and East Gondwana. **(d)** Further plate motion eventually resulted in the current positions of the modern-day continents.

If Extinct Species Can Be Revived by Cloning?

Scientists have cloned a number of animal species, including mice, dogs, cats, horses, and cows. Could the technology of cloning be used to bring back extinct species? In principle, yes, provided that perfectly preserved DNA of the extinct species is available. Such DNA could be transferred to an egg from a closely related, living species, and the egg implanted in a surrogate mother of that species.

For example, researchers have suggested that it might be possible to clone a woolly mammoth, using an elephant surrogate mother and DNA extracted from 20,000-year-old mammoths found frozen beneath the Siberian tundra. Most scientists, however, believe that any DNA recovered from a fossil mammoth would be far too degraded for use in cloning, and synthesizing an entire mammoth genome (its sequence is now almost fully known) is beyond the capabilities of current technology. The odds of success might be greater for another proposed project, which would use DNA from a preserved museum specimen to revive the Tasmanian tiger, an Australian mammal that has been extinct for more than 70 years. If cloning recently extinct species proves to be possible, would you support doing it?

period of years. With little light reaching the planet, temperatures would have dropped precipitously and the photosynthetic capture of energy (on which all life ultimately depends) would have declined drastically. The worldwide "impact winter" would have spelled doom for the dinosaurs and a host of other species.

17.6 HOW DID HUMANS EVOLVE?

Scientists are intensely interested in the origin and evolution of humans. The outline of human evolution that we present in this section represents an interpretation that is widely shared among paleontologists. However, fossil evidence of human evolution is comparatively scarce and therefore open to a variety of interpretations. Thus, some paleontologists would disagree with aspects of the scenario we present.

Humans Inherited Some Early Primate Adaptations for Life in Trees

Humans are members of a mammal group known as **primates,** which also includes lemurs, monkeys, and apes. The oldest primate fossils are 55 million years old, but because primate fossils are relatively rare compared with those of many other animals, the first primates probably arose considerably earlier but left no fossil record. Early primates probably fed on fruits and leaves, and were adapted for life in the trees. Many modern primates retain the tree-dwelling lifestyle of their ancestors (**Fig. 17-13**). The common heritage of humans and other primates is reflected in a set of physical characteristics that was present in the earliest primates and that persists in many modern primates, including humans.

Binocular Vision Provided Early Primates with Accurate Depth Perception

One of the earliest primate adaptations seems to have been large, forward-facing eyes (see Fig. 17-13). Jumping from branch to branch is risky business unless an animal can accurately judge where the next branch is located. Accurate depth

(a) **Tarsier**

(b) **Lemur**

(c) **Macaque**

◀ FIGURE 17-13 **Representative primates** The **(a)** tarsier, **(b)** lemur, and **(c)** lion-tail macaque monkey all have a relatively flat face, with forward-looking eyes providing binocular vision. All also have color vision and grasping hands. These features, retained from the earliest primates, are shared by humans.

perception was made possible by binocular vision, provided by forward-facing eyes with overlapping fields of view. Another key adaptation was color vision. We cannot, of course, tell if a fossil animal had color vision, but since modern primates have excellent color vision, it seems reasonable to assume that earlier primates did as well. Many primates feed on fruit, and color vision helps to detect ripe fruit among a bounty of green leaves.

Early Primates Had Grasping Hands

Early primates had long, grasping fingers that could wrap around and hold onto tree limbs. This adaptation to tree dwelling was the basis for later evolution of human hands that could perform both a *precision grip* (used by modern humans for delicate maneuvers such as manipulating small objects, writing, and sewing) and a *power grip* (used for powerful actions, such as swinging a club or thrusting with a spear).

A Large Brain Facilitated Hand–Eye Coordination and Complex Social Interactions

Primates have brains that are larger, relative to their body size, than the brains of almost all other animals. No one really knows for certain which environmental factors favored the evolution of large brains. It seems reasonable, however, that controlling and coordinating rapid locomotion through trees, the dexterous movements of the hands in manipulating objects, and binocular, color vision would be facilitated by increased brain power. Most primates also have fairly complex social systems, which require relatively high intelligence. If sociality promoted increased survival and reproduction, the benefits to individuals of successful social interaction might have favored the evolution of a larger brain.

The Oldest Hominin Fossils Are from Africa

On the basis of comparisons of DNA from modern chimps, gorillas, and humans, researchers estimate that the **hominin** line (humans and their fossil relatives) diverged from the ape lineage sometime between 5 million and 8 million years ago. The fossil record, however, suggests that the split must have occurred at the early end of that range. Paleontologists working in the African country of Chad in 2002 discovered fossils of a hominin, *Sahelanthropus tchadensis*, that lived more than 6 million years ago (**Fig. 17-14**). *Sahelanthropus* is clearly a hominin because it shares several anatomical features with later members of the group. But because this oldest known member of our family also exhibits other features that are more characteristic of apes, it may represent a point on our family tree that is close to the split between apes and hominins.

In addition to *Sahelanthropus,* two other hominin species—*Ardipithecus ramidus* and *Orrorin tugenensis*—are known from fossils appearing in rocks that are between 4 million and 6 million years old. Our knowledge of these hominins is limited, however, because only a few specimens have been found thus far, and most of these recent discoveries typically include only small portions of skeletons. A more extensive

▲ FIGURE 17-14 **The earliest hominin** This nearly complete skull of *Sahelanthropus tchadensis*, which is more than 6 million years old, is the oldest hominin fossil yet found.

record of early hominin evolution does not begin until about 4 million years ago. That date marks the beginning of the fossil record of the genus *Australopithecus* (**Fig. 17-15**), a group of African hominin species with brains larger than those of their prehominin forebears but still much smaller than those of modern humans.

The Earliest Hominins Could Stand and Walk Upright

The earliest australopithecines (as the various species of *Australopithecus* are collectively known) had legs that were shorter, relative to their height, than those of modern humans, but their knee joints allowed them to straighten their legs fully, permitting efficient bipedal (upright, two-legged) locomotion. Footprints almost 4 million years old, discovered in Tanzania by anthropologist Mary Leakey, show that even the earliest australopithecines could, and at least sometimes did, walk upright. Upright posture may have evolved even earlier. The discoverers of *Sahelanthropus* and *Orrorin* argue that the leg and foot bones of these earliest hominins have characteristics that indicate bipedal locomotion, but this conclusion will remain speculative until more complete skeletons of these species are found.

The reasons for the evolution of bipedal locomotion among the early hominins remain poorly understood. Perhaps hominins that could stand upright gained an advantage in gathering or carrying food in their forest habitat. Whatever its cause, the early evolution of upright posture was extremely important in the evolutionary history of hominins, because it freed their hands from use in walking. Later hominins were thus able to carry weapons, manipulate tools, and eventually achieve the cultural revolutions produced by modern *Homo sapiens*.

▼ FIGURE 17-15 A possible evolutionary tree for humans This hypothetical family tree shows facial reconstructions of representative specimens. Although many paleontologists consider this to be the most likely human family tree, there are several alternative interpretations of the known hominin fossils. Fossils of the earliest hominins are scarce and fragmentary, so the relationship of these species to later hominins remains unknown.

H. sapiens

H. heidelbergensis

H. neanderthalensis

Homo ergaster

H. erectus

H. habilis

A. robustus

A. africanus

A. boisei

Australopithecus afarensis

A. anamensis

............?
Orrorin tugenensis

............?
Sahelanthropus tchadensis

............?
Ardipithecus ramidus

millions of years ago

0   1   2   3   4   5   6

Several Species of *Australopithecus* Emerged in Africa

The oldest australopithecine species, represented by fossilized teeth, skull fragments, and arm bones, was unearthed near an ancient lake bed in Kenya from sediments that were dated as between 3.9 million and 4.1 million years old. It was named *Australopithecus anamensis* by its discoverers (*anam* means "lake" in the local Ethiopian language). The second most ancient australopithecine, called *Australopithecus afarensis*, was discovered in the Afar region of Ethiopia. Fossil remains of this species as old as 3.9 million years have been unearthed. The *A. afarensis* line apparently gave rise to at least two distinct forms: small, omnivorous species such as *A. africanus* (which was similar to *A. afarensis* in size and eating habits), and larger, herbivorous species such as *A. robustus* and *A. boisei*. All of the australopithecine species had gone extinct by 1.2 million years ago. Before disappearing, however, one of these species gave rise to a new branch of the hominin family tree, the genus *Homo* (see Fig. 17-15).

The Genus *Homo* Diverged from the Australopithecines 2.5 Million Years Ago

Hominins that are sufficiently similar to modern humans to be placed in the genus *Homo* first appear in African fossils that are about 2.5 million years old. Among the earliest African *Homo* fossils are *H. habilis* (see Fig. 17-15), a species whose body and brain were larger than those of the australopithecines but that retained the apelike long arms and short legs of their australopithecine ancestors. In contrast, the skeletal anatomy of *H. ergaster*, a species whose fossils first appear 2 million years ago, has limb proportions more like those of modern humans. This species is believed by many paleoanthropologists (scientists who study human origins) to be on the evolutionary branch that led ultimately to our own species, *H. sapiens*. In this view, *H. ergaster* was the common ancestor of two distinct branches of hominins. The first branch led to *H. erectus*, which was the first hominin species to leave Africa. The second branch from *H. ergaster* ultimately led to *H. heidelbergensis*, some of which migrated to Europe and gave rise to the Neanderthals, *H. neanderthalensis*. Meanwhile, back in Africa, another branch split off from the *H. heidelbergensis* lineage. This branch became *H. sapiens*—modern humans.

The Evolution of *Homo* Was Accompanied by Advances in Tool Technology

Hominin evolution is closely tied to the development of tools, a hallmark of hominin behavior. The oldest tools discovered so far were found in 2.5-million-year-old East African rocks, concurrent with the early emergence of the genus *Homo*. Early *Homo*, whose cheek teeth were much smaller than those of the genus's australopithecine ancestors, might first have used stone tools to break and crush tough foods that were hard to chew. Hominins constructed their earliest tools by striking one rock with another to chip off fragments and leave a sharp edge behind. During the next several hundred thousand years, tool-

making techniques in Africa gradually became more advanced. By 1.7 million years ago, tools had become more sophisticated. Flakes were chipped symmetrically from both sides of a rock to form double-edged tools ranging from hand axes, used for cutting and chopping, to points, probably used on spears (Figs. 17-16a,b). *Homo ergaster* and other bearers of these weapons presumably ate meat, probably acquired from both hunting and scavenging for the remains of prey killed by other predators. Double-edged tools were carried to Europe at least 600,000 years ago by migrating populations of *H. heidelbergen-*

(a) *Homo habilis*

(b) *Homo ergaster*

(c) *Homo neanderthalensis*

▲ FIGURE 17-16 Representative hominin tools (a) *Homo habilis* produced only fairly crude chopping tools called hand axes, usually unchipped on one end to hold in the hand. (b) *Homo ergaster* manufactured much finer tools. The tools were typically sharp all the way around the stone; at least some of these blades were probably tied to spears rather than held in the hand. (c) Neanderthal tools were works of art, with extremely sharp edges made by flaking off tiny bits of stone. In comparing these weapons, note the progressive increase in the number of flakes taken off the blades and the corresponding decrease in flake size. Smaller, more numerous flakes produce a sharper blade and suggest more insight into toolmaking, more patience, finer control of hand movements, or perhaps all three.

sis, and the Neanderthal descendants of these emigrants took stone-tool construction to new heights of skill and delicacy (**Fig. 17-16c**).

Neanderthals Had Large Brains and Excellent Tools

Neanderthals first appeared in the European fossil record about 150,000 years ago. By about 70,000 years ago, they had spread throughout Europe and western Asia. By 30,000 years ago, however, the species was extinct.

Contrary to the popular image of a hulking, stoop-shouldered "caveman," Neanderthals were quite similar to modern humans in many ways. Although more heavily muscled, Neanderthals walked fully erect, were dexterous enough to manufacture finely crafted stone tools, and had brains that, on average, were slightly larger than those of modern humans. Many European Neanderthal fossils show heavy brow ridges and a broad, flat skull, but others, particularly from areas around the eastern shores of the Mediterranean Sea, are somewhat more physically similar to *H. sapiens*.

Despite the physical and technological similarities between Neanderthals and *H. sapiens*, there is no solid archaeological evidence that Neanderthals ever developed an advanced culture that included such characteristically human endeavors as art, music, and rituals. Some anthropologists argue that, because their skeletal anatomy shows that they were physically capable of making the sounds required for speech, Neanderthals might have acquired language. This interpretation of Neanderthal anatomy, however, is not unanimously accepted. In general, the available evidence of the Neanderthal way of life is limited and open to different interpretations, and anthropologists are engaged in a sometimes heated debate about how advanced Neanderthal culture became.

Though some anthropologists argue that Neanderthals were simply a variety of *H. sapiens*, most agree that Neanderthals were a separate species. Dramatic evidence in support of this hypothesis has come from researchers who have isolated DNA from various Neanderthal skeletons that are between 20,000 and 38,000 years old. These extractions of ancient DNA have allowed researchers to compare the nucleotide sequences of Neanderthal genes with the sequences of the same genes in both fossil and modern humans. The comparisons have shown that Neanderthal sequences are very different from those of both modern and fossil humans, but that modern and fossil humans share similar sequences. These findings indicate that the evolutionary branch leading to Neanderthals diverged from the ancestral human line about 500,000 years ago, hundreds of thousands of years before the emergence of modern *H. sapiens*. This early divergence supports the conclusion that Neanderthals were a distinct species, *H. neanderthalensis*.

Modern Humans Emerged Less Than 200,000 Years Ago

The fossil record shows that anatomically modern humans appeared in Africa at least 160,000 years ago and possibly as long as 195,000 years ago. The location of these fossils suggests that

Homo sapiens originated in Africa, but most of our knowledge about our own early history comes from European and Middle Eastern fossils of *H. sapiens*, collectively known as Cro-Magnons (after the district in France in which their remains were first discovered). Cro-Magnons appeared about 90,000 years ago. They had domed heads, smooth brows, and prominent chins (just like us). Their tools were precision instruments similar to the stone tools used until recently in many parts of the world.

Behaviorally, Cro-Magnons seem to have been similar to, but more sophisticated than, Neanderthals. Artifacts from 30,000-year-old Cro-Magnon archaeological sites include elegant bone flutes, graceful carved ivory sculptures, and evidence of elaborate burial ceremonies (**Fig. 17-17**). Perhaps the most remarkable accomplishment of Cro-Magnons is the magnificent art left in caves in places such as Altamira in Spain and Lascaux and Chauvet in France (**Fig. 17-18**). The oldest cave paintings so far found are more than 30,000 years old, and even the oldest ones make use of sophisticated artistic techniques. No one knows exactly why these paintings were made, but they attest to minds as capable as our own.

Cro-Magnons and Neanderthals Lived Side by Side

Cro-Magnons coexisted with Neanderthals in Europe and the Middle East for perhaps as many as 50,000 years before the Neanderthals disappeared. Some researchers believe that Cro-Magnons interbred extensively with Neanderthals, so Neanderthals were essentially absorbed into the human genetic

▲ **FIGURE 17-17 Paleolithic burial** This 24,000-year-old grave shows evidence that Cro-Magnon people ritualistically buried their dead. The body was covered with a dye known as red ocher, then buried with a headdress made of snail shells and a flint tool in its hand.

▲ **FIGURE 17-18 The sophistication of Cro-Magnon people** Cave paintings by Cro-Magnons have been remarkably preserved by the relatively constant underground conditions of a cave in Lascaux, France.

mainstream. Other scientists disagree, citing mounting evidence such as the fossil DNA described earlier, and suggest that later-arriving Cro-Magnons simply overran and displaced the less-well-adapted Neanderthals.

Neither hypothesis does a good job of explaining how the two kinds of hominins managed to occupy the same geographical areas for such a long time. The persistence in one area of two similar but distinct groups for tens of thousands of years seems inconsistent with both interbreeding and direct competition. Perhaps the competition between *H. neanderthalensis* and *H. sapiens* was indirect, so that the two species were able to coexist for a time in the same habitat, until the superior ability of *H. sapiens* to exploit the available resources slowly drove Neanderthals to extinction.

Several Waves of Hominins Emigrated from Africa

The human family tree is rooted in Africa, but hominins found their way out of Africa on numerous occasions. For example, *H. erectus* reached tropical Asia almost 2 million years ago and apparently thrived there, eventually spreading across Asia (**Fig. 17-19a**). Similarly, *H. heidelbergensis* made it to Europe at least 780,000 years ago. It is increasingly clear that the genus *Homo* made repeated long-distance emigrations, beginning as soon as sufficiently capable limb anatomy evolved. What is less clear is how all this wandering is related to the origin of modern *H. sapiens*. According to the "African replacement" hypothesis (the basis of the scenario outlined earlier), *H. sapiens* emerged in Africa and dispersed less than 150,000 years ago, spreading into the Near East, Europe, and

Asia and replacing all other hominins (see Fig. 17-19a). But some paleoanthropologists believe that populations of *H. sapiens* evolved simultaneously in many regions from the already widespread populations of *H. erectus*. According to this "multiregional origin" hypothesis, continued migrations and interbreeding among *H. erectus* populations in different regions of the world maintained them as a single species as they gradually evolved into *H. sapiens* (**Fig. 17-19b**). Although an increasing number of studies of modern human DNA support the African replacement model of the origin of our

(a) African replacement hypothesis

(b) Multiregional hypothesis

▲ **FIGURE 17-19 Competing hypotheses for the evolution of *Homo sapiens* (a)** The "African replacement" hypothesis suggests that *H. sapiens* evolved in Africa, then migrated throughout the Near East, Europe, and Asia, displacing the other hominin species that were present in those regions. **(b)** The "multiregional" hypothesis suggests that populations of *H. sapiens* evolved in many regions simultaneously from the already widespread populations of *H. erectus*.

QUESTION Paleontologists recently discovered fossil hominins with features characteristic of modern humans in 160,000-year-old sediments in Africa. Which hypothesis does this new evidence support?

Case Study continued

Little People, Big Story

What is the ancestry of *H. floresiensis*, the Hobbit of Flores Island in Indonesia? Some clues point toward an intriguing scenario. First, the only other evidence of early hominin habitation on Flores consists of stone tools found at an 840,000-year-old site. The age and relative crudeness of the tools suggest that they were probably left by *H. erectus*, the only hominin known to be present in Asia that long ago. So, *H. floresiensis* may have descended from a population of *H. erectus* that became isolated on Flores. This conclusion is supported by some anatomical similarities between *H. floresiensis* and *H. erectus*. Oddly, *H. floresiensis* is more similar to *H. erectus* specimens from a distant, 1.8-million-year-old site in Central Asia than it is to much younger *H. erectus* specimens found in relatively nearby sites on other Indonesian islands. Perhaps *H. floresiensis* descended from a very early wave of *H. erectus* migrants.

species, both hypotheses are consistent with the fossil record. Therefore, the question remains unsettled.

The Evolutionary Origin of Large Brains May Be Related to Meat Consumption

The main physical features that distinguish us from our closest relatives, the apes, are our upright posture and large, highly developed brains. As described earlier, upright posture arose very early in hominin evolution, and hominins walked upright for several million years before large-brained *Homo* species arose. What circumstances might have caused the evolution of increased brain size? Many explanations have been proposed, but little direct evidence is available; hypotheses about the evolutionary origins of large brains are necessarily speculative.

One proposed explanation for the origin of large brains suggests that they evolved in response to increasingly complex social interactions. In particular, fossil evidence suggests that, beginning about 2 million years ago, hominin social life began to include a new type of activity—the cooperative hunting of large game. The resulting access to significant amounts of meat must have fostered a need to develop methods for distributing this valuable, limited resource among group members. Some anthropologists hypothesize that the individuals best able to manage this social interaction would have been more successful at gaining a large share of meat and using their share advantageously. Perhaps this social management was best accomplished by individuals with larger, more powerful brains, and natural selection therefore favored such individuals. Observations of chimpanzee societies have shown that the distribution of group-hunted meat often involves intricate social interactions in which meat is used to form alliances, repay favors, gain access to sexual partners, placate rivals, and so on. Perhaps the mental skill required to plan, assess, and remember such interactions was the driving force behind the evolution of our large, clever brains.

The Evolutionary Origin of Human Behavior Is Highly Speculative

Even after the evolution of comparatively large brains in species such as *H. erectus*, more than a million years passed before the origin of modern humans and their extremely large brains. And even after the first appearance of modern *H. sapiens*, more than 100,000 years passed before the appearance of any archaeological evidence of the distinctively human characteristics that were made possible by a large brain: language, abstract thought, and advanced culture. The evolutionary origin of these human traits is another unresolved question, in part because direct evidence of the transition to advanced culture may never be found. Early humans capable of language and symbolic thought would not necessarily have created artifacts that indicated these capabilities. We can uncover some clues by studying our ape relatives, which possess less-complex versions of many human behaviors and mental processes. Their behavior might resemble that of ancestral hominins. Nonetheless, the late, seemingly rapid origin of advanced human culture remains a puzzle.

The Cultural Evolution of Humans Now Far Outpaces Biological Evolution

In recent millennia, human evolution has come to be dominated by *cultural evolution*, the evolution of information and behaviors that are transmitted from generation to generation by learning. Our recent evolutionary success, for example, was engendered not so much by new physical adaptations as by a series of cultural and technological revolutions. The first such revolution was the development of tools, which began with the early hominins. Tools increased the efficiency with which food and shelter could be acquired and thus increased the number of individuals that could survive within a given ecosystem. About 10,000 years ago, human culture underwent a second revolution as people discovered how to grow crops and domesticate animals. This agricultural revolution dramatically increased the amount of food that could be extracted from the environment, and the human population surged, increasing from about 5 million at the dawn of agriculture to around 750 million by 1750. The subsequent Industrial Revolution gave rise to the modern economy and its attendant improvements in public health. Longer lives and lower infant mortality led to truly explosive population growth, and today our population is 6.8 billion and still growing.

Human cultural evolution and the accompanying increases in human population have had profound effects on the continuing biological evolution of other life-forms. Our agile hands and minds have transformed much of Earth's terrestrial and aquatic habitats. Humans have become the most powerful agent of natural selection. In the words of the late evolutionary biologist Stephen Jay Gould, "We have become, by the power of a glorious evolutionary accident called intelligence, the stewards of life's continuity on Earth. We did not ask for this role, but we cannot renounce it. We may not be suited for it, but here we are."

Case Study revisited
Little People, Big Story

The discovery of the hobbit-sized *Homo floresiensis* was exciting to many people in part because it suggested that our species may have more close relatives than we previously suspected and that at least some of them lived tantalizingly close to the present. Plus, the idea of a society of tiny humans seems to have an inherent appeal. But the discovery also raises a host of fascinating evolutionary questions.

For example, how can we account for the arrival on Flores of the *H. erectus* population that left tools behind and that may be ancestral to *H. floresiensis*? Unlike some islands, Flores was never connected to the mainland. Archaeologists generally agree that hominins did not construct boats until 60,000 years ago at the earliest. So how did *H. erectus* get to Flores nearly 800,000 years before the invention of boats? Perhaps they drifted across on clumps of floating vegetation.

Another interesting question about *H. floresiensis* is the cause of their small size. Large animal species that are isolated on islands sometimes evolve smaller body size. For example, the now-extinct elephants of Flores were only about 4 feet tall. Biologists suggest that the absence of large predators on most islands eliminates much of the benefit of large size, conferring an advantage on smaller individuals that require less food. Did this kind of dynamic foster the evolution of small stature in *H. floresiensis*? Are the bodies of hominins, which have weapons to defend against predators and tools to aid in acquiring food, subject to the same evolutionary pressures that shape the bodies of other animals?

Consider This

Homo floresiensis was found on an island. If you were searching for evidence of other undiscovered recent hominin species, would you concentrate your search on islands? Why or why not? In which regions of the world would you search?

CHAPTER REVIEW

Summary of Key Concepts

17.1 How Did Life Begin?

Before life arose, lightning, ultraviolet light, and heat formed organic molecules from water and the components of primordial Earth's atmosphere—methane, ammonia, hydrogen, and water vapor. The organic molecules formed probably included nucleic acids, amino acids, short proteins, and lipids. By chance, some molecules of RNA may have had enzymatic properties, catalyzing the assembly of copies of themselves from nucleotides in Earth's waters. These may have been the forerunners of life. Protein-lipid vesicles enclosing these ribozymes may have formed the first protocells.

17.2 What Were the Earliest Organisms Like?

The oldest fossils, about 3.5 billion years old, are of prokaryotic cells that fed by absorbing organic molecules that had been synthesized in the environment. Because there was no free oxygen in the atmosphere, their energy metabolism must have been anaerobic. As the cells multiplied, they depleted the organic molecules that had been formed by prebiotic synthesis. Some cells developed the ability to synthesize their own food molecules by using simple inorganic molecules and the energy of sunlight. These earliest photosynthetic cells were probably ancestors of today's cyanobacteria.

Photosynthesis releases oxygen as a by-product, and by about 2.2 billion years ago significant amounts of free oxygen were accumulating in the atmosphere. Aerobic metabolism, which generates more cellular energy than does anaerobic metabolism, probably arose about this time.

Eukaryotic cells had evolved by about 1.7 billion years ago. The first eukaryotic cells probably arose as symbiotic associations between predatory prokaryotic cells and other bacteria. Mitochondria may have evolved from aerobic bacteria engulfed by predatory cells. Similarly, chloroplasts may have evolved from photosynthetic cyanobacteria.

17.3 What Were the Earliest Multicellular Organisms Like?

Multicellular organisms evolved from eukaryotic cells and first appeared in the seas about 1.2 billion years ago. Multicellularity offers several advantages, including greater size. In plants, increased size offered some protection from predation. Specialization of cells allowed plants to anchor themselves in the nutrient-rich, well-lit waters of the shore. For animals, multicellularity allowed more efficient predation and more effective escape from predators. These in turn provided environmental pressures for faster locomotion, improved senses, and greater intelligence.

17.4 How Did Life Invade the Land?

The first land organisms were probably algae. The first multicellular land plants appeared about 475 million years ago. Life on land required special adaptations for support of the body, reproduction, and the acquisition, distribution, and retention of water, but the land also offered abundant sunlight and protection from aquatic herbivores. Soon after land plants evolved, arthropods invaded the land. Absence of predators and abundant land plants for food probably facilitated the invasion of the land by animals.

The earliest land vertebrates evolved from lobefin fishes, which had leglike fins and a primitive lung. A group of lobefins evolved into the amphibians about 350 million years ago. Reptiles evolved from amphibians, with several further adaptations for life on land: internal fertilization, waterproof eggs that could be laid on land, water-resistant skin, and better lungs. One reptile group, the birds, evolved feathers that provided insulation and facilitated flight. Mammals, whose bodies are insulated by hair, descended from a reptile group.

17.5 What Role Has Extinction Played in the History of Life?

The history of life has been characterized by constant turnover of species as species go extinct and are replaced by new ones. Mass extinctions, in which large numbers of species disappear within a relatively short time, have occurred periodically. Mass extinctions were probably caused by some combination of climate change and catastrophic events, such as volcanic eruptions and meteorite impacts.

17.6 How Did Humans Evolve?

One group of mammals evolved into the tree-dwelling primates. Some primates descended from the trees, and these were the ancestors of apes and humans. The oldest known hominin fossils are between 6 million and 7 million years old and were found in Africa. The australopithecines arose in Africa about 4 million years ago. These hominins walked erect, had larger brains than did their forebears, and fashioned primitive tools. One group of australopithecines gave rise to a line of hominins in the genus *Homo*. *Homo* arose in Africa, but populations of several *Homo* species migrated from Africa and spread to other geographic areas. In the last of these migrations, *Homo sapiens*, characterized by a large brain and advanced tool technology, dispersed from Africa to Asia and Europe.

Key Terms

amphibian *329*

arthropod *329*

conifer *328*

endosymbiont hypothesis 325

eukaryote *325*

exoskeleton *328*

hominin *334*

lobefin *329*

mammal *331*

mass extinction *331*

plate tectonics *332*

primate *333*

prokaryote *322*

protocell *321*

reptile *330*

ribozyme *321*

spontaneous
generation *318*

Thinking Through the Concepts

Fill-in-the-Blank

1. Because there was no oxygen in the earliest atmosphere, the first cells must have derived energy by _____ metabolism of organic molecules. Oxygen was introduced into the atmosphere when some microbes developed the ability to _____ and released oxygen as a by-product. Oxygen was _____ to many of the earliest cells, but some evolved the ability to use oxygen in _____ respiration, which provided far more _____.

2. The molecule _____ became a candidate for the first self-replicating information-carrying molecule when Tom Cech and Sidney Altman discovered that some of these molecules can act as _____, which they called _____.

3. Complex cells that contain a nucleus and other organelles are called _____ cells. A compelling explanation for the origin of these complex cells is the _____ hypothesis. One observation that supports this hypothesis is that mitochondria have their own _____.

4. The sperm of early land plants had to reach the egg by _____, limiting them to _____ environments. An important adaptation to dry land was the evolution of _____, which enclosed sperm in a drought-resistant coat.

5. Early plants that protected their seeds within cones are called _____. These relied on _____ to carry their pollen. This type of plant still dominates in _____ regions. Later, some plants evolved _____, which attracted animals, particularly _____ that carried their pollen. Animal pollination is much more _____ than wind pollination.

6. The first animals to live on land were _____ because their external skeletons, also called _____, supported the animals' weight, while protecting their bodies from _____.

7. Amphibians gave rise to _____, which had three important adaptations to life on dry land: shelled, waterproof _____; scaly, water-resistant _____; and more efficient _____.

Review Questions

1. What is the evidence that life might have originated from non-living matter on early Earth? What kind of evidence would you like to see before you would accept this hypothesis?

2. Explain the endosymbiont hypothesis for the origin of chloroplasts and mitochondria.

3. Name two advantages of multicellularity for plants and two for animals.

4. What advantages and disadvantages would terrestrial existence have had for the first plants to invade the land? For the first land animals?

5. Outline the major adaptations that emerged during the evolution of vertebrates, from fish to amphibians to reptiles to birds and mammals. Explain how these adaptations increased the fitness of the various groups for life on land.

6. Outline the evolution of humans from early primates. Include in your discussion such features as binocular vision, grasping hands, bipedal locomotion, toolmaking, and brain expansion.

Applying the Concepts

1. What is cultural evolution? Is cultural evolution more or less rapid than biological evolution? Why?

2. Do you think that studying our ancestors can shed light on the behavior of modern humans? Why or why not?

3. A biologist would probably answer the age-old question "What is life?" by saying, "The ability to self-replicate." Do you agree with this definition? If so, why? If not, how would you define life in biological terms?

4. Extinctions have occurred throughout the history of life on Earth. Why should we care if humans are causing a mass extinction event now?

5. The "African replacement" and "multiregional origin" hypotheses of the evolution of *Homo sapiens* make contrasting predictions about the extent and nature of genetic divergence among human races. One predicts that races are old and highly diverged genetically; the other predicts that races are young and little diverged genetically. What data would help you determine which hypothesis is closer to the truth?

6. In biological terms, what do you think was the most significant event in the history of life? Explain your answer.

 Go to www.masteringbiology.com for practice quizzes, activities, eText, videos, current events, and more.

Systematics: Seeking Order Amidst Diversity

▲ Biologists studying the evolutionary history of type 1 human immunodeficiency virus (HIV-1) discovered that the virus, which causes AIDS, probably originated in chimpanzees.

Case Study

Origin of a Killer

ONE OF THE WORLD'S MOST FRIGHTENING DISEASES is also one of its most mysterious. Acquired immune deficiency syndrome (AIDS) appeared seemingly out of nowhere, and when it was first recognized in the early 1980s, no one knew what caused it or where it came from. Scientists raced to solve the mystery and, within a few years, had identified the infectious agent that causes AIDS: human immunodeficiency virus (HIV). Once HIV had been identified, researchers turned their attention to the question of its origin.

Finding the source of HIV required an evolutionary approach. To ask, "Where did HIV come from?" is really to ask, "What kind of virus was the ancestor of HIV?" Biologists who examine questions of ancestry are known as *systematists*. Systematists strive to categorize organisms according to their evolutionary history, building classifications that accurately reflect the structure of the tree of life. When a systematist concludes that two species are closely related, it means that the two species share a recent common ancestor from which both species evolved.

The systematists who explored the ancestry of HIV discovered that its closest relatives are found not among other viruses that infect humans, but among those that infect monkeys and apes. In fact, the latest research on HIV's evolutionary history has concluded that the closest relative of HIV-1 (the type of HIV that is most responsible for the worldwide AIDS epidemic) is a virus strain that infects a particular chimp subspecies that inhabits a limited range in West Africa. Therefore, the ancestor of the virus that we now know as HIV-1 did not evolve from a preexisting human virus but must have somehow jumped from West African chimpanzees to humans.

At a Glance

18.1 HOW ARE ORGANISMS NAMED AND CLASSIFIED?

To study and discuss organisms, biologists must name them. The branch of biology that is concerned with naming and classifying organisms is known as **taxonomy.** The basis of modern taxonomy was established by the Swedish naturalist Carl von Linné (1707–1778), who called himself Carolus Linnaeus, a Latinized version of his given name. One of Linnaeus' most durable achievements was the introduction of the two-part scientific name.

Each Species Has a Unique, Two-Part Name

The **scientific name** of an organism designates its genus and species. A **genus** is a group that includes a number of very closely related species; each **species** within a genus includes populations of organisms that can potentially interbreed under natural conditions. For example, the genus *Sialia* (bluebirds) includes three species: the eastern bluebird (*Sialia sialis*), the western bluebird (*Sialia mexicana*), and the mountain bluebird (*Sialia currucoides*) (**Fig. 18-1**). Although the three species are similar, bluebirds normally breed only with members of their own species.

(a) Eastern bluebird   **(b) Western bluebird**   **(c) Mountain bluebird**

▲ **FIGURE 18-1 Three species of bluebird** Despite their obvious similarity, these three species of bluebird—from left to right, the eastern bluebird (*Sialia sialis*), the western bluebird (*Sialia mexicana*), and the mountain bluebird (*Sialia currucoides*)—remain distinct because they do not interbreed.

In a scientific name, the genus name appears first, followed by the species name. By convention, scientific names are always underlined or *italicized*. The first letter of the genus name is always capitalized, and the first letter of the species name is always lowercase. The species name is never used alone but is always paired with its genus name.

Each two-part scientific name is unique, so referring to an organism by its scientific name rules out any chance of ambiguity or confusion. For example, the bird *Gavia immer* is commonly known in North America as the common loon, in Great Britain as the northern diver, and by still other names in non-English-speaking countries. But the Latin scientific name *Gavia immer* is recognized by biologists worldwide, overcoming language barriers and allowing precise communication.

Classification Originated as a Hierarchy of Categories

In addition to devising a method for naming species, Linnaeus also developed a method for classifying them. He placed each species into a series of hierarchically arranged categories on the basis of its resemblance to other species. The categories form a nested hierarchy in which each level includes all of the other levels below it.

The Linnaean classification system came to include eight major categories, or *taxonomic ranks*: **domain, kingdom, phylum, class, order, family,** genus, and species. Because the ranks form a nested hierarchy, each domain contains a number of kingdoms; each kingdom contains a number of phyla; each phylum includes a number of classes; each class includes a number of orders; and so on. As we move down the hierarchy, smaller and smaller groups are included.

Modern Classification Emphasizes Patterns of Evolutionary Descent

Prior to the 1859 publication of Darwin's *On the Origin of Species*, classification served mainly to facilitate the study and discussion of organisms, much as a library catalog facilitates our ability to find a book. But after Darwin demonstrated that all organisms are linked by common ancestry, biologists began to recognize that classification ought to reflect and describe the pattern of evolutionary relatedness among organisms. Today, the process of classification focuses almost exclusively on reconstructing **phylogeny,** or evolutionary history. The science of reconstructing phylogeny is known as **systematics.** Systematists communicate their findings about phylogeny by constructing evolutionary trees (see Fig. 16-11).

As systematists have increasingly focused their efforts on building evolutionary trees, they have de-emphasized the Linnaean classification system. Systematists still name groups, which they call **clades,** that include species linked by descent from a common ancestor. Clades, like the taxonomic ranks in the Linnaean classification system, can be arranged in a hierarchy, with smaller clades nested within larger ones (**Fig. 18-2**). Many systematists, however, do not assign taxonomic ranks to the clades they name. These systematists concentrate on using

▲ FIGURE 18-2 **Clades form a nested hierarchy** Any group that includes all the descendants of a common ancestor is a clade. Some of the clades represented on this evolutionary tree are outlined in different colors. Note that smaller clades nest within larger clades.

data to construct accurate evolutionary trees, rather than on more subjective evaluations of whether a given clade should be called a kingdom, a phylum, a class, an order, or a family. As a result, use of Linnaean taxonomic ranks is declining. Nonetheless, the Linnaean ranks, with their long tradition of use in classical taxonomy, still appear in much scientific discourse.

Systematists Identify Features That Reveal Evolutionary Relationships

Systematists seek to reconstruct the tree of life, but they must do so without much direct knowledge of evolutionary history. Because systematists can't see into the past, they must infer the past as best they can, on the basis of similarities among living organisms. Not just any similarity will do, however. Some observed similarities stem from convergent evolution (see pp. 276–277) in organisms that are not closely related, and such similarities are not useful for inferring evolutionary history. Instead, systematists use similarities that exist because two kinds of organisms both inherited a characteristic from a common ancestor. Therefore, the scientists who devise classifications must distinguish informative similarities caused by common ancestry from uninformative similarities that result from convergent evolution. In the search for informative similarities, biologists look at many kinds of characteristics.

Anatomy Plays a Key Role in Systematics

Historically, the most important and useful distinguishing characteristics have been anatomical. Systematists look carefully at similarities in both external body structure (see Fig. 18-1) and internal structures, such as skeletons and muscles. For example, homologous structures such as the finger bones of dolphins, bats, seals, and humans provide evidence of a common ancestor (see Fig. 14-8). To detect relationships between more closely related species, biologists may use microscopes to discern finer details—for example, the number and shape of the "teeth" on the tongue-like radula of a snail, the shape and position of the bristles on a marine worm, or the external structure of pollen grains of a flowering plant (**Fig. 18-3**).

(a) Radula   **(b) Bristles**   **(c) Pollen grains**

▲ **FIGURE 18-3 Microscopic structures may be used to classify organisms (a)** The "teeth" on a snail's tongue-like radula (a structure used in feeding), **(b)** the bristles on a marine worm, and **(c)** the shape and surface features of pollen grains are characteristics that are potentially useful in classification. Such finely detailed structures can reveal similarities between species that are not apparent in larger and more obvious structures.

Molecular Similarities Are Also Useful for Reconstructing Phylogeny

The anatomical characteristics shared by related organisms are expressions of underlying genetic similarities, so it stands to reason that evolutionary relationships among species must also be reflected in genetic similarities. Of course, direct genetic comparisons were not possible for most of the history of biology. Since the 1980s, however, advances in the techniques of molecular genetics have revolutionized studies of evolutionary relationships.

As a result of these technical advances, today's systematists can use the nucleotide sequences of DNA (that is, organisms' genotypes) to investigate relatedness among different types of organisms. Closely related species have similar DNA sequences. In some cases, similarity of DNA sequences will be reflected in the structure of chromosomes. For example, both the DNA sequences and the chromosomes of chimpanzees and humans are extremely similar, showing that these two species are very closely related (**Fig. 18-4**). Some of the key methods of genetic analysis are explored in "Scientific Inquiry: Molecular Genetics Reveals Evolutionary Relationships" on p. 346. The process by which systematists use genetic and anatomical similarities to

▶ **FIGURE 18-4 Human and chimp chromosomes are similar** Chromosomes from different species can be compared by means of banding patterns that are revealed by staining. The comparison illustrated here, between human chromosomes (left member of each pair; H) and chimpanzee chromosomes (C), reveals that the two species are genetically very similar. In fact, the entire genomes of both species have been sequenced and are nearly 99% identical. The numbering system shown is that used for human chromosomes; note that human chromosome 2 corresponds to a combination of two chimp chromosomes.

Scientific Inquiry

Molecular Genetics Reveals Evolutionary Relationships

Evolution results from the accumulation of inherited changes in populations. Because DNA is the molecule of heredity, evolutionary changes must be reflected in changes in DNA. Systematists have long known that comparing DNA within a group of species would be a powerful method for inferring evolutionary relationships, but for most of the history of systematics, direct access to genetic information was nothing more than a dream. Today, however, **DNA sequencing**—determining the sequence of nucleotides in segments of DNA—is comparatively cheap, easy, and widely available. The *polymerase chain reaction* (PCR; see pp. 244–245) allows systematists to easily accumulate large samples of DNA from organisms, and automated machinery makes sequence determination a comparatively simple task. Sequencing has rapidly become one of the primary tools for uncovering phylogeny.

The logic underlying molecular systematics is straightforward. It is based on the observation that when a single species divides into two species, the gene pool of each resulting species begins to accumulate mutations. The particular mutations in each species, however, will differ because the species are now evolving independently, with no gene flow between them. As time passes, more and more genetic differences accumulate. So, a systematist who has obtained DNA sequences from representatives of both species can compare the two species' nucleotide sequences at any given location in the genome. Fewer differences indicate more closely related organisms.

Putting the simple principles outlined above into practice usually involves more sophisticated thinking. For example, sequence comparisons become far more complex when a researcher wishes to assess relationships among, say, 20 or 30 species. Fortunately, mathematicians and computer programmers have devised some very clever computer-assisted methods for comparing large numbers of sequences and deriving the phylogeny that is most likely to account for the observed sequence differences.

Molecular systematists must also use care in choosing which segment of DNA to sequence. Different parts of the genome evolve at different rates, and it is crucial to sequence a DNA segment whose rate of change is well matched to the phylogenetic question at hand. In general, slowly evolving genes work best for comparing distantly

related organisms, and rapidly changing portions of the genome are best for analyzing closer relationships. It is sometimes difficult to find any single gene that will yield sufficient information to provide an accurate picture of evolutionary change across the genome, so sequences from several different genes are often needed to construct reliable phylogenies, such as the one shown in **Figure E18-1**.

Today, sequence data are piling up with unprecedented rapidity, and systematists have access to sequences from an ever-increasing number of species. The entire genomes of more than 700 species have been sequenced, and whole-genome sequencing projects are under way for an additional 3,000 or so species. The Human Genome Project has been completed, and human DNA sequences are now a matter of public record. The revolution in molecular biology has fostered a great leap forward in our understanding of evolutionary history.

▲ **FIGURE E18-1 Relatedness can be determined by comparing DNA sequences** This evolutionary tree was derived from the nucleotide sequences of several different genes that are common to humans and apes.

Case Study continued
Origin of a Killer

Analysis of nucleotide sequences was absolutely required to construct the phylogeny of viruses that revealed the ancestor of HIV. The closely related viruses included in the phylogeny are all but indistinguishable on the basis of appearance and structure; the differences between them are revealed only by differences in their genetic material. Thus, scientific sleuthing about the origin of HIV would have been impossible prior to the modern era of routine DNA sequencing.

reconstruct evolutionary history are discussed in "A Closer Look at Phylogenetic Trees" on pp. 348–349. Some findings about genetic variation in humans are described in "Links to Everyday Life: Small World."

18.2 WHAT ARE THE DOMAINS OF LIFE?

If we picture the common ancestor of all living things as the trunk at the very base of the tree of life, we might ask: Which clades arose from the earliest branching of the trunk? Each of the earliest branches must have given rise to a huge clade of descendant species. These early-branching clades will be the largest ones that systematists can distinguish.

Before about 1970, systematists concluded from the available evidence that the earliest split in the tree of life divided all species into two groups: Animalia and Plantae. According to this view, bacteria, fungi, and photosynthetic eukaryotes were considered to be plants, and all other organisms were classified as animals. However, as knowledge of life's evolutionary history expanded, it became apparent that this early view had vastly oversimplified evolutionary history.

A Three-Domain System More Accurately Reflects Life's History

As new data accumulated and understanding of phylogeny grew, scientific assessment of life's fundamental categories was gradually revised. A key element of this revision stemmed from the pioneering work of microbiologist Carl Woese, who showed that biologists had overlooked a key event in the early history of life, one that demanded a new and more accurate classification of life.

Woese and other biologists interested in the evolutionary history of microorganisms studied the biochemistry of prokaryotic organisms. The researchers, by studying nucleotide sequences of the RNA that is found in organisms' ribosomes, discovered that prokaryotes actually include two very different kinds of organisms. Woese dubbed these two groups the Bacteria and the Archaea (**Fig. 18-5**).

(a) A bacterium

(b) An archaean

▲ FIGURE 18-5 **Two domains of prokaryotic organisms** Although similar in appearance, **(a)** *Vibrio cholerae* and **(b)** *Methanococcus jannaschii* are less closely related than a mushroom and an elephant. *Vibrio* is in the domain Bacteria, and *Methanococcus* is in Archaea.

Despite superficial similarities in their appearance under the microscope, Bacteria and Archaea are radically different. The two groups are no more closely related to one another than either one is to any eukaryote. The tree of life split into three parts very early in the history of life, long before the appearance of plants, animals, and fungi. This early

Links to *Everyday Life*

Small World

In light of humankind's intense curiosity about the origin of our species, it is not surprising that systematists have devoted a great deal of attention to uncovering the evolutionary history of *Homo sapiens*. Though much of this inquiry has focused on revealing the evolutionary connections between modern humans and the species to which we are most closely related, the techniques and methods of systematics have also been used to assess the evolutionary relationships among different populations within our species. Biologists have compared DNA sequences from human populations in many different parts of the world; different investigators have compared different portions of the human genome. As a result, a large amount of data has been gathered, and some interesting findings have emerged.

First, genetic divergence among human populations is very low compared to that of other animal species. For example, the range of genetic differences among all of Earth's humans is only one-tenth the size of the differences among the deer mice of North America (and many other species have even more genetic variability than deer mice). Clearly, all humans are genetically very similar, and the differences among different human populations are tiny.

It is also increasingly apparent that most of the human genetic variability that does exist can be found in African populations. The range of genetic differences found *within* sub-Saharan African populations is greater than the range between African populations and any non-African population. For many genes, all known variants are found in Africa, and no non-African population contains any distinctive variants; rather, non-African populations contain subsets of the African set. This finding strongly suggests that *Homo sapiens* originated in Africa, and that we have not lived anywhere else long enough to evolve very many differences from our African ancestors.

A Closer Look At *Phylogenetic Trees*

Systematists strive to develop a system of classification that reflects the phylogeny (evolutionary history) of organisms. Thus, the main job of systematists is to reconstruct phylogeny. Reconstructing the evolutionary history of all of Earth's organisms is, of course, a huge task, so each systematist typically chooses to work on some particular portion of the history.

The result of a phylogenetic reconstruction is usually represented by a diagram. These diagrams can take a number of different forms, but all of them show the sequence of branching events in which ancestral species split to give rise to descendant species. For this reason, diagrams of phylogeny are generally tree-like.

These trees can present the phylogeny of any specified set of *taxa* (singular, *taxon*). A taxon is a named species, such as *Homo sapiens*, or a named group of species, such as primates or beetles or ferns. Thus, phylogenetic trees can show evolutionary history at different scales. Systematists might reconstruct, for example, a tree of 10 species in a particular genus of clams, or a tree of 25 clades of animals, or a tree of the three domains of life.

After selecting the taxa to include, a systematist is ready to begin building a tree. Most systematists use the *cladistic* approach to reconstruct phylogenetic trees. Under the cladistic approach, relationships among taxa are revealed by the occurrence of similarities known as *synapomorphies*. A synapomorphy is a trait that is similar in two or more taxa because these taxa inherited a "derived" version of the trait that had changed from its original state in a common ancestor. The formation of synapomorphies is illustrated in **Figure E18-2.**

In the imaginary scenario illustrated in Figure E18-2, we can easily identify synapomorphies because we know the ancestral state of the trait and the subsequent changes that took place. In real life, however, systematists would not have direct knowledge of the ancestor, which lived in the distant past and whose identity is unknown. Without this direct knowledge, a systematist observing a similarity between two taxa is faced with a challenge. Is the observed similarity a synapomorphy, or does it have some other cause, such as convergent evolution or common inheritance of the ancestral state? The cladistic approach provides methods for identifying synapomorphies, but the possibility of mistaken interpretation remains. To guard against such errors, systematists use numerous traits to build a tree, thereby minimizing the influence of any single trait.

In the last phase of the tree-building process, the systematist compares different possible trees. For example, three taxa can be arranged in three different branching patterns (**Fig. E18-3**). Each branching pattern represents a different hypothesis about the evolutionary history of taxa A, B, and C. Which hypothesis is most likely to represent the true history of the three taxa? The one in which the taxa on adjacent branches share synapomorphies. For example, imagine that a systematist identified a number of synapomorphies that are shared by taxa A and B but are not found in C, but has found no synapomorphies that link taxa B and C or taxa A and C. In this case, tree 1 in Figure E18-3 is the best-supported hypothesis.

With large numbers of taxa, the number of possible trees grows dramatically. Similarly, a large number of traits also complicates the problem of identifying the tree best supported by the data. Fortunately, however, systematists have developed sophisticated computer programs to help cope with these complications.

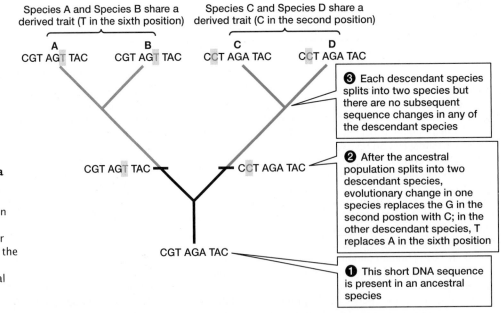

► FIGURE E18-2 **Related taxa are linked by shared derived traits (synapomorphies)** A derived trait is one that has been modified from the ancestral version of the trait. When two or more taxa share a derived trait, the shared trait is said to be a synapomorphy. The hypothetical scenario illustrated here shows how synapomorphies arise.

Species A and Species B share a derived trait (T in the sixth position)

Species C and Species D share a derived trait (C in the second position)

A
CGT AGT TAC

B
CGT AGT TAC

C
CCT AGA TAC

D
CCT AGA TAC

❸ Each descendant species splits into two species but there are no subsequent sequence changes in any of the descendant species

CGT AGT TAC

CCT AGA TAC

❷ After the ancestral population splits into two descendant species, evolutionary change in one species replaces the G in the second position with C; in the other descendant species, T replaces A in the sixth position

CGT AGA TAC

❶ This short DNA sequence is present in an ancestral species

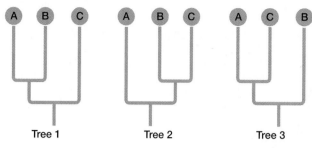

▲ FIGURE E18-3 **The three possible trees for three taxa**

Under the cladistic approach, phylogenetic trees play a key role in classification. Each designated group should contain only organisms that are more closely related to one another than to any organisms outside the group. So, for example, the members of the clade Canidae (which includes dogs, wolves, foxes, and coyotes) are more closely related to each other than to any member of any other clade. Another way to state this principle is to say that each designated group should contain *all* of the living descendants of a common ancestor (**Fig. E18-4a**). In the

terminology of cladistic systematics, such groups are said to be *monophyletic*.

Some names, especially names that predate the cladistic approach, designate groups that contain some, but not all, of the descendants of a common ancestor. Such groups are *paraphyletic*. For example, the group historically known as the reptiles—snakes, lizards, turtles, and crocodilians—is paraphyletic. To see why, examine the tree in **Figure E18-4b**. Find the branch that represents the common ancestor of snakes, lizards, turtles, and crocodilians (it is at the base of the tree). Then examine the tree again and make a list of all of the descendants of that common ancestor. Your list, if you performed this mental exercise correctly, includes the birds. That is, birds are part of the monophyletic group that includes all living descendants of the common ancestor that gave rise to snakes, lizards, turtles, and crocodilians. Therefore, the reptiles (Reptilia) constitute a monophyletic clade only if birds are included in the group. If we omit the birds, Reptilia is paraphyletic and, according to cladistic principles, is not a valid group name. Nonetheless, you will probably continue to encounter the word "reptiles" used in its older, technically incorrect sense, if only because so many people are accustomed to using it that way.

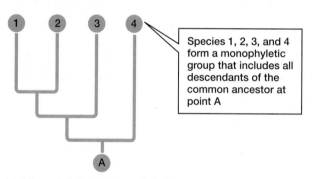

Species 1, 2, 3, and 4 form a monophyletic group that includes all descendants of the common ancestor at point A

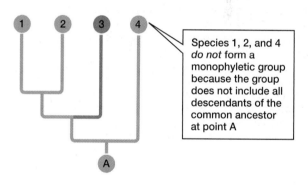

Species 1, 2, and 4 *do not* form a monophyletic group because the group does not include all descendants of the common ancestor at point A

(a) Monophyletic and paraphyletic groups

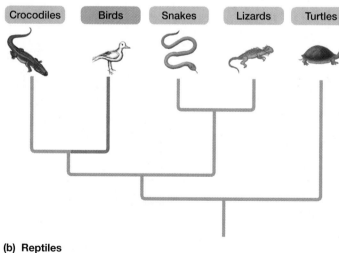

The group traditionally known as the *reptiles* is paraphyletic, but if birds are included, reptiles form a monophyletic group

▲ FIGURE E18-4 **Reptiles are a monophyletic group only if birds are included** Only groups that contain all of the descendants of a common ancestor are considered to be monophyletic groups.

EXERCISE Consider the following list of groups: (1) protists, (2) fungi, (3) great apes (chimpanzees, pygmy chimpanzees, gorillas, orangutans, and gibbons), (4) seedless plants (ferns, mosses, and liverworts), (5) prokaryotes (bacteria and archaea), and (6) animals. Using Figures 18-6, 18-7, E18-1, 21-5, 22-4, and 23-1 for reference, identify the monophyletic groups on the list.

(b) Reptiles

▶ **FIGURE 18-6** **The tree of life** The three domains of life represent the three main "trunks" on the tree of life.

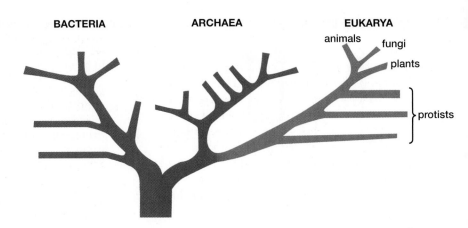

split is now reflected in a classification scheme that divides life into three domains: **Bacteria, Archaea,** and **Eukarya** (**Fig. 18-6**).

This text's descriptions of the diversity of life—which appear in Chapters 19 through 24—begin with an overview of the prokaryotic domains Archaea and Bacteria. Within the domain Eukarya, we provide separate discussions of three clades—plants, fungi, and animals—and of "protists" (a generic term that designates the diverse collection of eukaryote organisms that are not plants, fungi, or animals). **Figure 18-7** shows the evolutionary relationships among some members of the domain Eukarya.

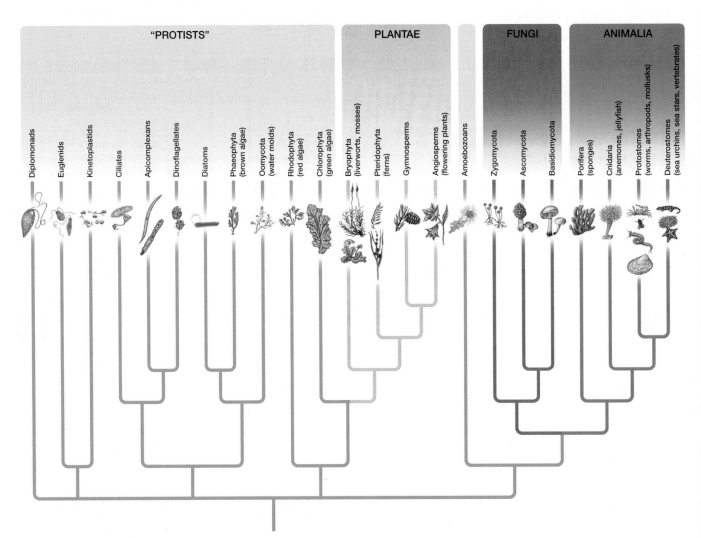

▲ **FIGURE 18-7** **An evolutionary tree of eukaryotes** Some of the major evolutionary lineages within the domain Eukarya are shown. The term "protist" refers to the many eukaryotes that are not plants, animals, or fungi.

18.3 WHY DO CLASSIFICATIONS CHANGE?

As the emergence of the three-domain system shows, the hypotheses of evolutionary relationships on which classification is based are subject to revision as new data become available. Even the largest, most inclusive clades—which represent old branchings of the tree of life—must sometimes be rearranged. Such changes at the top levels of classification occur only rarely, but at the other end of the classification hierarchy, among species designations, revisions are more frequent.

Species Designations Change When New Information Is Discovered

As researchers uncover new information, systematists regularly propose changes in species-level classifications. For example, until recently, systematists recognized two species of elephant, the African elephant and the Indian elephant. Now, however, they recognize three elephant species; the former African elephant is now divided into two species, the savanna elephant and the forest elephant. Why the change? Genetic analysis of elephants in Africa revealed that there is little gene flow between forest-dwelling and savanna-dwelling elephants. The two groups of elephants are no more genetically similar than lions and tigers.

The Biological Species Definition Can Be Difficult or Impossible to Apply

In some cases, systematists find themselves unable to say with certainty where one species ends and another begins. As discussed in Chapter 16, asexually reproducing organisms pose a particular challenge to systematists, because the criterion of interbreeding (the basis of the biological species definition that we have used in this text) cannot be used to distinguish among species. The irrelevance of this criterion in studies of asexual organisms leaves plenty of room for investigators to disagree about which asexual populations constitute a species, especially when comparing groups with similar phenotypes. For instance, some systematists recognize 200 species of the British blackberry (a plant that can produce seeds parthenogenetically—that is, without fertilization), but others recognize only 20 species.

The difficulty of applying the biological species definition to asexual organisms is a serious problem for systematists. After all, a significant portion of Earth's organisms reproduces without sex. Most bacteria, archaea, and protists, for example, reproduce asexually most of the time. Some systematists argue that we need a more universally applicable definition of species, one that won't exclude asexual organisms and that doesn't depend on the criterion of reproductive isolation.

The Phylogenetic Species Concept Offers an Alternative Definition

A number of alternative species definitions have been proposed over the history of evolutionary biology, but none has been sufficiently compelling to displace the biological species definition. One alternative definition, however, has been gaining adherents in recent years. The *phylogenetic species concept* defines a species as "the smallest diagnosable group that contains all the descendants of a single common ancestor." In other words, if we draw an evolutionary tree that describes the pattern of ancestry among a collection of organisms, each distinctive branch on the tree constitutes a separate species, regardless of whether the individuals represented by that branch can interbreed with individuals from other branches. As you might suspect, rigorous application of the phylogenetic species concept would vastly increase the number of different species recognized by systematists.

Proponents and opponents of the phylogenetic species concept are currently engaged in a vigorous debate about its merits. Perhaps one day it will replace the biological species concept as the "textbook definition" of species, or perhaps we will continue to rely on the biological species concept. In the meantime, classifications will continue to be debated and revised as systematists learn more and more about evolutionary relationships, particularly with the application of techniques derived from molecular biology. Although the precise evolutionary relationships of many organisms continue to elude us, classification is enormously helpful in ordering our thoughts and investigations into the diversity of life on Earth.

18.4 HOW MANY SPECIES EXIST?

Scientists do not know even within an order of magnitude how many species share our world. Each year, between 7,000 and 10,000 new species are named, most of them insects, many from tropical rain forests. The total number of named species is currently about 1.5 million. However, many scientists believe that 7 million to 10 million species may exist, and estimates range as high as 100 million. This total range of species diversity is known as **biodiversity.** Of all the species that have been identified thus far, about 5% are prokaryotes and protists. An additional 22% are plants and fungi, and the rest are animals. This distribution has little to do with the actual abundance of these organisms and a lot to do with the size of the organisms, how easy they are to classify, how accessible they are, and the number of scientists studying them. Historically, systematists have chiefly focused on large or conspicuous organisms in temperate regions, but biodiversity is greatest among small, inconspicuous organisms in the Tropics. In addition to the overlooked species on land and in shallow waters, an entire "continent" of species lies largely unexplored on the deep-sea floor. From the limited samples available, scientists estimate that hundreds of thousands of unknown species may reside there.

Although about 5,000 species of prokaryotes have been described and named, prokaryotic diversity remains largely unexplored. Consider a study by Norwegian scientists, who analyzed DNA to count the number of different bacteria species present in a small sample of forest soil. To distinguish among species, the researchers arbitrarily defined bacterial DNA as coming from separate species if it differed by at least 30% from that of any other bacterial DNA in the sample. Using this criterion, they reported more than 4,000 species of bacteria in their soil sample and an equal number of species in a sample of shallow marine sediment.

Our ignorance of the full extent of life's diversity adds a new dimension to the tragedy of the destruction of tropical rain forests. Although these forests cover only about 6% of Earth's land area, they are believed to be home to two-thirds of the world's existing species, most of which have never been studied or named. Because these forests are being destroyed so rapidly, Earth is losing many species that we will never even know existed! For example, in 1990, a new species of primate, the black-faced lion tamarin, was discovered in a small patch of dense rain forest on an island just off the east coast of Brazil (**Fig. 18-8**). Had the patch of forest been cut before this squirrel-sized monkey was discovered, its existence would have remained undocumented. At current rates of deforestation, most of the tropical rain forests, with their undescribed wealth of life, will be gone within the next century.

▶ **FIGURE 18-8 The black-faced lion tamarin** Researchers estimate that no more than 400 individuals remain in the wild; captive breeding may be the black-faced lion tamarin's only hope for survival.

Case Study revisited

Origin of a Killer

What evidence has persuaded evolutionary biologists that HIV originated in apes and monkeys? To understand the evolutionary thinking behind this conclusion, examine the evolutionary tree shown in **Figure 18-9**. This tree illustrates the phylogeny of HIV and its close relatives, the simian immunodeficiency viruses (SIVs), as revealed by a comparison of RNA sequences among different viruses.

Notice the positions on the tree of the four human viruses (two strains of HIV-1 and two of HIV-2; a strain is a genetically distinct subgroup of a particular type of virus). The branch leading to strain 1 of HIV-1 is directly adjacent to the branch leading to strain 1 of chimpanzee SIV. The adjacent branches indicate that strain 1 of HIV-1 is more closely related to a chimpanzee virus than to strain 2 of HIV-1. Similarly, strain 1 of HIV-2 is more closely related to pig-tailed macaque SIV than to strain 2 of HIV-2. Both HIV-1 and HIV-2 are more closely related to ape or monkey viruses than to one another.

The only way for the evolutionary history shown in the tree to have emerged is if viruses jumped between host species. If HIV had evolved strictly within human hosts, the human viruses would be each other's closest relatives. Because the human viruses do not cluster together on the phylogenetic tree, we can infer that cross-species infection occurred, probably on multiple occasions. The most likely means of transmission is human consumption of monkeys (HIV-2) and chimpanzees (HIV-1). Recently, a strain of SIV that is especially closely related to HIV-1 was found in members of a population of chimps that inhabit

forests in the southeastern corner of the Central African country of Cameroon. It is likely that viruses from this chimp population made the chimp-to-human jump that started the HIV epidemic.

Consider This

Can understanding the evolutionary origin of HIV help researchers devise better ways to treat and control the spread of AIDS? How might such understanding influence strategies for treatment and prevention? More generally, how can evolutionary thinking help advance medical research?

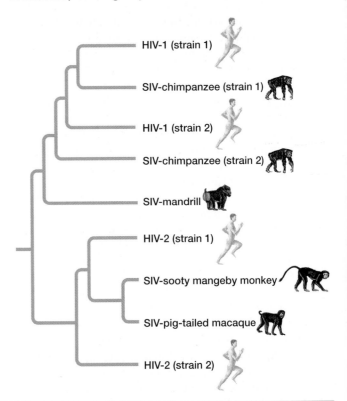

▶ **FIGURE 18-9 Evolutionary analysis helps reveal the origin of HIV** In this phylogeny of some immunodeficiency viruses, the viruses with human hosts do not cluster together. This lack of congruence between the evolutionary histories of the viruses and their host species suggests that the viruses must have jumped between host species. (Note that SIV stands for *simian immunodeficiency virus*.)

CHAPTER REVIEW

Summary of Key Concepts

18.1 How Are Organisms Named and Classified?

The scientific name of an organism is composed of its genus name and species name. Systematists use anatomical and molecular similarities among organisms to reconstruct the evolutionary relationships among species, and depict the results of their reconstructions in tree diagrams. On the basis of these evolutionary trees, systematists name clades (groups that include the species descended from a common ancestor). Clades nest within larger clades to form a nested hierarchy of categories. In Linnaean classification, the different clades in a hierarchy are assigned taxonomic ranks. The eight major ranks, in order of decreasing inclusiveness, are domain, kingdom, phylum, class, order, family, genus, and species.

18.2 What Are the Domains of Life?

The three domains of life, each representing one of three main branches of the tree of life, are Bacteria, Archaea, and Eukarya. Within the domain Eukarya, Fungi, Plantae, and Animalia are monophyletic clades. The assemblage known as "protists" comprises a variety of distinct clades.

18.3 Why Do Classifications Change?

Classifications are subject to revision as new information is discovered. Species boundaries may be hard to define, particularly in the case of asexually reproducing species. However, systematics is essential for precise communication and contributes to our understanding of the evolutionary history of life.

18.4 How Many Species Exist?

Although only about 1.5 million species have been named, estimates of the total number of species range up to 100 million. New species are being identified at the rate of 7,000 to 10,000 annually, mostly in tropical rain forests.

Key Terms

Archaea *350*	genus *343*
Bacteria *350*	kingdom *344*
biodiversity *351*	order *344*
clade *344*	phylogeny *344*
class *344*	phylum *344*
DNA sequencing *346*	scientific name *343*
domain *344*	species *343*
Eukarya *350*	systematics *344*
family *344*	taxonomy *343*

Thinking Through the Concepts

Fill-in-the-Blank

1. The science of naming and classifying organisms is called _____. The related science of reconstructing and depicting evolutionary history is called _____. A group consisting of all organisms descended from a particular common ancestor is a(n) _____.

2. A scientific name consists of a(n) _____ name followed by a(n) _____ name. Both parts of a scientific name are in the _____ language. The first letter of the first word in a scientific name is always _____, and both parts of the name are written in _____ letters.

3. In Linnaean classification, the eight major taxonomic ranks, in descending order of inclusiveness, are _____, _____, _____, _____, _____, _____, _____, and _____. The three domains of life are _____, _____, and _____.

4. Systematists determine the evolutionary relationships among species mainly on the basis of similarities in _____ and _____. The biological species definition is difficult to apply to organisms that _____. An alternative species definition, known as the _____, instead designates species on the basis of _____.

5. The number of named species is about_____, but the actual number of species on Earth is estimated to be between _____ and _____.

Review Questions

1. What contributions did Linnaeus and Darwin make to modern taxonomy?

2. What features would you study to determine whether a dolphin is more closely related to a fish or to a bear?

3. What techniques might you use to determine whether the extinct cave bear is more closely related to a grizzly bear or to a black bear?

4. Only a small fraction of the total number of species on Earth has been scientifically described. Why?

5. In England, "daddy longlegs" refers to a long-legged fly, but the same name refers to a spider-like animal in the United States. How do scientists attempt to avoid such confusion?

Applying the Concepts

1. There are many areas of disagreement about the classification of organisms. For example, there is no consensus about whether the red wolf is a distinct species or about how many kingdoms are within the domain Bacteria. What difference does it make whether biologists consider the red wolf a species, or into which kingdom a bacterial species falls? As Shakespeare put it, "What's in a name?"

2. BioEthics The pressures created by human population growth and economic expansion place storehouses of biological diversity such as the Tropics in peril. The seriousness of the situation is clear when we consider that probably only 1 out of every 20 tropical species is known to science at present. What arguments can you make for preserving biological diversity in poor

and developing countries, such as those in many areas of the Tropics? Does such preservation require that these countries sacrifice economic development? Suggest some solutions to the conflict between the growing demand for resources and the importance of conserving biodiversity.

3. During major floods, only the topmost branches of submerged trees may be visible above the water. If you were asked to sketch the branches below the surface of the water solely on the basis of the positions of the exposed tips, you would be attempting a reconstruction somewhat similar to the "family tree" by which taxonomists link various organisms according to their common ancestors (analogous to branching points). What sources of error do both exercises share? What advantages do modern taxonomists have?

4. The Florida panther, found only in the Florida Everglades, is currently classified as an endangered species, protecting it from human activities that could lead to its extinction. It has long been considered a subspecies of cougar (mountain lion), but recent mitochondrial DNA studies have shown that the Florida panther may actually be a hybrid between American and South American cougars. Should the Florida panther be protected by the Endangered Species Act?

(MB) *Go to www.masteringbiology.com for practice quizzes, activities, eText, videos, current events, and more.*

Animal Development

Case Study

The Faces of Fetal Alcohol Syndrome

"THE GUILT IS TREMENDOUS . . . I did it again and again. . . . I don't know how to tell them. It was something I could have prevented." Debbie, the young mother pictured here with her youngest child, Sabrina (upper photo), has had seven children. When she drank during pregnancy, so did her unborn children. Her daughter, Cory, has been diagnosed with **fetal alcohol syndrome (FAS)**, the most serious type of alcohol damage. At age 3, Cory was hyperactive and talked like a 1-year-old. Doctors believe that Cory's sister, Sabrina, is almost certainly a victim as well. She bears the features characteristic of FAS, including small eyes, a short nose, and a small head. At 7 months, she was weak, began having seizures, and could not eat solid food because she was unable to close her upper lip around a spoon.

John (lower photo) is another victim of FAS: His mother drank while she was pregnant with him, and she was drunk when she delivered him. John was fortunate, however, to have been adopted by a truly remarkable woman, Teresa Kellerman, who has become a leading parent advocate for children who have been damaged by alcohol. "Without intervention they end up homeless, jobless, addicted, arrested, pregnant or getting someone pregnant, living on the streets or dead, so many of them," says Kellerman, who founded the Fetal Alcohol Syndrome Community Resource Center in Tucson, Arizona.

Debbie entered rehabilitation and has resolved to stay sober and be a good parent to Sabrina and Cory. But even with the best parenting, John, Cory, Sabrina, and the thousands of other children born each year with FAS are unlikely ever to live without supervision, because the damage to their brains is irreparable. Tens of thousands of others with milder alcohol damage may become functional but will never reach their full potential.

As you study human development, think about how alcohol reaches a developing child when a pregnant woman drinks. How is the embryo nourished by its mother? To what extent is the embryo protected from environmental insults, whether alcohol and other drugs, toxins in cigarette smoke, or industrial pollutants? Are some stages of development more sensitive than others?

▲ John, who struggles with the lasting effects of fetal alcohol syndrome, helps his adoptive mother Teresa Kellerman educate people about the dangers of drinking during pregnancy. (Upper photo) Debbie regrets drinking while she was pregnant with her

42.1 WHAT ARE THE PRINCIPLES OF ANIMAL DEVELOPMENT?

Development is the process by which a multicellular organism grows and increases in organization and complexity. Development is usually considered to begin with a fertilized egg and end with a sexually mature adult. Three principal mechanisms contribute to development. First, individual cells multiply. Second, some of their daughter cells **differentiate,** or specialize in both structure and function, for example, as nerve cells or muscle fibers. Third, as they differentiate, groups of cells move about and become organized into multicellular structures, such as a brain or a biceps muscle.

All of the cells of an individual animal's body are genetically identical. How, then, can they differentiate into remarkably different structures with distinct functions? As we will see, the solution is to use different genes in different places in an animal's body, and at different times during an animal's life.

In this chapter, we will focus on the early developmental stages, from fertilized egg through birth. We will describe the major structures that appear during early vertebrate development and the processes that control gene expression at this time. We begin with a brief survey of the variety of ways in which animals develop from a fertilized egg to an adult.

42.2 HOW DO INDIRECT AND DIRECT DEVELOPMENT DIFFER?

Human babies, puppies, and kittens obviously develop as they grow up. However, in most respects, baby mammals and reptiles (including birds) are miniature versions of the adults of their species, undergoing a process called **direct development.** The majority of animal species, however, undergo **indirect development,** in which the newborn has a very different body structure than the adult.

During Indirect Development, Animals Undergo a Radical Change in Body Form

Indirect development occurs in amphibians, such as frogs and toads, and in most invertebrates. The females of animals that undergo indirect development typically produce huge numbers of eggs, each containing a small amount of food reserve called **yolk.** The yolk nourishes the developing embryo until it hatches into a small, sexually immature, feeding stage called a **larva** (plural, larvae; **Fig. 42-1**). Because the parents usually provide these vulnerable offspring with neither food nor protection from predators, most die in their larval stage. After feeding for a few weeks to several years, the handful of survivors undergo a revolution in body form, or **metamorphosis,** and become sexually mature adults.

Most larvae not only look very different from the adults, but also play different roles in their ecosystems. For instance, most adult butterflies sip nectar from flowers and unintentionally pollinate the flowers in return. Their caterpillar larvae munch on leaves, often of specific host plants (see Fig. 42-1).

Although we tend to regard the adult form as the "real animal" and the larval stage as "preparatory," most of the life span of some animals, especially insects, is spent in the larval form. An extreme example is provided by the North American

(a) Caterpillar (larva)

(b) Butterfly (adult)

◄ **FIGURE 42-1 Indirect development** The larvae of animals with indirect development are very different from the adult form, in structure, behaviors, and ecological niches. **(a)** Caterpillars of butterflies, such as the tiger swallowtail caterpillar shown here, feed on leaves, usually of a limited number of host plant species. **(b)** The principal food of most adult butterflies, including tiger swallowtails, is flower nectar.

periodical cicadas. Depending on the species, periodical cicadas spend 12 or 16 years as underground larvae, sucking juices from plant roots, and only 4 to 6 weeks as adults, mostly mating and laying eggs.

Newborn Animals That Undergo Direct Development Resemble Miniature Adults

Other animals, including some snails and fish, and all mammals and reptiles (including birds), undergo direct development, in which the newborn animal closely resembles the adult (**Fig. 42-2**). As the young animal matures, it may grow much bigger, but it does not fundamentally change its body form.

Juveniles of directly developing species are typically much larger than larvae, so they need much more nourishment before emerging into the world. Two strategies have evolved that meet the embryo's food requirement. Birds and most other reptiles, and many fish, produce eggs that contain relatively large amounts of yolk. Mammals, some snakes, and a few fish have relatively little yolk in their eggs. Instead, the embryos are nourished within the mother's body. Providing food for directly developing embryos places great demands on the mother. Many of these offspring, such as those of birds and mammals, require additional care and feeding after birth, placing additional demands on one, and often both, parents. Relatively few offspring are produced, but a higher proportion reach adulthood, because the parents devote more resources to each individual.

42.3 HOW DOES ANIMAL DEVELOPMENT PROCEED?

Most of the mechanisms of development—the control of gene expression to allow differentiation of individual cells and entire body parts—are fundamentally similar in vertebrates and invertebrates, and in animals with indirect or di-

rect development. Here, we will focus on the structures formed during vertebrate development.

Amphibians such as frogs, newts, and salamanders have long been favorite subjects for the study of development, because they can be induced to breed at any time of year, they have large, easily manipulated eggs and embryos, and the embryos develop in water, not inside their mothers. Most aspects of amphibian development are quite comparable to the development of other vertebrates, making most findings in amphibians applicable to other vertebrates, including humans. The descriptions and illustrations that follow will focus on amphibian development.

Cleavage of the Zygote Begins Development

The formation of an embryo begins with **cleavage,** a series of mitotic cell divisions of the fertilized egg, or **zygote** (**Fig. 42-3a**). The zygote is a very large cell. During cleavage, there is little or no cell growth between cell divisions, so as cleavage progresses, the available cytoplasm is split up into ever smaller cells, whose size gradually approaches that of cells in the adult. Eventually, a solid ball of small cells, the **morula** (**Fig. 42-3b**), is formed. As cleavage continues, a cavity opens within the morula, and the cells become the outer covering of a hollow structure called the **blastula** (**Fig. 42-3c**).

The details of cleavage differ by species and are partly determined by the amount of yolk, which hinders cytokinesis (cytoplasmic division). Eggs with extremely large yolks, such as a hen's egg, don't divide all the way through. Nevertheless, a hollow blastula (or its equivalent) is always produced. In birds and other reptiles, the blastula is flattened on top of the yolk.

Gastrulation Forms Three Tissue Layers

In amphibians and many other animals, the location of cells on the surface of the blastula forecasts their ultimate developmental fate in the adult. We have colored the cells of the blastula in

(a) Seahorses

(b) Snails

(c) Polar bears

◀ **FIGURE 42-2 Direct development** The offspring of animals with direct development closely resemble their parents from the moment of birth. **(a)** A male seahorse gives birth. The female seahorse deposits her eggs in his pouch, where he releases sperm to fertilize them. The fertilized eggs develop in the pouch for a few weeks, when vigorous muscular contractions of the pouch squirt out as many as 200 young. **(b)** Many land and freshwater snails hatch from small, yolk-rich eggs. **(c)** Mammalian mothers nourish their developing young within their bodies before birth, and with milk from their mammary glands after birth.

Figure 42-3c blue, yellow, and pink. These colors indicate the parts of the adult body that these cells are destined to produce during development (see below). In the blastula, all of these cells are on the surface (the lump of yellow cells on the bottom of the blastula is mostly yolk, and will gradually disappear during development). However, most of the structures that they will form are on the inside of the animal. These cells move to their proper destinations during the next stage of development, called **gastrulation** (literally, "producing the stomach").

Gastrulation begins when a dimple called the **blastopore** forms on one side of the blastula (see Fig. 42-3c). Surface cells then migrate through the blastopore in a continuous sheet, much as if you punched in an underinflated basketball. The resulting indentation enlarges to form a cavity that will eventually become the digestive tract (**Fig. 42-3d**).

The migrating cells form three tissue layers in the embryo, which is now called a **gastrula** (**Fig. 42-3e**). The cells that move through the blastopore to line the future digestive tract (yellow) are called **endoderm** (meaning "inner skin"); in addition to lining the digestive tract, endoderm also forms the lining of the respiratory tract and the liver and pancreas. The cells remaining on the outside (blue) are called **ectoderm** ("outer skin"); these mostly form surface structures such as the skin, hair, and nails, and the nervous system. Cells that migrate between the endoderm and ectoderm form the third layer (pink), the **mesoderm** ("middle skin"), which forms structures between these two, including muscles, the skeleton, and the circulatory system. **Table 42-1** lists the major structures produced from each layer.

Adult Structures Develop During Organogenesis

Organogenesis, the development of adult structures from the three embryonic tissue layers, proceeds by two major processes. First, a series of "master switch" genes turn on and

Table 42-1	Derivation of Adult Tissues from Embryonic Cell Layers
Embryonic Layer	**Adult Tissue**
Ectoderm	Epidermis of the skin; hair; lining of the mouth and nose; glands of the skin; nervous system
Mesoderm	Dermis of the skin; muscle, skeleton; circulatory system; gonads; kidneys; outer layers of the digestive and respiratory tracts
Endoderm	Lining of the digestive and respiratory tracts; liver; pancreas

(a) Zygote

◀ **FIGURE 42-3 Gastrulation in the frog (a)** A frog zygote, or fertilized egg, is a huge cell, as large as 0.1 inch (3 millimeters) in diameter in some species. **(b)** The zygote divides to form a solid ball of cells, the morula. The morula is about the same size as the zygote, although its individual cells are smaller. **(c)** The frog blastula is a hollow ball of cells with a lump of yolk-containing cells at one end. The blastula is still about the same size as the zygote. During normal development, the positions of the cells in the frog blastula foretell their future developmental fate (see the color-code legend). **(d)** During gastrulation, surface cells migrate into the blastula to form the endoderm and mesoderm layers of the gastrula. The cells remaining on the surface will form ectoderm. **(e)** The resulting three-layered embryo is now termed a gastrula.

(b) Cleavage of the zygote forms a morula

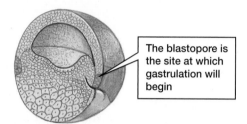

The blastopore is the site at which gastrulation will begin

(c) The blastula just before gastrulation

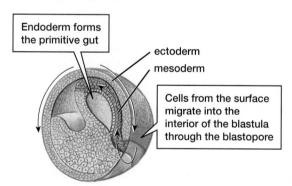

Endoderm forms the primitive gut

ectoderm

mesoderm

Cells from the surface migrate into the interior of the blastula through the blastopore

(d) Cells migrate at the start of gastrulation

primitive gut

(e) A three-layered gastrula has formed

ectoderm mesoderm endoderm

off, each controlling the transcription and translation of the many genes involved in producing, say, an arm or a backbone. We will return to these master genes in section 42.4.

Second, organogenesis prunes away superfluous cells, much as Michelangelo chiseled away "extra" marble, leaving behind his statue of David. In development, this sculpting requires the death of excess cells. Embryonic vertebrates, for example, have far more motor neurons than adults do. However, embryonic motor neurons are programmed to die unless they form a synapse with a skeletal muscle, which releases a chemical that prevents the death of the neuron. As another example, all amphibians, reptiles, and mammals pass through embryonic stages in which they have tails and webbed fingers and toes. In humans, these stages appear during the fourth to seventh weeks of development. A few weeks later, the cells of the tail and webbing have died: The tail disappears, and the hands and feet have separate fingers and toes.

Development in Reptiles and Mammals Depends on Extraembryonic Membranes

Fish live and reproduce in water, usually by spawning. Although many amphibians spend their adult lives on land, they too lay their eggs in water. In both cases, the embryo obtains nutrients from the yolk of the egg and oxygen from the water, and releases its wastes, including carbon dioxide, into the water.

Fully terrestrial vertebrate life was not possible until the evolution of the **amniotic egg.** This innovation arose first in reptiles, and persists today in that group (including birds) and its descendants, the mammals. It allows members of these groups to complete their development into the adult form in their own "private pond." The amniotic egg is characterized by four **extraembryonic membranes:** the chorion, amnion, allantois, and yolk sac (Table 42-2). In reptiles, the **chorion** lines the shell and exchanges oxygen and carbon dioxide between the embryo and the air. The **amnion** encloses the embryo in a watery environment. The **allantois** surrounds and isolates wastes. The **yolk sac** contains the yolk.

In placental mammals (all mammals except marsupials, such as kangaroos, and monotremes, such as platypuses), the embryo develops within the mother's body until birth. Nevertheless, all four extraembryonic membranes still persist—remnants of the reptilian genetic program for development—and in fact are essential for development. Table 42-2 compares the structures and functions of these extraembryonic membranes in reptiles and mammals.

Table 42-2 **Vertebrate Embryonic Membranes**

Reptile

Mammal

Membrane	Structure	Function	Structure	Function
Chorion	Membrane lining the inside of the shell	Acts as a respiratory surface; regulates the exchange of gases and water between the embryo and the air	Fetal contribution to the placenta	Provides for the exchange of gases, nutrients, and wastes between the embryo and the mother
Amnion	Sac surrounding the embryo	Encloses the embryo in fluid	Sac surrounding the embryo	Encloses the embryo in fluid
Allantois	Sac connected to the embryonic urinary tract; a capillary-rich membrane lining the inside of the chorion	Stores wastes (especially urine); acts as a respiratory surface	Membranous sac arising from the gut; varies in size	May store metabolic wastes; contributes to the umbilical cord blood vessels
Yolk sac	Membrane surrounding the yolk	Contains yolk as food; digests yolk and transfers its nutrients to the embryo	Small, membranous, fluid-filled sac	Helps absorb nutrients from the mother; forms blood cells; contributes to the umbilical cord

42.4 HOW IS DEVELOPMENT CONTROLLED?

A zygote contains all of the genes needed to produce an entire animal. Nearly every cell of the body also contains all of these genes—that's what makes cloning possible (see Chapter 9). In any given cell, however, some genes are used, or expressed, while others are not. The differentiation of cells during development arises because of these differences in gene expression.

You may recall from Chapter 12 that cells have several ways of controlling gene expression, including regulating which genes are transcribed into messenger RNA (mRNA). Proteins called transcription factors bind to DNA near the promoter regions where gene transcription begins. Different transcription factors bind to different genes and turn their transcription on or off. Which genes are transcribed determines the structure and function of the cell. This leads to one of the central questions about development: What causes different cells to transcribe different genes?

During the past decade, the techniques of molecular biology have revealed many of the genes and proteins involved in development, and some of the interactions among them. However, the fundamental principles were discovered about a century ago,

using tools no more sophisticated than forceps, tiny knives, and hair from a baby's head, as we explore in "Scientific Inquiry: Unraveling the Mechanisms of Animal Development" on pp. 820–821.

Molecules Positioned in the Egg and Produced by Nearby Cells Control Gene Expression During Embryonic Development

In animal embryos, the differentiation of individual cells and the development of entire structures are driven by one or both of two processes: (1) the actions of gene-regulating substances inherited from the mother in her egg, and (2) chemical communication between the cells of the embryo.

Maternal Molecules in the Egg May Direct Early Embryonic Differentiation

Recall from Chapter 41 that essentially all of the cytoplasm in a zygote (a fertilized egg) was already in the egg before fertilization; the sperm contributed little more than a nucleus. In most invertebrates and some vertebrates, specific mRNA and protein molecules become concentrated in different places in the egg's cytoplasm during oogenesis. Some of these proteins are transcription factors that regulate which genes are turned on and off.

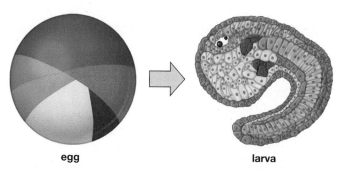

egg   **larva**

▲ **FIGURE 42-4 A "fate map" of the sea squirt egg** Gene-regulating substances in the cytoplasm of the egg of a sea squirt control early development. The coloring of the egg and larva shows which parts of the egg will give rise to which parts of the larva.

QUESTION If human development were as thoroughly determined as this, do you think that twins would be more or less common?

During the first few cleavage divisions after fertilization, the zygote and its daughter cells divide at specific places and in specific orientations. As a result, these early embryonic cells receive different maternal mRNAs and transcription factors. Therefore, different cells transcribe different genes, start differentiating into distinct cell types, and in many cases, ultimately give rise to specific adult structures. The positioning of maternal molecules in some eggs so strongly controls development that the egg can be mapped according to the major structures that will be produced by daughter cells inheriting each section of cytoplasm. For example, in the sea squirt egg diagrammed in **Figure 42-4,** cells that receive cytoplasm colored blue will form the skin, cells that receive cytoplasm colored green will form the nervous system, and so on.

In mammalian embryos, the current evidence indicates that all of the cells formed during cleavage are functionally equivalent. Which cells give rise to which parts of the later embryo appears to be a matter of chance, depending on where the cells happen to be located during the transition from the morula to the blastocyst (the mammalian equivalent of a blastula; see section 42.5).

Chemical Communication Between Cells Regulates Most Embryonic Development

At some point in all animal embryos, the developmental fate of each cell is determined by chemical interactions between cells, in a process called **induction.** During induction, certain cells release chemical messengers that alter the development of other, usually nearby, cells. Specific groups of genes are selectively activated in the recipient cells, causing them to differentiate in specific ways.

In amphibian embryos, it has been known since the early 1900s that a cluster of cells located near the blastopore (see Fig. 42-3c), called the *organizer*, determines whether nearby cells will become ectoderm or mesoderm, and even where the head and nervous system will form (see "Scientific Inquiry: Unraveling the Mechanisms of Animal Development"). How does the organizer accomplish this? The cells of the organizer release

proteins given fanciful names such as Noggin, Cerberus (in Greek mythology, the three-headed dog that guarded the entrance to the underworld), and Dickkopf (meaning "thickhead" in German). These proteins interact with a number of other messengers to stimulate or repress the expression of genes in nearby cells, often genes that encode transcription factors and that therefore exert widespread effects on gene expression. Which constellations of genes are expressed then determines the structures and functions of the cells. As these cells differentiate, they in turn release other chemicals that alter the fate of still other cells, in a cascade that ultimately culminates in the development of the tissues and organs of the adult body.

Homeobox Genes Regulate the Development of Entire Segments of the Body

Homeobox genes are found in animals as diverse as fruit flies, frogs, and humans. Although their functions differ somewhat in different animals, homeobox genes code for transcription factors that regulate the transcription of many other genes. Each homeobox gene has major responsibility for the development of a particular region of the body. Homeobox genes were discovered in fruit flies, where specific mutations cause entire parts of the body to be duplicated, replaced, or omitted. For example, one mutant homeobox gene causes the development of an extra body segment, complete with an extra set of wings.

In all animals studied to date, the homeobox genes are arranged on the chromosomes in a head-to-tail order. Early in development, homeobox genes are transcribed in a specific sequence within the animal body. For example, "head" homeobox genes are transcribed in the anterior part of the embryo, and "tail" homeobox genes are transcribed in the tail, although multiple homeobox genes are usually expressed in any given region (**Fig. 42-5**).

| lab | pb | | Dfd | Ser | Antp | Ubx | abd-A | Abd-B |

▲ **FIGURE 42-5 The sequence of homeobox genes on the chromosome corresponds to their role in the development of different body segments** In the fruit fly *Drosophila*, each homeobox gene is active in the body segment shown in the same color, in a head-to-tail order.

QUESTION Snakes have ribs all the way from just behind the head almost to the tip of the tail. Snakes also lack legs. Propose a possible genetic mechanism for this body structure, based on homeobox genes.

Scientific Inquiry

Unraveling the Mechanisms of Animal Development

Embryologists have long used amphibian eggs to study development. These eggs are very large (often over a millimeter in diameter) and many are pigmented in patterns that serve as natural markers for specific locations in the egg. They can also tolerate a lot of experimental manipulation and still develop fairly normally. In the 1920s, the German embryologist Hans Spemann used newt eggs to show that, at least in early embryos, all of the nuclei contain all of the genetic information needed to produce an entire embryo.

Molecules in the Egg Cytoplasm Regulate Early Development

Spemann wondered how genetically identical cells can produce structures as different as a brain, a leg, or a stomach. Might there be something in the egg cytoplasm that determines how genetic information is used?

Some fertilized amphibian eggs have three distinctively pigmented regions: dark on top, light on the bottom, and a crescent-shaped band of gray in between, on one side of the egg (Fig. E42-1). Usually, the first cleavage division is perpendicular to this gray crescent, so that both daughter cells receive some of it. Sometimes, however, the first cleavage plane misses the crescent: One daughter cell gets the entire crescent and the other doesn't get any.

Using fine forceps, Spemann lassoed two-celled salamander embryos with strands of hair from his baby daughter, Margrette, and tightened the nooses to separate the two cells. If both of the detached cells contained crescent material, both developed into normal embryos (Fig. E42-1a). But if only one cell contained crescent material, that cell would develop normally, whereas the other cell without crescent material would form a blob that Spemann called a "belly piece" (Fig. E42-1b). Spemann concluded that something, in a specific location of the cytoplasm, regulated the use of the genetic information that the two daughter cells received. In modern terms, gene-regulating molecules in specific locations in the egg cytoplasm altered gene expression and determined the developmental fates of the daughter cells.

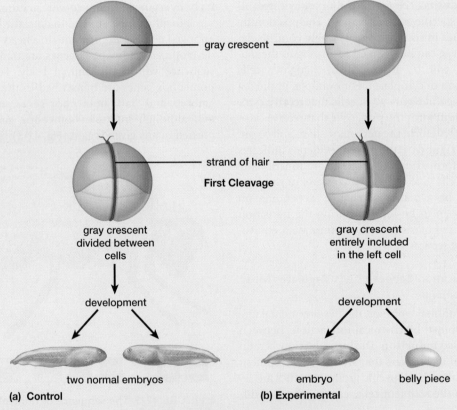

▲ FIGURE E42-1 **The egg cytoplasm controls early development in amphibians (a)** In salamanders and other amphibians, the first cleavage division usually bisects the gray crescent, so both daughter cells receive some of the crescent material. Separating the two cells produces two normal embryos. **(b)** Sometimes, the first division encloses the entire crescent in the cytoplasm of one daughter cell. If the two cells are separated, only the cell with the crescent material can form an embryo.

Certain Cells Determine the Development of Their Neighbors

What about later development? Surely the egg can't have infinitely precise positioning of myriads of molecules, dished out to daughter cells with such finesse that one particle of cytoplasm generates a leg, another an arm, and another an eye? Indeed not. Spemann and other embryologists had already done experiments in which bits of embryos, usually at the blastula stage, were transplanted to various locations in other embryos of the same species. They found that the fate of the transplanted cells was, in general, not predetermined: The transplants assumed the developmental fate of the area into which they were transplanted (Fig. E42-2a).

However, Spemann found that one small patch of cells, located near the blastopore (this patch is called the "dorsal lip"), followed its own developmental path, no matter where it was transplanted into the recipient embryo. In fact, transplanted dorsal lip cells caused the formation of a second head in the recipient embryo, and could actually produce a two-headed tadpole.

In the 1920s, Spemann and a graduate student, Hilde Mangold, performed a brilliant experiment showing that the transplanted dorsal lip cells actually changed the developmental fate of cells of the recipient embryo. Mangold cut out pieces of embryos from pale-colored newts and transplanted them into embryos of dark-colored newts, and vice versa. Transplants from the dorsal lip of the blastopore caused the surrounding tissue to form parts of a second head and, occasionally, to become almost complete secondary embryos (Fig. E42-2b). Spemann and Mangold concluded that the dorsal lip—now called Spemann's organizer—"organized" surrounding cells to form the head-to-tail axis of the embryo. We now know that Noggin, Cerberus, Dickkopf, and other molecules released by the organizer induce specific developmental pathways in nearby cells.

In 1935, Spemann was awarded the Nobel Prize for Physiology or Medicine. Hilde Mangold died tragically in a fire in 1924, and so she could not share the prize. (Nobel Prizes are not awarded posthumously.) In acknowledgment of Mangold's contributions, Spemann referred to "the experiments of Hilde Mangold" when describing these results.

❶ Cells from a region that normally becomes skin are removed from a light-colored blastula

❷ These cells are transplanted to a region of a dark-colored blastula that normally becomes nerve tissue

❸ Embryonic development proceeds

❹ The light-colored, transplanted cells differentiate into nerve tissue

(a) A typical transplantation experiment

❶ The dorsal lip of the blastopore is removed from a light-colored blastula

❷ The dorsal lip is transplanted inside a dark-colored blastula

❸ Embryonic development proceeds

❹ The transplanted dorsal lip of the blastopore causes the formation of a second embryo (pale) attached to the host embryo (dark)

(b) Transplantation of the dorsal lip of the blastopore

▲ FIGURE E42-2 Induction During most of development, the fate of any given cell is strongly influenced by the cells that surround it. **(a)** When part of a blastula is transplanted into a second blastula, the surrounding cells usually induce the transplant to assume the characteristics of the region into which the transplant was placed. **(b)** A transplanted dorsal lip of the blastopore, however, induces the surrounding cells to change their fates, and develop into most of the structures of a secondary embryo.

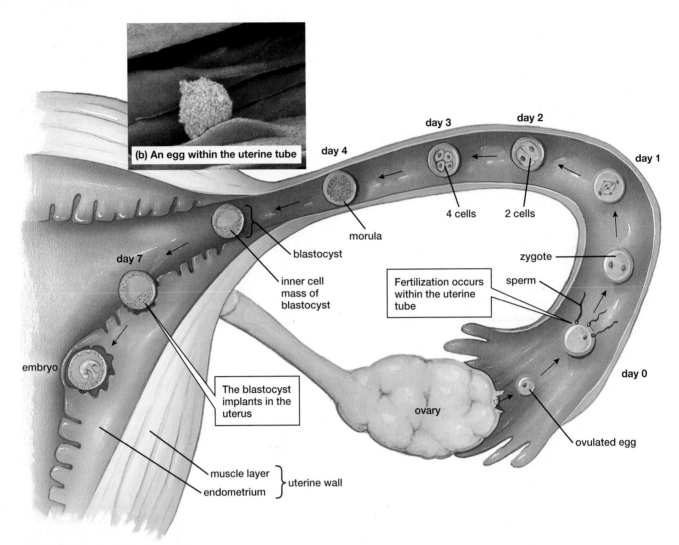

(b) An egg within the uterine tube

day 4

day 3

day 2

day 1

4 cells

2 cells

morula

blastocyst

day 7

inner cell
mass of
blastocyst

Fertilization occurs
within the uterine
tube

sperm

zygote

embryo

The blastocyst
implants in the
uterus

ovary

day 0

ovulated egg

muscle layer
endometrium } uterine wall

(a) The first week of development

▲ FIGURE 42-6 **The journey of the egg (a)** A human egg is fertilized in the uterine tube and slowly travels down to the uterus. Along the way, the zygote divides a few times, becoming first a morula and then a blastocyst. When the blastocyst reaches the uterine endometrium, it burrows in. **(b)** The egg, surrounded by cells from the follicle (the corona radiata), is cradled in the uterine tube on its way to the uterus.

QUESTION Recall the structure of an ovulated human egg and the process of fertilization from Chapter 41. What must happen before a blastocyst can implant?

42.5 HOW DO HUMANS DEVELOP?

Human development is controlled by the same mechanisms that control the development of other animals. In fact, our development strongly reflects our evolutionary heritage.

Differentiation and Growth Are Rapid During the First Two Months

A human egg is usually fertilized in the uterine tube and undergoes a few cleavage divisions there, becoming a morula on its way to the uterus (**Fig. 42-6**). By about the fifth day after fertilization, the zygote has developed into a hollow ball of cells, known as a **blastocyst** (the mammalian version of a

blastula; **Fig. 42-7a**). A mammalian blastocyst consists of an outer layer of cells surrounding a cluster of cells called the **inner cell mass.** The outer cell layer attaches to, and then burrows into, the endometrium of the uterus, a process called **implantation** (**Figs. 42-7a,b**). This outer cell layer will become the chorion. The complex intermingling of the chorion and the endometrium forms the placenta, which we will describe later in the chapter. The chorion also secretes chorionic gonadotropin (CG), which prevents the death of the corpus luteum (see pp. 802–803). The corpus luteum sustains the pregnancy by secreting progesterone and estrogen for the first couple of months, until the placenta takes over the secretion of these hormones.

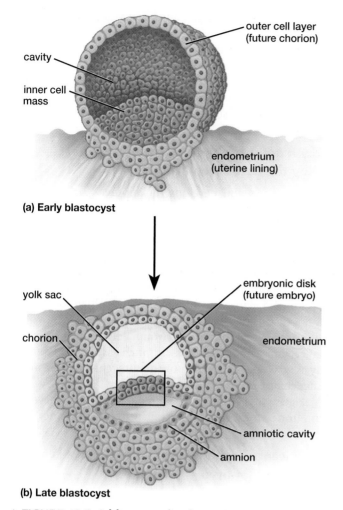

(a) Early blastocyst

(b) Late blastocyst

▲ **FIGURE 42-7 A blastocyst implants (a)** As it burrows into the uterine lining, the outer cell layer of the blastocyst forms the chorion, the embryonic contribution to the future placenta. **(b)** A few days later, the blastocyst has completely submerged beneath the uterine lining. The inner cell mass begins to develop into the yolk sac, the amnion, and the embryonic disk.

All of the cells of the inner cell mass have the potential to develop into any type of tissue. This remarkable flexibility allows the inner cell mass to produce both the entire embryo and the three remaining extraembryonic membranes. The inner cell mass is also the source of human embryonic stem cells, which researchers hope may one day be used to replace damaged adult tissues, as described in "Health Watch: The Promise of Stem Cells" on pp. 826–827.

After Implantation, Two Cavities Form and Gastrulation Occurs

During the second week, the inner cell mass grows and splits, forming two fluid-filled sacs that are separated by a double layer of cells called the **embryonic disk** (see Fig. 42-7b). One layer of cells is continuous with the yolk sac, although in placental mammals it contains no yolk. The second layer of cells is continuous with the amnion.

Gastrulation begins near the end of the second week after fertilization, and is usually complete by the end of the

third week. The two layers of the embryonic disk separate slightly, and a slit forms in the cell layer on the "amnion side" of the disk. (This slit is the blastocyst's equivalent of the amphibian blastopore.) Cells migrate through the slit into the interior of the disk, forming mesoderm, endoderm, and the fourth extraembryonic membrane, the allantois. The cells remaining on the surface become ectoderm.

Body Structures Begin to Form During Weeks Three to Eight

During the third week of development, the embryo begins to form the spinal cord and brain. The heart starts to beat about the beginning of the fourth week. At this time, the embryo bulges into the uterine cavity, bathed in fluid contained within the amnion (**Fig. 42-8**). Meanwhile, the

▲ **FIGURE 42-8 Human development during the fourth week** The embryo bulges into the uterus, and the placenta is restricted to one side. The body stalk and yolk stalk combine to form the umbilical cord, which exchanges wastes and nutrients between embryo and mother.

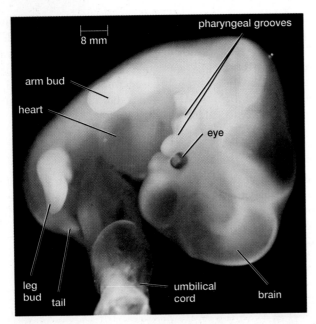

▲ **FIGURE 42-9 A 5-week-old human embryo** At the end of the fifth week, the human embryo is almost half head. A tail and pharyngeal (gill) grooves are clearly visible, evidence of our evolutionary relationship to other vertebrates.

umbilical cord forms from the fusion of the yolk stalk and body stalk. The yolk stalk connects the yolk sac (an evolutionary "leftover" from the yolk's role of nourishing embryonic reptiles) to the embryonic digestive tract. The body stalk contains the allantois, which contributes the blood vessels that will become the umbilical arteries and vein. The umbilical cord now connects the embryo to the placenta, which has formed from the merger of the chorion of the embryo and the lining of the uterus.

During the fourth and fifth weeks, the embryo develops a prominent tail and pharyngeal (gill) grooves (indentations behind the head that are homologous to a fish embryo's developing gills; **Fig. 42-9**). These structures are reminders that we share evolutionary ancestry with other vertebrates that retain their gills in adulthood. In humans, however, they disappear as development continues. By the seventh week, the embryo has rudimentary eyes and a rapidly developing brain, and the webbing between its fingers and toes is disappearing.

After Two Months, the Embryo Is Recognizably Human

As the second month draws to an end, nearly all of the major organs have at least begun to develop. Many structures, such as the arms and legs, are recognizably human in form. The gonads appear and develop into testes or ovaries. Sex hormones are secreted—either testosterone from the testes or estrogen from the ovaries. These hormones will affect the future development of the embryo; not only the reproductive organs, but also the brain and other parts of the body. After the second month of development, the embryo has

taken on a generally human appearance, and is now called a **fetus** (Fig. 42-10).

The first two months of pregnancy are a time of extremely rapid differentiation and growth for the embryo, and a time of considerable danger. Although vulnerable throughout development, the rapidly developing organs are especially sensitive to toxic substances during this time.

Growth and Development Continue During the Last Seven Months

The fetus grows and develops for another 7 months. The brain continues to develop rapidly and the head remains disproportionately large. As the brain and spinal cord grow, they begin to generate behaviors. As early as the third month of pregnancy, the fetus can move and respond to stimuli. Some instinctive behaviors appear, such as sucking, which will have obvious importance after birth. The lungs, stomach, intestine, and kidneys enlarge and become functional, although they will not be used until after birth. Nearly all fetuses 32 weeks or older can survive outside the womb with some medical assistance, and heroic measures can often save infants born as early as 26 weeks, although more mature fetuses have a much greater chance of healthy survival.

Figure 42-11 summarizes human embryonic development, from fertilization to the conclusion of pregnancy.

The Placenta Exchanges Materials Between Mother and Embryo

During the first few days after implantation, the embryo obtains nutrients directly from the endometrium. During the following week or so, the **placenta** begins to develop from interlocking structures produced by the embryo and the

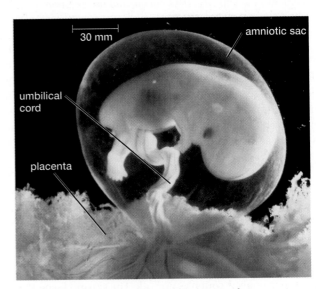

▲ **FIGURE 42-10 An 8-week-old human embryo** At the end of the eighth week, the embryo is clearly human in appearance and is now called a fetus. Most of the major organs of the adult body have begun to develop.

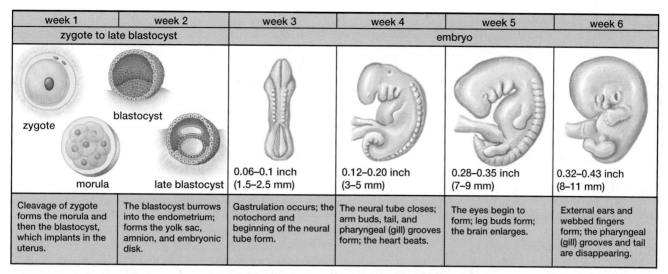

week 1	week 2	week 3	week 4	week 5	week 6
zygote to late blastocyst		embryo			
		0.06–0.1 inch (1.5–2.5 mm)	0.12–0.20 inch (3–5 mm)	0.28–0.35 inch (7–9 mm)	0.32–0.43 inch (8–11 mm)
Cleavage of zygote forms the morula and then the blastocyst, which implants in the uterus.	The blastocyst burrows into the endometrium; forms the yolk sac, amnion, and embryonic disk.	Gastrulation occurs; the notochord and beginning of the neural tube form.	The neural tube closes; arm buds, tail, and pharyngeal (gill) grooves form; the heart beats.	The eyes begin to form; leg buds form; the brain enlarges.	External ears and webbed fingers form; the pharyngeal (gill) grooves and tail are disappearing.

week 7	week 8	week 10	week 12	week 16
embryo		fetus		
0.67–0.79 inch (1.7–2.0 cm)	0.90–1.10 inches (2.3–2.8 cm)	1.25–1.75 inches (3.2–4.4 cm)	2–3 inches (5–7.6 cm)	4–5 inches (10.2–12.7 cm)
Webbed toes form; bones begin to stiffen; the back straightens; the eyelids begin to form.	All the major organs begin to form; the arms can bend; fingers are distinct. Facial features and outer ears take shape.	After 8 weeks, the embryo is called a fetus. Red blood cells form; toes separate; eyelids have developed; major brain parts are present; the hands can form fists.	The neck is well defined; all organs are present; male or female genitals are present; arms and legs move; teeth begin to form; a heartbeat can be detected electronically.	Sucking and swallowing movements occur; the liver and pancreas begin functioning. The body has grown relative to the head; major organs continue developing. The mother may feel movement; weight is about 5 oz.

week 20	week 24	week 30	week 36
fetus			
6–7 inches (15.2–17.8 cm)	8–9 inches (20.3–22.9 cm)	15–16 inches (38.1–40.6 cm)	16–19 inches (40.6–48.3 cm)
The fetus may suck its thumb; arms and legs can punch and kick; the body can change position. Fingernails are formed; fat is deposited under the skin; eyebrows and eyelashes appear.	Brain development continues, hearing develops, and the eyes can move. The fetus can hiccup, squint, smile, and frown. The fetus may have hair on its head. Unique foot- and fingerprints appear. Weight is about 1–1.5 pounds.	Brain development continues; the eyes open and close and see light; the fetus kicks and stretches. Breathing movements occur but the lungs are not mature. Bones are present but flexible. The baby may survive if born.	Eyes open and close corresponding to wake and sleep cycles; body fat increases; lungs and other organs are functional. The child can grasp and orient toward light. Weight is about 5–6 pounds, and the child is no longer considered premature if born. Full term is 38 weeks.

▲ FIGURE 42-11 **A calendar of development from zygote to birth**

Health Watch

The Promise of Stem Cells

Most cells in adult animals have become committed to a specific developmental pathway and cannot differentiate into other cell types. In contrast, a **stem cell** has not differentiated, and can give rise to more than one cell type. The medical potential of stem cells is vast—victims of heart attacks, strokes, spinal cord injuries, and degenerative diseases from arthritis to Parkinson's disease would benefit if their damaged tissues could be regenerated.

There are three sources of stem cells. First, **embryonic stem cells (ESCs)** are derived from the

inner cell mass (see Fig. 42-7). In the intact embryo, of course, the stem cells of the inner cell mass produce all of the cell types of the entire body. ESCs grown in cell culture can also generate any cell type in the body, if they are exposed to the correct mixture of proteins and other molecules that nudge them into one differentiation pathway or another (**Fig. E42-3**). Second, most parts of the body, including muscle, skin, liver, brain, and heart, contain small numbers of stem cells, usually called **adult stem cells (ASCs),** although they

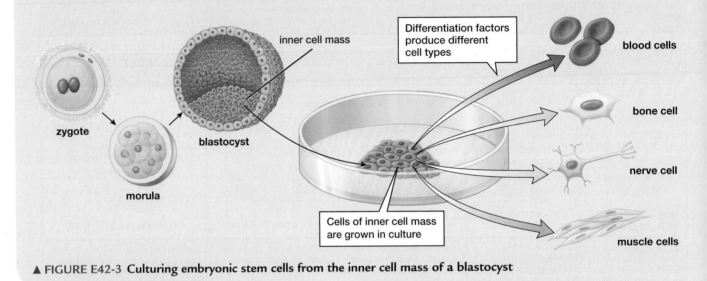

▲ FIGURE E42-3 Culturing embryonic stem cells from the inner cell mass of a blastocyst

endometrium (**Fig. 42-12**). The outer layer of the blastocyst forms the chorion, which grows finger-like **chorionic villi** that extend into the endometrium. Blood vessels of the umbilical cord connect the embryo's circulatory system with a dense network of capillaries in the villi. Meanwhile, implantation has eroded some of the blood vessels of the endometrium, producing pools of maternal blood that bathe the chorionic villi.

The embryo's blood and the mother's blood remain separated by the walls of the villi and their capillaries, so the two blood supplies do not actually mix to any great extent. However, this arrangement permits many small molecules to move between the mother's blood and the embryo's blood. Oxygen diffuses from the mother to the embryo. Nutrients, many aided by active transport, also travel from the mother to the embryo. Carbon dioxide and wastes, such as urea, diffuse from the embryo's blood to the mother's blood.

The membranes of the capillaries and chorionic villi act as barriers to some substances, including large proteins and cells. However, some disease-causing organisms and many harmful chemicals, including alcohol, can penetrate the placenta, as described in "Health Watch: The Placenta—Barrier or Open Door?" on p. 829.

The Placenta Secretes Hormones Essential to Pregnancy

By the end of the first trimester, the placenta usually secretes significant amounts of estrogen and progesterone, enough to

Case Study continued

The Faces of Fetal Alcohol Syndrome

Alcohol has many effects in the developing brain, including interfering with energy metabolism and disrupting the ability of cells to recognize their neighbors, migrate to their correct locations, and develop the correct connections to other brain cells. The resulting incorrect cell locations and connections can never be repaired. For example, the corpus callosum, the band of axons interconnecting the two cerebral hemispheres (see Fig. 38-12), is often smaller, and sometimes missing, in children with FAS, so the left and right sides of the brain cannot communicate properly with one another. Many brain cells die if correct connections are never made, resulting in a reduction in the size of many brain structures.

are also present in children. ASCs can differentiate into only a few cell types. Stem cells from bone marrow, which normally produce both red and white blood cells, have been used for decades in transplants to treat diseases such as leukemia.

Third, by inserting a handful of genes into them, adult (nonstem) cells can be transformed into **induced pluripotent stem cells (iPSCs),** which appear to be able to differentiate into all cell types. Up until early 2009, generating iPSCs required either at least one cancer-causing gene or the use of a potentially dangerous virus that inserts its DNA into the chromosomes of the host cell. Both of these techniques would probably make the resulting iPSCs unsafe for human applications. A major goal of iPSC researchers, therefore, is to produce iPSCs with methods that use neither viruses nor cancer-causing genes. In September 2009, a group at the Salk Institute and the University of California at San Diego reported that they had transformed fetal human neural stem cells into iPSCs using a single, noncarcinogenic gene. Although there are some differences between these iPSCs and ESCs, they offer the promise that it may someday be possible to make iPSCs safe for clinical use.

How might stem cells be used in medicine? In one experiment, researchers induced heart attacks in mice, and then injected ASCs into the damaged heart. The ASCs multiplied and partially repaired the heart muscle. Researchers also have been able to coax human ESCs to differentiate into insulin-secreting cells, and hope that this might be the first step to a cure for type 1 diabetes (see "Health Watch: Closer to a Cure for Diabetes" on p. 727).

However, there are significant obstacles to surmount before stem cells can become effective therapies. First, embryos must be destroyed to obtain ESCs (at least with today's technology). Many people object to this procedure, even when the embryos are "extras" that were created for *in vitro* fertilization and would be destroyed anyway.

Second, the immune system would reject ASCs or ESCs that are not genetically identical, or at least a very close match, to the recipient. This has led to proposals for **therapeutic cloning,** which would involve inserting the nucleus from one of a patient's own cells into an egg whose nucleus had been removed, to create ESCs that would not be rejected. Once again, an embryo would be destroyed to obtain ESCs, so this procedure is also controversial.

Third, are ESCs and iPSCs safe enough to use in people? In early 2009, the media reported that an Israeli boy had been taken to Russia and injected with ESCs three times since 2001 in an attempt to cure a rare brain disease. However, some of the ESCs grew into a tumor (benign, fortunately). Stem cell researchers and physicians stress that safety studies of stem cell therapies have not yet been carried out, so this procedure should never have been done. Some experimental stem cell therapies in mice do not induce tumors, so there's hope that stem cells can be made safe.

Despite these difficulties, researchers are enthusiastic about the future of stem cells for therapies. In the best-case scenario, if iPSCs can be made safe and still differentiate into any desired cell type, then the use of ESCs, the problem of rejection by the immune system, and the ethical issue of therapeutic cloning would all be solved.

---

sustain its own growth and development. About this time, the corpus luteum degenerates, so the future of the pregnancy now depends on the placental hormones. These hormones also stimulate development of the mammary glands. Finally, progesterone also inhibits premature contractions of the uterine muscles.

Pregnancy Culminates in Labor and Delivery

During the last months of pregnancy, the fetus usually becomes positioned head downward in the uterus, with the crown of the skull resting against (and being held up by) the cervix. Childbirth (**Fig. 42-13**) generally begins around the end of the ninth month. Birth results from a complex interplay between uterine stretching caused by the growing fetus, and maternal and fetal hormones that finally trigger **labor,** the contractions of the uterus that result in delivery of the child.

Unlike skeletal muscles, the smooth muscles of the uterus can contract spontaneously, and stretching enhances their tendency to contract. As the baby grows, it stretches the uterine muscles, which occasionally contract weeks before delivery. No one really knows what triggers labor in humans, but chemical signals from both the placenta and maturing fetus may be involved. Whatever the initial stimulus, the

placenta releases prostaglandins, which make the uterine muscles more likely to contract. As the uterus contracts, it pushes the fetus' head against the cervix, stretching it. This has two effects. First, the cervix expands so that the fetus' head can fit through. Second, stretching the cervix sends nervous signals

Have you ever wondered

Why Childbirth Is So Difficult?

Compared to the birth of other animals, childbirth is a lengthy ordeal. Why? Probably for two reasons. First, we walk upright, requiring a different shape to the pelvis as compared to four-footed animals. Thus, a woman's pelvic opening is both small (for her body size) and asymmetrical. Second, human infants have enormous heads, which actually must be squashed a bit to fit through the pelvic opening. Monkeys, with relatively small infant heads and large pelvic openings, give birth quickly and almost effortlessly. In contrast, human deliveries usually last several hours, cause considerable pain to the mother and probably the infant, and often require assistance. They don't call it "labor" for nothing!

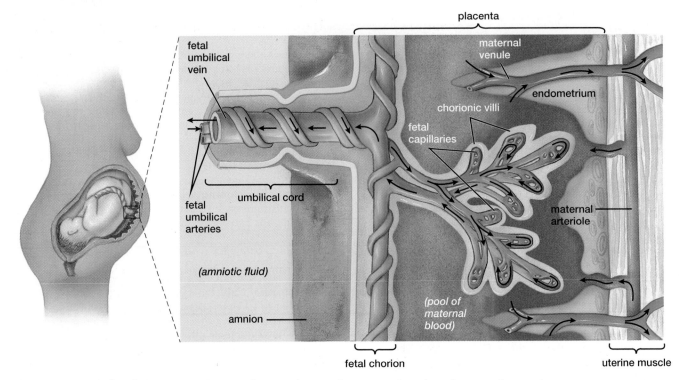

▲ FIGURE 42-12 **The placenta** The placenta allows exchange of wastes and nutrients between the fetal capillaries and the maternal blood pools, while keeping the fetal and maternal blood supplies separate. The umbilical arteries carry deoxygenated blood from the fetus to the placenta, and the umbilical vein carries oxygenated blood back to the fetus.

QUESTION A few types of mammals, such as kangaroos and platypuses, lack a placenta. What would you predict about the nature of development in nonplacental mammals?

to the mother's brain, causing the release of the hormone oxytocin (see Chapter 37). Oxytocin stimulates contractions of the uterine muscles, pushing the baby harder against the cervix, which stretches further, causing still more oxytocin to be released. This positive feedback cycle continues until the baby emerges from the vagina. The infant is in for a rude awakening. The uterus was soft, cushioned with fluid, and

warm. Suddenly, the baby must breathe on its own, regulate its own body temperature, and suckle to obtain food.

After a brief rest following childbirth, the uterus resumes its contractions and shrinks remarkably. During these contractions, the placenta is sheared from the uterine wall and expelled through the vagina. The umbilical cord now releases prostaglandins that cause the muscles surrounding

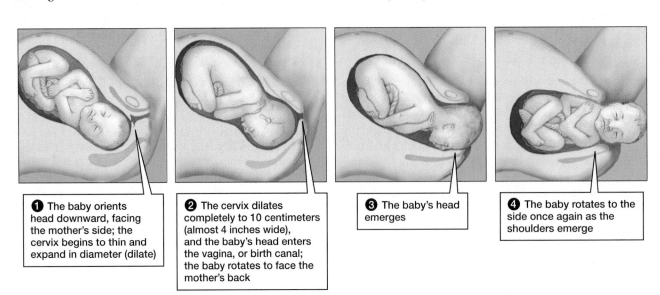

❶ The baby orients head downward, facing the mother's side; the cervix begins to thin and expand in diameter (dilate)

❷ The cervix dilates completely to 10 centimeters (almost 4 inches wide), and the baby's head enters the vagina, or birth canal; the baby rotates to face the mother's back

❸ The baby's head emerges

❹ The baby rotates to the side once again as the shoulders emerge

▲ FIGURE 42-13 **Human childbirth**

Health Watch

The Placenta—Barrier or Open Door?

The fetal and maternal blood supplies are separated by several membranes. However, many molecules, and even some infectious microbes, can pass through these thin membranes, moving from mother to fetus.

Microbes

Bacterial invaders include syphilis, some types of *Streptococcus* that cause blood infections, and *Listeria*, which in adults can cause fatal illness, usually transmitted in contaminated food. Viral invaders include those that cause genital herpes, German measles (rubella), hepatitis B, and HIV. Many of these microbes cause severe disorders in the fetus. For example, about 30% of fetuses infected with syphilis are stillborn, and about 40% suffer from mental retardation. *Listeria* can cause reduced fetal growth, premature delivery, and meningitis (a sometimes fatal infection of the membranes surrounding the brain). Infections with various types of viruses may cause premature birth, mental retardation, eye defects, and many other disorders.

Drugs

Many medicinal and recreational drugs are lipid soluble and can easily move across plasma membranes (see p. 84), including those of the placenta. The question is whether the drugs harm the fetus. Unfortunately, many people learn the answer the hard way. Thalidomide, for example, was commonly prescribed in Europe in the late 1950s and early 1960s as a sedative and antinausea medication to combat morning sickness. Its devastating effects on embryos were discovered only when many babies were born with missing or extremely abnormal limbs. In the late 1980s, the antiacne drug Accutane® was found to cause gross deformities in babies born to women using it.

Toxins in Cigarette Smoke

Many women smokers continue the habit during pregnancy, thus exposing their developing children to nicotine, carbon monoxide, and a host of carcinogens. As a result, these mothers have a higher incidence of miscarriages and tend to give birth to smaller infants, who have a higher risk of death shortly after birth. Children born to smokers also often have behavioral and intellectual deficits. See the "Health Watch: Smoking—A Life and Breath Decision" on p. 649 for more information about the health effects of smoking in children and adults.

Alcohol

Alcohol is soluble both in water and lipids. It dissolves in the blood and then easily passes through the placenta. As one FAS support group notes, "What you drink, baby drinks too." In fact, when a pregnant woman drinks, the blood of her unborn child has as much alcohol as her own. Worse, the fetus cannot metabolize alcohol as rapidly as an adult, so alcohol's effects in the fetus are greater and longer lasting.

More than 12% of U.S. women drink during pregnancy. Each year, they give birth to almost 40,000 infants with fetal alcohol spectrum disorders (FASD), which are a range of disabilities caused by prenatal alcohol exposure. Women who drink even lightly during pregnancy tend to have smaller babies. These children are also more likely to be anxious, depressed, or aggressive. If a pregnant woman drinks heavily on a regular basis (four or more drinks per day), or goes on alcoholic binges (five or more drinks at a time), her child has a significant risk of developing full-blown fetal alcohol syndrome, including below-average intelligence, hyperactivity, irritability, and poor impulse control. FAS children may also have reduced growth and defects of the heart and other organs. In extreme cases, children afflicted with FAS may have small, improperly developed brains (**Fig. E42-4**). The damage is irreversible and can be fatal.

FAS is the single most common cause of mental retardation in the United States. The U.S. Surgeon General advises pregnant women and those who are likely to become pregnant to avoid alcohol completely.

The Placenta Cannot Be Trusted to Protect the Embryo

A pregnant woman should assume that any drugs she takes will cross the placenta to her developing infant. Crucial stages of embryonic development can occur before a woman even realizes that she is pregnant, so any woman trying to become pregnant, or having unprotected sex, should take the same precautions as if she were already pregnant.

▲ **FIGURE E42-4 Alcohol impairs brain development** Comparing the brain of a 6-week-old child with severe fetal alcohol syndrome (left) and the brain of a normal child of the same age (right) shows the devastating effects of alcohol on the developing brain. (Photo courtesy of Dr. Sterling Clarren, University of Washington, Seattle, WA.)

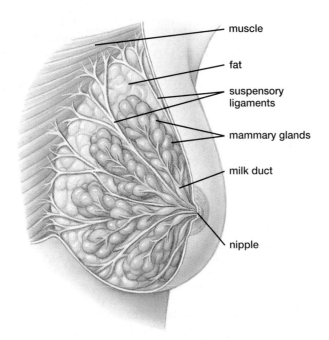

muscle

fat

suspensory
ligaments

mammary glands

milk duct

nipple

▲ **FIGURE 42-14 The structure of the mammary glands**
During pregnancy, fatty tissue, the milk-secreting glands, and
the milk ducts all increase in size.

fetal blood vessels in the umbilical cord to contract and shut off blood flow. Although tying off the umbilical cord is standard practice, it is not usually necessary; if it were, other mammals would not survive birth.

Milk Secretion Is Stimulated by the Hormones of Pregnancy

During pregnancy, large quantities of estrogen and progesterone are secreted by the placenta. Estrogen and progesterone, acting together with several other hormones, stimulate the milk-producing **mammary glands** in the breasts to grow, branch, and develop the capacity to secrete milk. The mammary glands are arranged in a circle around the nipple, each with a milk duct leading to the nipple (**Fig. 42-14**).

Prolactin, a hormone secreted by the anterior pituitary gland, promotes both mammary gland development and the actual secretion of milk, a process called **lactation.** Prolactin release is stimulated by the high levels of estrogen produced by the placenta, so you might think that milk secretion would begin even before the child is born. However, lactation is inhibited by progesterone, which is also secreted by the placenta. During childbirth, the placenta is ejected from the uterus. Progesterone levels plummet, allowing prolactin to cause lactation.

Milk is released when the infant's suckling stimulates nerve endings in the nipples, which signal the hypothalamus to cause the pituitary gland to release an extra surge of prolactin and oxytocin. Oxytocin causes muscles surrounding the mammary glands to contract, ejecting the milk into the ducts that lead to the nipples (see Fig. 37-8). The prolactin surge stimulates rapid milk production for the next feeding.

During the first few days after birth, the mammary glands secrete a yellowish fluid called **colostrum.** Colostrum is high in protein and contains antibodies from the mother that help protect the infant against some diseases as its immune system is developing. Colostrum is gradually replaced by mature milk, which is higher in fat and milk sugar (lactose) and lower in protein.

42.6 IS AGING THE FINAL STAGE OF HUMAN DEVELOPMENT?

Aging (**Fig. 42-15**) is the gradual accumulation of damage to essential biological molecules, particularly DNA in both the nucleus and mitochondria, resulting in defects in cell functioning, declining health, and ultimately death. This damage—from natural errors in DNA replication, radiation from the sun or the rocks beneath our feet, and chemicals in food, cigarettes, and industrial products—begins at fertilization. Many biological molecules are harmed by free radicals (see pp. 24–25), some produced by environmental pollutants, but most by energy-generating reactions in our cells, especially in mitochondria.

Some molecular injury can be tolerated. Young bodies may be able to repair damage or compensate for it. As an animal ages, however, its repair abilities diminish; eventually, the body's tolerance for damage is exceeded. At the organismal level, aging is manifested in many ways: Muscle and bone mass are lost, skin elasticity decreases, reaction time slows, and senses such as vision and hearing become less acute. A less-robust immune response renders the aging individual more vulnerable to disease. Eventually, the individual can no longer fight off natural assaults, and death occurs.

For thousands of years, people have attempted to delay aging and extend the human life span. Modern medical care can prevent or cure many diseases, and can fix or replace some damaged organs (think bypass surgery and transplants). Some dietary changes, particularly not eating very much food (euphemistically called "caloric restriction"), can prolong life, at least in animal experiments. However, what seems to be the maximum human life span, about 130 years, has not changed.

▲ **FIGURE 42-15 Youth meets age**

Several evolutionary hypotheses suggest that aging is unavoidable. For example, natural selection favors organisms that leave the largest number of healthy, successful offspring. Even a hypothetically immortal animal that wouldn't die from "inside," so to speak, will eventually succumb to predation, accident, or disease. Therefore, perhaps natural selection favors devoting more of the body's resources to reproduction than to the continuous bodily repair required for immortality. The fact that humans can live so long after they stop reproducing is probably evidence of the selective advantage conferred by the care and teaching given to the young by their elders.

Case Study revisited
The Faces of Fetal Alcohol Syndrome

When John Kellerman was born, the delivery room reeked of the alcohol polluting his amniotic fluid: John was born drunk. Even today, without medication, his behavior resembles that of a drunk person: silly, volatile, and lacking impulse control.

The writings of people with FAS or FASD (fetal alcohol spectrum disorders) poignantly convey the day-to-day difficulties that these innocent people face over a lifetime. In his poem "Help," John wrote:

"When my brain is not working right,
I need to let someone I trust
Help me
To stay safe and get calm again.
When my brain is not working right,
I feel like I am on a FASD Train
Going downhill,
And the engineer is asleep
And I can't wake him up,
And I can't put on the brakes."

CJ, an FAS victim from Canada, explained:

"I am small, I have a different face . . . and Lots of Learning
    problems.
Moms do not do this on purpose
Do not be mean or mad or blame them
I am 17 years old and have had FAS all my life
I will have it forever
It will never go away
Don't be mean or mad or blame me. . . ."

BioEthics Consider This

In many states, women who use illegal drugs or abuse alcohol during pregnancy may be subject to legal action to protect fetal rights. How do you think society should approach the dilemma of pregnant women who often unwittingly damage their unborn children through alcohol or other drugs? Is this child abuse? Based on what you know about development, how would you deal with a friend who continued to smoke, drink, or take other drugs during pregnancy?

CHAPTER REVIEW

Summary of Key Concepts

42.1 What Are the Principles of Animal Development?
Development is the process by which an organism grows and increases in organization and complexity, using three main mechanisms: (1) Individual cells multiply; (2) daughter cells differentiate; and (3) groups of cells move about and become organized into multicellular structures.

42.2 How Do Indirect and Direct Development Differ?
Animals undergo either indirect or direct development. In indirect development, eggs (usually with relatively little yolk) hatch into larvae, which undergo metamorphosis to become adults with notably different body forms. In direct development, the newborn animal is sexually immature but otherwise resembles a small adult. Animals with direct development tend to produce either large, yolk-filled eggs or nourish the developing embryo within the mother's body.

42.3 How Does Animal Development Proceed?
Animal development occurs in several stages. *Cleavage and blastula formation:* A fertilized egg undergoes cell divisions with little intervening growth, so the daughter cells become smaller. Cleavage results in the formation of the morula, a solid ball of cells. A cavity then opens up within the morula, forming a hollow ball of cells called a blastula. *Gastrulation:* A dimple forms in the blastula, and cells migrate from the surface into the interior of the ball, eventually forming a three-layered gastrula. These three cell layers—ectoderm, mesoderm, and endoderm—give rise to all the adult tissues. *Organogenesis:* The cell layers of the gastrula form organs characteristic of the animal species (see Table 42-1).

In mammals and reptiles (including birds), extraembryonic membranes (the chorion, amnion, allantois, and yolk sac) encase the embryo in a fluid-filled space and regulate the exchange of nutrients and wastes between the embryo and its environment.

42.4 How Is Development Controlled?
All the cells of an animal body contain a full set of genetic information, yet cells are specialized for particular functions. Cells differentiate by stimulating and repressing the transcription of specific genes, which is controlled by (1) differences in gene-regulating substances inherited from the mother in her egg and/or (2) chemical communication between the cells of the embryo, a process called induction. A particularly important group of genes, called homeobox genes, regulates the differentiation of body segments and their associated structures, such as wings or legs.

42.5 How Do Humans Develop?
A human egg is fertilized in the uterine tube. The resulting zygote develops into a blastocyst and implants in the endometrium. The

outer wall of the blastocyst will become the chorion and form the embryonic contribution to the placenta; the inner cell mass develops into the embryo and the three other extraembryonic membranes. During gastrulation, cells migrate and differentiate into ectoderm, mesoderm, and endoderm. During the third and fourth weeks, the endoderm forms a tube that will become the digestive tract, the heart begins to beat, and the rudiments of a nervous system appear. By the end of the second month, the major organs have begun to form, and the embryo—now called a fetus—appears human. In the next 7 months before birth, the fetus continues to grow; the lungs, stomach, intestine, kidneys, and nervous system enlarge, develop, and become functional. See Figure 42-11.

During pregnancy, mammary glands in the mother's breasts grow under the influence of estrogen, progesterone, and other hormones, such as prolactin. After about 9 months, uterine contractions are triggered by a complex interplay of uterine stretch and the release of prostaglandin and oxytocin. As a result, the uterus expels the baby and then the placenta. After its birth, the infant begins suckling and activates the release of prolactin, which stimulates milk production, and oxytocin, which triggers milk secretion.

42.6 Is Aging the Final Stage of Human Development?

Aging is the gradual accumulation of cellular damage (particularly to genetic material) over time that leads to loss of functionality of an organism and, eventually, to death. Some biologists hypothesize that aging results from natural selection favoring a sexually mature animal putting more resources into reproduction than into bodily repair.

Key Terms

adult stem cell (ASC) 826	fetus 824
aging 830	gastrula 816
allantois 817	gastrulation 816
amnion 817	homeobox gene 819
amniotic egg 817	implantation 822
blastocyst 822	indirect development 814
blastopore 816	induced pluripotent stem cell
blastula 815	(iPSC) 827
chorion 817	induction 819
chorionic villus (plural,	inner cell mass 822
chorionic villi) 826	labor 827
cleavage 815	lactation 830
colostrum 830	larva (plural, larvae) 814
development 814	mammary gland 830
differentiate 814	mesoderm 816
direct development 814	metamorphosis 814
ectoderm 816	morula 815
embryonic disk 823	organogenesis 816
embryonic stem cell	placenta 824
(ESC) 826	stem cell 826
endoderm 816	therapeutic cloning 827
extraembryonic	yolk 814
membrane 817	yolk sac 817
fetal alcohol syndrome	zygote 815
(FAS) 813	

Thinking Through the Concepts

Fill-in-the-Blank

1. A fertilized egg is a very large cell. One of the first events of animal development is the division of this cell, a process called _____, to produce a solid ball of much smaller cells, the _____. Soon, a cavity opens in this ball of cells, producing a hollow ball called the _____. Movements of cells in this hollow ball during gastrulation produce the three embryonic tissue layers, the _____, _____, and _____.

2. The evolution of the amniotic egg allows development to occur in fully terrestrial animals that do not lay eggs in water. The amniotic egg contains four extraembryonic membranes. In both reptiles and mammals, the _____ encloses the embryo in a watery environment. In mammals, the _____ forms the embryo's part of the placenta. The allantois contributes the blood vessels of the _____, which connects the embryo to the placenta. Finally, the _____ contains stored food in reptile eggs, but in mammals, this is "empty" and principally forms the lining of the digestive tract.

3. Undifferentiated cells that can multiply and produce daughter cells of many different types are called _____. Embryonic cells of this type can differentiate into any cell type of the body; they are derived from the _____.

4. Genes that control the development of entire body segments and their accompanying limbs (if any) are called _____. They usually code for proteins called _____ that regulate the transcription of many other genes.

5. Milk production in the mammary glands is stimulated by a hormone from the pituitary gland called _____. Another hormone, _____, stimulates contraction of both the uterine muscles during childbirth and the muscles around the mammary glands that cause milk to be ejected from the glands.

Review Questions

1. Distinguish between indirect and direct development, and give examples of each.

2. Describe the structure and function of the four extraembryonic membranes found in reptiles, including birds. Are these four present in placental mammals? In what ways are their roles similar in reptiles as compared to mammals? How do they differ?

3. What is gastrulation? Describe gastrulation in amphibians.

4. Name two structures derived from each of the three embryonic tissue layers—endoderm, ectoderm, and mesoderm.

5. Describe induction.

6. In humans, where does fertilization occur, and what stages of development occur before the fertilized egg reaches the uterus?

7. Describe how the human blastocyst gives rise to the embryo and its extraembryonic membranes.

8. Explain how the structure of the placenta prevents mixing of fetal and maternal blood while allowing for the exchange of substances between the mother and the fetus.

9. How do changes in the breast prepare a mother to nurse her newborn? How do hormones influence these changes and stimulate milk production?

10. Describe the events leading to the expulsion of the baby and the placenta from the uterus. Explain why this is an example of positive feedback.

Applying the Concepts

1. A researcher obtains two frog embryos at the gastrula stage of development. She carefully removes a cluster of cells from a location that she knows would normally become neural tube tissue and transplants it into the second gastrula in a location that would normally become skin. Does the second gastrula develop two neural tubes? Explain your answer.

2. In almost all animals that produce eggs with very little yolk, the blastula stage is roughly spherical. Mammalian eggs, however, contain virtually no yolk but have flat embryonic disks, which undergo gastrulation much like spherical blastulas do. Propose an explanation for this difference in shape.

3. BioEthics   Some people feel that the production of induced pluripotent stem cells means that research on embryonic stem cells is unnecessary. Take a position on this issue and defend it.

MB *Go to www.masteringbiology.com for practice quizzes, activities, eText, videos, current events, and more.*

Biological Vocabulary: Common Roots, Prefixes, and Suffixes

Biology has an extensive vocabulary often based on Greek or Latin rather than English words. Rather than memorizing every word as if it were part of a new, foreign language, you can figure out the meaning of many new terms if you learn a much smaller number of word roots, prefixes, and suffixes. We have provided common meanings in biology rather than literal translations from Greek or Latin. For each item in the list, the following information is given: meaning; part of word (prefix, suffix, or root); example from biology.

a–, an–: without, lack of (prefix); *abiotic*, without life

acro–: top, highest (prefix); *acrosome*, vesicle of enzymes at the tip of a sperm

ad–: to (prefix); *adhesion*, property of sticking to something else

allo–: other (prefix); *allopatric* (literally, "different fatherland"), restricted to different regions

amphi–: both, double, two (prefix); *amphibian*, a class of vertebrates that usually has two life stages (aquatic and terrestrial; e.g., a tadpole and an adult frog)

andro: man, male (root); *androgen*, a male hormone such as testosterone

ant–, anti–: against (prefix); *antibiotic* (literally "against life"), a substance that kills bacteria

antero–: front (prefix or root); *anterior*, toward the front of

aqu–, aqua–: water (prefix or root); *aquifer*, an underground water source, usually rock saturated with water

apic–: top, highest (prefix); *apical meristem*, the cluster of dividing cells at the tip of a plant shoot or root

arthr–: joint (prefix); *arthropod*, animals such as spiders, crabs, and insects, with exoskeletons that include jointed legs

–ase: enzyme (suffix); *protease*, an enzyme that digests protein

auto–: self (prefix); *autotrophic*, self-feeder (e.g., photo-synthetic)

bi–: two (prefix); *bipedal*, having two legs

bio–: life (prefix or root); *biology*, the study of life

blast: bud, precursor (root); *blastula*, embryonic stage of development, a hollow ball of cells

bronch: windpipe (root); *bronchus*, a branch of the trachea (windpipe) leading to a lung

carcin, –o: cancer (root); *carcinogenesis*, the process of producing a cancer

cardi, –a–, –o–: heart (root); *cardiac*, referring to the heart

carn–, –i–, –o–: flesh (prefix or root); *carnivore*, an animal that eats other animals

centi–: one hundredth (prefix); *centimeter*, a unit of length, 1 one-hundredth of a meter

cephal–, –i–, –o–: head (prefix or root); *cephalization*, the tendency for the nervous system to be located principally in the head

chloro–: green (prefix or root); *chlorophyll*, the green, light-absorbing pigment in plants

chondr–: cartilage (prefix); *Chondrichthyes*, class of vertebrates including sharks and rays, with a skeleton made of cartilage

chrom–: color (prefix or root); *chromosome*, a threadlike strand of DNA and protein in the nucleus of a cell (*Chromosome* literally means "colored body," because chromosomes absorb some of the colored dyes commonly used in microscopy.)

–cide: killer (suffix); *pesticide*, a chemical that kills "pests" (usually insects)

–clast: break down, broken (root or suffix); *osteoclast*, a cell that breaks down bone

co–: with or together with (prefix); *cohesion*, property of sticking together

coel–: hollow (prefix or root); *coelom*, the body cavity that separates the internal organs from the body wall

contra–: against (prefix); *contraception*, acting to prevent conception (pregnancy)

cortex: bark, outer layer (root); *cortex*, outer layer of kidney

crani–: skull (prefix or root); *cranium*, the skull

cuti: skin (root); *cuticle*, the outermost covering of a leaf

–cyte, cyto–: cell (root or prefix); *cytokinin*, a plant hormone that promotes cell division

de–: from, out of, remove (prefix); *decomposer*, an organism that breaks down organic matter

dendr: treelike, branching (root); *dendrite*, highly branched input structures of nerve cells

derm: skin, layer (root); *ectoderm*, the outer embryonic germ layer of cells

deutero–: second (prefix); *deuterostome* (literally, "second opening"), an animal in which the coelom is derived from the gut

di–: two (prefix); *dicot*, an angiosperm with two cotyledons in the seed

diplo–: both, double, two (prefix or root); *diploid*, having paired homologous chromosomes

dys–: difficult, painful (prefix); *dysfunction*, an inability to function properly

eco–: house, household (prefix); *ecology*, the study of the relationships between organisms and their environment

ecto–: outside (prefix); *ectoderm*, the outermost tissue layer of animal embryos

–elle: little, small (suffix); *organelle* (literally, "little organ"), a subcellular structure that performs a specific function

end–, endo–, ento–: inside, inner (prefix); *endocrine*, pertaining to a gland that secretes hormones inside the body

epi–: outside, outer (prefix); *epidermis*, outermost layer of skin

equi–: equal (prefix); *equidistant*, the same distance

erythro–: red (prefix); *erythrocyte*, red blood cell

eu–: true, good (prefix); *eukaryotic*, pertaining to a cell with a true nucleus

ex–, exo–: out of (prefix); *exocrine*, pertaining to a gland that secretes a substance (e.g., sweat) outside of the body

extra–: outside of (prefix); *extracellular*, outside of a cell

–fer: to bear, to carry (suffix); *conifer*, a tree that bears cones

gastr–: stomach (prefix or root); *gastric*, pertaining to the stomach

–gen–: to produce (prefix, root, or suffix); *antigen*, a substance that causes the body to produce antibodies

glyc–, glyco–: sweet (prefix); *glycogen*, a starch-like molecule composed of many glucose molecules bonded together

gyn, –o: female (prefix or root); *gynecology*, the study of the female reproductive tract

haplo–: single (prefix); *haploid*, having a single copy of each type of chromosome

hem–, hemato–: blood (prefix or root); *hemoglobin*, the molecule in red blood cells that carries oxygen

hemi–: half (prefix); *hemisphere*, one of the halves of the cerebrum

herb–, herbi–: grass (prefix or root); *herbivore*, an animal that eats plants

hetero–: other (prefix); *heterotrophic*, an organism that feeds on other organisms

hom–, homo–, homeo–: same (prefix); *homeostasis*, to maintain constant internal conditions in the face of changing external conditions

hydro–: water (usually prefix); *hydrophilic*, being attracted to water

hyper–: above, greater than (prefix); *hyperosmotic*, having a greater osmotic strength (usually higher solute concentration)

hypo–: below, less than (prefix); *hypodermic*, below the skin

inter–: between (prefix); *interneuron*, a neuron that receives input from one (or more) neuron(s) and sends output to another neuron (or many neurons)

intra–: within (prefix); *intracellular*, pertaining to an event or substance that occurs within a cell

iso–: equal (prefix); *isotonic*, pertaining to a solution that has the same osmotic strength as another solution

–itis: inflammation (suffix); *hepatitis*, an inflammation (or infection) of the liver

kin–, kinet–: moving (prefix or root); *cytokinesis*, the movements of a cell that divide the cell in half during cell division

lac–, lact–: milk (prefix or root); *lactose*, the principal sugar in mammalian milk

leuc–, leuco–, leuk–, leuko–: white (prefix); *leukocyte*, a white blood cell

lip–: fat (prefix or root); *lipid*, the chemical category to which fats, oils, and steroids belong

–logy: study of (suffix); *biology*, the study of life

lyso–, –lysis: loosening, split apart (prefix, root, or suffix); *lysis*, to break open a cell

macro–: large (prefix); *macrophage*, a large white blood cell that destroys invading foreign cells

medulla: marrow, middle substance (root); *medulla*, inner layer of kidney

mega–: large (prefix); *megaspore*, a large, haploid (female) spore formed by meiotic cell division in plants

–mere: segment, body section (suffix); *sarcomere*, the functional unit of a vertebrate skeletal muscle cell

meso–: middle (prefix); *mesophyll*, middle layers of cells in a leaf

meta–: change, after (prefix); *metamorphosis*, to change body form (e.g., developing from a larva to an adult)

micro–: small (prefix); *microscope*, a device that allows one to see small objects

milli–: one-thousandth (prefix); *millimeter*, a unit of measurement of length; 1 one-thousandth of a meter

mito–: thread (prefix); *mitosis*, cell division (in which chromosomes appear as threadlike bodies)

mono–: single (prefix); *monocot*, a type of angiosperm with one cotyledon in the seed

morph–: shape, form (prefix or root); *polymorphic*, having multiple forms

multi–: many (prefix); *multicellular*, pertaining to a body composed of more than one cell

myo–: muscle (prefix); *myofibril*, protein strands in muscle cells

neo–: new (prefix); *neonatal*, relating to or affecting a newborn child

neph–: kidney (prefix or root); *nephron*, functional unit of mammalian kidney

neur–, neuro–: nerve (prefix or root); *neuron*, a nerve cell

neutr–: of neither gender or type (usually root); *neutron*, an uncharged subatomic particle found in the nucleus of an atom

non–: not (prefix); *nondisjunction*, the failure of chromosomes to distribute themselves properly during cell division

oligo–: few (prefix); *oligomer*, a molecule made up of a few subunits (see also *poly–*)

omni–: all (prefix); *omnivore*, an animal that eats both plants and animals

oo–, ov–, ovo–: egg (prefix); *oocyte*, one of the stages of egg development

opsi–: sight (prefix or root); *opsin*, protein part of light-absorbing pigment in eye

opso–: tasty food (prefix or root); *opsonization*, process whereby antibodies and/or complement render bacteria easier for white blood cells to engulf

–osis: a condition, disease (suffix); *atherosclerosis*, a disease in which the artery walls become thickened and hardened

oss–, osteo–: bone (prefix or root); *osteoporosis*; a disease in which the bones become spongy and weak

para–: alongside (prefix); *parathyroid*, referring to a gland located next to the thyroid gland

pater, patr–: father (usually root); *paternal*, from or relating to a father

path–, –i–, –o–: disease (prefix or root); *pathology*, the study of disease and diseased tissue

–pathy: disease (suffix); *neuropathy*, a disease of the nervous system

peri–: around (prefix); *pericycle*, the outermost layer of cells in the vascular cylinder of a plant root

phago–: eat (prefix or root); *phagocyte*, a cell (e.g., some types of white blood cell) that eats other cells

–phil, philo–: to love (prefix or suffix); *hydrophilic* (literally, "water loving"), pertaining to a water-soluble molecule

–phob, phobo–: to fear (prefix or suffix); *hydrophobic* (literally, "water fearing"), pertaining to a water-insoluble molecule

photo–: light (prefix); *photosynthesis*, the manufacture of organic molecules using the energy of sunlight

–phyll: leaf (root or suffix); *chlorophyll*, the green, light-absorbing pigment in a leaf

–phyte: plant (root or suffix); *gametophyte* (literally, "gamete plant"), the gamete-producing stage of a plant life cycle

plasmo, –plasm: formed substance (prefix, root, or suffix); *cytoplasm*, the material inside a cell

ploid: chromosomes (root); *diploid*, having paired chromosomes

pneumo–: lung (root); *pneumonia*, a disease of the lungs

–pod: foot (root or suffix); *gastropod* (literally, "stomach-foot"), a class of mollusks, principally snails, that crawl on their ventral surfaces

poly–: many (prefix); *polysaccharide*, a carbohydrate polymer composed of many sugar subunits (see also *oligo–*)

post–, postero–: behind (prefix); *posterior*, pertaining to the hind part

pre–, pro–: before, in front of (prefix); *premating isolating mechanism*, a mechanism that prevents gene flow between species, acting to prevent mating (e.g., having different courtship rituals or different mating seasons)

prim–: first (prefix); *primary cell wall*, the first cell wall laid down between plant cells during cell division

pro–: before (prefix); *prokaryotic*, pertaining to a cell without (that evolved before the evolution of) a nucleus

proto–: first (prefix); *protocell*, a hypothetical evolutionary ancestor to the first cell

pseudo–: false (prefix); *pseudopod* (literally, "false foot"), the extension of the plasma membrane by which some cells, such as *Amoeba*, move and capture prey

quad–, quat–: four (prefix); *quaternary structure*, the "fourth level" of protein structure, in which multiple peptide chains form a complex three-dimensional structure

ren: kidney (root); *adrenal*, gland attached to the mammalian kidney

retro–: backward (prefix); *retrovirus*, a virus that uses RNA as its genetic material; this RNA must be copied "backward" to DNA during infection of a cell by the virus

sarco–: muscle (prefix); *sarcoplasmic reticulum*, a calcium-storing, modified endoplasmic reticulum found in muscle cells

scler–: hard, tough (prefix); *sclerenchyma*, a type of plant cell with a very thick, hard cell wall

semi–: one-half (prefix); *semiconservative replication*, the mechanism of DNA replication, in which one strand of the original DNA double helix becomes incorporated into the new DNA double helix

–some, soma–, somato–: body (prefix or suffix); *somatic nervous system*, part of the peripheral nervous system that controls the skeletal muscles that move the body

sperm, sperma–, spermato–: seed (usually root); *gymnosperm*, a type of plant producing a seed not enclosed within a fruit

stasis, stat–: stationary, standing still (suffix or prefix); *homeostasis*, the physiological process of maintaining constant internal conditions despite a changing external environment

stoma, –to–: mouth, opening (prefix or root); *stoma*, the adjustable pore in the surface of a leaf that allows carbon dioxide to enter the leaf

sub–: under, below (prefix); *subcutaneous*, beneath the skin

sym–: same (prefix); *sympatric* (literally "same father"), found in the same region

tel–, telo–: end (prefix); *telophase*, the last stage of mitosis and meiosis

test–: witness (prefix or root); *testis*, male reproductive organ (derived from the custom in ancient Rome that only males had standing in the eyes of the law; *testimony* has the same derivation)

therm–: heat (prefix or root); *thermoregulation*, the process of regulating body temperature

trans–: across (prefix); *transgenic*, having genes from another organism (usually another species); the genes have been moved "across" species

tri–: three (prefix); *triploid*, having three copies of each homologous chromosome

–trop–, tropic: change, turn, move (suffix); *phototropism*, the process by which plants orient toward the light

troph: food, nourishment (root); *autotrophic*, self-feeder (e.g., photosynthetic)

ultra–: beyond (prefix); *ultraviolet*, light of wavelengths beyond the violet

uni–: one (prefix); *unicellular*, referring to an organism composed of a single cell

vita: life (root); *vitamin*, a molecule required in the diet to sustain life

–vor: eat (usually root); *herbivore*, an animal that eats plants

zoo–, zoa–: animal (usually root); *zoology*, the study of animals

atomic number (number of protons)

element (chemical symbol)

atomic mass (total mass of protons + neutrons + electrons)

1	2	3	4	5	6	7	8	9	10	11	12	13	14	15	16	17	18
1 **H** 1.008																	2 **He** 4.003
3 **Li** 6.941	4 **Be** 9.012											5 **B** 10.81	6 **C** 12.01	7 **N** 14.01	8 **O** 16.00	9 **F** 19.00	10 **Ne** 20.18
11 **Na** 22.99	12 **Mg** 24.31											13 **Al** 26.98	14 **Si** 28.09	15 **P** 30.97	16 **S** 32.07	17 **Cl** 35.45	18 **Ar** 39.95
19 **K** 39.10	20 **Ca** 40.08	21 **Sc** 44.96	22 **Ti** 47.87	23 **V** 50.94	24 **Cr** 52.00	25 **Mn** 54.94	26 **Fe** 55.85	27 **Co** 58.93	28 **Ni** 58.69	29 **Cu** 63.55	30 **Zn** 65.39	31 **Ga** 69.72	32 **Ge** 72.61	33 **As** 74.92	34 **Se** 78.96	35 **Br** 79.90	36 **Kr** 83.80
37 **Rb** 85.47	38 **Sr** 87.62	39 **Y** 88.91	40 **Zr** 91.22	41 **Nb** 92.91	42 **Mo** 95.94	43 **Tc** (98)	44 **Ru** 101.1	45 **Rh** 102.9	46 **Pd** 106.4	47 **Ag** 107.9	48 **Cd** 112.4	49 **In** 114.8	50 **Sn** 118.7	51 **Sb** 121.8	52 **Te** 127.6	53 **I** 126.9	54 **Xe** 131.3
55 **Cs** 132.9	56 **Ba** 137.3	57 ***La** 138.9	72 **Hf** 178.5	73 **Ta** 180.9	74 **W** 183.8	75 **Re** 186.2	76 **Os** 190.2	77 **Ir** 192.2	78 **Pt** 195.1	79 **Au** 197.0	80 **Hg** 200.6	81 **Tl** 204.4	82 **Pb** 207.2	83 **Bi** 209.0	84 **Po** (209)	85 **At** (210)	86 **Rn** (222)
87 **Fr** (223)	88 **Ra** (226)	89 **†Ac** (227)	104 **Rf** (261)	105 **Db** (262)	106 **Sg** (263)	107 **Bh** (264)	108 **Hs** (265)	109 **Mt** (268)	110 **Ds** (281)	111 **Rg** (280)	112 ****** (277)	113 ******	114 ****** (285)	115 ******			

*Lanthanide series

58 **Ce** 140.1	59 **Pr** 140.9	60 **Nd** 144.2	61 **Pm** (145)	62 **Sm** 150.4	63 **Eu** 152.0	64 **Gd** 157.3	65 **Tb** 158.9	66 **Dy** 162.5	67 **Ho** 164.9	68 **Er** 167.3	69 **Tm** 168.9	70 **Yb** 173.0	71 **Lu** 175.0

†Actinide series

90 **Th** 232.0	91 **Pa** 231	92 **U** 238.0	93 **Np** (237)	94 **Pu** (244)	95 **Am** (243)	96 **Cm** (247)	97 **Bk** (247)	98 **Cf** (251)	99 **Es** (252)	100 **Fm** (257)	101 **Md** (258)	102 **No** (259)	103 **Lr** (262)

The periodic table of the elements was first devised by Russian chemist Dmitri Mendeleev. The atomic numbers of the elements (the numbers of protons in the nucleus) increase in normal reading order: left to right, top to bottom. The table is "periodic" because all the elements in a column possess similar chemical properties, and such similar elements therefore recur "periodically" in each row. For example, elements that usually form ions with a single positive charge—including H, Li, Na, K, and so on—occur as the first element in each row.

The gaps in the table are a consequence of the maximum numbers of electrons in the most reactive, usually outermost, electron shells of the atoms. It takes only two electrons to completely fill the first shell, so the first row of the table contains only two elements, H and He. It takes eight electrons to fill the second and third shells, so there are eight elements in the second and third rows. It takes 18 electrons to fill the fourth and fifth shells, so there are 18 elements in these rows.

The lanthanide series and actinide series of elements are usually placed below the main body of the table for convenience—it takes 32 electrons to completely fill the sixth and seventh shells, so the table would become extremely wide if all of these elements were included in the sixth and seventh rows.

The important elements found in living things are highlighted in color. The elements in pale red are the six most abundant elements in living things. The elements that form the five most abundant ions in living things are in purple. The trace elements important to life are shown as dark blue (more common) and lighter blue (less common). For radioactive elements, the atomic masses are given in parentheses, and represent the most common or the most stable isotope. Elements indicated as double asterisks have not yet been named.

Metric System Conversions

To Convert Metric Units:	Multiply by:	To Get English Equivalent:
Length		
Centimeters (cm)	0.3937	Inches (in)
Meters (m)	3.2808	Feet (ft)
Meters (m)	1.0936	Yards (yd)
Kilometers (km)	0.6214	Miles (mi)
Area		
Square centimeters (cm^2)	0.155	Square inches (in^2)
Square meters (m^2)	10.7639	Square feet (ft^2)
Square meters (m^2)	1.1960	Square yards (yd^2)
Square kilometers (km^2)	0.3831	Square miles (mi^2)
Hectare (ha) (10,000 m^2)	2.4710	Acres (a)
Volume		
Cubic centimeters (cm^3)	0.06	Cubic inches (in^3)
Cubic meters (m^3)	35.30	Cubic feet (ft^3)
Cubic meters (m^3)	1.3079	Cubic yards (yd^3)
Cubic kilometers (km^3)	0.24	Cubic miles (mi^3)
Liters (L)	1.0567	Quarts (qt), U.S.
Liters (L)	0.26	Gallons (gal), U.S.
Mass		
Grams (g)	0.03527	Ounces (oz)
Kilograms (kg)	2.2046	Pounds (lb)
Metric ton (tonne) (t)	1.10	Ton (tn), U.S.
Speed		
Meters/second (mps)	2.24	Miles/hour (mph)
Kilometers/hour (kmph)	0.62	Miles/hour (mph)

To Convert English Units:	Multiply by:	To Get Metric Equivalent:
Length		
Inches (in)	2.54	Centimeters (cm)
Feet (ft)	0.3048	Meters (m)
Yards (yd)	0.9144	Meters (m)
Miles (mi)	1.6094	Kilometers (km)
Area		
Square inches (in^2)	6.45	Square centimeters (cm^2)
Square feet (ft^2)	0.0929	Square meters (m^2)
Square yards (yd^2)	0.8361	Square meters (m^2)
Square miles (mi^2)	2.5900	Square kilometers (km^2)
Acres (a)	0.4047	Hectare (ha) (10,000 m^2)
Volume		
Cubic inches (in^3)	16.39	Cubic centimeters (cm^3)
Cubic feet (ft^3)	0.028	Cubic meters (m^3)
Cubic yards (yd^3)	0.765	Cubic meters (m^3)
Cubic miles (mi^3)	4.17	Cubic kilometers (km^3)
Quarts (qt), U.S.	0.9463	Liters (L)
Gallons (gal), U.S.	3.8	Liters (L)
Mass		
Ounces (oz)	28.3495	Grams (g)
Pounds (lb)	0.4536	Kilograms (kg)
Ton (tn), U.S.	0.91	Metric ton (tonne) (t)
Speed		
Miles/hour (mph)	0.448	Meters/second (mps)
Miles/hour (mph)	1.6094	Kilometers/hour (kmph)

Metric Prefixes

Prefix			Meaning
giga-	G	$10^9 =$	1,000,000,000
mega-	M	$10^6 =$	1,000,000
kilo-	k	$10^3 =$	1,000
hecto-	h	$10^2 =$	100
deka-	da	$10^1 =$	10
		$10^0 =$	1
deci-	d	$10^{-1} =$	0.1
centi-	c	$10^{-2} =$	0.01
milli-	m	$10^{-3} =$	0.001
micro-	μ	$10^{-6} =$	0.000001

°C · °F

160° — 320°
150° — 305°
140° — 290°
130° — 275° / 260°
120° — 245°
110° — 230°
100° — 212° ← water boils
90° — 200° / 185°
80° — 170°
70° — 155°
60° — 140°
50° — 125°
40° — 110° / 95°
30° — 80°
20° — 65°
10° — 50°
0° — 32° ← water freezes
-10° — 20° / 5°
-20° — -10°
-30° — -25°
-40° — -40°

$$°C = \frac{°F - 32}{1.8} \qquad °F = (1.8 \times °C) + 32$$

Classification of Major Groups of Eukaryotic Organisms*

Kingdom	Phylum or Class	Common Name
Excavata	Parabasalia	parabasalids
	Diplomonadida	diplomonads
Euglenozoa	Euglenida	euglenids
	Kinetoplastida	kinetoplastids
Stramenopila	Oomycota	water molds
	Phaeophyta	brown algae
	Bacillariophyta	diatoms
Alveolata	Apicomplexa	sporozoans
	Pyrrophyta	dinoflagellates
	Ciliophora	ciliates
Rhizaria	Foraminifera	foraminiferans
	Radiolaria	radiolarians
Amoebozoa	Tubulinea	amoebas
	Myxomycota	acellular slime molds
	Acrasiomycota	cellular slime molds
Rhodophyta		red algae
Chlorophyta		green algae
Plantae	Bryophyta	liverworts, mosses
	Pteridophyta	ferns
	Coniferophyta	evergreens
	Anthophyta	flowering plants
Fungi	Chytridiomycota	chytrids
	Zygomycota	zygote fungi
	Glomeromycota	glomeromycetes
	Ascomycota	sac fungi
	Basidiomycota	club fungi
Animalia	Porifera	sponges
	Cnidaria	hydras, sea anemones, sea jellies, corals
	Ctenophora	comb jellies
	Platyhelminthes	flatworms
	Annelida	segmented worms
	Oligochaeta	earthworms
	Polychaeta	tube worms
	Hirudinea	leeches
	Mollusca	mollusks
	Gastropoda	snails
	Pelecypoda	mussels, clams
	Cephalopoda	squid, octopuses
	Nematoda	roundworms
	Arthropoda	arthropods
	Insecta	insects
	Arachnida	spiders, ticks
	Crustacea	crabs, lobsters
	Myriapoda	millipedes, centipedes
	Chordata	chordates
	Urochordata	tunicates
	Cephalochordata	lancelets
	Myxini	hagfishes
	Petromyzontiformes	lampreys
	Chondrichthyes	sharks, rays
	Actinopterygii	ray-finned fishes
	Actinistia	coelacanths
	Dipnoi	lungfishes
	Amphibia	amphibians (frogs, salamanders)
	Reptilia	reptiles (turtles, crocodiles, birds, snakes, lizards)
	Mammalia	mammals

*This table lists only those taxonomic categories described in the textbook.

Glossary

abiotic (ā-bī´-ah´-tik): nonliving; the abiotic portion of an ecosystem includes soil, rock, water, and the atmosphere.

abscisic acid (ab-sis´-ik): a plant hormone that generally inhibits the action of other hormones, enforcing dormancy in seeds and buds and causing the closing of stomata.

abscission layer: a layer of thin-walled cells, located at the base of the petiole of a leaf, that produces an enzyme that digests the cell walls holding the leaf to the stem, allowing the leaf to fall off.

absorption: the process by which nutrients enter the body through the cells lining the digestive tract.

accessory pigment: a colored molecule other than chlorophyll *a*, that absorbs light energy and passes it to chlorophyll *a*.

acellular slime mold: a type of organism that forms a multinucleate structure that crawls in amoeboid fashion and ingests decaying organic matter; also called *plasmodial slime mold*. Acellular slime molds are members of the protist clade Amoebozoa.

acid deposition: the deposition of nitric or sulfuric acid, either in rain (acid rain) or in the form of dry particles, as a result of the production of nitrogen oxides or sulfur dioxide through burning, primarily of fossil fuels.

acid: a substance that releases hydrogen ions (H+) into solution; a solution with a pH less than 7.

acidic: referring to a solution with an H+ concentration exceeding that of OH-; referring to a substance that releases H+.

acquired immune deficiency syndrome (AIDS): an infectious disease caused by the human immunodeficiency virus (HIV); attacks and destroys T cells, thus weakening the immune system.

acrosome (ak´-rō-sōm): a vesicle, located at the tip of the head of an animal sperm, that contains enzymes needed to dissolve protective layers around the egg.

actin (ak´-tin): a major muscle protein whose interactions with myosin produce contraction; found in the thin filaments of the muscle fiber; see also *myosin*.

action potential: a rapid change from a negative to a positive electrical potential in a nerve cell. An action potential travels along an axon without a change in amplitude.

activation energy: in a chemical reaction, the energy needed to force the electron shells of reactants together, prior to the formation of products.

active site: the region of an enzyme molecule that binds substrates and performs the catalytic function of the enzyme.

active transport: the movement of materials across a membrane through the use of cellular energy, normally against a concentration gradient.

adaptation: a trait that increases the ability of an individual to survive and reproduce compared to individuals without the trait.

adaptive immune response: a response to invading toxins or microbes in which immune cells are activated by a specific invader, selectively destroy that invader, and then "remember" the invader, allowing a faster response if that type of invader reappears in the future; see also *innate immune response*.

adaptive immune system: a widely distributed system of organs (including the thymus, bone marrow, and lymph nodes), cells (including macrophages, dendritic cells, B cells, and T cells), and molecules (including cytokines and antibodies) that work together to combat microbial invasion of the body; the adaptive immune system responds to and destroys specific invading toxins or microbes; see also *innate immune response*.

adaptive radiation: the rise of many new species in a relatively short time; may occur when a single species invades different habitats and evolves in response to different environmental conditions in those habitats.

adenine (A): a nitrogenous base found in both DNA and RNA; abbreviated as A.

adenosine diphosphate (a-den´-ō-sēn dī-fos´-fāt; ADP): a molecule composed of the sugar ribose, the base adenine, and two phosphate groups; a component of ATP.

adenosine triphosphate (a-den´-ō-sēn trī-fos´-fāt; ATP): a molecule composed of the sugar ribose, the base adenine, and three phosphate groups; the major energy carrier in cells. The last two phosphate groups are attached by "high-energy" bonds.

adhesion: the tendency of polar molecules (such as water) to adhere to polar surfaces (such as glass).

adipose tissue (a´-dī-pōs): tissue composed of fat cells.

adrenal cortex: the outer part of the adrenal gland, which secretes steroid hormones that regulate metabolism and salt balance.

adrenal gland: a mammalian endocrine gland, adjacent to the kidney; secretes hormones that function in water regulation and in the stress response.

adrenal medulla: the inner part of the adrenal gland, which secretes epinephrine (adrenaline) and norepinephrine (noradrenaline) in the stress response.

adrenocorticotropic hormone (a-drēn-ō-kor-tik-ō-trō´-pik; ACTH): a hormone, secreted by the anterior pituitary, that stimulates the release of hormones by the adrenal cortex, especially in response to stress.

adult stem cell (ASC): any stem cell not found in an early embryo; can divide and differentiate into any of several cell types, but usually not all of the cell types of the body.

aerobic: using oxygen.

age structure: the distribution of males and females in a population according to age groups.

aggression: antagonistic behavior, normally among members of the same species, often resulting from competition for resources.

aggressive mimicry (mim´ik-rē): the evolution of a predatory organism to resemble a harmless animal or a part of the environment, thus gaining access to prey.

aging: the gradual accumulation of damage to essential biological molecules, particularly DNA in both the nucleus and mitochondria, resulting in defects in cell functioning, declining health, and ultimately death.

albinism: a recessive hereditary condition caused by defective alleles of the genes that encode the enzymes required for the synthesis of melanin, the principal pigment in mammalian skin and hair; albinism results in white hair and pink skin.

alcoholic fermentation: a type of fermentation in which pyruvate is converted to ethanol (a type of alcohol) and carbon dioxide, using hydrogen ions and electrons from NADH; the primary function of alcoholic fermentation is to regenerate NAD+ so that glycolysis can continue under anaerobic conditions.

aldosterone: a hormone, secreted by the adrenal cortex, that helps regulate ion concentration in the blood by stimulating the reabsorption of sodium by the kidneys and sweat glands.

alga (al´-ga; pl., algae, al´-jē): any photosynthetic protist.

allantois (al-an-tō´-is): one of the embryonic membranes of reptiles (including birds) and mammals; in reptiles, serves as a waste-storage organ; in mammals, forms most of the umbilical cord.

allele (al-ēl´): one of several alternative forms of a particular gene.

allele frequency: for any given gene, the relative proportion of each allele of that gene in a population

allergy: an inflammatory response produced by the body in response to invasion by foreign materials, such as pollen, that are themselves harmless.

allopatric speciation (al-ō-pat´-rik): the process by which new species arise following physical separation of parts of a population (geographical isolation).

allosteric regulation: the process by which enzyme action is enhanced or inhibited by small organic molecules that act as regulators by binding to the enzyme at a regulatory site distinct from the active site, and altering the shape and/or function of the active site.

alternation of generations: a life cycle, typical of plants, in which a diploid sporophyte (spore-producing) generation alternates with a haploid gametophyte (gamete-producing) generation.

altruism: a behavior that benefits other individuals while reducing the fitness of the individual that performs the behavior.

alveolate (al-vē′-ō-lāt): a member of the Alveolata, a large protist clade. The alveolates, which are characterized by a system of sacs beneath the cell membrane, include ciliates, dinoflagellates, and apicomplexans.

alveolus (al-vē′-ō-lus; pl., alveoli): a tiny air sac within the lungs, surrounded by capillaries, where gas exchange with the blood occurs.

amino acid: the individual subunit of which proteins are made, composed of a central carbon atom bonded to an amino group ($-NH_2$), a carboxyl group ($-COOH$), a hydrogen atom, and a variable group of atoms denoted by the letter R.

amino acid-derived hormone: a class of hormone that is synthesized by the body from single amino acids. Examples include epinephrine and thyroxine.

ammonia: NH_3; a highly toxic nitrogen-containing waste product of amino acid breakdown. In the mammalian liver, it is converted to urea.

amniocentesis (am-nē-ō-sen-tē′-sis): a procedure for sampling the amniotic fluid surrounding a fetus: A sterile needle is inserted through the abdominal wall, uterus, and amniotic sac of a pregnant woman, and 10 to 20 milliliters of amniotic fluid are withdrawn. Various tests may be performed on the fluid and the fetal cells suspended in it to provide information on the developmental and genetic state of the fetus.

amnion (am′-nē-on): one of the embryonic membranes of reptiles (including birds) and mammals; encloses a fluid-filled cavity that envelops the embryo.

amniotic egg (am-nē-ōt′-ik): the egg of reptiles, including birds; contains a membrane, the amnion, that surrounds the embryo, enclosing it in a watery environment and allowing the egg to be laid on dry land.

amoeba: an amoebozoan protist that uses a characteristic streaming mode of locomotion by extending a cellular projection called a *pseudopod*. Also known as *lobose amoebas*.

amoeboid cell: a protist or animal cell that moves by extending a cellular projection called a pseudopod.

amoebozoan: a member of the Amoebozoa, a protist clade. The amoebozoans, which generally lack shells and move by extending pseudopods, include the lobose amoebas and the slime molds.

amphibian: a member of the chordate clade Amphibia, which includes the frogs, toads, and salamanders, as well as the limbless caecelians.

amygdala (am-ig′-da-la): part of the forebrain of vertebrates that is involved in the production of appropriate behavioral responses to environmental stimuli.

amylase (am′-i-lās): an enzyme, found in saliva and pancreatic secretions, that catalyzes the breakdown of starch.

anaerobe (an–ə–rōb): an organism that can live and grow in the absence of oxygen.

anaerobic: not using oxygen.

analogous structure: structures that have similar functions and superficially similar appearance but very different anatomies, such as the wings of insects and birds. The similarities are the result of similar environmental pressures rather than a common ancestry.

anaphase (an′-a-fāz): in mitosis, the stage in which the sister chromatids of each chromosome separate from one another and are moved to opposite poles of the cell; in meiosis I, the stage in which homologous chromosomes, consisting of two sister chromatids, are separated; in meiosis II, the stage in which the sister chromatids of each chromosome separate from one another and are moved to opposite poles of the cell.

androgen: a male sex hormone.

angina (an-jī′-nuh): chest pain associated with reduced blood flow to the heart muscle; caused by an obstruction of the coronary arteries.

angiosperm (an′-jē-ō-sperm): a flowering vascular plant.

angiotensin (an-jē-ō-ten′-sun): a hormone that functions in water regulation in mammals by stimulating physiological changes that increase blood volume and blood pressure.

annual ring: a pattern of alternating light (early) and dark (late) xylem in woody stems and roots; formed as a result of the unequal availability of water in different seasons of the year, normally spring and summer.

antagonistic muscles: a pair of muscles, one of which contracts and in so doing extends the other, relaxed muscle; this arrangement makes possible movement of the skeleton at joints.

anterior pituitary: a lobe of the pituitary gland that produces prolactin and growth hormone as well as hormones that regulate hormone production in other glands.

anther (an′-ther): the uppermost part of the stamen, in which pollen develops.

antheridium (an-ther-id′-ē-um; pl., antheridia): a structure in which male sex cells are produced; found in nonvascular plants and certain seedless vascular plants.

antibiotic: chemicals that help to combat infection by destroying or slowing down the multiplication of bacteria, fungi, or protists.

antibody: a protein, produced by cells of the immune system, that combines with a specific antigen and normally facilitates the destruction of the antigen.

anticodon: a sequence of three bases in transfer RNA that is complementary to the three bases of a codon of messenger RNA.

antidiuretic hormone (an-tē-dī-ūr-et′-ik; ADH): a hormone produced by the hypothalamus and released into the bloodstream by the posterior pituitary when blood volume is low; increases the permeability of the distal tubule and the collecting duct to water, allowing more water to be reabsorbed into the bloodstream.

antigen: a complex molecule, normally a protein or polysaccharide, that stimulates the production of a specific antibody.

antioxidant: any molecule that reacts with free radicals, neutralizing their ability to damage biological molecules. Vitamins C and E are examples of dietary antioxidants.

anvil: the second of the small bones of the middle ear, linking the tympanic membrane (eardrum) to the oval window of the cochlea; also called the *incus*.

aphotic zone: the region of the ocean below 200 m, where sunlight does not penetrate.

apical dominance: the phenomenon whereby a growing shoot tip inhibits the sprouting of lateral buds.

apical meristem (āp′-i-kul mer′-i-stem): the cluster of meristem cells at the tip of a shoot or root (or one of their branches).

apicomplexan (ā-pē-kom-pleks′-an): a member of the protist clade Apicomplexa, which includes mostly parasitic, single-celled eukaryotes such as *Plasmodium*, which causes malaria in humans. Apicomplexans are part of a larger group known as the alveolates.

appendicular skeleton (ap-pen-dik′-ū-lur): the portion of the skeleton consisting of the bones of the extremities and their attachments to the axial skeleton; the appendicular skeleton therefore consists of the pectoral and pelvic girdles and the arms, legs, hands, and feet.

aquaporin: a channel protein in the plasma membrane of a cell that is selectively permeable to water.

aqueous humor (ā′-kwē-us): the clear, watery fluid between the cornea and lens of the eye; nourishes the cornea and lens.

aquifer (ok′–wi–fer): an underground deposit of fresh water, often used as a source for irrigation.

archaea: prokaryotes that are members of the domain Archaea, one of the three domains of living organisms; only distantly related to members of the domain Bacteria.

Archaea: one of life's three domains; consists of prokaryotes that are only distantly related to members of the domain Bacteria.

archegonium (ar-ke-gō'-nē-um; pl., archegonia): a structure in which female sex cells are produced; found in nonvascular plants and certain seedless vascular plants.

arteriole (ar-tēr'-ē-ōl): a small artery that empties into capillaries; constriction of arterioles regulates blood flow to various parts of the body.

artery (ar'-tuh-rē): a vessel with muscular, elastic walls that conducts blood away from the heart.

arthropod: a member of the animal phylum Arthropoda, which includes the insects, spiders, ticks, mites, scorpions, crustaceans, millipedes, and centipedes.

artificial selection: a selective breeding procedure in which only those individuals with particular traits are chosen as breeders; used mainly to enhance desirable traits in domesticated plants and animals; may also be used in evolutionary biology experiments.

ascomycete: a member of the fungus phylum Ascomycota, whose members form sexual spores in a saclike case known as an ascus.

ascus (as'-kus; pl., asci): a saclike case in which sexual spores are formed by members of the fungus phylum Ascomycota.

asexual reproduction: reproduction that does not involve the fusion of haploid gametes.

atherosclerosis (ath'-er-ō-skler-ō'-sis): a disease characterized by the obstruction of arteries by cholesterol deposits and thickening of the arterial walls.

atom: the smallest particle of an element that retains the properties of the element.

atomic mass: the total mass of all the protons, neutrons, and electrons within an atom.

atomic nucleus: the central part of an atom that contains protons and neutrons.

atomic number: the number of protons in the nuclei of all atoms of a particular element.

ATP synthase: a channel protein in the thylakoid membranes of chloroplasts and the inner membrane of mitochondria that uses the energy of H+ ions moving through the channel down their concentration gradient to produce ATP from ADP and inorganic phosphate.

atrial natriuretic peptide (ANP) (ā'-trē-ul nā-trē-ū-ret'-ik; ANP): a hormone, secreted by cells in the mammalian heart, that reduces blood volume by inhibiting the release of ADH and aldosterone.

atrioventricular (AV) node (ā'-trē-ō-ven-trik'-ū-lar nōd): a specialized mass of muscle at the base of the right atrium through which the electrical activity initiated in the sinoatrial node is transmitted to the ventricles.

atrioventricular valve: a heart valve that separates each atrium from each ventricle, preventing the backflow of blood into the atria during ventricular contraction.

atrium (ā'-trē-um; pl., atria): a chamber of the heart that receives venous blood and passes it to a ventricle.

attachment protein: a protein in the plasma membrane of a cell that attaches either to the cytoskeleton inside the cell, to other cells, or to the extracellular matrix.

auditory canal (aw'-di-tor-ē): a relatively large-diameter tube within the outer ear that conducts sound from the pinna to the tympanic membrane.

auditory nerve: the nerve leading from the mammalian cochlea to the brain; it carries information about sound.

auditory tube: a thin tube connecting the middle ear with the pharynx, which allows pressure to equilibrate between the middle ear and the outside air; also called the *Eustachian tube.*

autoimmune disease: a disorder in which the immune system attacks the body's own cells or molecules.

autonomic nervous system: the part of the peripheral nervous system of vertebrates that synapses on glands, internal organs, and smooth muscle and produces largely involuntary responses.

autosome (aw'-tō-sōm): a chromosome that occurs in homologous pairs in both males and females and that does not bear the genes determining sex.

autotroph (aw'-tō-trōf): literally, "self-feeder"; normally, a photosynthetic organism; a producer.

auxin (awk'-sin): a plant hormone that influences many plant functions, including phototropism, gravitropism, apical dominance, and root branching.

axial skeleton: the skeleton forming the body axis, including the skull, vertebral column, and rib cage.

axon: a long extension of a nerve cell, extending from the cell body to synaptic endings on other nerve cells or on muscles.

B cell: a type of lymphocyte that matures in the bone marrow, and that participates in humoral immunity; gives rise to plasma cells, which secrete antibodies into the circulatory system, and to memory cells.

bacteria (sing., bacterium): prokaryotes that are members of the domain Bacteria, one of the three domains of living organisms; only distantly related to members of the domain Archaea.

Bacteria: one of life's three domains; consists of prokaryotes that are only distantly related to members of the domain Archaea.

bacteriophage (bak-tir'-ē-ō-fāj): a virus that specifically infects bacteria.

ball-and-socket joint: a joint in which the rounded end of one bone fits into a hollow depression in another, as in the hip; allows movement in several directions.

bark: the outer layer of a woody stem, consisting of phloem, cork cambium, and cork cells.

Barr body: a condensed, inactivated X chromosome in the cells of female mammals, which have two X chromosomes.

basal body: a structure derived from a centriole that produces a cilium or flagellum and anchors this structure within the plasma membrane.

basal ganglia: several clusters of neurons in the interior of the cerebrum, plus the substantial nigra in the midbrain, that function in the control of movement. Damage to or degeneration of one or more basal ganglia causes disorders such as Parkinson's disease and Huntington's disease.

base: (1) a substance capable of combining with and neutralizing H+ ions in a solution; a solution with a pH greater than 7; (2) one of the nitrogen-containing, single- or double-ringed structures that distinguishes one nucleotide from another. In DNA, the bases are adenine, guanine, cytosine, and thymine.

basic: referring to a solution with an H+ concentration less than that of OH-; referring to a substance that combines with H+.

basidiomycete: a member of the fungus phylum Basidiomycota, which includes species that produce sexual spores in club-shaped cells known as basidia.

basidiospore (ba-sid'-ē-ō-spor): a sexual spore formed by members of the fungus phylum Basidiomycota.

basidium (pl., basidia): a diploid cell, typically club-shaped, formed by members of the fungus phylum Basidiomycota; produces basidiospores by meiosis.

basilar membrane (bas'-eh-lar): a membrane in the cochlea that bears hair cells that respond to the vibrations produced by sound.

behavior: any observable activity of a living animal.

bilateral symmetry: a body plan in which only a single plane through the central axis will divide the body into mirror-image halves.

bile (bīl): a liquid secretion, produced by the liver, that is stored in the gallbladder and released into the small intestine during digestion; consists of a complex mixture of bile salts, water, other salts, and cholesterol.

binary fission: the process by which a single bacterium divides in half, producing two identical offspring.

binocular vision: the ability to see objects simultaneously through both eyes, providing greater depth perception and more accurate judgment of the size and distance of an object than can be achieved by vision with one eye alone.

binomial system: the method of naming organisms by genus and species, often called the scientific name, usually using Latin words or words derived from Latin.

biocapacity: an estimate of the sustainable resources and waste-absorbing capacity actually available on Earth. Biocapacity calculations are subject to change as new technologies change the way people use resources.

biodegradable: able to be broken down into harmless substances by decomposers.

biodiversity: the diversity of living organisms; measured as the variety of different species, the variety of different alleles in species' gene pools, or the variety of different communities and nonliving environments in an ecosystem or in the entire biosphere.

biofilm: a community of prokaryotes of one or more species, in which the prokaryotes secrete and are embedded in slime that adheres to a surface.

biogeochemical cycle: the pathways of a specific nutrient (such as carbon, nitrogen, phosphorus, or water) through the living and nonliving portions of an ecosystem; also called a *nutrient cycle*.

biological clock: a metabolic timekeeping mechanism found in most organisms, whereby the organism measures the approximate length of a day (24 hours) even without external environmental cues such as light and darkness.

biological magnification: the increasing accumulation of a toxic substance in progressively higher trophic levels.

biomass: the total weight of all living material within a defined area.

biome (bī'-ōm): a terrestrial ecosystem that occupies an extensive geographical area and is characterized by a specific type of plant community; for example, deserts.

bioremediation: the use of organisms to remove or detoxify toxic substances in the environment.

biosphere (bī'-ō-sfēr): that part of Earth inhabited by living organisms; includes both living and nonliving components.

Biosphere Reserve: designated by the United Nations, a Biosphere Reserve is a region intended to maintain biodiversity and evaluate techniques for sustainable human development while maintaining local cultural values.

biotechnology: any industrial or commercial use or alteration of organisms, cells, or biological molecules to achieve specific practical goals.

biotic (bī-ah'-tik): living.

biotic potential: the maximum rate at which a population is able to increase, assuming ideal conditions that allow a maximum birth rate and minimum death rate.

birth rate: the number of births per individual in a specified unit of time, such as a year.

bladder: a hollow muscular organ that stores urine.

blade: the flat part of a leaf.

blastocyst (blas'-tō-sist): an early stage of human embryonic development, consisting of a hollow ball of cells, enclosing a mass of cells attached to its inner surface, which becomes the embryo.

blastopore: the site at which a blastula indents to form a gastrula.

blastula (blas'-tū-luh): in animals, the embryonic stage attained at the end of cleavage, in which the embryo usually consists of a hollow ball with a wall that is one or several cell layers thick.

blind spot: the area of the retina at which the axons of the ganglion cells merge to form the optic nerve; because there are no photoreceptors in the blind spot, objects focused at the blind spot cannot be seen.

blood: a specialized connective tissue, consisting of a fluid (plasma) in which blood cells are suspended; carried within the circulatory system.

blood clotting: a complex process by which platelets, the protein fibrin, and red blood cells block an irregular surface in or on the body, such as a damaged blood vessel, sealing the wound.

blood vessel: any of several types of tubes that carry blood throughout the body.

blood–brain barrier: relatively impermeable capillaries of the brain that protect the cells of the brain from potentially damaging chemicals that reach the bloodstream.

body mass index (BMI): a number derived from an individual's weight and height that is used to estimate body fat. The formula is weight (in kg) /height^2 (in meters^2).

bone: a hard, mineralized connective tissue that is a major component of the vertebrate endoskeleton; provides support and sites for muscle attachment.

boom-and-bust cycle: a population cycle characterized by rapid exponential growth followed by a sudden massive die-off; seen in seasonal species, such as many insects living in temperate climates, and in some populations of small rodents, such as lemmings.

Bowman's capsule: the cup-shaped portion of the nephron in which blood filtrate is collected from the glomerulus.

brain: the part of the central nervous system of vertebrates that is enclosed within the skull.

branch root: a root that arises as a branch of a preexisting root; occurs through divisions of pericycle cells and subsequent differentiation of the daughter cells.

bronchiole (bron'-kē-ōl): a narrow tube, formed by repeated branching of the bronchi, that conducts air into the alveoli.

bronchus (bron'-kus; pl., bronchi): a tube that conducts air from the trachea to each lung.

budding: asexual reproduction by the growth of a miniature copy, or bud, of the adult animal on the body of the parent. The bud breaks off to begin independent existence.

buffer: a compound that minimizes changes in pH by reversibly taking up or releasing H+ ions.

bulbourethral gland (bul-bō-ū-rē'-thrul): in male mammals, a gland that secretes a basic, mucous-containing fluid that forms part of the semen.

bulk flow: the movement of many molecules of a gas or liquid in unison (in bulk, hence the name) from an area of higher pressure to an area of lower pressure.

bundle sheath cells: cells that surround the veins of plants; in C$_4$ (but not in C$_3$) plants, bundle sheath cells contain chloroplasts.

C$_3$ pathway: in photosynthesis, the cyclic series of reactions whereby carbon from carbon dioxide is fixed as phosphoglyceric acid, the simple sugar glyceraldehyde-3-phosphate is generated, and the carbon-capture molecule, RuBP, is regenerated.

C$_3$ plant: a plant that relies on the C$_3$ pathway to fix carbon.

C$_4$ pathway: the series of reactions in certain plants that fixes carbon dioxide into a four-carbon molecule, which is later broken down for use in the Calvin cycle of photosynthesis. This reduces wasteful photorespiration in hot, dry environments.

C$_4$ plant: a plant that relies on the C$_4$ pathway to fix carbon.

calcitonin (kal-si-tōn'-in): a hormone, secreted by the thyroid gland, that inhibits the release of calcium from bone.

calorie (kal'-ō-rē): the amount of energy required to raise the temperature of 1 gram of water by 1 degree Celsius.

Calorie: a unit used to measure the energy content of foods; it is the amount of energy required to raise the temperature of 1 liter of water 1 degree Celsius; also called a *kilocalorie*, equal to 1,000 calories.

Calvin cycle: in photosynthesis, the cyclic series of reactions whereby carbon from carbon dioxide is fixed as phosphoglyceric acid, the simple sugar glyceraldehyde-3-phosphate is generated, and the carbon-capture molecule, RuBP, is regenerated.

cambium (kam'-bē-um; pl., cambia): a lateral meristem, parallel to the long axis of roots and stems, that causes secondary growth of woody plant stems and roots. See *cork cambium; vascular cambium.*

camouflage (cam'-a-flaj): coloration and/or shape that renders an organism inconspicuous in its environment.

cancer: a disease in which some of the body's cells escape from normal regulatory processes and divide without control.

capillary: the smallest type of blood vessel, connecting arterioles with venules; capillary walls, through which the exchange of nutrients and wastes occurs, are only one cell thick.

carbohydrate: a compound composed of carbon, hydrogen, and oxygen, with the approximate chemical formula $(CH_2O)_n$; includes sugars, starches, and cellulose.

carbon cycle: the biogeochemical cycle by which carbon moves from its reservoirs in the atmosphere and oceans through producers and into higher trophic levels, and then back to its reservoirs.

carbon fixation: the process by which carbon derived from carbon dioxide is captured in organic molecules during photosynthesis.

cardiac cycle (kar′-dē-ak): the alternation of contraction and relaxation of the heart chambers.

cardiac muscle (kar′-dē-ak): the specialized muscle of the heart; able to initiate its own contraction, independent of the nervous system.

carnivore (kar′-neh-vor): literally, "meat eater"; a predatory organism that feeds on herbivores or on other carnivores; a secondary (or higher) consumer.

carotenoid (ka-rot′-en-oid): a red, orange, or yellow pigment, found in chloroplasts, that serves as an accessory light-gathering pigment in thylakoid photosystems.

carpel (kar′pel): the female reproductive structure of a flower, composed of stigma, style, and ovary.

carrier: an individual who is heterozygous for a recessive condition; a carrier displays the dominant phenotype but can pass on the recessive allele to offspring.

carrier protein: a membrane protein that facilitates the diffusion of specific substances across the membrane. The molecule to be transported binds to the outer surface of the carrier protein; the protein then changes shape, allowing the molecule to move across the membrane.

carrying capacity *(K)*: the maximum population size that an ecosystem can support for a long period of time without damaging the ecosystem; determined primarily by the availability of space, nutrients, water, and light.

cartilage (kar′-teh-lij): a form of connective tissue that forms portions of the skeleton; consists of chondrocytes and their extracellular secretion of collagen.

Casparian strip (kas-par′-ē-un): a waxy, waterproof band, located in the cell walls between endodermal cells in a root, that prevents the movement of water and minerals into and out of the vascular cylinder through the extracellular space.

catalyst (kat′-uh-list): a substance that speeds up a chemical reaction without itself being permanently changed in the process; a catalyst lowers the activation energy of a reaction.

cell: the smallest unit of life, consisting, at a minimum, of an outer membrane that encloses a watery medium containing organic molecules, including genetic material composed of DNA.

cell body: the part of a nerve cell in which most of the common cellular organelles are located; typically a site of integration of inputs to the nerve cell.

cell cycle: the sequence of events in the life of a cell, from one cell division to the next.

cell division: splitting of one cell into two; the process of cellular reproduction.

cell plate: in plant cell division, a series of vesicles that fuse to form the new plasma membranes and cell wall separating the daughter cells.

cell theory: the scientific theory stating that every living organism is made up of one or more cells; cells are the functional units of all organisms; and all cells arise from preexisting cells.

cell-mediated immunity: an adaptive immune response in which foreign cells or substances are destroyed by contact with T cells.

cellular respiration: the oxygen-requiring reactions, occurring in mitochondria, that break down the end products of glycolysis into carbon dioxide and water while capturing large amounts of energy as ATP.

cellular slime mold: a type of organism consisting of individual amoeboid cells that can aggregate to form a sluglike mass, which in turn forms a fruiting body. Cellular slime molds are members of the protist clade Amoebozoa.

cellulose: an insoluble carbohydrate composed of glucose subunits; forms the cell wall of plants.

central nervous system (CNS): in vertebrates, the brain and spinal cord.

central vacuole (vak′-ū-ōl): a large, fluid-filled vacuole occupying most of the volume of many plant cells; performs several functions, including maintaining turgor pressure.

centriole (sen′-trē-ōl): in animal cells, a short, barrel-shaped ring consisting of nine microtubule triplets; a pair of centrioles is found near the nucleus and may play a role in the organization of the spindle; centrioles also give rise to the basal bodies at the base of each cilium and flagellum that give rise to the microtubules of cilia and flagella.

centromere (sen′-trō-mēr): the region of a replicated chromosome at which the sister chromatids are held together until they separate during cell division.

cephalization (sef-ul-ī-zā′-shun): concentration of sensory organs and nervous tissue in the anterior (head) portion of the body.

cerebellum (ser-uh-bel′-um): the part of the hindbrain of vertebrates that is concerned with coordinating movements of the body.

cerebral cortex (ser-ē′-brul kor′-tex): a thin layer of neurons on the surface of the vertebrate cerebrum, in which most neural processing and coordination of activity occurs.

cerebral hemisphere: one of two nearly symmetrical halves of the cerebrum, connected by a broad band of axons, the corpus callosum.

cerebrum (ser-ē′-brum): the part of the forebrain of vertebrates that is concerned with sensory processing, the direction of motor output, and the coordination of most of the body's activities; consists of two nearly symmetrical halves (the hemispheres) connected by a broad band of axons, the corpus callosum.

cervix (ser′-viks): a ring of connective tissue at the outer end of the uterus that leads into the vagina.

channel protein: a membrane protein that forms a channel or pore completely through the membrane and that is usually permeable to one or to a few water-soluble molecules, especially ions.

chaparral: a biome located in coastal regions, with very low annual rainfall; is characterized by shrubs and small trees.

checkpoint: a mechanism in the eukaryotic cell cycle by which protein complexes in the cell determine whether the cell has successfully completed a specific process that is essential to successful cell division, such as the accurate replication of chromosomes.

chemical bond: an attraction between two atoms or molecules that tends to hold them together. Types of bonds include covalent, ionic, and hydrogen.

chemical digestion: the process by which particles of food within the digestive tract are exposed to enzymes and other digestive fluids that break down large molecules into smaller subunits.

chemical energy: a form of potential energy that is stored in molecules and may be released during chemical reactions.

chemical reaction: the process that forms and breaks chemical bonds that hold atoms together in molecules.

chemiosmosis (ke-mē-oz-mō′-sis): a process of ATP generation in chloroplasts and mitochondria. The movement of electrons down an electron transport system is used to pump hydrogen ions across a membrane, thereby building up a concentration gradient of hydrogen ions; the hydrogen ions diffuse back across the membrane through the pores of ATP-synthesizing enzymes; the energy of their movement down their concentration gradient drives ATP synthesis.

chemosynthesis (kē-mō-sin-the-sis): the process of oxidizing inorganic molecules, such as hydrogen sulfide, to obtain energy. Producers in hydrothermal vent communities, where light is absent, use chemosynthesis instead of photosynthesis.

chemosynthetic (kēm′-ō-sin-the-tik): capable of oxidizing inorganic molecules to obtain energy.

chiasma (kī-as′-muh; pl., chiasmata): a point at which a chromatid of one chromosome crosses with a chromatid of the homologous chromosome during prophase I of meiosis; the site of exchange of chromosomal material between chromosomes.

chitin (kī′-tin): a compound found in the cell walls of fungi and the exoskeletons of insects and some other arthropods; composed of chains of nitrogen-containing, modified glucose molecules.

chlamydia (kla-mid′-ē-uh): a sexually transmitted disease, caused by a bacterium, that causes inflammation of the urethra in males and of the urethra and cervix in females.

chlorophyll (klor'-ō-fil): a pigment found in chloroplasts that captures light energy during photosynthesis; chlorophyll absorbs violet, blue, and red light but reflects green light.

chlorophyll *a* (klor'-ō-fil): the most abundant type of chlorophyll molecule in photosynthetic eukaryotic organisms and in cyanobacteria; chlorophyll *a* is found in the reaction centers of the photosystems.

chloroplast (klor'-ō-plast): the organelle in plants and plantlike protists that is the site of photosynthesis; surrounded by a double membrane and containing an extensive internal membrane system that bears chlorophyll.

cholecystokinin (kō'-lē-sis-tō-ki'-nin): a digestive hormone produced by the small intestine that stimulates the release of pancreatic enzymes.

chondrocyte (kon'-drō-sīt): a living cell of cartilage. Together with their extracellular secretions of collagen, chondrocytes form cartilage.

chorion (kor'-ē-on): the outermost embryonic membrane in reptiles (including birds) and mammals. In reptiles, the chorion functions mostly in gas exchange; in mammals, it forms most of the embryonic part of the placenta.

chorionic gonadotropin (kor–ē–on'–ik gō–na–dō–trō'–pin; CG): a hormone secreted by the chorion (one of the fetal membranes) that maintains the integrity of the corpus luteum during early pregnancy.

chorionic villus (kor-ē-on-ik; pl., **chorionic villi):** in mammalian embryos, a finger-like projection of the chorion that penetrates the uterine lining and forms the embryonic portion of the placenta.

chorionic villus sampling (kōr–ē–on'–ik; CVS): a procedure for sampling cells from the chorionic villi produced by a fetus: A tube is inserted into the uterus of a pregnant woman, and a small sample of villi is suctioned off for genetic and biochemical analyses.

choroid (kor'-oid): a darkly pigmented layer of tissue behind the retina; contains blood vessels and also pigment that absorbs stray light.

chromatid (krō'-ma-tid): one of the two identical strands of DNA and protein that forms a duplicated chromosome. The two sister chromatids of a duplicated chromosome are joined at the centromere.

chromatin (krō'-ma-tin): the complex of DNA and proteins that makes up eukaryotic chromosomes.

chromosome (krō'-mō-sōm): a DNA double helix together with proteins that help to organize and regulate the use of the DNA.

chylomicron: a particle produced by cells of the small intestine, consisting of proteins, triglycerides, and cholesterol; transports the products of lipid digestion into the lymphatic system and ultimately into the circulatory system.

chyme (kīm): an acidic, souplike mixture of partially digested food, water, and digestive secretions that is released from the stomach into the small intestine.

chytrid: a member of the fungus phylum Chytridomycota, which includes species with flagellated swimming spores.

ciliate (sil'-ē-et): a member of a protist group characterized by cilia and a complex unicellular structure. Ciliates are part of a larger group known as the alveolates.

cilium (sil'-ē-um; pl., **cilia):** a short, hair-like, motile projection from the surface of certain eukaryotic cells that contains microtubules in a 9 + 2 arrangement. The movement of cilia may propel cells through a fluid medium or move fluids over a stationary surface layer of cells.

citric acid cycle: a cyclic series of reactions, occurring in the matrix of mitochondria, in which the acetyl groups from the pyruvic acids produced by glycolysis are broken down to CO_2, accompanied by the formation of ATP and electron carriers; also called the Krebs cycle.

clade: a group that includes all the organisms descended from a common ancestor, but no other organisms; a monophyletic group.

class: in Linnaean classification, the taxonomic rank composed of related orders. Closely related classes form a phylum.

cleavage: the early cell divisions of embryos, in which little or no growth occurs between divisions; reduces the cell size and distributes gene-regulating substances to the newly formed cell.

climate: patterns of weather that prevail for long periods of time (from years to centuries) in a given region.

climax community: a diverse and relatively stable community that forms the endpoint of succession.

clitoris: an external structure of the female reproductive system that is composed of erectile tissue; a sensitive point of stimulation during sexual response.

clonal selection: the mechanism by which the adaptive immune response gains specificity; an invading antigen elicits a response from only a few lymphocytes, which proliferate to form a clone of cells that attack only the specific antigen that stimulated their production.

clone: offspring that are produced by mitosis and are, therefore, genetically identical to each other.

cloning: the process of producing many identical copies of a gene; also the production of many genetically identical copies of an organism.

closed circulatory system: a type of circulatory system, found in certain worms and vertebrates, in which the blood is always confined within the heart and vessels.

closed system: a hypothetical space where neither energy nor matter can enter or leave.

club fungus: a fungus of the phylum Basidiomycota, whose members (which include mushrooms, puffballs, and shelf fungi) reproduce by means of basidiospores.

clumped distribution: the distribution characteristic of populations in which individuals are clustered into groups; the groups may be social or based on the need for a localized resource.

cochlea (kahk'-lē-uh): a coiled, bony, fluid-filled tube found in the mammalian inner ear; contains mechanoreceptors (hair cells) that respond to the vibration of sound.

codominance: the relation between two alleles of a gene, such that both alleles are phenotypically expressed in heterozygous individuals.

codon: a sequence of three bases of messenger RNA that specifies a particular amino acid to be incorporated into a protein; certain codons also signal the beginning or end of protein synthesis.

coelom (sē'-lōm): in animals, a space or cavity, lined with tissue derived from mesoderm, that separates the body wall from the inner organs.

coenzyme: an organic molecule that is bound to certain enzymes and is required for the enzymes' proper functioning; typically, a nucleotide bound to a water-soluble vitamin.

coevolution: the evolution of adaptations in two species due to their extensive interactions with one another, such that each species acts as a major force of natural selection on the other.

cohesion: the tendency of the molecules of a substance to stick together.

cohesion–tension theory: a model for the transport of water in xylem; water is pulled up the xylem tubes, powered by the force of evaporation of water from the leaves (producing tension) and held together by hydrogen bonds between nearby water molecules (cohesion).

coleoptile (kō-lē-op'-tīl): a sheath surrounding the shoot in monocot seedlings that protects the shoot from abrasion by soil particles during germination.

collecting duct: a tube within the kidney that collects urine from many nephrons and conducts it through the renal medulla into the renal pelvis. Urine may become concentrated in the collecting ducts if antidiuretic hormone (ADH) is present.

collenchyma (kōl-en'-ki-muh): an elongated plant cell type, with thickened, flexible cell walls, that is alive at maturity and that supports the plant body.

colon: the longest part of the large intestine; does not include the rectum.

colostrum (kō-los'-trum): a yellowish fluid, high in protein and containing antibodies, that is produced by the mammary glands before milk secretion begins.

communication: the act of producing a signal that causes a receiver, normally another animal of the same species, to change its behavior in a way that is, on average, beneficial to both signaler and receiver

community: all the interacting populations within an ecosystem.

compact bone: the hard and strong outer bone; composed of osteons. Compare with *spongy bone*.

companion cell: a cell adjacent to a sieve-tube element in phloem; involved in the control and nutrition of the sieve-tube element.

competition: interaction among individuals who attempt to utilize a resource (for example, food or space) that is limited relative to the demand for that resource.

competitive exclusion principle: the concept that no two species can simultaneously and continuously occupy the same ecological niche.

competitive inhibition: the process by which two or more molecules that are somewhat similar in structure compete for the active site of an enzyme.

complement: a group of blood-borne proteins that participate in the destruction of foreign cells, especially those to which antibodies have bound.

complementary base pair: in nucleic acids, bases that pair by hydrogen bonding. In DNA, adenine is complementary to thymine and guanine is complementary to cytosine; in RNA, adenine is complementary to uracil, and guanine to cytosine.

complete flower: a flower that has all four floral parts (sepals, petals, stamens, and carpels).

compound: a substance whose molecules are formed by different types of atoms; can be broken into its constituent elements by chemical means.

compound eye: a type of eye, found in many arthropods, that is composed of numerous independent subunits called *ommatidia*. Each ommatidium contributes a piece of a mosaic-like image perceived by the animal.

concentration: the number of particles of a dissolved substance in a given unit of volume.

concentration gradient: the difference in concentration of a substance between two parts of a fluid or across a barrier such as a membrane.

conclusion: in the scientific method, a decision about the validity of a hypothesis, made on the basis of experiments or observations.

conducting portion: the portion of the respiratory system in lung-breathing vertebrates that carries air to the alveoli.

cone: a cone-shaped photoreceptor cell in the vertebrate retina; not as sensitive to light as are the rods. The three types of cones are most sensitive to different colors of light and provide color vision; see also *rod*.

conifer (kon'-eh-fer): a member of a group of nonflowering vascular plants whose members reproduce by means of seeds formed inside cones; retains its leaves throughout the year.

conjugation: in prokaryotes, the transfer of DNA from one cell to another via a temporary connection; in single-celled eukaryotes, the mutual exchange of genetic material between two temporarily joined cells.

connective tissue: a tissue type consisting of diverse tissues, including bone, cartilage, fat, and blood, that generally contain large amounts of extracellular material.

conservation biology: the application of knowledge from ecology and other areas of biology to understand and conserve biodiversity.

constant region: the part of an antibody molecule that is similar in all antibodies of a given class.

constant-loss population: A population characterized by a relatively constant death rate; constant-loss populations have a roughly linear survivorship curve.

consumer: an organism that eats other organisms; a heterotroph.

contest competition: a mechanism for resolving intraspecific competition by using social or chemical interactions to limit access of some individuals to important limited resources, such as food, mates, or territories.

contraception: the prevention of pregnancy.

contractile vacuole: a fluid-filled vacuole in certain protists that takes up water from the cytoplasm, contracts, and expels the water outside the cell through a pore in the plasma membrane.

control: that portion of an experiment in which all possible variables are held constant; in contrast to the "experimental" portion, in which a particular variable is altered.

convergent evolution: the independent evolution of similar structures among unrelated organisms as a result of similar environmental pressures; see *analogous structures*.

convolution: a folding of the cerebral cortex of the vertebrate brain.

copulation: reproductive behavior in which the penis of the male is inserted into the body of the female, where it releases sperm.

coral reef: an ecosystem created by animals (reef-building corals) and plants in warm tropical waters.

core reserve: a natural area protected from most human uses that encompasses enough space to preserve all of the biodiversity of the ecosystems in that area.

cork cambium: a lateral meristem in woody roots and stems that gives rise to cork cells.

cork cell: a protective cell of the bark of woody stems and roots; at maturity, cork cells are dead, with thick, waterproof cell walls.

cornea (kor'-nē-uh): the clear outer covering of the eye, located in front of the pupil and iris; begins the focusing of light on the retina.

corona radiata (kuh-rō'-nuh rā-dē-a'-tuh): the layer of cells surrounding an egg after ovulation.

corpus callosum (kor'pus kal-ō'-sum): the band of axons that connects the two cerebral hemispheres of vertebrates.

corpus luteum (kor'-pus loo'-tē-um): in the mammalian ovary, a structure that is derived from the follicle after ovulation and that secretes the hormones estrogen and progesterone.

cortex: the part of a primary root or stem located between the epidermis and the vascular cylinder.

cortisol (kor'-ti-sol): a steroid hormone released into the bloodstream by the adrenal cortex in response to stress. Cortisol helps the body cope with short-term stressors by raising blood glucose levels; it also inhibits the immune response.

cotyledon (kot-ul-ē'don): a leaflike structure within a seed that absorbs food molecules from the endosperm and transfers them to the growing embryo; also called *seed leaf*.

countercurrent exchange: a mechanism for the transfer of some property, such as heat or a dissolved substance, from one fluid to another, generally without the two fluids actually mixing; in countercurrent exchange, the two fluids flow past one another in opposite directions, and they transfer heat or solute from the fluid with the higher temperature or higher solute concentration to the fluid with the lower temperature or lower solute concentration.

coupled reaction: a pair of reactions, one exergonic and one endergonic, that are linked together such that the energy produced by the exergonic reaction provides the energy needed to drive the endergonic reaction.

covalent bond (kō-vā'-lent): a chemical bond between atoms in which electrons are shared.

crab lice: an arthropod parasite that can infest humans; can be transmitted by sexual contact.

craniate: an animal that has a skull.

critically endangered species: a species that faces an extreme risk of extinction in the wild in the immediate future.

cross-fertilization: the union of sperm and egg from two individuals of the same species.

crossing over: the exchange of corresponding segments of the chromatids of two homologous chromosomes during meiosis I; occurs at chiasmata.

cuticle (kū'-ti-kul): a waxy or fatty coating on the surfaces of aboveground epidermal cells of many land plants; aids in the retention of water.

cyclic adenosine monophosphate (cyclic AMP): a cyclic nucleotide, formed within many target cells as a result of the reception of amino acid derivatives or peptide hormones, that causes metabolic changes in the cell.

cytokine (sī'-tō-kīn): any of several chemical messenger molecules released by cells that facilitate communication with other cells and transfer signals within and between the various systems of the body. Cytokines are important in cellular differentiation and the adaptive immune response.

cytokinesis (sī-tō-ki-nē′-sis): the division of the cytoplasm and organelles into two daughter cells during cell division; normally occurs during telophase of mitosis.

cytokinin (sī-tō-ki′-nin): a group of plant hormones that promotes cell division, fruit development, and the sprouting of lateral buds; also delays the senescence of plant parts, especially leaves.

cytoplasm (sī′-tō-plaz-um): all of the material contained within the plasma membrane of a cell, exclusive of the nucleus.

cytoplasmic fluid: the fluid portion of the cytoplasm; the substance within the plasma membrane exclusive of the nucleus and organelles; also called cytosol.

cytosine (C): a nitrogenous base found in both DNA and RNA; abbreviated as C.

cytoskeleton: a network of protein fibers in the cytoplasm that gives shape to a cell, holds and moves organelles, and is typically involved in cell movement.

cytotoxic T cell: a type of T cell that, upon contacting foreign cells, directly destroys them.

daughter cell: one of the two cells formed by cell division.

day-neutral plant: a plant in which flowering occurs as soon as the plant has undergone sufficient growth and development, regardless of day length.

death rate: the number of deaths per individual in a specified unit of time, such as a year.

decomposer: an organism, usually a fungus or bacterium, that digests organic material by secreting digestive enzymes into the environment, in the process liberating nutrients into the environment.

deductive reasoning: the process of generating hypotheses about the results of a specific experiment or the nature of a specific observation.

deforestation: the excessive cutting of forests. In recent years, deforestation has occurred primarily in rain forests in the Tropics, to clear space for agriculture.

dehydration synthesis: a chemical reaction in which two molecules are joined by a covalent bond with the simultaneous removal of a hydrogen from one molecule and a hydroxyl group from the other, forming water; the reverse of hydrolysis.

deletion mutation: a mutation in which one or more pairs of nucleotides are removed from a gene.

demographic transition: a change in population dynamic in which a fairly stable population with both high birth rates and high death rates experiences rapid growth as death rates decline, and then returns to a stable (although much larger) population as birth rates decline.

demography: the study of the changes in human numbers over time, grouped by world regions, age, sex, educational levels, and other variables.

denature: to disrupt the secondary and/or tertiary structure of a protein while leaving its amino acid sequence intact. Denatured proteins can no longer perform their biological functions.

denatured: having the secondary and/or tertiary structure of a protein disrupted, while leaving the amino acid sequence unchanged. Denatured proteins can no longer perform their biological functions.

dendrite (den′-drīt): a branched tendril that extends outward from the cell body of a neuron; specialized to respond to signals from the external environment or from other neurons.

dendritic cell (den-drit′-ick): a type of phagocytic leukocyte that presents antigen to T and B cells, thereby stimulating an adaptive immune response to an invading microbe.

denitrifying bacteria (dē-nī′-treh-fī-ing): bacteria that break down nitrates, releasing nitrogen gas to the atmosphere.

density-dependent: referring to any factor, such as predation, that limits population size to an increasing extent as the population density increases.

density-independent: referring to any factor, such floods or fires, that limits a population's size regardless of its density.

deoxyribonucleic acid (dē-ox-ē-rī-bō-noo-klā′-ik; DNA): a molecule composed of deoxyribose nucleotides; contains the genetic information of all living cells.

dermal tissue system: a plant tissue system that makes up the outer covering of the plant body.

dermis (dur′-mis): the layer of skin beneath the epidermis; composed of connective tissue and containing blood vessels, muscles, nerve endings, and glands.

desert: a biome in which less than 10 inches (25 centimeters) of rain fall each year; characterized by cacti, succulents, and widely spaced, drought-resistant bushes.

desertification: the process by which relatively dry, drought-prone regions are converted to desert as a result of drought and overuse of the land, for example, by overgrazing or cutting of trees.

desmosome (dez′-mō-sōm): a strong cell-to-cell junction that attaches adjacent cells to one another.

detritus feeder (de-trī′-tus): one of a diverse group of organisms, ranging from worms to vultures, that live off the wastes and dead remains of other organisms.

deuterostome (doo′-ter-ō-stōm): an animal with a mode of embryonic development in which the coelom is derived from outpocketings of the gut; characteristic of echinoderms and chordates.

developing country: a country (including most in Central and South America, Asia, and Africa) that has a relatively low average living standard and limited access to modern technology and medical care.

development: the process by which an organism proceeds from fertilized egg through adulthood to eventual death.

diabetes mellitus (di-uh-bē′-tēs mel-ī′-tus): a disease characterized by defects in the production, release, or reception of insulin; characterized by high blood glucose levels that fluctuate with sugar intake.

diaphragm (dī′-uh-fram): in the respiratory system, a dome-shaped muscle forming the floor of the chest cavity; when the diaphragm contracts, it flattens, enlarging the chest cavity and causing air to be drawn into the lungs.

diastolic pressure (dī′-uh-stal-ik): the blood pressure measured during relaxation of the ventricles; the lower of the two blood pressure readings.

diatom (dī′-uh-tom): a member of a protist group that includes photosynthetic forms with two-part glassy outer coverings; important photosynthetic organisms in fresh water and salt water. Diatoms are part of a larger group known as the stramenopiles.

dicot (dī′-kaht): short for dicotyledon; a type of flowering plant characterized by embryos with two cotyledons, or seed leaves, that are usually modified for food storage.

differentiate: the process whereby a cell becomes specialized in structure and function.

differentiated cell: a mature cell specialized for a specific function; in plants, differentiated cells normally do not divide.

diffusion: the net movement of particles from a region of high concentration of that particle to a region of low concentration, driven by the concentration gradient; may occur entirely within a fluid or across a barrier such as a membrane.

digestion: the process by which food is physically and chemically broken down into molecules that can be absorbed by cells.

digestive system: a group of organs responsible for ingesting food, digesting food into simple molecules that can be absorbed into the circulatory system, and expelling undigested wastes from the body.

dinoflagellate (dī-nō-fla′-jel-et): a member of a protist group that includes photosynthetic forms in which two flagella project through armor-like plates; abundant in oceans; can reproduce rapidly, causing "red tides." Dinoflagellates are part of a larger group known as the alveolates.

diploid (dip′-loid): referring to a cell with pairs of homologous chromosomes.

diplomonad: a member of a protist group characterized by two nuclei and multiple flagella. Diplomonads, which include disease-causing parasites such as *Giardia*, are part of a larger group known as the excavates.

direct development: a developmental pathway in which the offspring is born as a miniature version of the adult and does not radically change in body form as it grows and matures.

directional selection: a type of natural selection that favors one extreme of a range of phenotypes.

disaccharide (dī-sak′-uh-rīd): a carbohydrate formed by the covalent bonding of two monosaccharides.

disruptive selection: a type of natural selection that favors both extremes of a range of phenotypes.

distal tubule: the last section of a mammalian nephron, following the loop of Henle and emptying urine into a collecting duct; most tubular secretion and a small amount of tubular reabsorption occur in the distal tubule.

disturbance: any event that disrupts an ecosystem by altering its community, its abiotic structure, or both; disturbance precedes succession.

disulfide bond: the covalent bond formed between the sulfur atoms of two cysteines in a protein; typically causes the protein to fold by bringing otherwise distant parts of the protein close together.

DNA helicase: an enzyme that helps unwind the DNA double helix during DNA replication.

DNA ligase: an enzyme that bonds the terminal sugar in one DNA strand to the terminal phosphate in a second DNA strand, creating a single strand with a continuous sugar-phosphate backbone.

DNA polymerase: an enzyme that bonds DNA nucleotides together into a continuous strand, using a preexisting DNA strand as a template.

DNA probe: a sequence of nucleotides that is complementary to the nucleotide sequence of a gene or other segment of DNA under study; used to locate the gene or DNA segment during gel electrophoresis or other methods of DNA analysis.

DNA profile: the pattern of short tandem repeats of specific DNA segments; using a standardized set of 13 short tandem repeats, DNA profiles identify individual people with great accuracy.

DNA replication: the copying of the double-stranded DNA molecule, producing two identical DNA double helices.

DNA sequencing: the process of determining the order of nucleotides in a DNA molecule.

domain: the broadest category for classifying organisms; organisms are classified into three domains: Bacteria, Archaea, and Eukarya.

dominance hierarchy: a social structure that arises when the animals in a social group establish individual ranks that determine access to resources; ranks are usually established through aggressive interactions.

dominant: an allele that can determine the phenotype of heterozygotes completely, such that they are indistinguishable from individuals homozygous for the allele; in the heterozygotes, the expression of the other (recessive) allele is completely masked.

dormancy: a state in which an organism does not grow or develop; usually marked by lowered metabolic activity and resistance to adverse environmental conditions.

dorsal root ganglion: a ganglion, located on the dorsal (sensory) branch of each spinal nerve, that contains the cell bodies of sensory neurons.

double fertilization: in flowering plants, the fusion of two sperm nuclei with the nuclei of two cells of the female gametophyte. One sperm nucleus fuses with the egg to form the zygote; the second sperm nucleus fuses with the two haploid nuclei of the central cell to form a triploid endosperm cell.

double helix (hē′-liks): the shape of the two-stranded DNA molecule; similar to a ladder twisted lengthwise into a corkscrew shape.

Down syndrome: a genetic disorder caused by the presence of three copies of chromosome 21; common characteristics include mental retardation, distinctively shaped eyelids, a small mouth with protruding tongue, heart defects, and low resistance to infectious diseases; also called *trisomy 21*.

duodenum: the first section of the small intestine, in which most food digestion occurs; receives chyme from the stomach, buffers and digestive enzymes from the pancreas, and bile from the liver and gallbladder.

duplicated chromosome: a eukaryotic chromosome following DNA replication; consists of two sister chromatids joined at the centromeres.

early-loss population: a population characterized by a high birth rate, a high death rate among juveniles, and lower death rates among adults; early-loss populations have a concave survivorship curve.

ecdysone (ek-dī′-sōn): a steroid hormone that triggers molting in insects and other arthropods.

ecological footprint: the area of productive land needed to produce the resources used and absorb the wastes (including carbon dioxide) generated by an individual person, or by an average person of a specific part of the world (for example, an individual country), or of the entire world, using current technologies.

ecological niche (nitch): the role of a particular species within an ecosystem, including all aspects of its interaction with the living and nonliving environments.

ecology (ē-kol′-uh-jē): the study of the interrelationships of organisms with each other and with their nonliving environment.

ecosystem (ē′-kō-sis-tem): all the organisms and their nonliving environment within a defined area.

ecosystem services: the processes through which natural ecosystems and their living communities sustain and fulfill human life. Ecosystem services include purifying air and water, replenishing oxygen, pollinating plants, reducing flooding, providing wildlife habitat, and many more.

ectoderm (ek′-tō-derm): the outermost embryonic tissue layer, which gives rise to structures such as hair, the epidermis of the skin, and the nervous system.

ectotherm: an animal that obtains most of its body warmth from its environment; body temperatures of ectotherms vary with the temperature of their surroundings.

effector (ē-fek′-tor): a part of the body (normally a muscle or gland) that carries out responses as directed by the nervous system.

egg: the haploid female gamete, usually large and nonmotile; contains food reserves for the developing embryo.

electromagnetic spectrum: the range of all possible wavelengths of electromagnetic radiation, from wavelengths longer than radio waves, to microwaves, infrared, visible light, ultraviolet, x-rays, and gamma rays.

electron carrier: a molecule that can reversibly gain or lose electrons. Electron carriers generally accept high-energy electrons produced during an exergonic reaction and donate the electrons to acceptor molecules that use the energy to drive endergonic reactions.

electron shell: a region in an atom within which electrons orbit; each shell corresponds to a fixed energy level at a given distance from the nucleus.

electron transport chain (ETC): a series of electron carrier molecules, found in the thylakoid membranes of chloroplasts and the inner membrane of mitochondria, that extract energy from electrons and generate ATP or other energetic molecules.

electron: a subatomic particle, found in an electron shell outside the nucleus of an atom, that bears a unit of negative charge and very little mass.

element: a substance that cannot be broken down, or converted, to a simpler substance by ordinary chemical means.

elimination: the expulsion of indigestible materials from the digestive tract, through the anus, and outside the body.

embryo (em′-brē-ō): in animals, the stages of development that begin with the fertilization of the egg cell and end with hatching or birth; in mammals, the early stages in which the developing animal does not yet resemble the adult of the species.

embryonic disk: in human embryonic development, the flat, two-layered group of cells that separates the amniotic cavity from the yolk sac; the cells of the embryonic disk produce most of the developing embryo.

embryonic stem cell (ESC): a cell derived from an early embryo that is capable of differentiating into any of the adult cell types.

emerging infectious disease: a previously unknown infectious disease (one caused by a microbe), or a previously known infectious disease whose frequency or severity has significantly increased in the past two decades.

emigration (em-uh-grā′-shun): migration of individuals out of an area.

endangered species: a species that faces a high risk of extinction in the wild in the near future.

endergonic (en-der-gon′-ik): pertaining to a chemical reaction that requires an input of energy to proceed; an "uphill" reaction.

endocrine disrupter: an environmental pollutant that interferes with endocrine function, often by disrupting the action of sex hormones.

endocrine gland: a ductless, hormone-producing gland consisting of cells that release their secretions into the extracellular fluid from which the secretions diffuse into nearby capillaries; most endocrine glands are composed of epithelial cells.

endocrine hormone: a molecule produced by cells of endocrine glands and released into the circulatory system. An endocrine hormone causes changes in target cells that bear specific receptors for the hormone.

endocrine system: an animal's organ system for cell-to-cell communication; composed of hormones and the cells that secrete them.

endocytosis (en-dō-sī-tō′-sis): the process in which the plasma membrane engulfs extracellular material, forming membrane-bound sacs that enter the cytoplasm and thereby move material into the cell.

endoderm (en′-dō-derm): the innermost embryonic tissue layer, which gives rise to structures such as the lining of the digestive and respiratory tracts.

endodermis (en-dō-der′-mis): the innermost layer of small, close-fitting cells of the cortex of a root that form a ring around the vascular cylinder; see also *Casparian strip*.

endometrium (en-dō-mē′-trē-um): the nutritive inner lining of the uterus.

endoplasmic reticulum (en-dō-plaz′-mik re-tik′-ū-lum; ER): a system of membranous tubes and channels in eukaryotic cells; the site of most protein and lipid synthesis.

endoskeleton (en′-dō-skel′-uh-tun): a rigid internal skeleton with flexible joints that allow for movement.

endosperm: a triploid food storage tissue in the seeds of flowering plants that nourishes the developing plant embryo.

endospore: a protective resting structure of some rod-shaped bacteria that withstands unfavorable environmental conditions.

endosymbiont hypothesis: the hypothesis that certain organelles, especially chloroplasts and mitochondria, arose as mutually beneficial associations between the ancestors of eukaryotic cells and captured bacteria that lived within the cytoplasm of the pre-eukaryotic cell.

endotherm: an animal that obtains most of its body heat from metabolic activities; body temperatures of endotherms usually remain relatively constant within a fairly wide range of environmental temperatures.

energy pyramid: a graphical representation of the energy contained in succeeding trophic levels, with maximum energy at the base (primary producers) and steadily diminishing amounts at higher levels.

energy-requiring transport: the transfer of substances across a cell membrane using cellular energy; includes active transport, endocytosis, and exocytosis.

energy: the capacity to do work.

entropy (en′-trō-pē): a measure of the amount of randomness and disorder in a system.

environmental resistance: any factor that tends to counteract biotic potential, limiting population growth and the resulting population size.

enzyme (en′zīm): a biological catalyst, usually a protein, that speeds up the rate of specific biological reactions.

epicotyl (ep′-ē-kot-ul): the part of the embryonic shoot located above the attachment point of the cotyledons but below the tip of the shoot.

epidermal tissue: dermal tissue in plants that forms the epidermis, the outermost cell layer that covers leaves, young stems, and young roots.

epidermis (ep-uh-der′-mis): in animals, specialized stratified epithelial tissue that forms the outer layer of the skin; in plants, the outermost layer of cells of a leaf, young root, or young stem.

epididymis (e-pi-di′-di-mus): a series of tubes that connect with and receive sperm from the seminiferous tubules of the testis, and empty into the vas deferens.

epiglottis (ep-eh-glah′-tis): a flap of cartilage in the lower pharynx that covers the opening to the larynx during swallowing; directs food into the esophagus.

epinephrine (ep-i-nef′-rin): a hormone, secreted by the adrenal medulla, that is released in response to stress and that stimulates a variety of responses, including the release of glucose from the liver and an increase in heart rate.

epithelial tissue (eh-puh-thē′-lē-ul): a tissue type that forms membranes that cover the body surface and line body cavities, and that also gives rise to glands.

equilibrium population: a population in which allele frequencies and the distribution of genotypes do not change from generation to generation.

erythrocyte (eh-rith′-rō-sīt): a red blood cell, which contains the oxygen-binding protein hemoglobin and thus transports oxygen in the circulatory system.

erythropoietin (eh-rith′-rō-pō-ē′-tin): a hormone produced by the kidneys in response to oxygen deficiency; stimulates the production of red blood cells by the bone marrow.

esophagus: a muscular, tubular portion of the mammalian digestive tract located between the pharynx and the stomach; no digestion occurs in the esophagus.

essential amino acid: an amino acid that is a required nutrient; the body is unable to manufacture essential amino acids, so they must be supplied in the diet.

essential fatty acid: a fatty acid that is a required nutrient; the body is unable to manufacture essential fatty acids, so they must be supplied in the diet.

essential nutrient: any nutrient that cannot be synthesized by the body, including certain fatty acids and amino acids, vitamins, minerals, and water.

estrogen: a female sex hormone, produced by follicle cells of the ovary, that stimulates follicle development, oogenesis, the development of secondary sex characteristics, and growth of the uterine lining.

estuary (es′-choo-ar-ē): a wetland formed where a river meets the ocean; the salinity is quite variable, but lower than in seawater and higher than in fresh water.

ethology (ē-thol′-ō-jē): the study of animal behavior.

ethylene: a plant hormone that promotes the ripening of some fruits and the dropping of leaves and fruit; promotes senescence of leaves.

euglenid (ū′-gle-nid): a member of a protist group characterized by one or more whiplike flagella, which are used for locomotion, and by a photoreceptor, which detects light; are photosynthetic. Euglenids are part of a larger group known as euglenozoans.

euglenozoan: a member of the Euglenozoa, a protist clade. The euglenozoans, which are characterized by mitochondrial membranes that appear under the microscope to be shaped like a stack of disks, include the euglenids and the kinetoplastids.

Eukarya (ū-kar′-ē-a): one of life's three domains; consists of all eukaryotes (plants, animals, fungi, and protists).

eukaryote (ū-kar′-ē-ōt): an organism whose cells are eukaryotic; plants, animals, fungi, and protists are eukaryotes.

eukaryotic (ū-kar-ē-ot′-ik): referring to cells of organisms of the domain Eukarya (plants, animals, fungi, and protists). Eukaryotic cells have genetic material enclosed within a membrane-bound nucleus and contain other organelles.

eutrophic lake: a lake that receives sufficiently large inputs of sediments, organic material, and inorganic nutrients from its surroundings to support dense communities, especially of plants and phytoplankton; contains murky water with poor light penetration.

evolution: (1) the descent of modern organisms, with modification, from preexisting life-forms; (2) the theory that all organisms are related by common ancestry and have changed over time; (3) any change in the genetic makeup (the proportions of different genotypes) in a population from one generation to the next.

excavate: a member of the Excavata, a protist clade. The excavates, which generally lack mitochondria, include the diplomonads and the parabasalids.

excitatory postsynaptic potential (EPSP): an electrical signal produced in a postsynaptic cell that makes the resting potential of the postsynaptic neuron less negative and, hence, makes the neuron more likely to produce an action potential.

excretion: the elimination of waste substances from the body; can occur from the digestive system, skin glands, urinary system, or lungs.

exergonic (ex-er-gon´-ik): pertaining to a chemical reaction that releases energy (either as heat or in the form of increased entropy); a "downhill" reaction.

exhalation: the act of releasing air from the lungs, which results from a relaxation of the respiratory muscles.

exocrine gland: a gland that releases its secretions into ducts that lead to the outside of the body or into a body cavity, such as the digestive or reproductive system; most exocrine glands are composed of epithelial cells.

exocytosis (ex-ō-sī´-tō´-sis): the process in which intracellular material is enclosed within a membrane-bound sac that moves to the plasma membrane and fuses with it, releasing the material outside the cell.

exon: a segment of DNA in a eukaryotic gene that codes for amino acids in a protein (see also intron).

exoskeleton (ex´-ō-skel´-uh-tun): a rigid external skeleton that supports the body, protects the internal organs, and has flexible joints that allow for movement.

experiment: in the scientific method, the use of carefully controlled observations or manipulations to test the predictions generated by a hypothesis.

exponential growth: a continuously accelerating increase in population size; this type of growth generates a curve shaped like the letter "J."

extensor: a muscle that straightens (increases the angle of) a joint.

external fertilization: the union of sperm and egg outside the body of either parent.

extinction: the death of all members of a species.

extracellular digestion: the physical and chemical breakdown of food that occurs outside a cell, normally in a digestive cavity.

extracellular fluid: fluid that bathes the cells of the body; in mammals, extracellular fluid leaks from capillaries and is similar in composition to blood plasma, but lacking the large proteins found in plasma.

extraembryonic membrane: in the embryonic development of reptiles (including birds) and mammals, one of the chorion (functions in gas exchange), amnion (provision of the watery environment needed for development), allantois (waste storage), or yolk sac (storage of the yolk).

facilitated diffusion: the diffusion of molecules across a membrane, assisted by protein pores or carriers embedded in the membrane.

family: in Linnaean classification, the taxonomic rank composed of related genera. Closely related families make up an order.

farsighted: the inability to focus on nearby objects, caused by the eyeball being slightly too short or the cornea too flat.

fat (molecular): a lipid composed of three saturated fatty acids covalently bonded to glycerol; fats are solid at room temperature.

fatty acid: an organic molecule composed of a long chain of carbon atoms, with a carboxylic acid (COOH) group at one end; may be saturated (all single bonds between the carbon atoms) or unsaturated (one or more double bonds between the carbon atoms).

feces: semisolid waste material that remains in the intestine after absorption is complete and is voided through the anus. Feces consist principally of indigestible wastes and bacteria.

feedback inhibition: in enzyme-mediated chemical reactions, the condition in which the product of a reaction inhibits one or more of the enzymes involved in synthesizing the product.

fermentation: anaerobic reactions that convert the pyruvic acid produced by glycolysis into lactic acid or alcohol and CO_2, using hydrogen ions and electrons from NADH; the primary function of fermentation is to regenerate NAD+ so that glycolysis can continue under anaerobic conditions.

fertilization: the fusion of male and female haploid gametes, forming a zygote.

fetal alcohol syndrome (FAS): a cluster of symptoms, including mental retardation and physical abnormalities, that occur in infants born to mothers who consumed large amounts of alcoholic beverages during pregnancy.

fetus: the later stages of mammalian embryonic development (after the second month for humans), when the developing animal has come to resemble the adult of the species.

fever: an elevation in body temperature caused by chemicals (pyrogens) that are released by white blood cells in response to infection.

fibrillation (fi-bri-lā´-shun): the rapid, uncoordinated, and ineffective contraction of heart muscle cells.

fibrin (fī´-brin): a clotting protein formed in the blood in response to a wound; binds with other fibrin molecules and provides a matrix around which a blood clot forms.

fibrinogen (fī-brin´-ō-jen): the inactive form of the clotting protein fibrin. Fibrinogen is converted into fibrin by the enzyme thrombin, which is produced in response to injury.

fibrous root system: a root system, commonly found in monocots, that is characterized by many roots of approximately the same size arising from the base of the stem.

filament: in flowers, the stalk of a stamen, which bears an anther at its tip.

filtrate: the fluid produced by filtration; in the kidneys, the fluid produced by the filtration of blood through the glomerular capillaries.

filtration: within Bowman's capsule in each nephron of a kidney, the process by which blood is pumped under pressure through permeable capillaries of the glomerulus, forcing out water and small solutes, including wastes and nutrients.

first law of thermodynamics: the principle of physics that states that within any closed system, energy can be neither created nor destroyed, but can be converted from one form to another; also called the law of conservation of energy.

fission: asexual reproduction by dividing the body into two smaller, complete organisms.

fitness: the reproductive success of an organism, relative to the average reproductive success in the population.

flagellum (fla-jel´-um; pl., flagella): a long, hair-like, motile extension of the plasma membrane; in eukaryotic cells, it contains microtubules arranged in a 9 + 2 pattern. The movement of flagella propel some cells through fluids.

flavin adenine dinucleotide (FAD or FADH₂): an electron carrier molecule produced in the mitochondrial matrix by the Krebs cycle; subsequently donates electrons to the electron transport chain.

flexor: a muscle that flexes (decreases the angle of) a joint.

florigen: one of a group of plant hormones that may stimulate or inhibit flowering in response to day length.

flower: the reproductive structure of an angiosperm plant.

flower bud: a cluster of meristem cells (a bud) that forms a flower.

fluid mosaic model: a model of cell membrane structure; according to this model, membranes are composed of a double layer of phospholipids in which various proteins are embedded. The phospholipid bilayer is a somewhat fluid matrix that allows the movement of proteins within it.

fluid: a liquid or gas.

follicle: in the ovary of female mammals, the oocyte and its surrounding accessory cells.

follicle-stimulating hormone (FSH): a hormone, produced by the anterior pituitary, that stimulates spermatogenesis in males and the development of the follicle in females.

food chain: a linear feeding relationship in a community, using a single representative from each of the trophic levels.

food vacuole: a membranous sac, within a single cell, in which food is enclosed. Digestive enzymes are released into the vacuole, where intracellular digestion occurs.

food web: a representation of the complex feeding relationships within a community, including many organisms at various trophic levels, with many of the consumers occupying more than one level simultaneously.

foraminiferan (for-am-i-nif'-er-un): a member of a protist group characterized by pseudopods and elaborate calcium carbonate shells. Foraminiferans are generally aquatic (largely marine) and are part of a larger group known as rhizarians.

forebrain: during development, the anterior portion of the brain. In mammals, the forebrain differentiates into the thalamus, the limbic system, and the cerebrum. In humans, the cerebrum contains about half of all the neurons in the brain.

fossil: the remains of a dead organism, normally preserved in rock; may be petrified bones or wood; shells; impressions of body forms, such as feathers, skin, or leaves; or markings made by organisms, such as footprints.

fossil fuel: a fuel such as coal, oil, and natural gas, derived from the remains of ancient organisms.

founder effect: the result of an event in which an isolated population is founded by a small number of individuals; may result in genetic drift if allele frequencies in the founder population are by chance different from those of the parent population.

fovea (fō'-vē-uh): in the vertebrate retina, the central region on which images are focused; contains closely packed cones.

free nucleotides: nucleotides that have not been joined together to form a DNA or RNA strand.

free radical: a molecule containing an atom with an unpaired electron, which makes it highly unstable and reactive with nearby molecules. By removing an electron from the molecule it attacks, it creates a new free radical and begins a chain reaction that can lead to the destruction of biological molecules crucial to life.

fruit: in flowering plants, the ripened ovary (plus, in some cases, other parts of the flower), which contains the seeds.

functional group: one of several groups of atoms commonly found in an organic molecule, including hydrogen, hydroxyl, amino, carboxyl, and phosphate groups, that determine the characteristics and chemical reactivity of the molecule.

gallbladder: a small sac located next to the liver that stores and concentrates the bile secreted by the liver. Bile is released from the gallbladder to the small intestine through the bile duct.

gamete (gam'-ēt): a haploid sex cell, usually a sperm or an egg, formed in sexually reproducing organisms.

gametophyte (ga-mēt'-ō-fīt): the multicellular haploid stage in the life cycle of plants.

ganglion (gang'-lē-un; pl., ganglia): a cluster of neurons.

ganglion cell: in the vertebrate retina, the nerve cells whose axons form the optic nerve.

gap junction: a type of cell-to-cell junction in animals in which channels connect the cytoplasm of adjacent cells.

gas-exchange portion: the portion of the respiratory system in lung-breathing vertebrates where gas is exchanged in the alveoli of the lungs.

gastric gland: one of numerous small glands in the stomach lining; contains cells that secrete mucus, hydrochloric acid, or pepsinogen (the inactive form of the protease pepsin).

gastrin: a hormone produced by the stomach that stimulates acid secretion in response to the presence of food.

gastrovascular cavity: a saclike chamber with digestive functions, found in some invertebrates such as cnidarians (sea jellies, anemones, and related animals); a single opening serves as both mouth and anus.

gastrula (gas'-troo-luh): in animal development, a three-layered embryo with ectoderm, mesoderm, and endoderm cell layers. The endoderm layer usually encloses the primitive gut.

gastrulation (gas-troo-la'-shun): the process whereby a blastula develops into a gastrula, including the formation of endoderm, ectoderm, and mesoderm.

gel electrophoresis: a technique in which molecules (such as DNA fragments) are placed in wells in a thin sheet of gelatinous material and exposed to an electric field; the molecules migrate through the gel at a rate determined by certain characteristics, most commonly size.

gene flow: the movement of alleles from one population to another owing to the migration of individual organisms.

gene pool: the total of all alleles of all genes in a population; for a single gene, the total of all the alleles of that gene that occur in a population.

gene: the unit of heredity; a segment of DNA located at a particular place on a chromosome that encodes the information for the amino acid sequence of a protein and, hence, particular traits.

generative cell: in flowering plants, one of the haploid cells of a pollen grain; undergoes mitotic cell division to form two sperm cells.

genetic code: the collection of codons of mRNA, each of which directs the incorporation of a particular amino acid into a protein during protein synthesis or causes protein synthesis to start or stop.

genetic drift: a change in the allele frequencies of a small population purely by chance.

genetic engineering: the modification of the genetic material of an organism, usually using recombinant DNA techniques.

genetic recombination: the generation of new combinations of alleles on homologous chromosomes due to the exchange of DNA during crossing over.

genital herpes: a sexually transmitted disease, caused by a virus, that can cause painful blisters on the genitals and surrounding skin.

genotype (jēn'-ō-tīp): the genetic composition of an organism; the actual alleles of each gene carried by the organism.

genus (jē-nus): in Linnaean classification, the taxonomic rank composed of related species. Closely related genera make up a family.

germination: the growth and development of a seed, spore, or pollen grain.

gibberellin (jib-er-el'-in): one of a group of plant hormones that stimulates seed germination, fruit development, flowering, and cell division and elongation in stems.

gill: in aquatic animals, a branched tissue richly supplied with capillaries around which water is circulated for gas exchange.

gland: a cluster of cells that are specialized to secrete substances such as sweat, mucus, enzymes, or hormones.

glia: cells of the nervous system that provide nutrients for neurons, regulate the composition of the extracellular fluid in the brain and spinal cord, modulate communication between neurons, and insulate axons, thereby speeding up the conduction of action potentials. Also called *glial cells.*

glial cell: a cell of the nervous system that provides support and insulation for neurons, and regulates the composition of the extracellular fluid in the nervous system.

global warming: a gradual rise in global atmospheric temperature as a result of an amplification of the natural greenhouse effect due to human activities.

glomeromycete: a member of the fungus phylum Glomeromycota, which includes species that form mycorrhizal associations with plant roots and that form bush-shaped branching structures inside plant cells.

glomerulus (glō-mer'-ū-lus): a dense network of thin-walled capillaries, located within the Bowman's capsule of each nephron of the kidney, where blood pressure forces water and small solutes, including wastes and nutrients, through the capillary walls into the nephron.

glucagon (gloo'-ka-gon): a hormone, secreted by the pancreas, that increases blood sugar by stimulating the breakdown of glycogen (to glucose) in the liver.

glucocorticoid (gloo-kō-kor'-tik-oid): a class of hormones, released by the adrenal cortex in response to the presence of ACTH, that makes additional energy available to the body by stimulating the synthesis of glucose.

glucose: the most common monosaccharide, with the molecular formula $C_6H_{12}O_6$; most polysaccharides, including cellulose, starch, and glycogen, are made of glucose subunits covalently bonded together.

glycerol (glis′-er-ol): a three-carbon alcohol to which fatty acids are covalently bonded to make fats and oils.

glycogen (glī′-kō-jen): a highly branched polymer of glucose that is stored by animals in the muscles and liver and metabolized as a source of energy.

glycolysis (glī-kol′-i-sis): reactions, carried out in the cytoplasm, that break down glucose into two molecules of pyruvic acid, producing two ATP molecules; does not require oxygen but can proceed when oxygen is present.

glycoprotein: a protein to which a carbohydrate is attached.

goiter: a swelling of the thyroid gland caused by iodine deficiency, which affects the functioning of the thyroid gland and its hormones.

Golgi apparatus (gōl′-jē): a stack of membranous sacs, found in most eukaryotic cells, that is the site of processing and separation of membrane components and secretory materials.

gonad: an organ where reproductive cells are formed; in males, the testes, and in females, the ovaries.

gonadotropin-releasing hormone (gō-na-dō-trō′-pin; GnRH): a hormone produced by the neurosecretory cells of the hypothalamus, which stimulates cells in the anterior pituitary to release follicle-stimulating hormone (FSH) and luteinizing hormone (LH). GnRH is involved in the menstrual cycle and in spermatogenesis.

gonorrhea (gon-uh-rē′-uh): a sexually transmitted bacterial infection of the reproductive organs; if untreated, can result in sterility.

gradient: a difference in concentration, pressure, or electrical charge between two regions.

grassland: a biome, located in the centers of continents, that primarily supports grasses; also called a *prairie*.

gravitropism: growth with respect to the direction of gravity.

gray matter: the outer portion of the brain and inner region of the spinal cord; composed largely of neuron cell bodies, which give this area a gray color.

greenhouse effect: the process in which certain gases such as carbon dioxide and methane trap sunlight energy in a planet's atmosphere as heat; the glass in a greenhouse does the same. The result, global warming, is being enhanced by the production of these gases by humans.

greenhouse gas: a gas, such as carbon dioxide or methane, that traps sunlight energy in a planet's atmosphere as heat; a gas that participates in the greenhouse effect.

ground tissue system: a plant tissue system, consisting of parenchyma, collenchyma, and sclerenchyma cells, that makes up the bulk of a leaf or young stem, excluding vascular or dermal tissues. Most ground tissue cells function in photosynthesis, support, or carbohydrate storage.

growth hormone: a hormone, released by the anterior pituitary, that stimulates growth, especially of the skeleton.

growth rate: a measure of the change in population size per individual per unit of time.

guanine (G): a nitrogenous base found in both DNA and RNA; abbreviated as G.

guard cell: one of a pair of specialized epidermal cells that surrounds the central opening of a stoma in the epidermis of a leaf or young stem, and regulates the size of the opening.

gymnosperm (jim′-nō-sperm): a nonflowering seed plant, such as a conifer, gnetophyte, cycad, or gingko.

gyre (jī r): a roughly circular pattern of ocean currents, formed because continents interrupt the flow of the current; rotates clockwise in the Northern Hemisphere and counterclockwise in the Southern Hemisphere.

habitat fragmentation: the process by which human development and activities produce patches of wildlife habitat that may not be large enough to sustain minimum viable populations.

habituation (heh-bich-oo-ā′-shun): a type of simple learning characterized by a decline in response to a repeated stimulus.

hair cell: a type of mechanoreceptor cell found in the inner ear that produces an electrical signal when stiff hairlike cilia projecting from the surface of the cell are bent. Hair cells in the cochlea respond to sound vibrations; those in the vestibular system respond to motion and gravity.

hair follicle (fol′-i-kul): a cluster of specialized epithelial cells located in the dermis of mammalian skin, which produces a hair.

hammer: the second of the small bones of the middle ear, linking the tympanic membrane (eardrum) with the oval window of the cochlea; also called the *malleus*.

haploid hap′-loid: referring to a cell that has only one member of each pair of homologous chromosomes.

Hardy–Weinberg principle: a mathematical model proposing that, under certain conditions, the allele frequencies and genotype frequencies in a sexually reproducing population will remain constant over generations.

heart: a muscular organ responsible for pumping blood within the circulatory system throughout the body.

heart attack: a severe reduction or blockage of blood flow through a coronary artery, depriving some of the heart muscle of its blood supply.

heartwood: older secondary xylem that usually no longer conducts water or minerals, but that contributes to the strength of a tree trunk.

heat of fusion: the energy that must be removed from a compound to transform it from a liquid into a solid at its freezing temperature.

heat of vaporization: the energy that must be supplied to a compound to transform it from a liquid into a gas at its boiling temperature.

Heimlich maneuver: a method of dislodging food or other obstructions that have entered the airway.

helix (hē′-liks): a coiled, springlike secondary structure of a protein.

helper T cell: a type of T cell that helps other immune cells recognize and act against antigens.

hemocoel (hē′-mō-sēl): a cavity within the bodies of certain invertebrates in which a fluid, called hemolymph, bathes tissues directly; part of an open circulatory system.

hemodialysis (hē-mō-dī′-al′-luh-sis): a procedure that simulates kidney function in individuals with damaged or ineffective kidneys; blood is diverted from the body, artificially filtered, and returned to the body.

hemoglobin (hē′-mō-glō-bin): the iron-containing protein that gives red blood cells their color; binds to oxygen in the lungs and releases it in the tissues.

hemolymph: in animals with an open circulatory system, the fluid that is located in the hemocoel and that bathes all the body cells, therefore serving as both blood and extracellular fluid.

hemophilia: a recessive, sex-linked disease in which the blood fails to clot normally.

herbivore (erb′-i-vor): literally, "plant-eater"; an organism that feeds directly and exclusively on producers; a primary consumer.

hermaphrodite (her-maf′-ruh-dit′): an organism that possesses both male and female sexual organs. Some hermaphroditic animals can fertilize themselves; others must exchange sex cells with a mate.

hermaphroditic (her-maf′-ruh-dit′-ik): possessing both male and female sexual organs. Some hermaphroditic animals can fertilize themselves; others must exchange sex cells with a mate.

heterotroph (het′-er-ō-trōf′): literally, "other-feeder"; an organism that eats other organisms; a consumer.

heterozygous (het′-er-ō-zī′-gus): carrying two different alleles of a given gene; also called *hybrid*.

hindbrain: the posterior portion of the brain, containing the medulla, pons, and cerebellum.

hinge joint: a joint at which the bones fit together in a way that allows movement in only two dimensions, as at the elbow or knee.

hippocampus (hip-ō-kam′-pus): the part of the forebrain of vertebrates that is important in emotion and especially learning.

histamine (his′-ta-mēn): a substance released by certain cells in response to tissue damage and invasion of the body by foreign substances; promotes the dilation of arterioles and the leakiness of capillaries and triggers some of the events of the inflammatory response.

homeobox gene (hō'-mē-ō-boks): a sequence of DNA coding for a transcription factor protein that activates or inactivates many other genes that control the development of specific, major parts of the body.

homeostasis (hōm-ē-ō-stā'-sis): the maintenance of the relatively constant internal environment that is required for the optimal functioning of cells.

hominin: a human or a prehistoric relative of humans; the oldest known hominin is *Sahelanthropus*, whose fossils are more than 6 million years old.

homologous chromosome: a chromosome that is similar in appearance and genetic information to another chromosome with which it pairs during meiosis; also called *homologue*.

homologous structure: structures that may differ in function but that have similar anatomy, presumably because the organisms that possess them have descended from common ancestors.

homologue (hō-'mō-log): a chromosome that is similar in appearance and genetic information to another chromosome with which it pairs during meiosis; also called *homologous chromosome*.

homozygous (hō-mō-zī'-gus): carrying two copies of the same allele of a given gene; also called *true-breeding*.

hormone: a chemical that is secreted by one group of cells and transported to other cells, whose activity is influenced by reception of the hormone.

host: the prey organism on or in which a parasite lives; the host is harmed by the relationship.

human immunodeficiency virus (HIV): a pathogenic virus that causes acquired immune deficiency syndrome (AIDS) by attacking and destroying the immune system's helper T cells.

human papillomavirus (pap-il-lo'-ma; HPV): a virus that infects the reproductive organs, often causing genital warts; causes most, if not all, cases of cervical cancer.

humoral immunity: an immune response in which foreign substances are inactivated or destroyed by antibodies that circulate in the blood.

Huntington disease: an incurable genetic disorder, caused by a dominant allele, that produces progressive brain deterioration, resulting in the loss of motor coordination, flailing movements, personality disturbances, and eventual death.

hybrid: an organism that is the offspring of parents differing in at least one genetically determined characteristic; also used to refer to the offspring of parents of different species.

hydrogen bond: the weak attraction between a hydrogen atom that bears a partial positive charge (due to polar covalent bonding with another atom) and another atom (oxygen, nitrogen, or fluorine) that bears a partial negative charge; hydrogen bonds may form between atoms of a single molecule or of different molecules.

hydrologic cycle (hī–drō–loj'–ik): the biogeochemical cycle by which water travels from its major reservoir, the oceans, through the atmosphere to reservoirs in freshwater lakes, rivers, and groundwater, and back into the oceans. The hydrologic cycle is driven by solar energy. Nearly all water remains as water throughout the cycle (rather than being used in the synthesis of new molecules).

hydrolysis (hī-drol'-i-sis): the chemical reaction that breaks a covalent bond by means of the addition of hydrogen to the atom on one side of the original bond and a hydroxyl group to the atom on the other side; the reverse of dehydration synthesis.

hydrophilic (hī-drō-fil'-ik): pertaining to molecules that dissolve readily in water, or to molecules that form hydrogen bonds with water; polar.

hydrophobic (hī-drō-fō'-bik): pertaining to molecules that do not dissolve in water or form hydrogen bonds with water; nonpolar.

hydrophobic interaction: the tendency for hydrophobic molecules to cluster together when immersed in water.

hydrostatic skeleton (hī-drō-stat'-ik): in invertebrate animals, a body structure in which fluid-filled compartments provide support for the body and change shape when acted on by muscles, which alters the animal's body shape and position, or causes the animal to move.

hydrothermal vent community: a community of unusual organisms, living in the deep ocean near hydrothermal vents, that depends on the chemosynthetic activities of sulfur bacteria.

hypertension: arterial blood pressure that is chronically elevated above the normal level.

hypertonic (hī-per-ton'-ik): referring to a solution that has a higher concentration of dissolved particles (and therefore a lower concentration of free water) than has the cytoplasm of a cell.

hypha (hī'-fuh; pl., hyphae): in fungi, a threadlike structure that consists of elongated cells, typically with many haploid nuclei; many hyphae make up the fungal body.

hypocotyl (hī'-pō-kot-ul): the part of the embryonic shoot located below the attachment point of the cotyledons but above the root.

hypothalamus: (hī-pō-thal'-a-mus): a region of the brain that controls the secretory activity of the pituitary gland; synthesizes, stores, and releases certain peptide hormones; directs autonomic nervous system responses.

hypothesis (hī-poth'-eh-sis): in the scientific method, a supposition based on previous observations that is offered as an explanation for an observed phenomenon and is used as the basis for further observations or experiments.

hypotonic (hī-pō-ton'-ik): referring to a solution that has a lower concentration of dissolved particles (and therefore a higher concentration of free water) than has the cytoplasm of a cell.

immigration (im-uh-grā'-shun): migration of individuals into an area.

immune system: a system of cells, including macrophages, B cells, and T cells, and molecules, such as antibodies and cytokines, that work together to combat microbial invasion of the body.

imperfect flower: a flower that is missing either stamens or carpels.

implantation: the process whereby the early embryo embeds itself within the lining of the uterus.

imprinting: a type of learning in which an animal acquires a particular type of information during a specific sensitive phase of development.

incomplete dominance: a pattern of inheritance in which the heterozygous phenotype is intermediate between the two homozygous phenotypes.

incomplete flower: a flower that is missing one of the four floral parts (sepals, petals, stamens, or carpels).

indirect development: a developmental pathway in which an offspring goes through radical changes in body form as it matures.

induced pluripotent stem cell (ploo-rē-pō'-tent; iPSC): a type of stem cell produced from nonstem cells by the insertion of a specific set of genes that cause the cells to become capable of unlimited cell division and to be able to be differentiated into many different cell types, possibly any cell type of the body.

induction: the process by which a group of cells causes other cells to differentiate into a specific tissue type.

inductive reasoning: the process of creating a generalization based on many specific observations that support the generalization, coupled with an absence of observations that contradict it.

inflammatory response: a nonspecific, local response to injury to the body, characterized by the phagocytosis of foreign substances and tissue debris by white blood cells and by the walling off of the injury site by the clotting of fluids that escape from nearby blood vessels.

ingestion: the movement of food into the digestive tract, usually through the mouth.

inhalation: the act of drawing air into the lungs by enlarging the chest cavity.

inheritance: the genetic transmission of characteristics from parent to offspring.

inhibiting hormone: a hormone, secreted by the neurosecretory cells of the hypothalamus, that inhibits the release of specific hormones from the anterior pituitary.

inhibitory postsynaptic potential (IPSP): an electrical signal produced in a postsynaptic cell that makes the resting potential more negative and, hence, makes the neuron less likely to fire an action potential.

innate (in-āt'): inborn; instinctive; an innate behavior is performed correctly the first time it is attempted.

innate immune response: nonspecific defenses against many different invading microbes, including phagocytic white blood cells, natural killer cells, the inflammatory response, and fever.

inner cell mass: in human embryonic development, the cluster of cells, on the inside of the blastocyst, that will develop into the embryo.

inner ear: the innermost part of the mammalian ear; composed of the bony, fluid-filled tubes of the cochlea and the vestibular apparatus.

inorganic: describing any molecule that does not contain both carbon and hydrogen.

insertion: the site of attachment of a muscle to the relatively movable bone on one side of a joint.

insertion mutation: a mutation in which one or more pairs of nucleotides are inserted into a gene.

insight learning: a type of learning in which a problem is solved by understanding the relationships among the components of the problem rather than through trial and error.

insulin: a hormone, secreted by the pancreas, that lowers blood sugar by stimulating many cells to take up glucose and by stimulating the liver to convert glucose to glycogen.

integration: the process of adding up all of the electrical signals in a neuron, including sensory inputs and postsynaptic potentials, to determine the output of the neuron (action potentials and/or synaptic transmission).

integument (in-teg'-ū-ment): in plants, the outer layers of cells of the ovule that surround the female gametophyte; develops into the seed coat.

intensity: the strength of stimulation or response.

intercalated disc: junctions connecting individual cardiac muscle cells that serve both to attach adjacent cells to one another and to allow electrical signals to pass between cells.

intermediate filament: part of the cytoskeleton of eukaryotic cells that is composed of several types of proteins and probably functions mainly for support.

intermembrane space: the fluid-filled space between the inner and outer membranes of a mitochondrion.

internal fertilization: the union of sperm and egg inside the body of the female.

interneuron: in a neural network, a nerve cell that is postsynaptic to a sensory neuron and presynaptic to a motor neuron. In actual circuits, there may be many interneurons between individual sensory and motor neurons.

internode: the part of a stem between two nodes.

interphase: the stage of the cell cycle between cell divisions in which chromosomes are duplicated and other cell functions occur, such as growth, movement, and acquisition of nutrients.

interspecific competition: competition among individuals of different species.

interstitial cell (in-ter-sti'-shul): in the vertebrate testis, a testosterone-producing cell located between the seminiferous tubules.

intertidal zone: an area of the ocean shore that is alternately covered by water during high tides and exposed to the air during low tides.

intracellular digestion: the chemical breakdown of food within single cells.

intraspecific competition: competition among individuals of the same species.

intron: a segment of DNA in a eukaryotic gene that does not code for amino acids in a protein (see also exon).

invasive species: organisms with a high biotic potential that are introduced (deliberately or accidentally) into ecosystems where they did not evolve and where they encounter little environmental resistance and tend to displace native species.

inversion: a mutation that occurs when a piece of DNA is cut out of a chromosome, turned around, and reinserted into the gap.

invertebrate (in-vert'-uh-bret): an animal that lacks a vertebral column.

ion (ī-on): a charged atom or molecule; an atom or molecule that has either an excess of electrons (and, hence, is negatively charged) or has lost electrons (and is positively charged).

ionic bond: a chemical bond formed by the electrical attraction between positively and negatively charged ions.

iris: the pigmented muscular tissue of the vertebrate eye that surrounds and controls the size of the pupil, through which light enters the eye.

islet cell: a cell in the endocrine portion of the pancreas that produces either insulin or glucagon.

isolating mechanism: a morphological, physiological, behavioral, or ecological difference that prevents members of two species from interbreeding.

isotonic (ī-sō-ton'-ik): referring to a solution that has the same concentration of dissolved particles (and therefore the same concentration of free water) as has the cytoplasm of a cell.

isotope (ī'-suh-tōp): one of several forms of a single element, the nuclei of which contain the same number of protons but different numbers of neutrons.

J-curve: the J-shaped growth curve of an exponentially growing population in which increasing numbers of individuals join the population during each succeeding time period.

Jacob syndrome: a set of characteristics typical of human males possessing one X and two Y chromosomes (XYY); most XYY males are phenotypically normal, but XYY males have a higher than average incidence of high testosterone levels, severe acne, and above-average height.

joint: a flexible region between two rigid units of an exoskeleton or endoskeleton, allowing for movement between the units.

karyotype: a preparation showing the number, sizes, and shapes of all of the chromosomes within a cell.

kelp forest: a diverse ecosystem consisting of stands of tall brown algae and associated marine life. Kelp forests occur in oceans worldwide in nutrient-rich cool coastal waters.

keratin (ker'-uh-tin): a fibrous protein in hair, nails, and the epidermis of skin.

keystone species: a species whose influence on community structure is greater than its abundance would suggest.

kidney: one of a pair of organs of the excretory system that is located on either side of the spinal column and filters blood, removing wastes and regulating the composition and water content of the blood.

kin selection: a type of natural selection that favors traits that enhance the survival or reproduction of an individual's relatives, even if the traits reduce the fitness of the individuals bearing them.

kinetic energy: the energy of movement; includes light, heat, mechanical movement, and electricity.

kinetochore (ki-net'-ō-kor): a protein structure that forms at the centromere regions of chromosomes; attaches the chromosomes to the spindle.

kinetoplastid: a member of a protist group characterized by distinctively structured mitochondria. Kinetoplastids are mostly flagellated and include parasitic forms such as *Trypanosoma*, which causes sleeping sickness. Kinetoplastids are part of a larger group known as euglenozoans.

kingdom: the second broadest taxonomic category, consisting of related phyla. Related kingdoms make up a domain.

Klinefelter syndrome: a set of characteristics typically found in individuals who have two X chromosomes and one Y chromosome; these individuals are phenotypically males but are sterile and have several female-like traits, including broad hips and partial breast development.

Krebs cycle: a cyclic series of reactions, occurring in the matrix of mitochondria, in which the acetyl groups from the pyruvic acids produced by glycolysis are broken down to CO_2, accompanied by the formation of ATP and electron carriers; also called the citric acid cycle.

labium (pl., labia): one of a pair of folds of skin of the external structures of the mammalian female reproductive system.

labor: a series of contractions of the uterus that result in birth.

lactation: the secretion of milk from the mammary glands.

lacteal (lak-tēl'): a lymph capillary; found in each villus of the small intestine.

lactic acid fermentation: anaerobic reactions that convert the pyruvic acid produced by glycolysis into lactic acid, using hydrogen ions and electrons from NADH; the primary function of lactic acid fermentation is to regenerate NAD+ so that glycolysis can continue under anaerobic conditions.

lactose (lak'-tōs): a disaccharide composed of glucose and galactose; found in mammalian milk.

lactose intolerance: the inability to digest lactose (milk sugar) because lactase, the enzyme that digests lactose, is not produced in sufficient amounts; symptoms include bloating, gas pains, and diarrhea.

lactose operon: in prokaryotes, the set of genes that encodes the proteins needed for lactose metabolism, including both the structural genes and a common promoter and operator that control transcription of the structural genes.

large intestine: the final section of the digestive tract; consists of the colon and the rectum, where feces are formed and stored.

larva (lar'-vuh; pl., larvae): an immature form of an animal that subsequently undergoes metamorphosis into its adult form; includes the caterpillars of moths and butterflies, the maggots of flies, and the tadpoles of frogs and toads.

larynx (lar'-inks): the portion of the air passage between the pharynx and the trachea; contains the vocal cords.

late-loss population: a population in which most individuals survive into adulthood; late-loss populations have a convex survivorship curve.

lateral bud: a cluster of meristem cells at the node of a stem; under appropriate conditions, it grows into a branch.

lateral meristem: a meristem tissue that forms cylinders parallel to the long axis of roots and stems; normally located between the primary xylem and primary phloem (vascular cambium) and just outside the phloem (cork cambium); also called *cambium*.

law of conservation of energy: the principle of physics that states that within any closed system, energy can be neither created nor destroyed, but can be converted from one form to another; also called the first law of thermodynamics.

law of independent assortment: the independent inheritance of two or more traits, assuming that each trait is controlled by a single gene with no influence from gene(s) controlling the other trait; states that the alleles of each gene are distributed to the gametes independently of the alleles for other genes; this law is true only for genes located on different chromosomes or very far apart on a single chromosome.

law of segregation: the principle that each gamete receives only one of each parent's pair of alleles of each gene.

laws of thermodynamics: the physical laws that define the basic properties and behavior of energy.

leaf: an outgrowth of a stem, normally flattened and photosynthetic.

leaf primordium (pri-mor'-dē-um; pl., pri-mor-dia): a cluster of dividing cells, surrounding a terminal or lateral bud, that develops into a leaf.

learning: the process by which behavior is modified in response to experience.

legume (leg'-ūm): a member of a family of plants characterized by root swellings in which nitrogen-fixing bacteria are housed; includes peas, soybeans, lupines, alfalfa, and clover.

lens: a clear object that bends light rays; in eyes, a flexible or movable structure used to focus light on the photoreceptor cells of the retina.

leptin: a peptide hormone released by fat cells that helps the body monitor its fat stores and regulate weight.

leukocyte (loo'-kō-sīt): any of the white blood cells circulating in the blood.

lichen (lī'-ken): a symbiotic association between an alga or cyanobacterium and a fungus, resulting in a composite organism.

life table: a data table that groups organisms born at the same time and tracks them throughout their life span, recording how many continue to survive in each succeeding year (or other unit of time). Various parameters such as sex may be used in the groupings. Human life tables may include many other parameters (such as socioeconomic status) used by demographers.

ligament: a tough connective tissue band connecting two bones.

light reactions: the first stage of photosynthesis, in which the energy of light is captured as ATP and NADPH; occurs in thylakoids of chloroplasts.

lignin: a hard material that is embedded in the cell walls of vascular plants and that provides support in terrestrial species; an early and important adaptation to terrestrial life.

limbic system: a diverse group of brain structures, mostly in the lower forebrain, that includes the thalamus, hypothalamus, amygdala, hippocampus, and parts of the cerebrum and is involved in basic emotions, drives, behaviors, and learning.

limnetic zone: the part of a lake in which enough light penetrates to support photosynthesis.

linkage: the inheritance of certain genes as a group because they are parts of the same chromosome. Linked genes do not show independent assortment.

lipase (lī'-pās): an enzyme that catalyzes the breakdown of lipids such as fats.

lipid (li'-pid): one of a number of organic molecules containing large nonpolar regions composed solely of carbon and hydrogen, which make lipids hydrophobic and insoluble in water; includes oils, fats, waxes, phospholipids, and steroids.

littoral zone: the part of a lake, usually close to the shore, in which the water is shallow and plants find abundant light, anchorage, and adequate nutrients.

liver: an organ with varied functions, including bile production, glycogen storage, and the detoxification of poisons.

lobefin: fish with fleshy fins that have well-developed bones and muscles. Lobefins include two living clades: the coelacanths and the lungfishes.

local hormone: a general term for messenger molecules produced by most cells and released into the cells' immediate vicinity. Local hormones, which include prostaglandins and cytokines, influence nearby cells bearing appropriate receptors.

locus (plural, loci): the physical location of a gene on a chromosome.

logistic population growth: population growth characterized by an early exponential growth phase, followed by slower growth as the population approaches its carrying capacity, and finally reaching a stable population at the carrying capacity of the environment; this type of growth generates a curve shaped like a stretched-out letter "S."

long-day plant: a plant that will flower only if the length of uninterrupted darkness is shorter than a species-specific critical period; also called a *short-night plant*.

long-term memory: the second phase of learning; a more-or-less permanent memory formed by a structural change in the brain, brought on by repetition.

loop of Henle (hen'-lē): a specialized portion of the tubule of some nephrons in birds and mammals that creates an osmotic concentration gradient in the fluid immediately surrounding it. This gradient in turn makes possible the production of urine that is more osmotically concentrated than blood plasma.

lung: in terrestrial vertebrates, one of the pair of respiratory organs in which gas exchange occurs; consists of inflatable chambers within the chest cavity.

luteinizing hormone (loo'-tin-īz-ing; LH): a hormone produced by the anterior pituitary that stimulates testosterone production in males and the development of the follicle, ovulation, and the production of the corpus luteum in females.

lymph (limf): a pale fluid found within the lymphatic system; composed primarily of interstitial fluid and white blood cells.

lymph node: a small structure located on a lymph vessel, containing macrophages and lymphocytes (B and T cells). Macrophages filter the lymph by removing microbes; lymphocytes are the principal components of the adaptive immune response to infection.

lymphatic system: a system consisting of lymph vessels, lymph capillaries, lymph nodes, and the thymus and spleen; helps protect the body against infection, absorbs fats, and returns excess fluid and small proteins to the blood circulatory system.

lymphocyte (lim'-fō-sit): a type of white blood cell (natural killer cell, B cell, or T cell) that is important in either the innate or adaptive immune response.

lysosome (lī'-sō-sōm): a membrane-bound organelle containing intracellular digestive enzymes.

macronutrient: a nutrient required by an organism in relatively large quantities.

macrophage (mak′-rō-fāj): a type of white blood cell that engulfs microbes and destroys them by phagocytosis; also presents microbial antigens to T cells, helping stimulate the immune response.

major histocompatibility complex (MHC): a group of proteins, normally located on the surfaces of body cells, that identify the cell as "self"; also important in stimulating and regulating the immune response.

Malpighian tubule (mal-pig′-ē-un): the functional unit of the excretory system of insects, consisting of a small tube protruding from the intestine; wastes and nutrients move from the surrounding blood into the tubule, which drains into the intestine, where nutrients are reabsorbed back into the blood, while the wastes are excreted along with feces.

maltose (mal′-tōs): a disaccharide composed of two glucose molecules.

mammal: a member of the chordate clade Mammalia, which includes vertebrates with hair and mammary glands.

mammary gland (mam′-uh-rē): a milk-producing gland used by female mammals to nourish their young.

marsupial (mar-soo′-pē-ul): a member of the clade Marsupialia, which includes mammals whose young are born at an extremely immature stage and undergo further development in a pouch, where they remain attached to a mammary gland; kangaroos, opossums, and koalas are marsupials.

mass extinction: a relatively sudden extinction of many species, belonging to multiple major taxonomic groups, as a result of environmental change. The fossil record reveals five mass extinctions over geologic time.

mast cell: a cell of the immune system that releases histamine and other molecules used in the body's response to trauma and that are a factor in allergic reactions.

matrix: The fluid contained within the inner membrane of the mitochrondrion.

mechanical digestion: the process by which food in the digestive tract is physically broken down into smaller pieces.

medulla (med-ū′-luh): the part of the hindbrain of vertebrates that controls automatic activities such as breathing, swallowing, heart rate, and blood pressure.

megakaryocyte (meg-a-kar′-ē-ō-sīt): a large cell type in the bone marrow, which pinches off pieces of itself that enter the circulation as platelets.

megaspore: a haploid cell formed by meiotic cell division from a diploid megaspore mother cell; through mitotic cell division and differentiation, it develops into the female gametophyte.

megaspore mother cell: a diploid cell, within the ovule of a flowering plant, that undergoes meiotic cell division to produce four haploid megaspores.

meiosis (mī-ō′-sis): in eukaryotic organisms, a type of nuclear division in which a diploid nucleus divides twice to form four haploid nuclei.

meiotic cell division: meiosis followed by cytokinesis.

melatonin (mel-uh-tōn′-in): a hormone, secreted by the pineal gland, that is involved in the regulation of circadian cycles.

memory B cell: a type of white blood cell that is produced by clonal selection as a result of the binding of an antibody on a B cell to an antigen on an invading microorganism. Memory B cells persist in the bloodstream and provide future immunity to invaders bearing that antigen.

memory T cell: a type of white blood cell that is produced by clonal selection as a result of the binding of a receptor on a T cell to an antigen on an invading microorganism. Memory T cells persist in the bloodstream and provide future immunity to invaders bearing that antigen.

menstrual cycle: in human females, a roughly 28-day cycle during which hormonal interactions among the hypothalamus, pituitary gland, and ovary coordinate ovulation and the preparation of the uterus to receive and nourish a fertilized egg. If pregnancy does not occur, the uterine lining is shed during menstruation.

menstruation: in human females, the monthly discharge of uterine tissue and blood from the uterus.

meristem cell (mer′-i-stem): an undifferentiated cell that remains capable of cell division throughout the life of a plant.

mesoderm (mēz′-ō-derm): the middle embryonic tissue layer, lying between the endoderm and ectoderm, and normally the last to develop; gives rise to structures such as muscles, the skeleton, the circulatory system, and the kidneys.

mesophyll (mez′-ō-fil): loosely packed, usually photosynthetic cells located beneath the epidermis of a leaf.

messenger RNA (mRNA): a strand of RNA, complementary to the DNA of a gene, that conveys the genetic information in DNA to the ribosomes to be used during protein synthesis; sequences of three bases (codons) in mRNA that specify particular amino acids to be incorporated into a protein.

metabolic pathway: a sequence of chemical reactions within a cell, in which the products of one reaction are the reactants for the next reaction.

metabolic rate: the speed at which cellular reactions that release energy occur.

metabolism: the sum of all chemical reactions that occur within a single cell or within all the cells of a multicellular organism.

metamorphosis (met-a-mor′-fō-sis): in animals with indirect development, a radical change in body form from larva to sexually mature adult, as seen in amphibians (e.g., tadpole to frog) and insects (e.g., caterpillar to butterfly).

metaphase (met′-a-fāz): in mitosis, the stage in which the chromosomes, attached to spindle fibers at kinetochores, are lined up along the equator of the cell; also the approximately comparable stages in meiosis I and meiosis II.

microbe: a microorganism.

microfilament: part of the cytoskeleton of eukaryotic cells that is composed of the proteins actin and (in some cases) myosin; functions in the movement of cell organelles, locomotion by extension of the plasma membrane, and sometimes contraction of entire cells.

micronutrient: a nutrient required by an organism in relatively small quantities.

microspore: a haploid cell formed by meiotic cell division from a microspore mother cell; through mitotic cell division and differentiation, it develops into the male gametophyte.

microspore mother cell: a diploid cell contained within an anther of a flowering plant; undergoes meiotic cell division to produce four haploid microspores.

microtubule: a hollow, cylindrical strand, found in eukaryotic cells, that is composed of the protein tubulin; part of the cytoskeleton used in the movement of organelles, cell growth, and the construction of cilia and flagella.

microvillus (mī-krō-vi′-lus; pl., microvilli): a microscopic projection of the plasma membrane, which increases the surface area of a cell.

midbrain: during development, the central portion of the brain; contains an important relay center, the reticular formation.

middle ear: the part of the mammalian ear composed of the tympanic membrane, the Eustachian tube, and three bones (hammer, anvil, and stirrup) that transmit vibrations from the auditory canal to the oval window.

mimicry (mim′-ik-rē): the situation in which a species has evolved to resemble something else, typically another type of organism.

mineral: an inorganic substance, especially one in rocks or soil, or dissolved in water. In nutrition, minerals such as sodium, calcium, and potassium are essential nutrients that must be obtained in the diet.

mineralocorticoids: steroid hormones produced by the adrenal cortex that regulate salt retention in the kidney, thereby regulating the salt concentration in the blood and other extracellular fluids.

minimum viable population (MVP): the smallest isolated population that can persist indefinitely and survive likely natural events such as fires and floods.

mitochondrion (mī-tō-kon′-drē-un; pl., **mitochondria):** an organelle, bounded by two membranes, that is the site of the reactions of aerobic metabolism.

mitosis (mī-tō′-sis): a type of nuclear division, used by eukaryotic cells, in which one copy of each chromosome (already duplicated during interphase before mitosis) moves into each of two daughter nuclei; the daughter nuclei are therefore genetically identical to each other.

mitotic cell division: mitosis followed by cytokinesis.

molecule (mol′-e-kūl): a particle composed of one or more atoms held together by chemical bonds; the smallest particle of a compound that displays all the properties of that compound.

molt: to shed an external body covering, such as an exoskeleton, skin, feathers, or fur.

monocot: short for monocotyledon; a type of flowering plant characterized by embryos with one seed leaf, or cotyledon.

monomer (mo′-nō-mer): a small organic molecule, several of which may be bonded together to form a chain called a polymer.

monosaccharide (mo-nō-sak′-uh-rīd): the basic molecular unit of all carbohydrates, normally composed of a chain of carbon atoms bonded to hydrogen and hydroxyl groups.

monotreme: a member of the clade Monotremata, which includes mammals that lay eggs; platypuses and spiny anteaters are monotremes.

morula (mor′-ū-luh): in animals, an embryonic stage during cleavage, when the embryo consists of a solid ball of cells.

motor neuron: a neuron that receives instructions from sensory neurons or interneurons and activates effector organs, such as muscles or glands.

motor unit: a single motor neuron and all the muscle fibers on which it forms synapses.

mouth: the opening through which food enters a tubular digestive system.

multicellular: many-celled; most members of the kingdoms Fungi, Plantae, and Animalia are multicellular, with intimate cooperation among cells.

multiple alleles: many alleles of a single gene, perhaps dozens or hundreds, as a result of mutations.

muscle fiber: an individual muscle cell.

muscle tissue: tissue composed of one of three types of contractile cells (smooth, skeletal, or cardiac).

mutation: a change in the base sequence of DNA in a gene; often used to refer to a genetic change that is significant enough to alter the appearance or function of the organism.

mutualism (mū′-choo-ul-iz-um): a symbiotic relationship in which both participating species benefit.

mycelium (mī-sēl′-ē-um; pl., **mycelia):** the body of a fungus, consisting of a mass of hyphae.

mycorrhiza (mī-kō-rī′-zuh; pl., **mycorrhizae):** a symbiotic association between a fungus and the roots of a land plant that facilitates mineral extraction and absorption.

myelin (mī′-uh-lin): a wrapping of insulating membranes of specialized nonneural cells around the axon of a vertebrate nerve cell; increases the speed of conduction of action potentials.

myofibril (mū-ō-fī′-bril): a cylindrical subunit of a muscle cell, consisting of a series of sarcomeres, surrounded by sarcoplasmic reticulum.

myometrium (mī-ō-mē′-trē-um): the muscular outer layer of the uterus.

myosin (mī′-ō-sin): one of the major proteins of muscle, the interaction of which with the protein actin produces muscle contraction; found in the thick filaments of the muscle fiber; see also *actin*.

myosin head: the part of a myosin protein that binds to the actin subunits of a thick filament; flexion of the myosin head moves the thin filament toward the center of the sarcomere, causing muscle fiber contraction.

Na⁺-K⁺ pump: an active transport protein that uses the energy of ATP to transport Na^+ out of a cell and K^+ into a cell; produces and maintains the concentration gradients of these ions across the plasma membrane, such that the concentration of Na^+ is higher outside a cell than inside, and the concentration of K^+ is higher inside a cell than outside.

natural causality: the scientific principle that natural events occur as a result of preceding natural causes.

natural killer cell: a type of white blood cell that destroys some virus-infected cells and cancerous cells on contact; part of the innate immune system's nonspecific internal defense against disease.

natural selection: the unequal survival and reproduction of organisms with different phenotypes, caused by environmental forces. Natural selection refers specifically to cases in which the differing phenotypes are heritable; that is, they are caused at least partly by genetic differences, with the result that better adapted phenotypes become more common in the population.

nearshore zone: the region of coastal water that is relatively shallow but constantly submerged, and that can support large plants or seaweeds; includes bays and coastal wetlands.

nearsighted: the inability to focus on distant objects caused by an eyeball that is slightly too long or a cornea that is too curved.

negative feedback: a physiological process in which a change causes responses that tend to counteract the change and restore the original state. Negative feedback in physiological systems maintains homeostasis.

nephridium (nef-rid′-ē-um; pl., **nephridia):** an excretory organ found in earthworms, mollusks, and certain other invertebrates; somewhat resembles a single vertebrate nephron.

nephron (nef′-ron): the functional unit of the kidney; where blood is filtered and urine is formed.

nerve: a bundle of axons of nerve cells, bound together in a sheath.

nerve cord: a major nervous pathway consisting of a cord of nervous tissue extending lengthwise through the body, paired in many invertebrates and unpaired in chordates.

nerve net: a simple form of nervous system, consisting of a network of neurons that extends throughout the tissues of an organism such as a cnidarian.

nerve tissue: the tissue that makes up the brain, spinal cord, and nerves; consists of neurons and glial cells.

net primary productivity: the energy stored in the autotrophs of an ecosystem over a given time period.

neuromuscular junction: the synapse formed between a motor neuron and a muscle fiber.

neuron (noor′-on): a single nerve cell.

neurosecretory cell: a specialized nerve cell that synthesizes and releases hormones.

neurotransmitter: a chemical that is released by a nerve cell close to a second nerve cell, a muscle, or a gland cell and that influences the activity of the second cell.

neutral mutation: a mutation that does not detectably change the function of the encoded protein.

neutron: a subatomic particle that is found in the nuclei of atoms, bears no charge, and has a mass approximately equal to that of a proton.

neutrophil (nū′-trō-fil): a type of white blood cell that engulfs invading microbes and contributes to the nonspecific defenses of the body against disease.

nicotinamide adenine dinucleotide (NAD+ or NADH): an electron carrier molecule produced in the cytoplasmic fluid by glycolysis and in the mitochondrial matrix by the Krebs cycle; subsequently donates electrons to the electron transport chain.

nitrogen cycle: the biogeochemical cycle by which nitrogen moves from its primary reservoir of nitrogen gas in the atmosphere via nitrogen-fixing bacteria to reservoirs in soil and water, through producers and into higher trophic levels, and then back to its reservoirs.

nitrogen fixation: the process that combines atmospheric nitrogen with hydrogen to form ammonium (NH_4^+).

nitrogen-fixing bacterium: a bacterium that possesses the ability to remove nitrogen (N_2) from the atmosphere and combine it with hydrogen to produce ammonium (NH_4^+).

no-till: a method of growing crops that leaves the remains of harvested crops in place, with the next year's crops being planted directly in the remains of last year's crops without significant disturbance of the soil.

node: in plants, a region of a stem at which the petiole of a leaf is attached; usually, a lateral bud is also found at a node.

nodule: a swelling on the root of a legume or other plant that consists of cortex cells inhabited by nitrogen-fixing bacteria.

noncompetitive inhibition: the process by which an inhibitory molecule binds to a site on an enzyme that is distinct from the active site. As a result, the enzyme's active site is distorted, making it less able to catalyze the reaction involving its normal substrate.

nondisjunction: an error in meiosis in which chromosomes fail to segregate properly into the daughter cells.

nonpolar covalent bond: a covalent bond with equal sharing of electrons.

nonvascular plant: a plant that lacks lignin and well-developed conducting vessels. Nonvascular plants include mosses, hornworts, and liverworts.

norepinephrine (nor-ep-i-nef-rin´): a neurotransmitter, released by neurons of the parasympathetic nervous system, that prepares the body to respond to stressful situations; also called *noradrenaline*.

northern coniferous forest: a biome with long, cold winters and only a few months of warm weather; dominated by evergreen coniferous trees; also called *taiga*.

notochord (nōt´-ō-kord): a stiff but somewhat flexible, supportive rod that extends along the head-to-tail axis and is found in all members of the phylum Chordata at some stage of development.

nuclear envelope: the double-membrane system surrounding the nucleus of eukaryotic cells; the outer membrane is typically continuous with the endoplasmic reticulum.

nuclear pore complex: an array of proteins that line pores in the nuclear membrane and control which substances enter and leave the nucleus.

nucleic acid (noo-klā´-ik): an organic molecule composed of nucleotide subunits; the two common types of nucleic acids are ribonucleic acid (RNA) and deoxyribonucleic acid (DNA).

nucleoid (noo-klē-oid): the location of the genetic material in prokaryotic cells; not membrane enclosed.

nucleolus (noo-klē´-ō-lus; pl., **nucleoli):** the region of the eukaryotic nucleus that is engaged in ribosome synthesis; consists of the genes encoding ribosomal RNA, newly synthesized ribosomal RNA, and ribosomal proteins.

nucleotide substitution: a mutation in which a single base pair in DNA has been changed.

nucleotide: a subunit of which nucleic acids are composed; a phosphate group bonded to a sugar (deoxyribose in DNA), which is in turn bonded to a nitrogen-containing base (adenine, guanine, cytosine, or thymine in DNA). Nucleotides are linked together, forming a strand of nucleic acid, by bonds between the phosphate of one nucleotide and the sugar of the next nucleotide.

nucleus (atomic): the central region of an atom, consisting of protons and neutrons.

nucleus (cellular): the membrane-bound organelle of eukaryotic cells that contains the cell's genetic material.

nutrient: a substance acquired from the environment and needed for the survival, growth, and development of an organism.

nutrient cycle: the pathways of a specific nutrient (such as carbon, nitrogen, phosphorus, or water) through the living and nonliving portions of an ecosystem; also called a *biogeochemical cycle*.

observation: in the scientific method, the recognition of and a statement about a specific phenomenon, usually leading to the formulation of a question about the phenomenon.

oil: a lipid composed of three fatty acids, some of which are unsaturated, covalently bonded to a molecule of glycerol; oils are liquid at room temperature.

oligotrophic lake: a lake that is very low in nutrients and hence supports little phytoplankton, plant, and algal life; contains clear water with deep light penetration.

ommatidium (ōm-ma-tid´-ē-um; pl., **ommatidia):** an individual light-sensitive subunit of a compound eye; consists of a lens and several receptor cells.

omnivore: an organism that consumes both plants and animals.

oogenesis (ō-ō-jen´-i-sis): the process by which egg cells are formed.

oogonium (ō-ō-gō´-nē-um; pl., **oogonia):** in female animals, a diploid cell that gives rise to a primary oocyte.

open circulatory system: a type of circulatory system found in some invertebrates, such as arthropods and most mollusks, that includes an open space (the hemocoel) in which blood directly bathes body tissues.

operant conditioning: a laboratory training procedure in which an animal learns to perform a response (such as pressing a lever) through reward or punishment.

operator: a sequence of DNA nucleotides in a prokaryotic operon that binds regulatory proteins that control the ability of RNA polymerase to transcribe the structural genes of the operon.

operon (op´-er-on): in prokaryotes, a set of genes, often encoding the proteins needed for a complete metabolic pathway, including both the structural genes and a common promoter and operator that control transcription of the structural genes.

optic nerve: the nerve leading from the eye to the brain; it carries visual information.

order: in Linnaean classification, the taxonomic rank composed of related families. Related orders make up a class.

organ: a structure (such as the liver, kidney, or skin) composed of two or more distinct tissue types that function together.

organ system: two or more organs that work together to perform a specific function; for example, the digestive system.

organelle (or-guh-nel´): a membrane-enclosed structure found inside a eukaryotic cell that performs a specific function.

organic molecule: a molecule that contains both carbon and hydrogen.

organic: describing a molecule that contains both carbon and hydrogen.

organism (or´-guh-niz-um): an individual living thing.

organogenesis (or-gan-ō-jen´-uh-sis): the process by which the layers of the gastrula (endoderm, ectoderm, mesoderm) rearrange to form organs.

origin: the site of attachment of a muscle to the relatively stationary bone on one side of a joint.

osmolarity: a measure of the total number of dissolved solute particles in a solution.

osmoregulation: homeostatic maintenance of the water and salt content of the body within a limited range.

osmosis (oz-mō´-sis): the diffusion of water across a differentially permeable membrane, normally down a concentration gradient of free water molecules. Water moves into the solution that has a lower concentration of free water from a solution that has a higher concentration of free water.

osteoblast (os´-tē-ō-blast): a cell type that produces bone.

osteoclast (os´-tē-ō-klast): a cell type that dissolves bone.

osteocyte (os´-tē-ō-sīt): a mature bone cell.

osteoporosis (os´-tē-ō-por-ō´-sis): a condition in which bones become porous, weak, and easily fractured; most common in elderly women.

outer ear: the outermost part of the mammalian ear, including the external ear and auditory canal leading to the tympanic membrane.

oval window: the membrane-covered entrance to the cochlea.

ovary: (1) in animals, the gonad of females. (2) in flowering plants, a structure at the base of the carpel that contains one or more ovules and develops into the fruit.

ovary: in animals, the gonad of females.

overexploitation: hunting or harvesting natural populations at a rate that exceeds those populations' ability to replenish their numbers.

ovulation: the release of a secondary oocyte, ready to be fertilized, from the ovary.

ovule: a structure within the ovary of a flower, inside which the female gametophyte develops; after fertilization, develops into the seed.

oxytocin (oks-ē-tō´-sin): a hormone, released by the posterior pituitary, that stimulates the contraction of uterine and mammary gland muscles.

ozone hole: a region of severe ozone loss in the stratosphere caused by ozone-depleting chemicals; maximum ozone loss occurs from September to early October over Antarctica.

ozone layer: the ozone-enriched layer of the upper atmosphere (stratosphere) that filters out much of the sun's ultraviolet radiation.

pacemaker: a cluster of specialized muscle cells in the upper right atrium of the heart that produce spontaneous electrical signals at a regular rate; the sinoatrial node.

pain receptor: a receptor cell that stimulates activity in the brain that is perceived as the sensation of pain; responds to very high or very low temperatures, mechanical damage (such as extreme stretching of tissue), and/or certain chemicals, such as potassium ions or bradykinin, that are produced as a result of tissue damage; also called *nociceptor*.

pancreas (pan'-krē-us): a combined exocrine and endocrine gland located in the abdominal cavity next to the stomach. The endocrine portion secretes the hormones insulin and glucagon, which regulate glucose concentrations in the blood. The exocrine portion secretes pancreatic juice (a mixture of water, enzymes, and sodium bicarbonate) into the small intestine; the enzymes digest fat, carbohydrate, and protein; the bicarbonate neutralizes acidic chyme entering the intestine from the stomach.

pancreatic juice: a mixture of water, sodium bicarbonate, and enzymes released by the pancreas into the small intestine.

parabasalid: a member of a protist group characterized by mutualistic or parasitic relationships with the animal species inside which they live. Parabasalids are part of a larger group known as the excavates.

parasite (par'-uh-sīt): an organism that lives in or on a larger organism (its host), harming the host but usually not killing it immediately.

parasympathetic division: the division of the autonomic nervous system that produces largely involuntary responses related to the maintenance of normal body functions, such as digestion; often called the *parasympathetic nervous system*.

parathyroid gland: one of four small endocrine glands, embedded in the surface of the thyroid gland, that produces parathyroid hormone, which (with calcitonin from the thyroid gland) regulates calcium ion concentration in the blood.

parathyroid hormone: a hormone released by the parathyroid gland that stimulates the release of calcium from bone.

parenchyma (par-en'-ki-muh): a plant cell type that is alive at maturity, normally with thin cell walls, that carries out most of the metabolism of a plant. Most dividing meristem cells in a plant are parenchyma.

parthenogenesis (par-the-nō-jen'-uh-sis): an asexual specialization of sexual reproduction, in which a haploid egg undergoes development without fertilization.

passive transport: the movement of materials across a membrane down a gradient of concentration, pressure, or electrical charge without using cellular energy.

pathogen: an organism (or a toxin) capable of producing disease.

pathogenic (path'-ō-jen-ik): capable of producing disease; referring to an organism with such a capability (a pathogen).

pedigree: a diagram showing genetic relationships among a set of individuals, normally with respect to a specific genetic trait.

pelagic (puh-la'-jik): free-swimming or floating.

penis: an external structure of the male reproductive and urinary systems; serves to deposit sperm into the female reproductive system and deliver urine to the outside of the body.

peptide (pep'-tīd): a chain composed of two or more amino acids linked together by peptide bonds.

peptide bond: the covalent bond between the nitrogen of the amino group of one amino acid and the carbon of the carboxyl group of a second amino acid, joining the two amino acids together in a peptide or protein.

peptide hormone: a hormone consisting of a chain of amino acids; includes small proteins that function as hormones.

pericycle (per'-i-sī-kul): the outermost layer of cells of the vascular cylinder of a root.

periderm: the outer cell layers of roots and stems that have undergone secondary growth; consists primarily of cork cambium and cork cells.

peripheral nervous system (PNS): in vertebrates, the part of the nervous system that connects the central nervous system to the rest of the body.

peristalsis: rhythmic coordinated contractions of the smooth muscles of the digestive tract that move substances through the digestive tract.

permafrost: a permanently frozen layer of soil, usually found in tundra of the arctic or high mountains.

petal: part of a flower, typically brightly colored and fragrant, that attracts potential animal pollinators.

petiole (pet'-ē-ōl): the stalk that connects the blade of a leaf to the stem.

pH scale: a scale, with values from 0 to 14, used for measuring the relative acidity of a solution; at pH 7 a solution is neutral, pH 0 to 7 is acidic, and pH 7 to 14 is basic; each unit on the scale represents a tenfold change in H+ concentration.

phagocyte (fā'-gō-sīt): a type of immune system cell that destroys invading microbes by using phagocytosis to engulf and digest the microbes. Also called a *phagocytic cell*.

phagocytosis (fa-gō-sī-tō'-sis): a type of endocytosis in which extensions of a plasma membrane engulf extracellular particles, enclose them in a membrane-bound sac, and transport them into the interior of the cell.

pharyngeal gill slit (far-in'-jē-ul): one of a series of openings, located just posterior to the mouth, that connects the throat to the outside environment; present (as some stage of life) in all chordates.

pharynx (far'-inks): in vertebrates, a chamber that is located at the back of the mouth, shared by the digestive and respiratory systems; in some invertebrates, the portion of the digestive tube just posterior to the mouth.

phenotype (fēn'-ō-tīp): the physical characteristics of an organism; can be defined as outward appearance (such as flower color), as behavior, or in molecular terms (such as glycoproteins on red blood cells).

pheromone (fer'-uh-mōn): a chemical produced by an organism that alters the behavior or physiological state of another member of the same species.

phloem (flō'-um): a conducting tissue of vascular plants that transports a concentrated solution of sugars (primarily sucrose) and other organic molecules up and down the plant.

phospholipid (fos-fō-li'-pid): a lipid consisting of glycerol bonded to two fatty acids and one phosphate group, which bears another group of atoms, typically charged and containing nitrogen. A double layer of phospholipids is a component of all cellular membranes.

phospholipid bilayer: a double layer of phospholipids that forms the basis of all cellular membranes. The phospholipid heads, which are hydrophilic, face the water of extracellular fluid or the cytoplasm; the tails, which are hydrophobic, are buried in the middle of the bilayer.

phosphorus cycle (fos'–for-us): the biogeochemical cycle by which phosphorus moves from its primary reservoir—phosphate-rich rock—to reservoirs of phosphate in soil and water, through producers and into higher trophic levels, and then back to its reservoirs.

photic zone: the region of an ocean where light is strong enough to support photosynthesis.

photon (fō'-ton): the smallest unit of light energy.

photopigment (fō'-tō-pig-ment): a chemical substance in a photoreceptor cell that, when struck by light, changes shape and produces a response in the cell.

photoreceptor: a receptor cell that responds to light; in vertebrates, rods and cones.

photorespiration: a series of reactions in plants in which O_2 replaces CO_2 during the Calvin cycle, preventing carbon fixation; this wasteful process dominates when C_3 plants are forced to close their stomata to prevent water loss.

photosynthesis: the complete series of chemical reactions in which the energy of light is used to synthesize high-energy organic molecules, usually carbohydrates, from low-energy inorganic molecules, usually carbon dioxide and water.

photosystem: in thylakoid membranes, a cluster of chlorophyll, accessory pigment molecules, proteins, and other molecules that collectively capture light energy, transfer some of the energy to electrons, and transfer the energetic electrons to an adjacent electron transport chain.

phototropism: growth with respect to the direction of light.

phylogeny (fī-lah′-jen-ē): the evolutionary history of a group of species.

phylum (fī′-lum): in Linnaean classification, the taxonomic rank composed of related classes. Related phyla make up a kingdom.

phytochrome (fī′-tō-krōm): a light-sensitive plant pigment that mediates many plant responses to light, including flowering, stem elongation, and seed germination.

phytoplankton (fī′-tō-plank-ten): photosynthetic protists that are abundant in marine and freshwater environments.

pigment molecule: a light-absorbing, colored molecule, such as chlorophyll, carotenoid, or melanin molecules.

pineal gland (pī-nē′-al): a small gland within the brain that secretes melatonin; controls the seasonal reproductive cycles of some mammals.

pinna: a flap of skin-covered cartilage on the surface of the head that collects sound waves and funnels them to the auditory canal.

pinocytosis (pi-nō-sī-tō′-sis): the nonselective movement of extracellular fluid, enclosed within a vesicle formed from the plasma membrane, into a cell.

pioneer: an organism that is among the first to colonize an unoccupied habitat in the first stages of succession.

pit: an area in the cell walls between two plant cells where the two cells are separated only by a thin, porous cell wall.

pith: cells forming the center of a root or stem.

pituitary gland: an endocrine gland, located at the base of the brain, that produces several hormones, many of which influence the activity of other glands.

placenta (pluh-sen′-tuh): in mammals, a structure formed by a complex interweaving of the uterine lining and the embryonic membranes, especially the chorion; functions in gas, nutrient, and waste exchange between embryonic and maternal circulatory systems, and also secretes the hormones estrogen and progesterone, which are essential to maintaining pregnancy.

placental (pluh-sen′-tul): referring to a mammal possessing a complex placenta (that is, species that are not marsupials or monotremes).

plankton: microscopic organisms that live in marine or freshwater environments; includes phytoplankton and zooplankton.

plant hormone: a chemical produced by specific plants cells that influences the growth, development, or metabolic activity of other cells, typically some distance away in the plant body.

plaque (plak): a deposit of cholesterol and other fatty substances within the wall of an artery.

plasma: the fluid, noncellular portion of the blood.

plasma cell: an antibody-secreting descendant of a B cell.

plasma membrane: the outer membrane of a cell, composed of a bilayer of phospholipids in which proteins are embedded.

plasmid (plaz′-mid): a small, circular piece of DNA located in the cytoplasm of many bacteria; usually does not carry genes required for the normal functioning of the bacterium, but may carry genes, such as those for antibiotic resistance, that assist bacterial survival in certain environments.

plasmodesma (plaz-mō-dez′-muh; pl., plasmodesmata): a cell-to-cell junction in plants that connects the cytoplasm of adjacent cells.

plasmodium (plaz-mō′-dē-um): a sluglike mass of cytoplasm containing thousands of nuclei that are not confined within individual cells.

plastid (plas′-tid): in plant cells, an organelle bounded by two membranes that may be involved in photosynthesis (chloroplasts), pigment storage, or food storage.

plate tectonics: the theory that Earth's crust is divided into irregular plates that are converging, diverging, or slipping by one another; these motions cause continental drift, the movement of continents over Earth's surface.

platelet (plāt′-let): a cell fragment that is formed from megakaryocytes in bone marrow; platelets lack a nucleus; they circulate in the blood and play a role in blood clotting.

pleated sheet: a form of secondary structure exhibited by certain proteins, such as silk, in which many protein chains lie side by side, with hydrogen bonds holding adjacent chains together.

pleiotropy (ple′-ō-trō-pē): a situation in which a single gene influences more than one phenotypic characteristic.

point mutation: a mutation in which a single base pair in DNA has been changed.

polar body: in oogenesis, a small cell, containing a nucleus but virtually no cytoplasm, produced by both the first meiotic division (of the primary oocyte) and the second meiotic division (of the secondary oocyte).

polar covalent bond: a covalent bond with unequal sharing of electrons, such that one atom is relatively negative and the other is relatively positive.

pollen: the male gametophyte of a seed plant; also called a *pollen grain*.

pollen grain: the male gametophyte of a seed plant.

pollination: in flowering plants, when pollen grains land on the stigma of a flower of the same species; in conifers, when pollen grains land within the pollen chamber of a female cone of the same species.

polygenic inheritance: a pattern of inheritance in which the interactions of two or more functionally similar genes determine phenotype.

polymer (pah′-li-mer): a molecule composed of three or more (perhaps thousands) smaller subunits called monomers, which may be identical (for example, the glucose monomers of starch) or different (for example, the amino acids of a protein).

polymerase chain reaction (PCR): a method of producing virtually unlimited numbers of copies of a specific piece of DNA, starting with as little as one copy of the desired DNA.

polyploidy (pahl′-ē-ploid-ē): having more than two sets of homologous chromosomes.

polysaccharide (pahl-ē-sak′-uh-rīd): a large carbohydrate molecule composed of branched or unbranched chains of repeating monosaccharide subunits, normally glucose or modified glucose molecules; includes starches, cellulose, and glycogen.

pons: a portion of the hindbrain, just above the medulla, that contains neurons that influence sleep and the rate and pattern of breathing.

population bottleneck: the result of an event that causes a population to become extremely small; may cause genetic drift that results in changed allele frequencies and loss of genetic variability.

population cycle: regularly recurring, cyclic changes in population size.

population: all the members of a particular species within an ecosystem, found in the same time and place and actually or potentially interbreeding.

positive feedback: a physiological mechanism in which a change causes responses that tend to amplify the original change.

post-anal tail: a tail that extends beyond the anus, and contains muscle tissue and the most posterior part of the nerve cord; found in all chordates at some stage of development.

posterior pituitary: a lobe of the pituitary gland that is an outgrowth of the hypothalamus and that releases antidiuretic hormone and oxytocin.

postmating isolating mechanism: any structure, physiological function, or developmental abnormality that prevents organisms of two different species, once mating has occurred, from producing vigorous, fertile offspring.

postsynaptic neuron: at a synapse, the nerve cell that changes its electrical potential in response to a chemical (the neurotransmitter) released by another (presynaptic) cell.

postsynaptic potential (PSP): an electrical signal produced in a postsynaptic cell by transmission across the synapse; it may be excitatory (EPSP), making the cell more likely to produce an action potential, or inhibitory (IPSP), tending to inhibit an action potential.

potential energy: "stored" energy; normally chemical energy or energy of position within a gravitational field.

prairie: a biome, located in the centers of continents, that primarily supports grasses; also called *grassland*.

precapillary sphincter (sfink´-ter): a ring of smooth muscle between an arteriole and a capillary that regulates the flow of blood into the capillary bed.

predation (pre-dā´-shun): the act of eating another living organism.

predator: an organism that eats other organisms.

prediction: in the scientific method, a statement describing an expected observation or the expected outcome of an experiment, assuming that a specific hypothesis is true.

premating isolating mechanism: any structure, physiological function, or behavior that prevents organisms of two different species from exchanging gametes.

pressure-flow theory: a model for the transport of sugars in phloem; the movement of sugars into a phloem sieve tube causes water to enter the tube by osmosis, while the movement of sugars out of another part of the same sieve tube causes water to leave by osmosis. The resulting pressure gradient causes the bulk movement of water and dissolved sugars from the end of the sieve tube into which sugar is transported (a source) toward the end of the sieve tube from which sugar is removed (a sink).

presynaptic neuron: a nerve cell that releases a chemical (the neurotransmitter) at a synapse, causing changes in the electrical activity of another (postsynaptic) cell.

prey: organisms that are eaten, and often killed, by another organism (a predator).

primary consumer: an organism that feeds on producers; an herbivore

primary electron acceptor: A molecule in the reaction center of each photosystem that accepts an electron from one of the two reaction center chlorophyll *a* molecules and transfers the electron to an adjacent electron transport chain.

primary growth: growth in length and development of the initial structures of plant roots and shoots; results from cell division of apical meristems and differentiation of the daughter cells.

primary oocyte (ō´-ō-sī t): a diploid cell, derived from the oogonium by growth and differentiation, that undergoes meiotic cell division, producing the egg.

primary spermatocyte (sper-ma´-tō-sī t): a diploid cell, derived from the spermatogonium by growth and differentiation, that undergoes meiotic cell division, producing four sperm.

primary structure: the amino acid sequence of a protein.

primary succession: succession that occurs in an environment, such as bare rock, in which no trace of a previous community is present.

primate: a member of the mammalian clade Primates, characterized by the presence of an opposable thumb, forward-facing eyes, and a well-developed cerebral cortex; includes lemurs, monkeys, apes, and humans.

prion (prē´-on): a protein that, in mutated form, acts as an infectious agent that causes certain neurodegenerative diseases, including kuru and scrapie.

producer: a photosynthetic organism; an autotroph.

product: an atom or molecule that is formed from reactants in a chemical reaction.

profundal zone: the part of a lake in which light is insufficient to support photosynthesis.

progesterone (prō-ge´-ster-ōn): a hormone, produced by the corpus luteum in the ovary, that promotes the development of the uterine lining in females.

prokaryote (prō-kar´-ē-ōt): an organism whose cells are prokaryotic (their genetic material is not enclosed in a membrane-bound nucleus and they lack other membrane-bound organelles); bacteria and archaea are prokaryotes.

prokaryotic (prō-kar-ē-ot´-ik): referring to cells of the domains Bacteria or Archaea. Prokaryotic cells have genetic material that is

not enclosed in a membrane-bound nucleus; they also lack other membrane-bound organelles.

prolactin: a hormone, released by the anterior pituitary, that stimulates milk production in human females.

promoter: a specific sequence of DNA at the beginning of a gene, to which RNA polymerase binds and starts gene transcription.

prophase (prō´-fāz): the first stage of mitosis, in which the chromosomes first become visible in the light microscope as thickened, condensed threads and the spindle begins to form; as the spindle is completed, the nuclear envelope breaks apart, and the spindle microtubules invade the nuclear region and attach to the kinetochores of the chromosomes. Also, the first stage of meiosis:In meiosis I, the homologous chromosomes pair up, exchange parts at chiasmata, and attach to spindle microtubules; in meiosis II, the spindle re-forms and chromosomes attach to the microtubules.

prostaglandin (pro-stuh-glan´-din): a family of modified fatty acid hormones manufactured by many cells of the body.

prostate gland (pros´-tāt): a gland that produces part of the fluid component of semen; prostatic fluid is basic and contains a chemical that activates sperm movement.

protease (prō´-tē-ās): an enzyme that digests proteins.

protein: a polymer composed of amino acids joined by peptide bonds.

protist: a eukaryotic organism that is not a plant, animal, or fungus. The term encompasses a diverse array of organisms and does not represent a monophyletic group.

protocell: the hypothetical evolutionary precursor of living cells, consisting of a mixture of organic molecules within a membrane.

proton: a subatomic particle that is found in the nuclei of atoms; it bears a unit of positive charge, and has a relatively large mass, roughly equal to the mass of the neutron.

protonephridium (prō-tō-nef-rid´-ē-um; pl., protonephridia): the functional unit of the excretory system of some invertebrates, such as flatworms; consists of a tubule that has an external opening to the outside of the body, but lacks an internal opening within the body. Fluid is filtered from the body cavity into the tubule by a hollow cell at the end of the tubule, such as a flame cell in flatworms, and released outside the body.

protostome (prō´-tō-stōm): an animal with a mode of embryonic development in which the coelom is derived from splits in the mesoderm; characteristic of arthropods, annelids, and mollusks.

protozoan (prō-tuh-zō´-an; pl., protozoa): a nonphotosynthetic, single-celled protist.

proximal tubule: the initial part of a mammalian nephron, between Bowman's capsule and the loop of Henle; most tubular reabsorption and a small amount of tubular secretion occur in the proximal tubule.

pseudocoelom (soo´-dō-sēl´-ōm): in animals, a "false coelom," that is, a space or cavity, partially but not fully lined with tissue derived from mesoderm, that separates the body wall from the inner organs; found in roundworms.

pseudoplasmodium (soo´-dō-plaz-mō´-dē-um): an aggregation of individual amoeboid cells that form a sluglike mass.

pseudopod (sood´-ō-pod): an extension of the plasma membrane by which certain cells, such as amoebas, locomote and engulf prey.

puberty: a stage of development characterized by sexual maturation, rapid growth, and the appearance of secondary sexual characteristics.

Punnett square method: a method of predicting the genotypes and phenotypes of offspring in genetic crosses.

pupa (pl., pupae): a developmental stage in some insect species in which the organism stops moving and feeding and may be encased in a cocoon; occurs between the larval and the adult phases.

pupil: the adjustable opening in the center of the iris, through which light enters the eye.

quaternary structure (kwat´-er-nuh-rē): the complex three-dimensional structure of a protein consisting of more than one peptide chain.

question: in the scientific method, a statement that identifies a particular aspect of an observation that a scientist wishes to explain.

radial symmetry: a body plan in which any plane along a central axis will divide the body into approximately mirror-image halves. Cnidarians and many adult echinoderms exhibit radial symmetry.

radioactive: pertaining to an atom with an unstable nucleus that spontaneously disintegrates, with the emission of radiation.

radiolarian (rā-dē-ō-lar'-ē-un): a member of a protist group characterized by pseudopods and typically elaborate silica shells. Radiolarians are largely aquatic (mostly marine) and are part of a larger group known as rhizarians.

rain shadow: a local dry area, usually located on the downwind side of a mountain range that blocks the prevailing moisture-bearing winds.

random distribution: the distribution characteristic of populations in which the probability of finding an individual is equal in all parts of an area.

reactant: an atom or molecule that is used up in a chemical reaction to form a product.

reaction center: two chlorophyll *a* molecules and a primary electron acceptor complexed with proteins and located near the center of each photosystem within the thylakoid membrane. Light energy is passed to one of the chlorophylls, which donates an energized electron to the primary electron acceptor, which then passes the electron to an adjacent electron transport chain.

receptor: (1) a protein, located in a membrane or the cytoplasm of a cell, that binds to specific molecules (for example, a hormone or neurotransmitter), triggering a response in the cell, such as endocytosis, changes in metabolic rate, cell division, or electrical changes; (2) a cell that responds to an environmental stimulus (chemicals, sound, light, pH, and so on) by changing its electrical potential.

receptor potential: an electrical potential change in a receptor cell, produced in response to the reception of an environmental stimulus (chemicals, sound, light, heat, and so on). The size of the receptor potential is proportional to the intensity of the stimulus.

receptor protein: a protein, located in a membrane or the cytoplasm of a cell, that binds to specific molecules (for example, a hormone or neurotransmitter), triggering a response in the cell, such as endocytosis, changes in metabolic rate, cell division, or electrical changes.

receptor-mediated endocytosis: the selective uptake of molecules from the extracellular fluid by binding to a receptor located at a coated pit on the plasma membrane and pinching off the coated pit into a vesicle that moves into the cytoplasm.

recessive: an allele that is expressed only in homozygotes and is completely masked in heterozygotes.

recognition protein: a protein or glycoprotein protruding from the outside surface of a plasma membrane that identifies a cell as belonging to a particular species, to a specific individual of that species, and in many cases to one specific organ within the individual.

recombinant DNA: DNA that has been altered by the addition of DNA from a different organism, typically from a different species.

recombination: the formation of new combinations of the different alleles of each gene on a chromosome; the result of crossing over.

rectum: the terminal portion of the vertebrate digestive tube where feces are stored until they are eliminated.

reflex: a simple, stereotyped movement of part of the body that occurs automatically in response to a stimulus.

regeneration: the regrowth of a body part after loss or damage; also, asexual reproduction by means of the regrowth of an entire body from a fragment.

regulatory gene: in prokaryotes, a gene encoding a protein that binds to the operator of one or more operons, controlling the ability of RNA polymerase to transcribe the structural genes of the operon.

regulatory T cell: a type of T cell that suppresses the adaptive immune response, especially by self-reactive lymphocytes, and appears to be important in the prevention of autoimmune disorders.

releasing hormone: a hormone, secreted by the hypothalamus, that causes the release of specific hormones by the anterior pituitary.

renal artery: the artery carrying blood to each kidney.

renal cortex: the outer layer of the kidney, in which the largest portion of each nephron is located, including Bowman's capsule and the distal and proximal tubules.

renal medulla: the layer of the kidney just inside the renal cortex, in which loops of Henle produce a highly concentrated extracellular fluid, allowing the production of concentrated urine.

renal pelvis: the inner chamber of the kidney, in which urine from the collecting ducts accumulates before it enters the ureter.

renal vein: the vein carrying blood away from each kidney.

renin: in mammals, an enzyme that is released by the kidneys when blood pressure falls. Renin catalyzes the formation of angiotensin, which causes arterioles to constrict, thereby elevating blood pressure.

replacement-level fertility (RLF): the average number of offspring per female that is required to maintain a stable population.

repressor protein: in prokaryotes, a protein encoded by a regulatory gene, which binds to the operator of an operon and prevents RNA polymerase from transcribing the structural genes.

reproductive isolation: the failure of organisms of one population to breed successfully with members of another; may be due to premating or postmating isolating mechanisms.

reptile: a member of the chordate group that includes the snakes, lizards, turtles, alligators, birds, and crocodiles.

reservoir: the major source and storage site of a nutrient in an ecosystem, normally in the abiotic portion.

resource partitioning: the coexistence of two species with similar requirements, each occupying a smaller niche than either would if it were by itself; a means of minimizing the species' competitive interactions.

respiration: in terrestrial vertebrates, the act of moving air into the lungs (inhalation) and out of the lungs (exhalation); during respiration, oxygen diffuses from the air in the lungs into the circulatory system and carbon dioxide diffuses from the circulatory system into the air in the lungs.

respiratory center: a cluster of neurons, located in the medulla of the brain, that sends rhythmic bursts of nerve impulses to the respiratory muscles, resulting in breathing.

respiratory membrane: within the lungs, the fusion of the epithelial cells of the alveoli and the endothelial cells that form the walls of surrounding capillaries.

resting potential: an electrical potential, or voltage, in unstimulated nerve cells; the inside of the cell is always negative with respect to the outside.

restriction enzyme: an enzyme, usually isolated from bacteria, that cuts double-stranded DNA at a specific nucleotide sequence; the nucleotide sequence that is cut differs for different restriction enzymes.

restriction fragment length polymorphism (RFLP): a difference in the length of DNA fragments that were produced by cutting samples of DNA from different individuals of the same species with the same set of restriction enzymes; fragment length differences occur because of differences in nucleotide sequences, and hence in the ability of restriction enzymes to cut the DNA, among individuals of the same species.

restriction fragment: a piece of DNA that has been isolated by cleaving a larger piece of DNA with restriction enzymes.

reticular formation (reh-tik'-ū-lar): a diffuse network of neurons extending from the hindbrain, through the midbrain, and into the lower reaches of the forebrain; involved in filtering sensory input and regulating what information is relayed to conscious brain centers for further attention.

retina (ret'-in-uh): a multilayered sheet of nerve tissue at the rear of camera-type eyes, composed of photoreceptor cells plus associated nerve cells that refine the photoreceptor information and transmit it to the optic nerve.

rhizarian: a member of Rhizaria, a protist clade. Rhizarians, which use thin pseudopods to move and capture prey and which often have hard shells, include the foraminiferans and the radiolarians.

ribonucleic acid (RNA) (rī-bō-noo-klā'-ik; RNA): a molecule composed of ribose nucleotides, each of which consists of a phosphate group, the sugar ribose, and one of the bases adenine, cytosine, guanine, or uracil; involved in converting the information in DNA into protein; also the genetic material of some viruses.

ribosomal RNA (rī–bō–sō′–mul; rRNA): a type of RNA that combines with proteins to form ribosomes.

ribosome (rī′–bō–sōm): a complex consisting of two subunits, each composed of ribosomal RNA and protein, found in the cytoplasm of cells or attached to the endoplasmic reticulum, that is the site of protein synthesis, during which the sequence of bases of messenger RNA is translated into the sequence of amino acids in a protein.

ribozyme: an RNA molecule that can catalyze certain chemical reactions, especially those involved in the synthesis and processing of RNA itself.

RNA polymerase: in RNA synthesis, an enzyme that catalyzes the bonding of free RNA nucleotides into a continuous strand, using RNA nucleotides that are complementary to those of the template strand of DNA.

rod: a rod-shaped photoreceptor cell in the vertebrate retina, sensitive to dim light but not involved in color vision; see also *cone*.

root: the part of the plant body, normally underground, that provides anchorage, absorbs water and dissolved nutrients and transports them to the stem, produces some hormones, and in some plants serves as a storage site for carbohydrates.

root cap: a cluster of cells at the tip of a growing root, derived from the apical meristem; protects the growing tip from damage as it burrows through the soil.

root hair: a fine projection from an epidermal cell of a young root that increases the absorptive surface area of the root.

root pressure: pressure within a root caused by the transport of minerals into the vascular cylinder, accompanied by the entry of water by osmosis.

root system: all of the roots of a plant.

round window: a flexible membrane at the end of the cochlea opposite the oval window that allows the fluid in the cochlea to move in response to movements of the oval window.

rubisco: in the carbon fixation step of the Calvin cycle, the enzyme that catalyzes the reaction between ribulose bisphosphate (RuBP) and carbon dioxide, thereby fixing the carbon of carbon dioxide in an organic molecule; short for ribulose bisphosphate carboxylase.

ruminant (roo′-min-ant): an herbivorous animal with a digestive tract that includes multiple stomach chambers, one of which contains cellulose-digesting bacteria, and that regurgitates the contents ("cud") of the first chamber for additional chewing ("ruminating").

S-curve: the S-shaped growth curve produced by logistic population growth, usually describing a population of organisms introduced into a new area; consists of an initial period of exponential growth, followed by a decreasing growth rate, and finally, relative stability around a growth rate of zero.

sac fungus: a member of the fungus phylum Ascomycota, whose members form spores in a saclike case called an ascus.

saccule: a patch of hair cells in the vestibule of the inner ear; bending of the hairs of the hair cells permits detection of the direction of gravity and the degree of tilt of the head.

sapwood: young secondary xylem that transports water and minerals in a tree trunk.

sarcomere (sark′-ō-mēr): the unit of contraction of a muscle fiber; a subunit of the myofibril, consisting of thick and thin filaments, bounded by Z lines.

sarcoplasmic reticulum (sark′-ō-plas′-mik re-tik′-ū-lum; SR): the specialized endoplasmic reticulum in muscle cells; forms interconnected hollow tubes. The sarcoplasmic reticulum stores calcium ions and releases them into the interior of the muscle cell, initiating contraction.

saturated: referring to a fatty acid with as many hydrogen atoms as possible bonded to the carbon backbone (therefore, a saturated fatty acid has no double bonds in its carbon backbone).

savanna: a biome that is dominated by grasses and supports scattered trees; typically has a rainy season during which most of the year's precipitation falls, followed by a dry season during which virtually no precipitation occurs.

scientific method: a rigorous procedure for making observations of specific phenomena and searching for the order underlying those phenomena.

scientific name: the two-part Latin name of a species; consists of the genus name followed by the species name.

scientific theory of evolution: the theory that modern organisms descended, with modification, from preexisting life-forms.

scientific theory: a general explanation of natural phenomena developed through extensive and reproducible observations; more general and reliable than a hypothesis.

sclera: a tough, white connective tissue layer that covers the outside of the eyeball and forms the white of the eye.

sclerenchyma (skler-en′-ki-muh): a plant cell type with thick, hardened cell walls that normally dies as the last stage of differentiation; may support or protect the plant body.

scramble competition: a free-for-all scramble for limited resources among individuals of the same species.

scrotum (skrō′-tum): in male mammals, the pouch of skin containing the testes.

second law of thermodynamics: the principle of physics that states that any change in a closed system causes the quantity of concentrated, useful energy to decrease and the amount of randomness and disorder (entropy) to increase.

second messenger: an intracellular chemical, such as cyclic AMP, that is synthesized or released within a cell in response to the binding of a hormone or neurotransmitter (the first messenger) to receptors on the cell surface; brings about specific changes in the metabolism of the cell.

secondary consumer: an organism that feeds on primary consumers; a carnivore.

secondary growth: growth in the diameter and strength of a stem or root due to cell division in lateral meristems and differentiation of their daughter cells.

secondary oocyte (ō′-ō-sīt): a large haploid cell derived from the diploid primary oocyte by meiosis I.

secondary spermatocyte (sper-ma′-tō-sīt): a large haploid cell derived from the diploid primary spermatocyte by meiosis I.

secondary structure: a repeated, regular structure assumed by a protein chain, held together by hydrogen bonds; for example, a helix.

secondary succession: succession that occurs after an existing community is disturbed—for example, after a forest fire; secondary succession is much more rapid than primary succession.

secretin: a hormone produced by the small intestine that stimulates the production and release of digestive secretions by the pancreas and liver.

seed: the reproductive structure of a seed plant, protected by a seed coat; contains an embryonic plant and a supply of food for it.

seed coat: the thin, tough, and waterproof outermost covering of a seed, formed from the integuments of the ovule.

segmentation (seg-men-tā′-shun): an animal body plan in which the body is divided into repeated, typically similar units.

selectively permeable: the quality of a membrane that allows certain molecules or ions to move through it more readily than others.

self-fertilization: the union of sperm and egg from the same individual.

semen: the sperm-containing fluid produced by the male reproductive tract.

semicircular canal: in the inner ear, one of three fluid-filled tubes, each with a bulge at one end containing a patch of hair cells; movement of the head moves fluid in the canal and consequently bends the hairs of the hair cells.

semiconservative replication: the process of replication of the DNA double helix; the two DNA strands separate, and each is used as a template for the synthesis of a complementary DNA strand. Consequently, each daughter double helix consists of one parental strand and one new strand.

semilunar valve: a valve located between the right ventricle of the heart and the pulmonary artery, or between the left ventricle and the aorta; prevents the backflow of blood into the ventricles when they relax.

seminal vesicle: in male mammals, a gland that produces a basic, fructose-containing fluid that forms part of the semen.

seminiferous tubule (sem-i-ni′-fer-us): in the vertebrate testis, a series of tubes in which sperm are produced.

senescence: in plants, a specific aging process, typically including deterioration and the dropping of leaves and flowers.

sensory neuron: a nerve cell that responds to a stimulus from the internal or external environment.

sensory receptor: a cell (typically, a neuron) specialized to respond to particular internal or external environmental stimuli by producing an electrical potential.

sepal (sē′-pul): one of the group of modified leaves that surrounds and protects a flower bud; in dicots, usually develops into a green, leaflike structure when the flower blooms; in monocots, usually similar to a petal.

septum (pl., **septa**)**:** a partition that separates the fungal hypha into individual cells; pores in septa allow the transfer of materials between cells.

Sertoli cell: in the seminiferous tubule, a large cell that regulates spermatogenesis and nourishes the developing sperm.

severe combined immune deficiency (SCID): a disorder in which no immune cells, or very few, are formed; the immune system is incapable of responding properly to invading disease organisms, and the individual is very vulnerable to common infections.

sex chromosome: either of the pair of chromosomes that usually determines the sex of an organism; for example, the X and Y chromosomes in mammals.

sex-linked: referring to a pattern of inheritance characteristic of genes located on one type of sex chromosome (for example, X) and not found on the other type (for example, Y); in mammals, in almost all cases, the gene controlling the trait is on the X chromosome, so this pattern is often called X-linked. In X-linked inheritance, females show the dominant trait unless they are homozygous recessive, whereas males express whichever allele, dominant or recessive, that is found on their single X chromosome.

sexual reproduction: a form of reproduction in which genetic material from two parent organisms is combined in the offspring; usually, two haploid gametes fuse to form a diploid zygote.

sexual selection: a type of natural selection that acts on traits involved in finding and acquiring mates.

sexually transmitted disease (STD): a disease that is passed from person to person by sexual contact; also known as *sexually transmitted infection (STI)*.

shoot system: all the parts of a vascular plant exclusive of the root; normally aboveground. Consists of stem, leaves, buds, and (in season) flowers and fruits; functions include photosynthesis, transport of materials, reproduction, and hormone synthesis.

short tandem repeat (STR): a DNA sequence consisting of a short sequence of nucleotides (usually 2 to 5 nucleotides in length) repeated multiple times, with all of the repetitions side by side on a chromosome; variations in the number of repeats of a standardized set of 13 STRs produce DNA profiles used to identify people by their DNA.

short-day plant: a plant that will flower only if the length of uninterrupted darkness exceeds a species-specific critical period; also called a *long-night plant*.

sickle-cell anemia: a recessive disease caused by a single amino acid substitution in the hemoglobin molecule. Sickle-cell hemoglobin molecules tend to cluster together, distorting the shape of red blood cells and causing them to break and clog capillaries.

sieve plate: in plants, a structure between two adjacent sieve-tube elements in phloem, where holes formed in the cell walls interconnect the cytoplasm of the sieve-tube elements.

sieve-tube element: in phloem, one of the cells of a sieve tube.

simple diffusion: the diffusion of water, dissolved gases, or lipid-soluble molecules through the phospholipid bilayer of a cellular membrane.

simple epithelium: a type of epithelial tissue, one cell layer thick, that lines many hollow organs such as those of the respiratory, digestive, urinary, reproductive, and circulatory systems.

sink: in plants, any structure that uses up sugars or converts sugars to starch, and toward which phloem fluids will flow.

sinoatrial (SA) node (sī′-nō-āt′-rē-ul nōd): a small mass of specialized muscle in the wall of the right atrium; generates electrical signals rhythmically and spontaneously and serves as the heart's pacemaker.

skeletal muscle: the type of muscle that is attached to and moves the skeleton and is under the direct, normally voluntary, control of the nervous system; also called *striated muscle*.

skeleton: a supporting structure for the body, on which muscles act to change the body configuration; may be external or internal.

small intestine: the portion of the digestive tract, located between the stomach and large intestine, in which most digestion and absorption of nutrients occur.

smooth muscle: the type of muscle that surrounds hollow organs, such as the digestive tract, bladder, and blood vessels; not striped in appearance (hence the name "smooth") and normally not under voluntary control.

solute: a substance dissolved in a solvent.

solution: a solvent containing one or more dissolved substances (solutes).

solvent: a liquid capable of dissolving (uniformly dispersing) other substances in itself.

somatic nervous system: that portion of the peripheral nervous system that controls voluntary movement by activating skeletal muscles.

source: in plants, any structure that actively synthesizes sugar, and away from which phloem fluid will be transported.

spawning: a method of external fertilization in which male and female parents shed gametes into water, and sperm must swim through the water to reach the eggs.

speciation: the process of species formation, in which a single species splits into two or more species.

species (spē′-sēs): the basic unit of taxonomic classification, consisting of a population or group of populations that evolves independently of other populations. In sexually reproducing organisms, a species can be defined as a population or group of populations of organisms that interbreed freely with one another under natural conditions but that do not interbreed with members of other populations.

specific heat: the amount of energy required to raise the temperature of 1 gram of a substance by 1°C.

sperm: the haploid male gamete, normally small, motile, and containing little cytoplasm.

spermatid: a haploid cell derived from the secondary spermatocyte by meiosis II; differentiates into the mature sperm.

spermatogenesis: the process by which sperm cells form.

spermatogonium (pl., **spermatogonia**)**:** a diploid cell, lining the walls of the seminiferous tubules, that gives rise to a primary spermatocyte.

spermatophore: a package of sperm formed by the males of some invertebrate animals; the spermatophore can be inserted into the female reproductive tract, where it releases its sperm.

sphincter muscle: a circular ring of muscle surrounding a tubular structure, such as the esophagus, stomach, or intestine; contraction and relaxation of a sphincter muscle controls the movement of materials through the tube.

spinal cord: the part of the central nervous system of vertebrates that extends from the base of the brain to the hips and is protected by the bones of the vertebral column; contains the cell bodies of motor neurons that form synapses with skeletal muscles, the circuitry for some simple reflex behaviors, and axons that communicate with the brain.

spindle microtubule: microtubules organized in a spindle shape that separate chromosomes during mitosis or meiosis.

spiracle (spi′-ruh-kul): an opening in the body wall of insects through which air enters the tracheae.

spleen: the largest organ of the lymphatic system, located in the abdominal cavity; contains macrophages that filter the blood by removing microbes and aged red blood cells, and lymphocytes (B and T cells) that reproduce during times of infection.

spongy bone: porous, lightweight bone tissue in the interior of bones; the location of bone marrow. Compare with *compact bone.*

spontaneous generation: the proposal that living organisms can arise from nonliving matter.

sporangium (spor-an′-jē-um; pl., **sporangia):** a structure in which spores are produced.

spore: (1) in plants and fungi, a haploid cell capable of developing into an adult without fusing with another cell (without fertilization); (2) in bacteria and some other organisms, a stage of the life cycle that is resistant to extreme environmental conditions.

sporophyte (spor′-ō-fīt): the multicellular diploid stage in the life cycle of a plant; produces haploid, asexual spores through meiosis.

stabilizing selection: a type of natural selection that favors the average phenotype in a population.

stamen (stā′-men): the male reproductive structure of a flower, consisting of a filament and an anther, in which pollen grains develop.

starch: a polysaccharide that is composed of branched or unbranched chains of glucose molecules; used by plants as a carbohydrate-storage molecule.

start codon: the first AUG codon in a messenger RNA molecule.

startle coloration: a form of mimicry in which a color pattern (in many cases resembling large eyes) can be displayed suddenly by a prey organism when approached by a predator.

stem: the portion of the plant body, normally located aboveground, that bears leaves and reproductive structures such as flowers and fruit.

stem cell: an undifferentiated cell that is capable of dividing and giving rise to one or more distinct types of differentiated cell(s).

sterilization: a generally permanent method of contraception in which the pathways through which the sperm (vas deferens) or egg (oviducts) must travel are interrupted; the most effective form of contraception.

steroid: a lipid consisting of four fused carbon rings, with various functional groups attached.

steroid hormone: a class of hormone whose chemical structure (four fused carbon rings with various functional groups) resembles cholesterol; steroids, which are lipids, are secreted by the ovaries and placenta, the testes, and the adrenal cortex.

stigma (stig′-muh): the pollen-capturing tip of a carpel.

stirrup: the third of the small bones of the middle ear, linking the tympanic membrane with the oval window; the stirrup is directly connected to the oval window; also called the *stapes.*

stoma (stō′-muh; pl., **stomata):** an adjustable opening in the epidermis of a leaf or young stem, surrounded by a pair of guard cells, that regulates the diffusion of carbon dioxide and water into and out of the leaf or stem.

stomach: the muscular sac between the esophagus and small intestine where food is stored and mechanically broken down and in which protein digestion begins.

stop codon: a codon in messenger RNA that stops protein synthesis and causes the completed protein chain to be released from the ribosome.

stramenopile: a member of Stramenopila, a large protist clade. Stramenopiles, which are characterized by hair-like projections on their flagella, include the water molds, the diatoms, and the brown algae.

strand: a single polymer of nucleotides; DNA is composed of two strands wound about each other in a double helix; RNA is usually single stranded.

stratified epithelium: a type of epithelial tissue composed of several cell layers, usually strong and waterproof; mostly found on the surface of the skin.

stroke: an interruption of blood flow to part of the brain caused by the rupture of an artery or the blocking of an artery by a blood clot. Loss of blood supply leads to rapid death of the area of the brain affected.

stroma (strō′-muh): the semifluid material inside chloroplasts in which the thylakoids are located; the site of the reactions of the Calvin cycle.

structural gene: in the prokaryotic operon, the genes that encode enzymes or other cellular proteins.

style: a stalk connecting the stigma of a carpel with the ovary at its base.

subclimax: a community in which succession is stopped before the climax community is reached; it is maintained by regular disturbance—for example, a tallgrass prairie maintained by periodic fires.

substrate: the atoms or molecules that are the reactants for an enzyme-catalyzed chemical reaction.

succession (suk-seh′-shun): a structural change in a community and its nonliving environment over time. During succession, species replace one another in a somewhat predictable manner until a stable, self-sustaining climax community is reached.

sucrose: a disaccharide composed of glucose and fructose.

sugar-phosphate backbone: a chain of sugars and phosphates in DNA and RNA; the sugar of one nucleotide bonds to the phosphate of the next nucleotide in a DNA or RNA strand. The bases in DNA or RNA are attached to the sugars of the backbone.

sugar: a simple carbohydrate molecule, either a monosaccharide or a disaccharide.

surface tension: the property of a liquid to resist penetration by objects at its interface with the air, due to cohesion between molecules of the liquid.

survivorship curve: the curve that results when the number of individuals of each age in a population is graphed against their age, usually expressed as a percentage of their maximum life span.

survivorship table: a data table that groups organisms born at the same time and tracks them throughout their life span, recording how many continue to survive in each succeeding year (or other unit of time). Various parameters such as sex may be used in the groupings. Human life tables may include many other parameters (such as socioeconomic status) used by demographers.

sustainable development: human activities that meet present needs for a reasonable quality of life without exceeding nature's limits and without compromising the ability of future generations to meet their needs.

sympathetic division: the division of the autonomic nervous system that produces largely involuntary responses that prepare the body for stressful or highly energetic situations; often called the *sympathetic nervous system.*

sympatric speciation (sim-pat′-rik): the process by which new species arise in populations that are not physically divided; the genetic isolation required for sympatric speciation may be due to ecological isolation or chromosomal aberrations (such as polyploidy).

synapse (sin′-aps): the site of communication between nerve cells. At a synapse, one cell (presynaptic) normally releases a chemical (the neurotransmitter) that changes the electrical potential of the second (postsynaptic) cell.

synaptic cleft: in a synapse, a small gap between the presynaptic and postsynaptic neurons.

synaptic terminal: a swelling at the branched ending of an axon; where the axon forms a synapse.

syphilis (si′-ful-is): a sexually transmitted bacterial infection of the reproductive organs; if untreated, can damage the nervous and circulatory systems.

systematics: the branch of biology concerned with reconstructing phylogenies and with naming clades.

systolic pressure (sis′-tal-ik): the blood pressure measured at the peak of contraction of the ventricles; the higher of the two blood pressure readings.

T cell: a type of lymphocyte that matures in the thymus, and that recognizes and destroys specific foreign cells or substances or that regulates other cells of the immune system.

T tubule: a deep infolding of the muscle plasma membrane; conducts the action potential inside a cell.

T-cell receptor: a protein receptor, located on the surface of a T cell, that binds a specific antigen and triggers the immune response of the T cell.

taiga (tī′-guh): a biome with long, cold winters and only a few months of warm weather; dominated by evergreen coniferous trees; also called *northern coniferous forest.*

taproot system: a root system, commonly found in dicots, that consists of a long, thick main root and many smaller lateral roots that grow from the main root.

target cell: a cell on which a particular hormone exerts its effect.

taste bud: a cluster of taste receptor cells and supporting cells that is located in a small pit beneath the surface of the tongue and that communicates with the mouth through a small pore.

taxonomy (tax-on′-uh-mē): the branch of biology concerned with naming and classifying organisms.

tectorial membrane (tek-tor′-ē-ul): one of the membranes of the cochlea in which the hairs of the hair cells are embedded. In sound reception, movement of the basilar membrane relative to the tectorial membrane bends the hairs.

telomere (tē-le-mēr): the nucleotides at the end of a chromosome that protect the chromosome from damage during condensation, and prevent the end of one chromosome from attaching to the end of another chromosome.

telophase (tēl-ō-fāz): in mitosis and both divisions of meiosis, the final stage, in which the spindle fibers usually disappear, nuclear envelopes re-form, and cytokinesis generally occurs. In mitosis and meiosis II, the chromosomes also relax from their condensed form.

temperate deciduous forest: a biome having cold winters and warm summers, with enough summer rainfall for trees to grow and shade out grasses; characterized by trees that drop their leaves in winter (deciduous trees), an adaptation that minimizes water loss when the soil is frozen.

temperate rain forest: a temperate biome with abundant liquid water year-round, dominated by conifers.

template strand: the strand of the DNA double helix from which RNA is transcribed.

tendon: a tough connective tissue band connecting a muscle to a bone.

terminal bud: meristem tissue and surrounding leaf primordia that are located at the tip of a plant shoot or a branch.

territoriality: the defense of an area in which important resources are located.

tertiary consumer (ter′-shē-er-ē): a carnivore that feeds on other carnivores (secondary consumers).

tertiary structure (ter′-shē-er-ē): the complex three-dimensional structure of a single peptide chain; held in place by disulfide bonds between cysteines.

test cross: a breeding experiment in which an individual showing the dominant phenotype is mated with an individual that is homozygous recessive for the same gene. The ratio of offspring with dominant versus recessive phenotypes can be used to determine the genotype of the phenotypically dominant individual.

testis (pl., testes): the gonad of male animals.

testosterone: in vertebrates, a hormone produced by the interstitial cells of the testis; stimulates spermatogenesis and the development of male secondary sex characteristics.

thalamus: the part of the forebrain that relays sensory information to many parts of the brain.

therapeutic cloning: the production of a clone for medical purposes. Typically, the nucleus from one of a patient's own cells would be inserted into an egg whose nucleus had been removed; the resulting cell would divide and produce embryonic stem cells that would be compatible with the patient's tissues and therefore would not be rejected by the patient's immune system.

thick filament: in the sarcomere, a bundle of myosin that interacts with thin filaments, producing muscle contraction.

thigmotropism: growth in response to touch.

thin filament: in the sarcomere, a protein strand that interacts with thick filaments, producing muscle contraction; composed primarily of actin, plus the accessory proteins troponin and tropomyosin.

threatened species: all species classified as critically endangered, endangered, or vulnerable.

threshold: the electrical potential at which an action potential is triggered; the threshold is usually about 10 to 20 mV less negative than the resting potential.

thrombin: an enzyme produced in the blood as a result of injury to a blood vessel; catalyzes the production of fibrin, a protein that assists in blood clot formation.

thylakoid (thī′-luh-koid): a disk-shaped, membranous sac found in chloroplasts, the membranes of which contain the photosystems, electron transport chains, and ATP-synthesizing enzymes used in the light reactions of photosynthesis.

thymine (T): a nitrogenous base found only in DNA; abbreviated as T.

thymosin (thī-mō-sin): a hormone, secreted by the thymus, that stimulates the maturation of T lymphocytes of the immune system.

thymus (thī′-mus): an organ of the lymphatic system that is located in the upper chest in front of the heart and that secretes thymosin, which stimulates maturation of T lymphocytes of the immune system.

thyroid gland: an endocrine gland, located in front of the larynx in the neck, that secretes the hormones thyroxine (affecting metabolic rate) and calcitonin (regulating calcium ion concentration in the blood).

thyroid-stimulating hormone (TSH): a hormone, released by the anterior pituitary, that stimulates the thyroid gland to release hormones.

thyroxine (thī-rox′-in): a hormone, secreted by the thyroid gland, that stimulates and regulates metabolism.

tight junction: a type of cell-to-cell junction in animals that prevents the movement of materials through the spaces between cells.

tissue: a group of (normally similar) cells that together carry out a specific function; a tissue may also include extracellular material produced by its cells.

tissue system: a group of two or more tissues that together perform a specific function.

tonsil: a patch of lymphatic tissue, located at the entrance to the pharynx, that contains macrophages and lymphocytes; destroys many microbes entering the body through the mouth and stimulates an adaptive immune response to them.

trachea (trā′-kē-uh): in terrestrial vertebrates, a flexible tube, supported by rings of cartilage, that conducts air between the larynx and the bronchi.

tracheae (tra-ke-ē): the respiratory organ of insects, consisting of a set of air-filled tubes leading from openings in the body called spiracles and branching extensively throughout the body.

tracheid (trā′-kē-id): an elongated cell type in xylem, with tapered ends that overlap the tapered ends of other tracheids, forming tubes that transport water and minerals. Pits in the cell walls of tracheids allow easy movement of water and minerals into and out of the cells, including from one tracheid to the next.

trans fat: a type of fat produced during the process of hydrogenating oils that may increase the risk of heart disease. The fatty acids of trans fats include an unusual configuration of double bonds that is not normally found in fats of biological origin.

transcription: the synthesis of an RNA molecule from a DNA template.

transfer RNA (tRNA): a type of RNA that binds to a specific amino acid, carries it to a ribosome, and positions it for incorporation into the growing protein chain during protein synthesis. A set of three bases in tRNA (the anticodon) is complementary to the set of three bases in mRNA (the codon) that codes for that specific amino acid in the genetic code.

transformation: a method of acquiring new genes, whereby DNA from one bacterium (normally released after the death of the bacterium) becomes incorporated into the DNA of another, living, bacterium.

transgenic: referring to an animal or a plant that contains DNA derived from another species, usually inserted into the organism through genetic engineering.

translation: the process whereby the sequence of bases of messenger RNA is converted into the sequence of amino acids of a protein.

translocation: a mutation that occurs when a piece of DNA is removed from one chromosome and attached to another chromosome.

transpiration (trans'-per-ā-shun): the evaporation of water through the stomata, chiefly in leaves.

transport protein: a protein that regulates the movement of water-soluble molecules through the plasma membrane.

trial-and-error learning: a type of learning in which behavior is modified in response to the positive or negative consequences of an action.

trichomoniasis (trik-ō-mō-nī'-uh-sis): a sexually transmitted disease, caused by the protist *Trichomonas*, that causes inflammation of the mucous membranes that line the urinary tract and genitals.

triglyceride (trī-glis'-er-ī d): a lipid composed of three fatty-acid molecules bonded to a single glycerol molecule.

trisomy 21: see *Down syndrome.*

trisomy X: a condition of females who have three X chromosomes instead of the normal two; most such women are phenotypically normal and are fertile.

trophic level: literally, "feeding level"; the categories of organisms in a community, and the position of an organism in a food chain, defined by the organism's source of energy; includes producers, primary consumers, secondary consumers, and so on.

tropical deciduous forest: a biome, warm all year-round, with pronounced wet and dry seasons; characterized by trees that shed their leaves during the dry season (deciduous trees), an adaptation that minimizes water loss.

tropical rain forest: a biome with evenly warm, evenly moist conditions year-round, dominated by broadleaf evergreen trees; the most diverse biome.

tropical scrub forest: a biome, warm all year-round, with pronounced wet and dry seasons (drier conditions than in tropical deciduous forests); characterized by short, deciduous, often thorn-bearing trees with grasses growing beneath them.

true-breeding: pertaining to an individual all of whose offspring produced through self-fertilization are identical to the parental type. True-breeding individuals are homozygous for a given trait.

tube cell: the outermost cell of a pollen grain, containing the sperm. When the pollen grain germinates, the tube cell produces a tube penetrating through the tissues of the carpel, from the stigma, through the style, and to the opening of an ovule in the ovary.

tubular reabsorption: the process by which cells of the tubule of the nephron remove water and nutrients from the filtrate within the tubule and return those substances to the blood.

tubular secretion: the process by which cells of the tubule of the nephron remove wastes from the blood, actively secreting those wastes into the tubule.

tubule (toob'-ūl): the tubular portion of the nephron; includes a proximal portion, the loop of Henle, and a distal portion. Urine is formed from the blood filtrate as it passes through the tubule.

tundra: a biome with severe weather conditions (extreme cold and wind, and little rainfall) that cannot support trees.

turgor pressure: pressure developed within a cell (especially the central vacuole of plant cells) as a result of osmotic water entry.

Turner syndrome: a set of characteristics typical of a woman with only one X chromosome; women with Turner syndrome are sterile, with a tendency to be very short and to lack typical female secondary sexual characteristics.

tympanic membrane (tim-pan'-ik): the eardrum; a membrane that stretches across the opening of the middle ear and transmits vibrations to the bones of the middle ear.

unicellular: single-celled; most members of the domains Bacteria and Archaea and the kingdom Protista are unicellular.

uniform distribution: the distribution characteristic of a population with a relatively regular spacing of individuals, commonly as a result of territorial behavior.

unsaturated: referring to a fatty acid with fewer than the maximum number of hydrogen atoms bonded to its carbon backbone (therefore, an unsaturated fatty acid has one or more double bonds in its carbon backbone).

upwelling: an upward flow that brings cold, nutrient-laden water from the ocean depths to the surface.

urea (ū-rē'-uh): a water-soluble, nitrogen-containing waste product of amino acid breakdown; one of the principal components of mammalian urine.

ureter (ū'-re-ter): a tube that conducts urine from a kidney to the urinary bladder.

urethra (ū-rē'-thruh): the tube leading from the urinary bladder to the outside of the body; in males, the urethra also receives sperm from the vas deferens and conducts both sperm and urine (at different times) to the tip of the penis.

urinary system: the organ system that produces, stores, and eliminates urine, which contains cellular wastes, excess water and nutrients, and toxic or foreign substances. The urinary system is critical for maintaining homeostatic conditions within the bloodstream. In mammals, it includes the kidneys, ureters, bladder, and urethra.

urine: the fluid produced and excreted by the urinary system, containing water and dissolved wastes, such as urea.

uterine tube: the tube leading from the ovary to the uterus, into which the secondary oocyte (egg cell) is released; also called the *oviduct,* or, in humans, the *Fallopian tube.*

uterus: in female mammals, the part of the reproductive tract that houses the embryo during pregnancy.

utricle: a patch of hair cells in the vestibule of the inner ear; bending of the hairs of the hair cells permits detection of the direction of gravity and the degree of tilt of the head.

vaccine: an injection into the body that contains antigens characteristic of a particular disease organism and that stimulates an immune response appropriate to that disease organism.

vacuole (vak'-ū-ōl): a vesicle that is typically large and consists of a single membrane enclosing a fluid-filled space.

vagina: the passageway leading from the outside of a female mammal's body to the cervix of the uterus; serves as the receptacle for semen and as the birth canal.

variable: a factor in a scientific experiment that is deliberately manipulated in order to test a hypothesis.

variable region: the part of an antibody molecule that differs among antibodies; the ends of the variable regions of the light and heavy chains form the specific binding site for antigens.

vas deferens (vaz de'-fer-enz): the tube connecting the epididymis of the testis with the urethra.

vascular bundle: a strand of xylem and phloem in leaves and stems; in leaves, commonly called a *vein.*

vascular cambium: a lateral meristem that is located between the xylem and phloem of a woody root or stem and that gives rise to secondary xylem and phloem.

vascular cylinder: the centrally located conducting tissue of a young root; consists of primary xylem and phloem, surrounded by a layer of pericycle cells.

vascular plant (vas'-kū-lar): a plant that has conducting vessels for transporting liquids; also called a tracheophyte.

vascular tissue system: a plant tissue system consisting of xylem (which transports water and minerals from root to shoot) and phloem (which transports water and sugars throughout the plant).

vein: in vertebrates, a large-diameter, thin-walled vessel that carries blood from venules back to the heart; in plants, a vascular bundle in a leaf.

ventricle (ven'-tre-kul): the lower muscular chamber on each side of the heart that pumps blood out through the arteries. The right ventricle sends blood to the lungs; the left ventricle pumps blood to the rest of the body.

venule (ven'-ūl): a narrow vessel with thin walls that carries blood from capillaries to veins.

vertebral column (ver-tē'-brul): a column of serially arranged skeletal units (the vertebrae) that enclose the nerve cord in vertebrates; the backbone.

vertebrate: an animal that has a vertebral column.

vesicle (ves'-i-kul): a small, membrane-bound sac within the cytoplasm.

vessel: in plants, a tube of xylem composed of vertically stacked vessel elements with heavily perforated or missing end walls, leaving a continuous, uninterrupted hollow cylinder.

vessel element: one of the cells of a xylem vessel; elongated, dead at maturity, with thick lateral cell walls for support but with end walls that are either heavily perforated or missing.

vestibular apparatus: part of the inner ear, consisting of the vestibule and the semicircular canals, involved in the detection of gravity, tilt of the head, and movement of the head.

vestigial structure (ves-tij´-ē-ul): a structure that serves no apparent purpose but is homologous to functional structures in related organisms and provides evidence of evolution.

villus (vi´-lus; pl., villi): a finger-like projection of the wall of the small intestine that increases its absorptive surface area.

viroid (vī´-roid): a particle of RNA that is capable of infecting a cell and of directing the production of more viroids; responsible for certain plant diseases.

virus (vī´-rus): a noncellular parasitic particle that consists of a protein coat surrounding genetic material; multiplies only within a cell of a living organism (the host).

vitamin: one of a group of diverse chemicals that must be present in trace amounts in the diet to maintain health; used by the body in conjunction with enzymes in a variety of metabolic reactions.

vitreous humor (vit´-rē-us): a clear, jelly-like substance that fills the large chamber of the eye between the lens and the retina; helps to maintain the shape of the eyeball.

vocal cords: a pair of bands of elastic tissue that extend across the opening of the larynx and produce sound when air is forced between them. Muscles alter the tension on the vocal cords and control the size and shape of the opening, which in turn determines whether sound is produced and what its pitch will be.

vulnerable species: a species that is likely to become endangered unless conditions that threaten its survival improve.

waggle dance: a symbolic form of communication used by honeybee foragers to communicate the location of a food source to their hive mates.

warning coloration: bright coloration that warns predators that the potential prey is distasteful or even poisonous.

water mold: a member of a protist group that includes species with filamentous shapes that give them a superficially fungus-like appearance. Water molds, which include species that cause economically important plant diseases, are part of a larger group known as the stramenopiles.

wax: a lipid composed of fatty acids covalently bonded to long-chain alcohols.

weather: short-term fluctuations in temperature, humidity, cloud cover, wind, and precipitation in a region over periods of hours to days.

wetland: a region (sometimes called a marsh, swamp, or bog) in which the soil is covered by, or saturated with, water for a significant part of the year.

white matter: the portion of the brain and spinal cord that consists largely of myelin-covered axons and that gives these areas a white appearance.

wildlife corridor: a strip of protected land linking larger areas. Wildlife corridors allow animals to move freely and safely between habitats that would otherwise be isolated by human activities.

work: energy transferred to an object, usually causing the object to move.

working memory: the first phase of learning; short-term memory that is electrical or biochemical in nature.

X chromosome: the female sex chromosome in mammals and some insects.

xylem (zī-lum): a conducting tissue of vascular plants that transports water and minerals from root to shoot.

Y chromosome: the male sex chromosome in mammals and some insects.

yolk: protein-rich or lipid-rich substances contained in eggs that provide food for the developing embryo.

yolk sac: one of the embryonic membranes of reptiles (including birds) and mammals. In reptiles, the yolk sac is a membrane surrounding the yolk in the egg; in mammals, it forms part of the umbilical cord and the digestive tract but does not contain yolk.

Z line: a fibrous protein structure to which the thin filaments of skeletal muscle are attached; forms the boundary of a sarcomere.

zona pellucida (pel-oo´-si-duh): a clear, noncellular layer between the corona radiata and the egg.

zooplankton: nonphotosynthetic protists that are abundant in marine and freshwater environments.

zygomycete: a fungus of the phylum Zygomycota, which includes the species that cause fruit rot and bread mold.

zygosporangium (zī´-gō-spor-an-jee-um): a tough, resistant reproductive structure produced by fungi in the phylum Zygomycota; encloses diploid nuclei that undergo meiosis and give rise to haploid spores.

zygote (zī´-gōt): in sexual reproduction, a diploid cell (the fertilized egg) formed by the fusion of two haploid gametes.

Answers to Selected Questions

Chapter 1

Figure Caption Questions

Figure 1-1 Global warming will impact the entire biosphere. The growing human population—whose energy use is driving global warming and whose demand for space and resources is causing widespread habitat destruction—would also be an appropriate answer.

Figure 1-3 You might answer "no" at this point, but keep this art in mind as you read the section on endosymbiosis in Chapter 17.

Figure 1-5 The antibacterial chemicals produced by fungi probably evolved because they improved the fungi's ability to compete with bacteria for access to resources such as food and space (by excluding bacteria from areas where the fungi are present).

Figure E1-1 Redi's experiment demonstrated that the maggots were caused by something that was excluded by a gauze cover, but the possibility remained that some agent other than flies produced the maggots. An effective follow-up experiment might involve a series of closed, meat-containing systems that were identical in all respects other than the addition of a single possible causal element. Perhaps one container would have flies added, one roaches, one dust or soot, and so on. And, of course, a control would have nothing added.

Fill-in-the-Blank

1. atom; cell; carbon, organic molecules; tissues
2. scientific theory; hypothesis; scientific method
3. evolution; natural selection
4. deoxyribonucleic acid, DNA; genes
5. homeostasis; stimuli; energy, materials; organized, complex

Chapter 2

Figure Caption Questions

Figure 2-2 Atoms with outer shells that are not full are unstable. They become stable by filling (or emptying) their outer shells. Except for hydrogen, atoms in biological molecules have outer shells that are stable when filled with eight electrons.

Figure 2-4 Free radicals have atoms (often oxygen atoms) with one or more unpaired electrons in their outer shells, making them very unstable and causing them to capture electrons from nearby molecules to complete their outer shells. This can cause damage to biological molecules, including DNA, which are critical to proper cellular functioning.

Figure E2-2 Go to Table 2-1 and compare the atomic mass of H_2 and He (note that the mass of H_2 would be double the mass of H, and so would have an atomic mass of 2). Because H_2 is lighter than He, it would float more readily in air (which is composed primarily of N_2 and O_2).

Fill-in-the-Blank

1. protons, neutrons; atomic number; electrons, electron shells
2. ion; positive; negative; ionic
3. isotopes; energy; radioactive
4. inert; reactive; share
5. free radicals; DNA; antioxidants
6. polar; hydrogen; cohesion

Chapter 3

Figure Caption Questions

Figure 3-7 During hydrolysis of sucrose, water would be split; a hydrogen atom from water would be added to the oxygen from glucose (that formerly linked the two subunits) and the remaining OH from water would be added to the carbon (formerly bonded to oxygen) of the fructose subunit.

Figure 3-12 The enzyme would hydrolyze the triglyceride into a glycerol and three fatty acids, using up three water molecules.

Figure 3-15 As lipids, steroids are soluble in the lipid-based cell membrane and can cross it (and the nuclear membrane) to act inside the cell. Other types of hormones (mostly peptides) are not lipid soluble and cannot easily cross the cell membrane.

Figure 3-20 Heat energy can break chemical bonds, and the hydrogen bonds that account for secondary (and higher level) protein structure are especially susceptible to heat. Because a protein's functional ability usually depends on its shape, breaking shape-controlling hydrogen bonds disrupts function.

Fill-in-the-Blank

1. monomer, polymers; polysaccharides; hydrolysis; cellulose, starch, glycogen; sucrose, lactose, maltose
2. oil; wax; fat; steroids; cholesterol; phospholipid
3. dehydration, water; amino acids; primary; helix, pleated sheet; pleated sheet; denatured
4. double bonds (or double covalent bonds); hydrogen bonds; disulfide bonds; hydrogen bonds; peptide bonds
5. ribose or deoxyribose sugar, base, phosphate; adenosine triphosphate (ATP); adenine, guanine, cytosine, thymine; deoxyribonucleic acid (DNA), ribonucleic acid (RNA); phosphate
6. genetic material (DNA, RNA, or nucleic acids); vCJD; bovine spongiform encephalitis (BSE); scrapie

Chapter 4

Figure Caption Questions

Figure 4-4 Of the four structures listed, only the ribosome is found in all of the main branches of life (i.e., found in bacteria, archaea, and all eukaryotes). Thus, ribosomes must have been present in the common ancestor of all living cells, and nuclei, mitochondria, and chloroplasts must have arisen later.

Figure 4-7 Fluid would not move upward because the beating of the flagella would direct fluid straight out from the cell membranes. Mucus and trapped particles would accumulate in the trachea.

Figure 4-9 By forming chromosomes during cell division, the DNA can be parcelled evenly to the resulting daughter cells, with each receiving a complete copy of the genetic information.

Figure 4-13 Because membranes are fundamentally similar, they can merge with one another. This allows molecules in vesicles to be transferred from one membrane-enclosed structure (such as endoplasmic reticulum) to another (such as the Golgi apparatus). The material can be exported from the cell when the vesicle merges with the plasma membrane.

Fill-in-the-Blank

1. phospholipids, proteins; phospholipid; protein; protein
2. cytoskeleton; microfilaments, intermediate filaments, microtubules; microtubules
3. ribosomes; endoplasmic reticulum; nucleolus; Golgi apparatus; cell wall; messenger RNA
4. rough endoplasmic reticulum; vesicles, Golgi apparatus; carbohydrate; plasma
5. mitochondria; chloroplasts; cell wall; nucleoid; cilia; cytoplasm
6. mitochondria, chloroplasts; double, ATP, DNA; size

Chapter 5

Figure Caption Questions

Figure 5-9 The distilled water made the solution hypotonic to the blood cells, causing enough water to flow in to burst their fragile cell membranes.

Figure 5-10 The rigid cell wall of plant cells counteracts the pressure exerted by water entering by osmosis, so the cell does not burst. Animal cells lack a cell wall, and when placed in a highly hypotonic solution will absorb water by osmosis until the cell membrane bursts.

Figure 5-15 Exocytosis uses cellular energy, whereas diffusion is passive. In addition, while materials move through a membrane during diffusion out of a cell, in exocytosis, materials are expelled without passing directly through the plasma membrane. Exocytosis allows materials that are too large to pass through membranes to be eliminated from the cell.

Fill-in-the-Blank

1. phospholipids; receptor, recognition, enzymes, attachment, transport
2. selectively permeable; diffusion; osmosis; aquaporins; active transport
3. kinks (or bends or double bonds); pressure, temperature
4. channel, carrier; simple, lipids
5. active transport, endocytosis, exocytosis; active transport
6. simple diffusion; simple diffusion; facilitated diffusion (may also move by active transport); facilitated diffusion
7. endocytosis; yes; pinocytosis, phagocytosis; vesicles

Chapter 6

Figure Caption Questions

Figure 6-6 Other sources of energy that might overcome activation energy include mechanical energy (e.g., shaking), electricity, and radiation.

Figure 6-10 No, endergonic reactions do not occur spontaneously because they require an input of energy, whether or not a catalyst is present.

Fill-in-the-Blank

1. created, destroyed; kinetic, potential
2. more, less; organized; entropy
3. activation; electron shells; heat or movement of molecules
4. exergonic; endergonic; exergonic; endergonic; coupled
5. adenosine triphosphate; energy carrier; adenosine diphosphate, phosphate; energy
6. proteins; activation energy; active site; shape, electrical charges

Chapter 7

Figure Caption Questions

Figure 7-9 No. Because oxygen is generated during the light reactions, these bubbles would not form in darkness.

Figure 7-11 The C_4 pathway is less efficient than the C_3 pathway; C_4 uses one extra ATP per CO_2 molecule (to regenerate PEP from pyruvate). Thus, when CO_2 is abundant and photorespiration is not a problem, C_3 plants produce sugar at a lower energy cost, and they outcompete C_4 plants.

Fill-in-the-Blank

1. stomata, oxygen (O_2), carbon dioxide (CO_2); water loss (evaporation); chloroplasts, mesophyll; bundle sheath
2. red, blue, violet; green; carotenoids
3. photosystem II, chlorophyll a, primary electron acceptor; electron transport chain (ETC, or ETC II); H+ (hydrogen ions); chemiosmosis
4. water (H_2O), carbon dioxide (CO_2); carbon fixation; rubisco, oxygen
5. both; both; C_4 plants, CAM plants
6. ATP, NADPH, Calvin; RuBP; G3P, glucose

Chapter 8

Figure Caption Questions

Figure 8-6 Without oxygen, ATP production halts. Oxygen is the final acceptor in the electron transport chain. If it is not present, electrons cannot proceed along the chain, and production of ATP by chemiosmosis ceases.

Figure 8-10 In oxygen-rich environments, aerobic bacteria would prevail because their respiration produces far more ATP per glucose molecule. Some anaerobes would survive but would generate far less energy, while others would be poisoned by the oxygen. In oxygen-poor environments, aerobic bacteria are limited by the oxygen shortage (unless they can switch to fermentation), and anaerobes would prevail.

Fill-in-the-Blank

1. glycolysis, cellular respiration; cytoplasmic fluid, mitochondria; cellular respiration
2. anaerobic; glycolysis, two; fermentation, NAD
3. ethanol, carbon dioxide; lactic acid; lactic acid
4. erythropoietin (EPO), red blood, oxygen; cellular respiration
5. matrix, intermembrane space, concentration gradient; chemiosmosis; ATP synthase
6. Krebs, citric acid; acetyl CoA; two; NADH, $FADH_2$

Chapter 9

Figure Caption Questions

Figure 9-8 If the sister chromatids of one replicated chromosome failed to separate, then one daughter cell would not receive any copy of that chromosome, whereas the other daughter cell would receive both copies.

Figure 9-15 If one pair of homologues failed to separate at anaphase I, one of the resulting daughter cells (and the gametes produced from it) would have both homologues and the other daughter cell (and the gametes produced from it) would not have any copies of that homologue.

Fill-in-the-Blank

1. binary fission
2. mitotic, differentiation
3. homologues OR homologous chromosomes; autosomes; sex chromosomes
4. prophase, metaphase, anaphase, telophase; cytokinesis; telophase
5. kinetochore; polar
6. four; meiosis I; gametes OR sperm and eggs
7. prophase; chiasmata; crossing over
8. shuffling of homologues; crossing over; fusion of gametes

Chapter 10

Figure Caption Questions

Figure 10-8 Half of the gametes produced by a Pp plant will have the P allele, and half will have the p allele. All of the gametes produced by a pp plant will have the p allele. Therefore, half of the offspring of a $Pp \times pp$ cross will be Pp (purple) and half will be pp (white), whereas all of the offspring of a $PP \times pp$ cross will be Pp (purple). See Figure 10-9.

Figure 10-11 A plant with wrinkled green seeds has the genotype $ssyy$. A plant with smooth yellow seeds could be $SSYY$, $SsYY$, $SSYy$, or $SsYy$. Set up four Punnett squares to see if the smooth yellow plant's genotype can be revealed by a test cross.

Figure 10-12 Chromosomes, not individual genes, assort independently during meiosis. Therefore, if the genes for seed color and seed shape were on the same chromosome, they would tend to be inherited together, and would not assort independently.

Figure 10-24 One of Victoria and Albert's sons, Leopold, had hemophilia. To be male, Leopold must have inherited Albert's Y chromosome. The X chromosome, not the Y chromosome, bears the gene for blood clotting, so Leopold must have inherited the hemophilia allele from his mother, Victoria.

Fill-in-the-Blank

1. locus; alleles; mutations
2. genotype; phenotype; heterozygous
3. independently; as a group; linked
4. an X and a Y, two X; sperm
5. sex linked
6. incomplete dominance; codominance; polygenic inheritance

Chapter 11

Figure Caption Questions

Figure 11-5   It takes more energy to break apart a C–G base pair, because these are held together by three hydrogen bonds, compared with the two hydrogen bonds that bind A to T.

Figure E11-7   DNA polymerase always moves in the 3′ to 5′ direction on a parental strand. Because the two strands of a DNA double helix are oriented in opposite directions, the 5′ direction on one strand leads toward the replication fork and the 5′ direction on the other strand leads away from the fork. Therefore, DNA polymerase must move in opposite directions on the two strands.

Fill-in-the-Blank

1. nucleotides; sugar (deoxyribose), phosphate, base (order not important)
2. phosphate, sugar (order not important); double helix
3. thymine, cytosine; complementary
4. semiconservative
5. DNA helicase; DNA polymerase; DNA ligase
6. mutations; nucleotide substitution, point mutation

Chapter 12

Figure Caption Questions

Figure 12-3   RNA polymerase always travels in the 3′ to 5′ direction on the template strand. Because the two DNA strands run in opposite directions, if the other DNA strand were the template strand, then RNA polymerase must travel in the opposite direction (that is, right to left in this illustration).

Figure 12-4   Cells produce far larger amounts of some proteins than others. Obvious examples include cells that produce antibodies or protein hormones, which they secrete into the bloodstream in vast quantities, affecting functioning throughout the body. If a cell needs to produce more of certain proteins, it will probably synthesize more mRNA, which will then be translated into that protein.

Figure 12-7   Grouped in codons, the original mRNA sequence visible here is CGA AUC UAG UAA. Changing all G to U would produce the sequence CUA AUC UAU UAA. The two changes are in the first codon (CGA to CUA) and the third codon (UAG to UAU). Refer to the genetic code illustrated in Table 12-3. First, CGA encodes arginine, while CUA encodes leucine, so the first G → U change would substitute leucine for arginine in the protein. Second, UAG is a stop codon, but UAU encodes tyrosine. Therefore, the second G → U change would add tyrosine to the protein instead of stopping translation. The final codon in the illustration, UAA, is a stop codon, so the new protein would end with tyrosine.

Figure E12-1   The mold would be able to grow if any of ornithine, citrulline, or arginine were added to the medium.

Fill-in-the-Blank

1. transcription; translation; ribosome
2. messenger RNA; transfer RNA; ribosomal RNA (order not important); microRNA
3. three; codon; anticodon
4. RNA polymerase; template; promoter; termination signal
5. start, stop; transfer; peptide
6. point; insertion; deletion

Chapter 13

Figure Caption Questions

Figure 13-3   *Thermus aquaticus* lives in hot springs, and its DNA polymerase has evolved to be efficient at high temperatures. The DNA polymerase would probably work more slowly at both higher and lower temperatures than the springs in which *T. aquaticus* resides; 70°C is close to optimal.

Figure 13-7   As they do for other genes, each person normally has two copies of each STR gene, one on each of a pair of homologous chromosomes. A person may be homozygous (two copies of the same allele) or heterozygous (one copy of each of two alleles) for each STR. The bands on the gel represent individual alleles of an STR gene. Therefore, a single person can have one band (if homozygous) or two bands (if heterozygous). If a person is homozygous for an STR allele, then he has two copies of the same allele. The DNA from both (identical) alleles will run in the same place on the gel and, therefore, that (single) band will have twice as much DNA as each of the two bands of DNA from a heterozygote. The more DNA, the brighter the band.

Figure 13-11   A heterozygote has one normal globin allele and one sickle-cell allele. Therefore, MstII would produce two DNA bands from the normal allele and one from the sickle-cell allele, for a total of three bands of different sizes. The amount of DNA in each of the bands from heterozygotes would be half as much as from the homozygotes, because DNA from heterozygotes contains only one copy of each type of allele, whereas homozygous normal DNA has two copies of the normal allele, and homozygous sickle-cell DNA has two copies of the sickle-cell allele. Therefore, bands from heterozygotes should be about half as bright as bands from homozygotes.

Fill-in-the-Blank

1. genetically modified organisms OR transgenic organisms
2. transformation; plasmids
3. polymerase chain reaction
4. short tandem repeats (STRs); length, or size, or number of repeats; DNA profile
5. electrophoresis OR gel electrophoresis; DNA probe, base pairing, OR hydrogen bonds

Chapter 14

Figure Caption Questions

Figure 14-6   No. Mutations, the ultimate source of the phenotypic variation on which natural selection acts, occur in all organisms, including those that reproduce asexually.

Figure 14-7   No. Evolution can include changes in traits that are not revealed in morphology, such as physiological systems and metabolic pathways. More generally, evolution in the sense of changes in a species' gene pool is inevitable in all lineages; genetic evolution is not necessarily reflected in morphological change.

Figure 14-9   Possibilities include coccyx (tailbone)—homologous with tail bones of a cat (or any tetrapod); goosebumps—homologous with erectile hairs of a chimp (or any mammal; used for aggressive displays and insulation); appendix—homologous with the cecum of a rabbit (and other herbivorous mammals; extension of large intestine used for storage); wisdom teeth—homologous with grinding rear molars of a leaf-eating monkey (or other mammals); ear-wiggling muscles (the muscles around the ear that some people can use to make their ears move)—homologous with muscles in a dog (and other mammals) that enable the external ear to orient toward sound.

Figure 14-10   Analogous. Bird tails consist of feathers; dog tails consist of bone/muscle/skin.

Fill-in-the-Blank

1. wing, arm; analogous, convergent; vestigial
2. common ancestor; amino acids, ATP
3. catastrophism; uniformitarianism; old
4. evolution; mutations, DNA
5. natural selection; artificial selection
6. many traits are inherited; Gregor Mendel

Chapter 15

Figure Caption Questions

Figure 15-3   The surviving colonies would be in different places on each treated plate, and there would be a different number of surviving colonies on each plate (because the antibiotic-caused mutations would arise unpredictably, depending on which bacteria happened to interact with the antibiotic such that mutations were caused). Another possibility would be for all of the colonies to survive (if the antibiotic always caused mutations in every colony).

Figure 15-5   For a locus with two alleles, one dominant and one recessive, there are two possible phenotypes. A mating between a heterozygote and a homozygote-recessive yields offspring with a 50:50 ratio of the two phenotypes.

	B	*b*
b	*Bb* (black)	*bb* (brown)
b	*Bb* (black)	*bb* (brown)

Figure 15-6   Allele *B* should behave roughly as it does in the size 4 population, its frequency drifting to fixation or loss in almost all cases. But, because the population is a bit larger, the allele should, on average, take a longer time (greater number of generations) to reach fixation or loss. The longer period of drift should also allow for more reversals of direction (e.g., frequency drifting down, then up, then down again, etc.) than in the size 4 population.

Figure 15-7   Mutations inevitably and continually add variability to a population and, after the population becomes larger, the counteracting, diversity-reducing effects of drift decrease. The net result is an increase in genetic diversity.

Figure 15-11   Greater for males. A female's reproductive success is limited by her maximum litter size, but a male's potential reproductive success is limited only by the number of available females. When, as in bighorn sheep, males battle for access to females, the most successful males can impregnate many females, whereas unsuccessful males may not fertilize any females at all. Thus, the difference between the most and least successful male can be very large. In contrast, even the most successful female can have only one litter of offspring per breeding season, which is not that many more offspring than a female who fails to reproduce.

Figure 15-13   There is always a limit to directional selection. As a trait becomes more extreme, eventually the cost of increasing it further outweighs the benefits (for example, the cost of obtaining extra food may outweigh the benefit of larger size), or it may be physically impossible for the trait to become more extreme (for example, a limb's length may be limited by the maximum length that a bone can attain without breaking under its own weight).

Fill-in-the-Blank

1. Hardy–Weinberg principle, equilibrium, allele; no
2. alleles; nucleotides; mutations; homozygous, heterozygous
3. genotype, phenotype; phenotype
4. genetic drift; small; founder effect, population bottleneck; founder effect
5. the same species; natural selection, coevolution; adaptations
6. reproduction; environment

Chapter 16

Figure Caption Questions

Figure 16-9   Possibilities include continental drift; climate changes (especially glacial advances) that cause habitat fragmentation; formation of islands by volcanic activity or rising sea level; movements of organisms to existing islands (including "islands" of isolated habitats such as lakes, mountaintops, deep-ocean vents); and formation of barriers to movement (e.g., new mountain ranges, deserts, rivers). These processes are indeed sufficiently common and widespread to account for a multitude of speciation events over the history of life.

Figure 16-10   The key question is whether the two populations inhabiting two species of trees (apple and hawthorn) interbreed. Tests might involve careful observation of flies under natural conditions, lab experiments in which captive flies of the two types are provided with opportunities to interbreed, or genetic comparisons to determine the degree of gene flow between the two types of flies.

Figure 16-14   Natural selection cannot look forward and ensure that the only traits that evolve are those that ensure survival of the species as a whole. Instead, natural selection ensures only the preservation of traits that help individuals survive and reproduce more successfully than individuals lacking the trait. So if, in a particular species, highly specialized individuals survive and reproduce better than less-specialized individuals, the specialized phenotype will eventually dominate, even if it ultimately puts the species at greater risk of extinction.

Fill-in-the-Blank

1. populations, independently; reproductive isolation; asexually
2. behavioral isolation; hybrid inviability; temporal isolation; gametic incompatibility; mechanical incompatibility
3. genetically isolated, diverge; allopatric speciation; genetic drift, natural selection
4. adaptive radiation; habitat (or environment)
5. small, specialized; habitat destruction

Chapter 17

Figure Caption Questions

Figure 17-2   The presence of oxygen would prevent the accumulation of organic compounds by quickly oxidizing them or their precursors. All of the successful abiotic synthesis experiments used oxygen-free "atmospheres."

Figure 17-5   The bacterial sequence would be most similar to that of the plant mitochondrion, because (as the descendant of the immediate ancestor of the mitochondrion) the bacterium shares with the mitochondrion a more recent common ancestor than with the chloroplast or the nucleus.

Figure 17-8   Most likely because of competition with seed plants, which had not yet arisen during the period when ferns and club mosses reached large sizes. After seed plants arose, competition from them eventually eliminated other types of plants from many ecological niches, presumably including those niches that favored evolution of large size.

Figure 17-9   No. The mudskipper merely demonstrates the plausibility of a hypothetical intermediate step in the proposed scenario for the origin of land-dwelling tetrapods. But the existence of a modern example similar in form to the hypothetical intermediate form does not provide information about the actual identity of that intermediate form.

Figure 17-11   On average, the rate at which new species arise has been larger than the rate at which species have gone extinct.

Figure 17-19   The African replacement hypothesis. These fossils are the oldest modern humans found so far, and their presence in Africa suggests that modern humans were present in Africa before they were present anywhere else, which, if true, would mean that they originated in Africa.

Figure E17-1   713 million years old. (1:1 ratio means that $\frac{1}{2}$ of the original uranium-235 is left, so its half-life has passed.)

Fill-in-the-Blank

1. anaerobic; photosynthesize; poisonous (toxic, harmful), aerobic (cellular) respiration, energy
2. RNA (ribonucleic acid), enzymes (catalysts), ribozymes
3. eukaryotic; endosymbiotic; aerobic; DNA (deoxyribonucleic acid)
4. swimming, moist (wet); pollen
5. conifers; wind; cold, northern; flowers, insects; efficient
6. arthropods, exoskeletons, drying
7. reptiles, egg; skin; lungs

Chapter 18

Figure Caption Questions

Figure E18-4   Fungi and animals are monophyletic; protists, great apes, seedless plants, and prokaryotes are not. (Descendants of the most recent common ancestor of protists include all the other eukaryotes; for great apes, include humans; for prokaryotes, include eukaryotes; for seedless plants, include the seed plants).

Fill-in-the-Blank

1. taxonomy; systematics; clade
2. genus, species; Latin; capitalized, italic
3. domain, kingdom, phylum, class, order, family, genus, species; Archaea, Bacteria, Eukarya
4. anatomy, DNA sequence; reproduce asexually; phylogenetic species concept, phylogeny (evolutionary tree)
5. 1.5 million, 7 million, 100 million

Chapter 19

Figure Caption Questions

Figure 19-4 Protective structures like endospores are most likely to evolve in environments in which protection is especially advantageous. Compared to other environments inhabited by bacteria, soils are especially vulnerable to drying out, which can be fatal to unprotected bacteria. Bacteria that could resist long dry periods would gain an evolutionary advantage.

Figure 19-5 Enzymes from bacteria that live in hot environments are active at high temperatures (temperatures that usually denature enzymes in organisms from more temperate environments). This ability to function at high temperatures makes the enzymes useful in test tube reactions (such as PCR) that are run at high temperatures.

Figure 19-7 The main advantage is efficiency. In binary fission, every individual produces new individuals. In sexual reproduction, only some individuals (e.g., females) produce offspring. So the average individual produces twice as many offspring by fission as it would by sexual reproduction.

Figure 19-9 The concentration of nitrogen gas would increase, because the major process for removing atmospheric nitrogen would end, whereas the processes that add nitrogen gas to the atmosphere would continue.

Figure 19-12 Viruses lack ribosomes and the rest of the "machinery" required to manufacture proteins.

Figure 19-13 Many viruses replicate by integrating their genetic material into the host cell's genome. Thus, if biotechnologists can insert foreign genetic material into such a virus, the virus will naturally tend to transfer the foreign genes to the cells they infect.

Fill-in-the-Blank

1. bacteria, cell walls, archaea
2. smaller; rod-shaped, corkscrew-shaped, spherical
3. flagella; biofilms; endospores
4. anaerobic; photosynthetic
5. binary fission, conjugation
6. nitrogen-fixing; cellulose
7. tuberculosis, cholera, bubonic plague, syphilis, gonorrhea, pneumonia, Lyme disease, etc.; meat, produce
8. DNA, RNA, protein; host; bacteriophage

Chapter 20

Figure Caption Questions

Figure 20-2 Sex is the process that combines the genomes of two different individuals. In plants and animals, this mixing of genomes occurs only during reproduction. But in many protists (and prokaryotes), genome mixing may occur through conjugation and other processes that take place independently of reproduction (which in many cases occurs by simple mitotic cell division).

Figure 20-7 Convergent evolution. Water molds and fungi live in similar environments and acquire nutrients in similar ways. These ecological similarities have fostered the evolution of superficially similar structures, even though the two taxa are only distantly related.

Fill-in-the-Blank

1. pseudopods; decomposers, parasites
2. algae; protozoa
3. secondary endosymbiosis, photosynthetic protist
4. diplomonad (or excavate); kinetoplastid (or euglenozoan); apicomplexan (or alveolate)
5. water mold (or oomycete or stramenopile); amoebozoan
6. dinoflagellates, diatoms; green algae

Chapter 21

Figure Caption Questions

Figure 21-5 Bryophytes lack lignin (which provides stiffness and support) and conducting cells (which transport materials to distant parts of the body). Conducting cells and stiff stems seem to be required to achieve more than minimal height.

Figure 21-7 All of the pictured structures are sporophytes. In ferns, horsetails, and club mosses, the gametophyte is small and inconspicuous.

Figure 21-9 The most common adaptations are hard, protective shells and incorporation of toxic and/or distasteful chemicals.

Figure 21-12 Both types of pollination persist in angiosperms because the cost–benefit balance and, therefore, the most adaptive pollination system differ, depending on the ecological circumstances of a species.

Type of Pollination	Advantages	Disadvantages
Wind	Not dependent on the presence of animals; no investment in nectar or showy flowers; pollen can disperse over large distances	A larger investment in pollen because most fails to reach an egg; higher chance of failure to fertilize any egg
Animal	Each pollen grain has a much greater chance of reaching a suitable egg	Depends on the presence of animals; must invest in nectar and showy flowers

Fill-in-the-Blank

1. green algae; nonvascular plants, vascular plants; embryos, alternation of generations
2. cuticle, stomata, water; conducting cells, lignin; water, nutrients
3. swim to the egg; seeds, pollen; gymnosperms, angiosperms; attract pollinators; facilitate seed dispersal
4. hornworts, liverworts, mosses; club mosses, horsetails, ferns; angiosperms

Chapter 22

Figure Caption Questions

Figure 22-1 Its filamentous shape helps the fungal body to penetrate and extend into its food sources, and is also a shape that maximizes the ratio of surface area to interior volume (which maximizes the area available for absorbing nutrients). The extreme thinness of the filaments ensures that no cell is very far from the surface at which nutrients are absorbed.

Figure 22-8 No. The common source of the two hyphae means that they will both inherit the same mating type. Hyphae must be of different mating types in order to reproduce sexually.

Figure 22-9 Haploid (although there might be some diploid cells in the basidia concealed in the gills of these haploid mushrooms).

Figure 22-19 In nature, bacteria compete with fungi for access to food and living space. The antibiotic chemicals produced by fungi serve as a defense against competition from bacteria.

Fill-in-the-Blank

1. reproduction; spores
2. mycelium, hyphae, septa; chitin
3. mitotic, one; meiotic, zygote, one
4. glomeromycetes; chytrids; basidiomycetes
5. lichens; mycorrhizae; endophytes
6. wood (cellulose and lignin); yeasts; athlete's foot, jock itch, vaginal infections, ringworm, histoplasmosis, valley fever (many possible answers)

Chapter 23

Figure Caption Questions

Figure 23-4 Sponges are "primitive" only in the sense that their lineage arose early in the evolutionary history of animals and their body plan is comparatively simple. But early origin and simplicity do not determine effectiveness, and the sponge body plan and way of life are clearly suitable for excellent survival and reproduction in many habitats.

Figure 23-6 (a) polyp, (b) medusa, (c) polyp, (d) medusa

Figure 23-10   Parasitic tapeworms have no gut and absorb nutrients across their body surfaces. Their ribbon-like shape maximizes surface area for absorption and allows the worm body to extend through the greatest possible area of the host's body (to be in contact with as many nutrients as possible).

Figure 23-11   Two openings allow one-way travel of food through the gut. One-way movement allows more efficient digestion than two-way movement; digestive waste from which all nutrients have been extracted can be excreted quickly without the need for reverse travel back along the gut, and food can be processed more quickly.

Figure 23-12   Water travels easily through the moist epidermis of a leech. When a high concentration of salt is dissolved in the moisture on the outside of a leech's body, water moves rapidly out of the leech's body by osmosis, dehydrating and ultimately killing the animal.

Fill-in-the-Blank

1. three, endoderm, mesoderm, ectoderm; two, mesoderm
2. cephalized; sensing the environment, ingesting food; cavity, mesoderm
3. protostome; deuterostome, echinoderms, chordates
4. invertebrates, vertebrates; invertebrates; sponges, single-celled organisms; cnidarians, annelids
5. bivalves, gastropods, cephalopods; arthropods; insects, arachnids, crustaceans
6. annelids, arthropods (chordates also correct); closed circulatory; open circulatory, hemocoel
7. mollusks, cnidarians, echinoderms, arthropods (chordates also correct)

Chapter 24

Figure Caption Questions

Figure 24-7   A freshwater fish's body is immersed in a hypotonic solution, so water tends to continuously enter the body by osmosis. The physiological challenge is to get rid of all this excess water. For a saltwater fish, the challenge is reversed. The surrounding solution is hypertonic, so water tends to leave the body. The physiological challenge is to retain sufficient water.

Figure 24-9   One advantage is that adults and juveniles occupy different habitats and therefore do not compete with one another for resources (the niche occupied by an individual over its lifetime is broadened).

Figure 24-12   Flight is a very expensive trait (consumes a lot of energy, requires many special structures). In circumstances in which the benefits of flight are low, such as in habitats without predators or in species whose size is very large, natural selection may favor individuals that forgo an investment in flight, and flightlessness can arise.

Fill-in-the-Blank

1. hollow, dorsal; anus, notochord
2. tunicates, lancelets, hagfishes (order not important); skull; hagfishes
3. lungfishes; cartilage; ray-finned fishes; jaws
4. mammals, amphibians, reptiles, amphibians
5. monotremes; salamanders; bats

Chapter 25

Figure Caption Questions

Figure 25-1   One possibility is that the variation necessary for selection has never arisen. (If no members of the species by chance gain the ability to discriminate between their own chicks and cuckoo chicks, then selection has no opportunity to favor the novel behavior.) Another possibility is that the cost of the behavior is relatively low. (If parasitism by cuckoos is rare, a parent that feeds any begging chick in its nest is, on average, much more likely to benefit than suffer.)

Figure 25-7   Because the crossbreeding experiment shows that differences in orientation direction between the two populations stem from genetic differences, birds from the western population should orient in a southwesterly direction, regardless of the environment in which they are raised.

Figure 25-21   If females do indeed gain any benefits from their mates, those benefits would necessarily be genetic (because the male provides no material benefits). Male fitness may vary, and to the extent that this fitness can be passed to offspring, females would benefit by choosing the most fit males. If a male's fitness is reflected in his ability to build and decorate a bower, females would benefit by preferring to mate with males that build especially good bowers.

Figure 25-24   Canines forage mainly by smell; apes are mostly visual foragers. Modes of sexual signaling are affected not only by the nature of the information to be encoded, but also by the sensory biases and sensitivities of the species involved. Communication systems may evolve to take advantage of traits that originally evolved for other functions.

Fill-in-the-Blank

1. genes, environment; stimulus; innate
2. energy, predators, injury; practice, skills, adult; brains, learning
3. habituation, repeated; imprinting; sensitive period
4. aggressive; displays, injuring (wounding, damaging); weapons (such as fangs, claws), larger
5. territoriality (territorial behavior); mate, raise young, feed, store food; male; same species
6. For pheromones, any of the following advantages is correct: long lasting, use little energy to produce, species specific, don't attract predators, may convey messages over long distances. Any of the following disadvantages is correct: cannot convey changing information, conveys fewer different types of information. For visual displays, any of the following advantages is correct: instantaneous, can change rapidly, many different messages can be sent, is quiet. Any of the following disadvantages is correct: makes animals conspicuous to predators, generally ineffective in darkness or dense vegetation, requires that recipient be in visual range (close by).

Chapter 26

Figure Caption Questions

Figure 26-4   Many variables interact in complex ways to produce real population cycles. Weather, for example, affects the lemmings' food supply and thus their ability to survive and reproduce. Predation of lemmings is influenced by both the number of predators and the availability of other prey, which in turn is influenced by multiple environmental variables.

Figure 26-13   Emigration relieves population pressure in an overpopulated area, spreading the migrating animals into new habitats that may have more resources. Human emigration within and between countries is often driven by the desire or need for more resources, although social factors—such as wars and religious or racial persecution—also fuel human emigration. (This is a subjective question that can lead to discussion of the extent to which overpopulation drives human emigration.)

Figure 26-16   This is a subjective question. Many scenarios are possible based on different assumptions about increases in technology, changes in birth and death rates, and the resiliency of the ecosystems that sustain us.

Figure 26-20   When fertility exceeds RLF, there are more children than parents. As the additional children mature and become parents themselves, this more numerous generation produces still more additional children, and so on.

Figure 26-21   High birth rates in developing countries are sustained by cultural expectations, lack of health education, and lack of access to contraception. Lower birth rates in developed countries are encouraged by easy access to contraception, the relatively high cost of raising children, and more varied career opportunities for women. (Students should be able to expand on, or add to, these factors.)

Figure 26-22   U.S. population growth is in the rapidly rising "exponential" phase of the S-curve. Stabilization will require some combination of reduction in immigration rates and birth rates. An increase in death rates is less likely, but cannot be ruled out entirely in any future scenario. (Students should be encouraged to speculate about the timing and the reason for various time frames.)

Fill-in-the-Blank

1. Any two of the following: freezing, drought, flood, fire, storms, habitat destruction; predation and competition
2. survivorship curves; early-loss; late-loss
3. exponential; no; J-curve; no
4. carrying capacity; logistic, S-
5. clumped; uniform; random
6. pyramid (triangle); stable; pyramidal (triangular)
7. births, immigrants, deaths, emigrants; decreases, increases, increases

Chapter 27

Figure Caption Questions

Figure 27-1   Because they did not evolve in the habitat to which they were introduced, invasive species may occupy a niche that is nearly identical to that of a native species; for example, zebra mussels compete with other freshwater mussels or clams. A successful invasive species may have adaptations that allow it to outcompete the native species, such as a higher growth rate or reproductive rate. Further, all native species are likely to have local predators, whereas the introduced species may not. The absence of predators would also help the invasive species outcompete a native species if they occupy very similar niches.

Figure 27-3   Examples of coevolution between predators and prey include the keen eyesight of the hawk and the camouflage coloration of a mouse. Grasses have evolved tough silicon embedded in their leaves, and grazing herbivores have teeth that grow continuously throughout life so that they are not completely worn down by the abrasive grasses. A moth may detect a bat's echolocation signals and fly erratically, while the bat shifts its echolocation pitch to a pitch that the moth cannot detect. Milkweed plants have evolved a toxin to deter predators, and monarch butterfly caterpillars are not susceptible to the toxin.

Figure 27-5   Although scientists have not observed these examples of evolution as they occurred, a likely scenario is that chance mutation caused some animals to more closely resemble their surroundings than did other members of their species. These individuals were less likely to be seen and eaten by predators. As a result, more survived and reproduced, passing their genetically determined appearance on to their offspring. Over large spans of time, more chance mutations that enhanced their resemblance to the environment further reduced predation, again selecting for individuals bearing these genetic traits.

Figure 27-12   Although tasty prey have often evolved to blend in with their surroundings, poisonous prey species (such as the monarch caterpillar, which stores milkweed toxin in its body) frequently advertise their presence with bright "warning colors." These bright colors make it easy for predators to learn to actively avoid animals bearing them.

Figure 27-15   Forests in which fires are suppressed grow extremely dense stands of trees, which tend to be less healthy because they are competing with one another for light, nutrients, and water. A fire under these conditions will burn hotter and more extensively, leaving fewer living plants and seeds to recolonize the area, slowing succession. Smaller, more frequent fires clear spaces within a forest and allow patches of localized succession to occur, increasing the habitat for a variety of animals and increasing the species diversity of plants.

Fill-in-the-Blank

1. natural selection; coevolution; competition, predation, parasitism, mutualism
2. carnivores, herbivores; camouflage; larger, abundant (or numerous)
3. niches; interspecific competition; resource partitioning
4. warning coloration; startle coloration; Batesian mimicry; aggressive mimicry
5. mutualism; parasitism; predation; parasitism; mutualism; competition
6. succession; primary succession; secondary succession; climax; subclimax

Chapter 28

Figure Caption Questions

Figure 28-2   Whenever energy is utilized, the second law of thermodynamics applies: When energy is converted from one form to another, the amount of useful energy decreases. Much of this energy is lost as heat.

Figure 28-3   On land, high productivity is supported by optimal temperatures for plant growth, a long growing season, and plenty of moisture, such as is found in rain forests. Lack of water limits desert productivity. In aquatic ecosystems, high productivity is supported by an abundance of nutrients and adequate light, such as is found in estuaries. Lack of nutrients limits the productivity of the open ocean in the photic zone.

Figure 28-5   There are many possibilities, including many combinations that are not linked by arrows in the figure. One example is grass (producer) → grasshopper (primary consumer) → meadowlark (secondary consumer) → hawk (tertiary consumer). Another is grass (producer) → grasshopper (primary consumer) → spider (secondary consumer) → shrew (tertiary consumer).

Figure 28-9   Humanity's need to grow crops to feed our growing population has led to the trapping of nitrogen for fertilizer using industrial processes. Additionally, large-scale livestock feedlots generate enormous amounts of nitrogenous waste. Nitrogen oxides are also generated when fossil fuels are burned in power plants, vehicles, and factories, as well as when forests are burned. Consequences include the overfertilization of lakes and rivers, and the creation of dead zones in nearshore coastal waters that receive excessive nutrient runoff from land. Another important consequence is acid deposition, in which nitrogen oxides formed by combustion produce nitric acid in the atmosphere; this acid is then deposited on land or in water.

Fill-in-the-Blank

1. sunlight, photosynthesis; nutrients, nutrient cycles OR biogeochemical cycles
2. autotrophs, producers; net primary productivity
3. trophic levels; food chain; food webs
4. 10; the second law of thermodynamics
5. herbivores, primary consumers; heterotrophs, consumers; detritus feeders; fungi, bacteria
6. nitrogen-fixing bacteria, denitrifying bacteria; ammonia, nitrates
7. atmosphere, oceans; CO_2 (carbon dioxide); limestone, fossil fuels

Chapter 29

Figure Caption Questions

Figure 29-6   Both live in arid environments, so their evolution has selected for fleshy, water-storing bodies. In each case, leaf area has been reduced, limiting evaporation. Both of these plants would be attractive to desert animals because they store water; as a result of this predation pressure, both carry defensive spines.

Figure 29-9   Most nutrients in tropical rain forests are not stored in the soil. The optimal temperature and moisture of tropical climates allow plants to make such efficient use of nutrients that nearly all nutrients are stored in plant bodies and, to a lesser extent, in the bodies of the animals they support.

Figure 29-17   Tallgrass prairie is vulnerable to two major encroachments. First, if humans suppress natural wildfires, then adequate rainfall allows forests to take over. Second, these biomes provide the world's most fertile soils and have excellent growing conditions for farming, which has now displaced native vegetation.

Figure 29-29   Nearshore ecosystems have an abundance of the two limiting factors for life in water: nutrients and light to support photosynthetic organisms. Upwelling from ocean depths or runoff from the land (or both) provide nutrients. The shallow water in these areas allows adequate light to penetrate to support rooted plants and anchored algae, which in turn provide food and shelter for a wealth of other marine life.

Figure 29-30   Bleaching refers to the loss of symbiotic algae that normally inhabit the corals' tissues. The algae (dinoflagellates) provide the corals with energy-rich compounds that store energy from photosynthesis. Loss of these symbiotic algae can eventually kill the coral. Bleaching is a common response to water that is excessively warm and, thus, global warming may contribute to the demise of coral reefs.

Fill-in-the-Blank

1. seasons; Tropics; ocean currents OR the presence of the ocean; rain shadow
2. appropriate temperatures, liquid water; light, nutrients; tropical rain forests; coral reefs
3. tropical rain forest, soil; deciduous forest; shortgrass prairie; desert; savanna; tundra
4. littoral zone; phytoplankton, zooplankton; limnetic zone, profundal zone; oligotrophic; eutrophic; wetlands
5. phytoplankton; bioluminescence; chemosynthesis, hydrogen sulfide; high pressure

Chapter 30

Figure Caption Questions

Figure 30-8   Any rare organism faces a greater chance of extinction in a small reserve. For example, large carnivores need a large prey population to support them (see energy pyramids in Chapter 28), which in turn needs a large area of suitable habitat. Large herbivores are likely to be rare for similar reasons; for example, it takes a very large area of vegetation to support a population of elephants. A chance event (storm, fire, disease) may well kill all of the members of such a population in a small reserve.

Figure 30-11   If a species becomes extinct in one of the small reserves, members of the species in nearby reserves can move through the corridor and recolonize the now-vacant reserve.

Fill-in-the-Blank

1. genetic, species, ecosystem; genetic
2. ecosystem services; many possible answers, including food, wood, medicines, soil formation, erosion and flood control, climate regulation, genetic resources, recreation
3. ecological economics
4. habitat destruction, overexploitation, invasive species, pollution, global warming; habitat destruction
5. minimum viable population; habitat fragmentation; wildlife corridors
6. sustainable

Chapter 31

Figure Caption Questions

Figure 31-2   If the mammal's heat-sensing nerve endings were rendered nonfunctional, the nervous system would not send a signal to the hypothalamus when the body reached the set-point temperature. Consequently, the hypothalamus would send continuous "turn on" signals to the body's heat-generating and heat-retention mechanisms, which would continue to increase body temperature indefinitely (presumably until stored energy reserves are exhausted or the animal dies).

Figure 31-8   Blood is considered a form of connective tissue because it is composed largely of a matrix of extracellular fluid (plasma) in which cells and proteins are suspended.

Fill-in-the-Blank

1. homeostasis; negative feedback
2. cells, tissues, organs, organ systems
3. connective; epithelial; connective; connective; epithelial; muscle; nerve; connective
4. exocrine; endocrine, hormones
5. cardiac; skeletal; cardiac and skeletal; cardiac and smooth; smooth; skeletal

Chapter 32

Figure Caption Questions

Figure 32-4   Due to an exercise-induced increase in muscle size, the hearts of well-conditioned athletes are larger than those of

sedentary people, so a greater volume of blood is pumped with each heartbeat. This allows the body's resting demand for oxygen to be met by a slower heart rate.

Figure 32-8   Iron is a key component of hemoglobin, which is necessary for building red blood cells capable of transporting oxygen. When red blood cells die, their iron is recycled, which allows new red blood cells to be made. However, iron recycling in the body is not 100% efficient, so dietary iron is necessary to replace that lost through excretion or bleeding. Otherwise, more red blood cells will die than new red blood cells can be produced, resulting in anemia.

Figure 32-10   The hormone erythropoietin stimulates production of additional red blood cells. These extra cells increase the blood's capacity to carry oxygen to muscles, thereby increasing the amount of time that the muscles can work without becoming fatigued, which occurs when their oxygen supply is depleted and they can no longer carry out cellular respiration to produce ATP.

Figure 32-16   The principles of diffusion (see pp. 82–83) tell us that molecules move down gradients from high to low concentration. Because the tissues through which capillaries pass generally consume oxygen, the concentration of oxygen is higher inside the capillaries than outside them, and oxygen diffuses along its concentration gradient from the inside of the capillary to the outside. Conversely, tissues generally produce carbon dioxide, so the concentration of carbon dioxide is higher outside the capillaries than inside them, and carbon dioxide diffuses along its concentration gradient from the outside of the capillary to the inside.

Fill-in-the-Blank

1. right atrium; left ventricle; right atrium; right ventricle; left ventricle
2. sinoatrial node; cardiac muscle cells; atria; atrioventricular; AV bundle (atrioventricular bundle); fibrillation
3. capillaries; arteries; veins; venules; arterioles; arteries
4. platelets; thrombin; fibrinogen, fibrin
5. platelets; leukocytes; erythrocytes; leukocytes; erythrocytes; leukocytes; erythrocytes
6. extracellular fluid, capillaries; lymphatic capillaries; one-way valves; spleen

Chapter 33

Figure Caption Questions

Figure 33-5   Because juveniles of many amphibian species breathe through gills, and because both juveniles and adults often rely on supplemental respiration through the skin, most amphibians live in moist habitats, such as marshes, swamps, ponds, and rain forests.

Figure 33-10   Body cells can only function within a narrow pH range, so blood pH must be tightly controlled. If hydrogen ions entered the plasma along with the bicarbonate ions, the pH (a function of the hydrogen ion concentration) of the plasma would become acidic.

Figure 33-11   Like any skeletal muscle, the diaphragm muscle is longer when relaxed than when contracted. At rest, the diaphragm is domed upward into the chest cavity, reducing the cavity's volume. Contracting the diaphragm muscle makes it shorter, which can occur only by flattening its domed shape, thereby increasing the volume of the chest cavity.

Fill-in-the-Blank

1. the pharynx; the epiglottis; trachea, bronchi, bronchioles, alveoli
2. capillaries; hemoglobin; bicarbonate; cellular respiration
3. alveoli; alveolus, capillary; two; surfactant
4. diaphragm, expand (larger also acceptable); passive, relax; respiratory center, medulla; carbon dioxide
5. lung cancer, chronic bronchitis, asthma, emphysema (any three); ear infections, asthma, coughs, colds, allergies, bronchitis (any three)

Chapter 34

Figure Caption Questions

Figure 34-5   This food contains relatively little total fat, and the fats that are present are primarily unsaturated; there are no trans fats (see p. 46 for more information on types of fat). The food has a substantial percentage of the recommended daily amounts of a variety of vitamins and iron. Yes, it would be a good contribution to a balanced diet. Note, however, that it lacks any significant protein and contains very little fiber.

Figure 34-10 Birds grind food using a muscular gizzard, often containing small sharp stones that substitute for teeth.

Figure 34-11 Because the microorganism populations live in the first chamber of the ruminant's digestive system, many of them are passed to the other chambers, where they are digested and become an additional source of nutrients, particularly organic nutrients that the microbes synthesize but that the cow cannot synthesize or obtain in the food it eats.

Figure 34-16 A likely outcome is that the needed absorptive surface area would have been achieved by some other sort of adaptation, perhaps a much longer intestine and a correspondingly larger abdominal cavity to hold it. One could also speculate about other features that might have been required to accommodate the extra long intestine (e.g., skeletal and muscular features to support it).

Fill-in-the-Blank

1. energy, raw materials; vitamins; minerals; essential
2. intracellular; gastrovascular cavity; tubular; cellulose
3. amylase, starch; protein; pepsinogen, pepsin; small intestine
4. ingestion, mechanical digestion, chemical digestion, absorption, elimination
5. pharynx, digestive, respiratory; epiglottis, swallowing; peristalsis; sphincter muscles
6. duodenum; sodium bicarbonate, chyme, carbohydrates, lipids (OR fats and oils), proteins
7. bile (OR bile salts); liver, gallbladder; epithelial; lacteal, lymphatic

Chapter 35

Figure Caption Questions

Figure 35-7 If you consumed excess water, a drop in blood osmolarity would occur that would be detected by receptors in the hypothalamus. Activation of these receptors would cause less ADH to be released from the posterior pituitary. In the kidneys, less ADH would result in fewer aquaporins in the membranes of the distal tubules and collecting ducts, making them almost impermeable to water. This would result in production of large amounts of watery urine until normal blood osmolarity was restored.

Fill-in-the-Blank

1. nephridia; Malpighian tubules; protonephridia; nephridia
2. renal cortex, renal medulla, renal pelvis; ureter, bladder, urethra
3. glomerulus, Bowman's capsule, proximal tubule, loop of Henle, distal tubule
4. proximal tubule; collecting duct; loop of Henle; medulla
5. urea; H+ (hydrogen ions); NaCl (salt); water
6. homeostasis; renin, angiotensin; erythropoietin, red blood cells
7. hypothalamus, posterior pituitary, antidiuretic (ADH); distal tubule, collecting duct, aquaporins, concentrated

Chapter 36

Figure Caption Questions

Figure 36-4 In most capillaries, there are small gaps between the cells that make up the capillary walls (see Chapter 32). The inflammatory response causes these gaps to become larger, which allows white blood cells to move more easily between cells of the capillary walls.

Figure 36-6 The combination of constant and variable components allows an antibody to accomplish not only functions that are unique to a particular antibody molecule (i.e., recognize and bind to a specific antigen), but also functions that are common to all antibodies in a given class (i.e., carry out the appropriate response to neutralize the invader, such as enhancing phagocytosis). Variable regions provide the unique properties; constant regions provide the universal properties.

Figure 36-12 Cytotoxic T cells are activated by antigens on the target cell's surface. The plasma membranes of cancer cells often bear distinctive, abnormal molecules that are not recognized as "self" by the immune system; thus, they act as antigens that stimulate the adaptive immune response to kill the cancerous cells.

Fill-in-the-Blank

1. skin; digestive, respiratory, urogenital (order not important)
2. phagocytes; natural killer cells; inflammatory response; fever
3. antigens; antibodies, T-cell receptors (order not important)
4. light, heavy (order not important); variable, constant (order not important); variable
5. humoral, plasma cells; cell-mediated; cytotoxic; helper; memory
6. vaccine
7. allergy; immune deficiency; autoimmune disease

Chapter 37

Figure Caption Questions

Figure 37-7 Dwarfism can be treated by administering growth hormone to affected individuals; it is much more difficult to halt the production of excess hormone (especially of a pituitary hormone such as growth hormone). Disruption of the pituitary is likely to disrupt the release of many other hormones as well. (Some cases of gigantism are caused by pituitary tumors, which can be treated by surgery.)

Figure 37-11 There are several possible hypotheses, including: (1) A tumor in the anterior pituitary caused multiplication of the TSH-secreting cells; (2) a tumor in the hypothalamus caused multiplication of the cells that secrete TSH-releasing hormone; and (3) an iodine-deficient diet caused the thyroid to produce too little thyroxine, so that the negative feedback system regulating TSH release is shut off.

Figure 37-12 If the receptors could not bind glucagon, then target cells, such as those in the liver, would not be able to respond to glucagon. When blood glucose levels are too low, liver cells and other cells cannot convert glycogen to glucose, so blood glucose levels would stay low.

Fill-in-the-Blank

1. endocrine system; target cells, receptors
2. peptide, amino acid derived, steroid (order not important); peptide hormones, amino acid-derived hormones (order not important); second messengers; steroid hormones; changes in gene transcription (OR synthesis of messenger RNA)
3. hypothalamus; neurosecretory cells, oxytocin, antidiuretic hormone (order of hormones not important)
4. adrenocorticotropic hormone, follicle-stimulating hormone, luteinizing hormone, growth hormone, prolactin, thyroid-stimulating hormone
5. insulin; diabetes mellitus; glucagon, glycogen
6. testes, testosterone; ovaries, estrogen, progesterone
7. glucocorticoids, mineralocorticoids, testosterone (order of hormones not important); norepinephrine, epinephrine (order of hormones not important)

Chapter 38

Figure Caption Questions

Figure 38-4 Based on the evidence, the toxin must act on the postsynaptic part of the synapse, by blocking neurotransmitter receptors. If the toxin acted by blocking release of neurotransmitters from the presynaptic neuron, then adding neurotransmitter to the synapse would have generated a postsynaptic action potential. If the toxin acted by preventing sodium channels from opening, then it would not have been possible to stimulate an action potential in the presynaptic neuron.

Figure 38-5 Sensitive areas have a higher density of touch-sensitive sensory neurons. This would allow two types of increased sensitivity: (1) The higher density of receptors would mean that touching any particular place on the sensitive skin area would be more likely to stimulate at least one touch receptor; and (2) a higher density of receptors would also mean that a touch of a particular force would stimulate a larger number of neurons. The touch thus would generate a larger number of action potentials in the sensitive area and would be perceived as a stronger stimulus.

Figure 38-10   A severed or damaged spinal cord prevents the sensation of pain from being relayed to the brain but does not disrupt the reflex circuit, which requires transmission within only a small portion of the spinal cord.

Fill-in-the-Blank

1. neuron; dendrite; cell body; axon, synaptic terminal
2. negative; threshold; positive
3. neurotransmitter; receptors; excitatory postsynaptic potential; inhibitory postsynaptic potential
4. somatic nervous system; autonomic nervous system, sympathetic, parasympathetic
5. cerebellum, pons, medulla (order not important); cerebellum
6. frontal, parietal, temporal, occipital (order not important); occipital; frontal

Chapter 39

Figure Caption Questions

Figure 39-10   For nearsightedness, the cornea is flattened (made less convex), which causes the light rays to converge less before they reach the lens. For farsightedness, the edges of the cornea are reduced, which leaves the cornea with a more rounded, convex shape that causes the light rays to converge more before they reach the lens.

Figure 39-11   You do not experience a hole in your vision because (1) the blind spots in your two eyes do not see the same place in your visual field, so one of the eyes always sees the "hole" in the visual field of the other eye; and (2) your eyes constantly move around, so no part of the visual field is in the blind spot of either eye for very long. The brain "fills in" the missing visual information with what the eye saw just a fraction of a second before.

Figure 39-12   Distance perception is useful for many behaviors, not just predation. Fruit-eating bats fly around during the daytime, and binocular vision is useful for avoiding obstacles such as branches. Monkeys often jump from branch to branch, and need to know how far it is to the next branch.

Fill-in-the-Blank

1. receptor potential; frequency
2. mechanoreceptors; photoreceptors; chemoreceptors
3. pinna, eardrum (tympanic membrane); hammer (malleus), anvil (incus), stirrup (stapes) (order *is* important); oval window; hair cells
4. cornea, aqueous humor, iris; lens, vitreous humor; cornea, lens (order not important)
5. rods, cones (order not important); rods; cones, fovea
6. sweet, salty, sour, bitter, umami (order not important); olfaction OR smell

Chapter 40

Figure Caption Questions

Figure 40-2   Water helps to support some of the weight of a thick exoskeleton. For land-dwelling arthropods, the weight of a thick exoskeleton would require much more energy expenditure just to stand, let alone move.

Figure 40-6   A highly stretched muscle would have the thin and thick filaments pulled so far out that not all of the myosin heads would overlap a thin filament and, hence, could not attach to actin when a contraction begins. Fewer myosin heads pulling on the thin filaments would generate less force of contraction than if all of the heads could pull on the thin filaments.

Figure 40-10   Two reasons: (1) Compact bone is much heavier than spongy bone, so it would require much more energy for an animal to stand or move; and (2) compact bone, being virtually solid, would leave no room for bone marrow, which is where blood cells are produced.

Fill-in-the-Blank

1. hydrostatic skeleton, endoskeleton, exoskeleton (order not important); antagonistic
2. skeletal, cardiac (order not important); cardiac, smooth (order not important); cardiac, smooth (order not important)
3. muscle fiber; myofibrils, sarcomeres; Z lines
4. actin, myosin; ATP
5. neuromuscular junctions; T tubules, sarcoplasmic reticulum
6. cartilage, bone, ligaments (order not important); collagen
7. hinge, ball-and-socket; flexor, extensor

Chapter 41

Figure Caption Questions

Figure 41-1   Mitotic cell division.

Figure 41-3   Asexual reproduction produces offspring that are genetically identical to the mother, all containing all of her genes. This is an efficient way for her to maximize the number of her genes in the population, but provides no significant opportunity for any of her offspring to have new genotypes that might enhance survival or reproduction. Because the weather is favorable and food is so abundant in the spring and summer, natural selection is not very strong, so this is probably not a major difficulty. When autumn arrives, weather and food become more problematic. Sexual reproduction produces genetically variable offspring, some of which may be better adapted to the conditions and be favored by natural selection.

Figure 41-6   Courtship rituals help ensure that animals mate with other individuals of their own species. Courtship rituals are reproductive isolating mechanisms that help prevent potentially disadvantageous hybrid mating. The courtship activities in some species stimulate ovulation.

Figure 41-13   Testosterone inhibits the release of GnRH and FSH. Without adequate FSH, the Sertoli cells are not stimulated and, hence, spermatogenesis slows down or stops.

Figure 41-17   Estrogen and progesterone inhibit the release of GnRH, FSH, and LH. Without enough FSH, follicles will not develop. Even if a follicle somehow does develop, without LH, the follicle will not mature, meiosis I will not be completed, and ovulation will not occur. Without an ovulated secondary oocyte, fertilization and pregnancy cannot occur.

Fill-in-the-Blank

1. asexual; bud; fission
2. testis; testosterone (androgen also acceptable); seminiferous tubules
3. nucleus, acrosome; mitochondria
4. epididymis, vas deferens, seminal vesicles, prostate gland, bulbourethral gland (order of glands not important), urethra
5. ovary; estrogen, progesterone (order not important); secondary oocyte; polar body; oviduct OR uterine tube OR fallopian tube; uterus
6. corpus luteum; chorionic gonadotropin

Chapter 42

Figure Caption Questions

Figure 42-4   Twins would probably never occur, because even the first cell division of cleavage would produce daughter cells with different developmental fates, with the result that each of the daughter cells would be able to give rise to some, but not all, of the structures of the human adult.

Figure 42-5   *Ribs:* Homeobox genes are usually active in a head-to-tail sequence, such that gene A might be active in the head region, gene B would be active in the torso, gene C would be active in the pelvic region, and so on. If, for example, gene B causes production of ribs, then perhaps in snakes, gene B is active all the way from the end of the (very short) neck to the tail segments.

Lack of legs: A specific homeobox gene would normally be responsible for triggering the production of the entire leg (or at least most of it). A severe mutation (for example, a premature stop codon) in this particular homeobox gene would prevent leg formation.

Figure 42-8   The ovulated egg is surrounded by the zona pellucida and the corona radiata (through which the sperm must penetrate to fertilize the egg). However, it is the outer layer of the blastocyst that attaches to, and implants in, the uterus. Therefore, the blastocyst must emerge out of the zona pellucida and corona radiata at some point before implantation.

Figure 42-13   Monotremes such as platypuses lay eggs; the embryos are not nourished inside the mother at all. In marsupials such as kangaroos, the embryo is enclosed within an amnion that segregates it from the mother's blood (and thus from attack by the mother's immune system), but nutrients cannot pass across the amnion. However, marsupials produce only a primitive placenta-like structure, much like a large yolk sac, rather than a true placenta that allows efficient exchange of nutrients, wastes, and gases between embryo and mother. Therefore, marsupial offspring are born after a short gestation, in a much less developed state than are the offspring of placental mammals. Development continues outside the uterus (typically inside an external pouch).

Fill-in-the-Blank

1. cleavage, morula; blastula; ectoderm, mesoderm, endoderm (order not important)
2. amnion; chorion; umbilical cord; yolk sac
3. stem cells; inner cell mass
4. homeobox genes; transcription factors
5. prolactin; oxytocin

Chapter 43
Figure Caption Questions

Figure 43-7   The onion stores nutrients for use by the shoot produced during the second year, after which the plant dies. An onion bulb at the end of the second year would be practically nonexistent.

Figure 43-9   No. In a climate that was truly uniformly warm and wet year-round, the vascular cambium would divide at the same rate year-round, and the daughter secondary xylem cells would grow the same way year-round. All of the secondary xylem cells would have the same size and cell wall thickness, and so they would all be the same color.

Figure 43-19   The fungus acquires sugars from the plant root. Cortex cells typically receive sugars and store them (possibly converting them to starch). Therefore, the fungus would likely benefit most from a close association with cortex cells. Cortex cells can also take up minerals, so any minerals made available by the fungus could be taken up by the cortex cells.

Figure 43-23 CO_2 is required for photosynthesis. When stomata close, photosynthesis in the leaf slows and eventually stops because closed stomata prevent CO_2 in the air from entering the leaf and reaching the mesophyll cells where photosynthesis occurs. Closed stomata also greatly reduce transpiration from the leaf. Because transpiration provides the driving force for the upward movement of water in xylem, which in turn provides the major driving force for water entry into the roots, closing the stomata would slow down water entry into the roots.

Fill-in-the-Blank

1. meristem; apical meristem, lateral meristem; apical meristem; lateral meristem
2. dermal, ground, vascular (order not important); dermal; vascular; ground
3. xylem, tracheids, vessel elements (order not important for the last two answers); hydrogen bonds, transpiration; stomata

4. phloem; sieve tube element, companion cells
5. root cap; root hairs, active transport; mycorrhizae

Chapter 44
Figure Caption Questions

Figure 44-3   Separate bloom times reduce the chances of self-pollination and, hence, self-fertilization, which would result in inbreeding. Plants that do not inbreed in many cases have more successful offspring. Inbred individuals are more likely to have homozygous recessive alleles that harm the plant's growth or reproduction.

Figure 44-6   Colorful petals and sweet scents have evolved because they attract pollinators; thus, they would not be useful to a wind-pollinated plant, which has no need to attract animal pollinators. Further, petals, scents, and nectar require energy to produce, so they would be selected against. Therefore, wind-pollinated plants would not be expected to have them.

Figure 44-15   When nectar is at the base of a long, tubular flower, it is accessible to hummingbirds (which have long bills and tongues), but not to most insects and other small animals that might like to eat it. A flower whose nectar is inaccessible to insects is more likely to have nectar available for a visiting hummingbird; it is thus more likely that hummingbirds will learn to repeatedly visit this type of flower, ensuring that the flowers will be pollinated and the plant will reproduce.

Figure 44-18   *Hints:* How do maple fruits "fly"? Do they fly further with or without their wings? Does wind make them fly further? If so, how do the wings affect their flight distance on a windy day?

Figure 44-19   Water flows only downhill. Therefore, floating fruits move downhill. A species using water as its primary means of dispersal will move downhill generation after generation, until eventually its most common habitat would be the ocean shore. This, of course, is precisely where coconut palms are found.

Fill-in-the-Blank

1. alternation of generations; sporophyte; meiotic cell division; gametophyte
2. pollen grain; anthers; stigma; style; integuments
3. zygote; endosperm; cotyledons
4. ovary; ovule; integuments
5. germination; root; coleoptile; bend OR hook

Chapter 45
Figure Caption Questions

Figure 45-7   The added auxin would replace the auxin normally produced by the apical meristem of the intact shoot tip, so apical dominance would persist. Lateral buds would be inhibited from sprouting into branches.

Figure 45-10   Ripe tomatoes are often damaged in shipping. Blocking ethylene production would prevent ripening. Green tomatoes could be ripened after they reach the market by exposing them to ethylene.

Fill-in-the-Blank

1. inhibits, apical dominance; stimulates; positive phototropism
2. gibberellin; divide, auxin
3. ethylene; abscission layer; ripening, (any two of the following are correct, but this listing from the text is not exclusive) bananas, apples, pears, tomatoes, OR avocados
4. root apical meristem; inhibits, stimulates, branches OR buds
5. abscisic acid; dormancy

Photo Credits

Detailed Contents Photos: p. v: Tischenko Irina/Shutterstock; p. vi: Victoria Alexandrova/Shutterstock; p. vii: Dr. Jeremy Burgess/Science Photo Library/Photo Researchers, Inc.; p. viii: Image courtesy Indigo® Instruments: http://www.indigo.com; p. ix: Photos.com; p. x: Photos.com; p. xi: Allen Blake Sheldon/Allen Blake Sheldon Nature Photography; p. xii: Roland Birke/Peter Arnold, Inc.; p. xiii: Meppu/iStockphoto.com; p. xiv: David Fleetham/Alamy Images; p. xv: Andy Sands/Nature Picture Library; p. xvi: Jan Martin Will/Shutterstock; p. xvii: Dr. David M. Phillips/Visuals Unlimited/Getty Images; p. xviii: Michael Durham/Minden Pictures; p. xix: James Cavallini/Photo Researchers, Inc.; p. xx: Dennis Kunkel/Phototake NYC; p. xxi: H. Stanley Johnson/Purestock/SuperStock p. xxii: John Cancalosi/Photolibrary.com

Unit Openers: Unit 1: Dennis Kunkel/Phototake NYC; Unit 2: GK Hart/Vicky Hart/Photonica/Getty Images; Unit 3: Frans Lanting/CORBIS; Unit 4: Georgette Douwma/Getty Images; Unit 5: Marty Sohl Photography; Unit 6: Purestock/Getty Images

Chapter 1 opener: WHO/Christopher Black; opener inset: Frederick A. Murphy/Centers for Disease Control; 1-2: Electron micrograph by Wm. P. Wergin, courtesy E. H. Newcomb, University of Wisconsin-Madison/ Biological Photo Service; 1-3: Hunter Cole; 1-5: Christine Case/Visuals Unlimited; 1-6: Frank Cucinotta/NASA; 1-7: Francois Gohier/Photo Researchers, Inc.; 1-8: Wim van Egmond/Getty Images Inc. Visuals Unlimited; 1-9: AP Wide World Photos; E1-3: Frans Lanting/CORBIS; E1-3 inset: Unclesam/Fotolia; E1-4: Mark R/Shutterstock

Chapter 2 opener: Underwood & Underwood/CORBIS; 2-4: Mediacolor's/ Alamy Images; 2-5c: Piotr Sosnowski/Wikimedia Commons/Wikemedia Commons; 2-8a: Stephen Dalton/Photo Researchers, Inc.; 2-8b: Teresa and Gerald Audesirk; 2-10: Renn Sminkey/CDV LLC, Creative Digital Visions; 2-13a: Comstock Images/Jupiter Unlimited; 2-13b: Hans Huber/Photoshot Archive Creative; E2-1c: Warren Grant/National Institute of Health; E2-2: UPI/ CORBIS-NY; E2-3: Don Mason/Brand X Pictures/Jupiter Images - PictureArts Corporation/Brand X Pictures Royalty Free; E2-3 inset: iStockphoto.com

Chapter 3 opener: gordondix/iStockphoto.com; 3-8a: Dr. Jeremy Burgess/ Science Photo Library/Photo Researchers, Inc.; 3-9a: Mike Norton/Shutterstock; 3-9b: Jeremy Burgess/Science Photo Library/Photo Researchers, Inc. 3-9c: Biophoto Associates/Photo Researchers, Inc.; 3-10: Mark Jones/Minden Pictures; 3-11a: Sylvie Bouchard/Fotolia; 3-11b: Tischenko Irina/Shutterstock; 3-16a: Tracy Morgan/Dorling Kindersley; 3-16b: gabriela schaufelberger/iStockphoto.com; 3-16c: Xiaodong Ye/iStockphoto.com; E3-1: Renn Sminkey/Creative Digital Visions, Pearson Education; E3-2: GJLP/Photo Researchers, Inc.; E3-3: Coka/Fotolia

Chapter 4 opener: © 2006 Advanced Tissue Sciences, a Division of Advanced BioHealing; opener inset: © 2006 Advanced Tissue Sciences, a Division of Advanced BioHealing; 4-5b: Molecular Probes, Inc.; 4-6: William L. Dentler/Biological Photo Service; 4-7a: Ellen R. Dirksen/Visuals Unlimited; 4-7b: Yorgos Nikas/Getty Images Inc.; 4-8b: Dr. Elena Kiseleva/SPL/Photo Researchers, Inc.; 4-9: Lester V. Bergman/Bettmann/CORBIS; 4-10: Oscar L. Miller, Jr., University of Virginia; 4-11b: R. Bolender and Donald Fawcett/Visuals Unlimited; 4-12: Lee W. Wilcox; 4-16: The Keith R. Porter Endowment for Cell BIology; 4-17: © E.H. Newcomb & W.P. Wergin/ Biological Photo Service, Terraphotographics; 4-18: Biophoto Associates/ Photo Researchers, Inc.; 4-19b: CNRI/Science Photo Library/Photo Researchers, Inc.; 4-19c: Visuals Unlimited/CORBIS; 4-19d: John Cardamone,Jr./ Biological Photo Service; 4-19e: "TEM showing the thylakoid membranes of strain CCMEE 5410". Phycobilisomes were not observed (Bar, 100nm). From PNAS 01/18/05; Vol 102 (3) page 852, Fig 2A by Scott R. Miller, et al. Copyright © 2005 National Academy of Sciences, U.S.A.; 4-20: Sam Ogden/Photo Researchers, Inc.; E4-1aT: Plate XI, Micrographia by Robert Hooke 1665 Project Gutenberg.; E4-1aB: Cecil Fox/Science Source/Photo Researchers, Inc.; E4-1bT: Brian J. Ford; E4-1bB: Brian J. Ford; E4-1c: Courtesy of DOE's Pacific Northwest National L/Pacific Northwest National Laboratory; E4-2a: M.I. Walker/Photo Reserachers, Inc.; E4-2b: Manfred Kage/Peter Arnold, Inc.; E4-2c: David M. Phillips/Visual Unlimited; E4-2d: National Library of Medicine

Chapter 5 opener: Daniel J. Lyons/Photoshot Holdings Ltd/Bruce Coleman USA; opener inset: Larry F. Jemigan/Photolibrary.com; 5-9a: Joseph Kurantsin-Mills, The George Washington Univeristy Medical Center; 5-9b: Joseph Kurantsin-Mills, The George Washington Univeristy Medical Center; 5-9c: Joseph Kurantsin-Mills, The George Washington Univeristy

Medical Center; 5-10a: Nigel Cattlin/Holt Studios International/Photo Researchers, Inc.; 5-10b: Nigel Cattlin/Holt Studios International/Photo Researchers, Inc.; 5-12b: BCC Microimaging, Corp. Reproduced with permission.; 5-13b1: M.M. Perry and A.B. Gilbert, Journal of Cell Science, 39:257-272 (1979). © 1979 The Company of Biologists Limited.; 5-13b2: M.M. Perry and A.B. Gilbert, Journal of Cell Science, 39:257-272 (1979). © 1979 The Company of Biologists Limited.; 5-13b3: M.M. Perry and A.B. Gilbert, Journal of Cell Science, 39:257-272 (1979). © 1979 The Company of Biologists Limited.; 5-13b4: M.M. Perry and A.B. Gilbert, Journal of Cell Science, 39:257-272 (1979). © 1979 The Company of Biologists Limited.; 5-14b: Visuals Unlimited/CORBIS; 5-14c: Dennis Kunkel/Phototake NYC; 5-15: L. A. Hufnagel, Ultrastructural Aspects of Chemoreception in Ciliated Protists (Ciliophora), Journal of Electron Microscopy Technique, 1991. Photomicrograph by Jurgen Bohmer and Linda Hufnagel, University of Rhode Island.; 5-19a: American College of Physicians; 5-19b: Photo Courtesy of Justin Schwarts, www.rattlesnakebite.org; E5-1: Victoria Alexandrova/ Shutterstock; E5-2: Stephen J. Boitano/Getty Images; E5-3a: Reproduced by permission from: Water permeability of aquaporin-I (AQPI) expressed in Xenous oocytes. Fig 3, part D of Trends in Biochem Science 1994 Oct; 19(10):421-5 by Chrispeels MJ and Agre P. Copyright © 1994 by Elsevier Science Ltd. Photo courtesy of G.M. Preston

Chapter 6 opener: Jason DeCrow/AP Wide World Photos; 6-1: Tim Davis/ CORBIS; E6-1: Baumgartner Olivia/CORBIS; UN6-1: Gail Shumway/Getty Images

Chapter 7 opener: Joe Tucciarone; 7-1a: Nikolay Okhitin/Shutterstock; 7-1c: J. Michael Eichelberger/Visuals Unlimited; 7-2a: Dr. Jeremy Burgess/Science Photo Library/ Photo Researchers, Inc.; 7-2b: Dr. Jeremy Burgess/Photo Researchers, Inc. 7-5: Teresa and Gerald Audesirk; 7-9: Colin Milkins/Oxford Scientific Films/Animals Animals/Earth Scenes; E7-1: Daniel Beltra/Getty Images

Chapter 8 opener: Newscom; 8-10: Julián Rovagnati/Shutterstock; E8-3: William Leaman /Alamy Images; E8-4: Gordon Swanson/Shutterstock

Chapter 9 opener: Young Ho/SIPA Press; 9-2a: David Scharf/Peter Arnold, Inc.; 9-2b: M. I. Walker/Photo Researchers, Inc.; 9-2c: Carolina Biological Supply Company/Phototake NYC; 9-2d: Teresa and Gerald Audesirk; 9-4: Andrew Syred/Photo Researchers, Inc.; 9-6: CNRI/Science Photo Library/Photo Researchers, Inc.; 9-8a: Michael W. Davidson, Florida State University/Molecular Expressions (http://www.microscopy.fsu.edu).; 9-8b: Michael W. Davidson, Florida State University/Molecular Expressions (http://www.microscopy.fsu.edu).; 9-8c: Michael W. Davidson, Florida State University/Molecular Expressions (http://www.microscopy.fsu.edu).; 9-8d: Michael W. Davidson, Florida State University/Molecular Expressions (http://www.microscopy.fsu.edu).; 9-8e: Michael W. Davidson, Florida State University/Molecular Expressions (http://www.microscopy.fsu.edu).; 9-8f: Michael W. Davidson, Florida State University/Molecular Expressions (http://www.microscopy.fsu.edu).; 9-8g: Michael W. Davidson, Florida State University/Molecular Expressions (http://www.microscopy.fsu.edu).; 9-8h: Michael W. Davidson, Florida State University/Molecular Expressions (http:// www.microscopy.fsu.edu).; E9-1: Photograph courtesy of The Roslin Institute

Chapter 10 opener: Ronald Modra/Sports Illustrated; 10-2: Archiv/Photo Researchers, Inc.; 10-15: Image courtesy Indigo® Instruments: http://www .indigo.com/; 10-19b: Sarah Leen/National Geographic Image Collection; 10-20: David Hosking /Alamy Images; 10-22a: Rick Guidotti for Positive Exposure; 10-22b: Jeremy Voisey/iStockphoto.com; 10-23a: Dennis Kunkel/Phototake NYC; 10-23b: Wlater Reinhart/Phototake NYC; 10-24: Gunn and Stewart/Mary Evans/Photo Researchers, Inc.; 10-26a: CNRI/Science Photo Library/Photo Researchers, Inc.; 10-26b: philidor/Fotolia E10-1: VES HERMAN/Landov Media; E10-2a: Custom Medical Stock Photo; E10-2b: Custom Medical Stock Photo

Chapter 11 opener: Yann Arthus-Bertrand/CORBIS/Yann Arthus-Betrand/Bettmann/CORBIS; 11-4a: Photo by M.H.F. Wilkins. Courtesy of King's College London, England; 11-4b: The Nobel Foundation 2008; 11-4c: Jenifer Glynn/National Library of Medicine; 11-5c: Michael Freeman/Phototake NYC; 11-7: Dr. Gopal Murti/Science Photo Library/Photo Researchers, Inc.; 11-9: Stuart Isett/Polaris Images; E11-3: National Cancer Institute

Chapter 12 opener: Photograph by Pete Moss, Courtesy Sony BMG and Luke Martineau; 12-4: Oscar L. Miller, Jr., University of Virginia; 12-5b: From Hamkalo and Miller, Electronmicroscopy of Genetic Material, Figure 6a, p. 379. Reproduced with permission, from Annual Review of Biochemistry,

Index